1983
YEARBOOK
OF
SCIENCE
AND THE
FUTURE

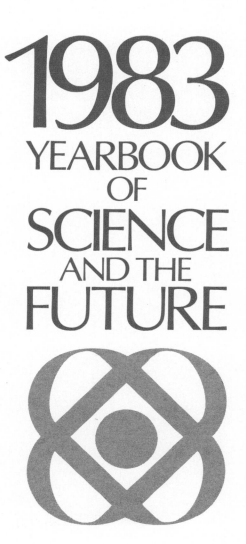

1983
YEARBOOK
OF
SCIENCE
AND THE
FUTURE

Encyclopædia Britannica, Inc.
Chicago

Auckland   Geneva   London   Manila   Paris   Rome   Seoul   Sydney   Tokyo   Toronto

The University of Chicago
The Yearbook of Science and the Future
is published with the editorial advice of the faculties of
the University of Chicago.

1983
YEARBOOK OF SCIENCE AND THE FUTURE

CONTENTS
Feature Articles

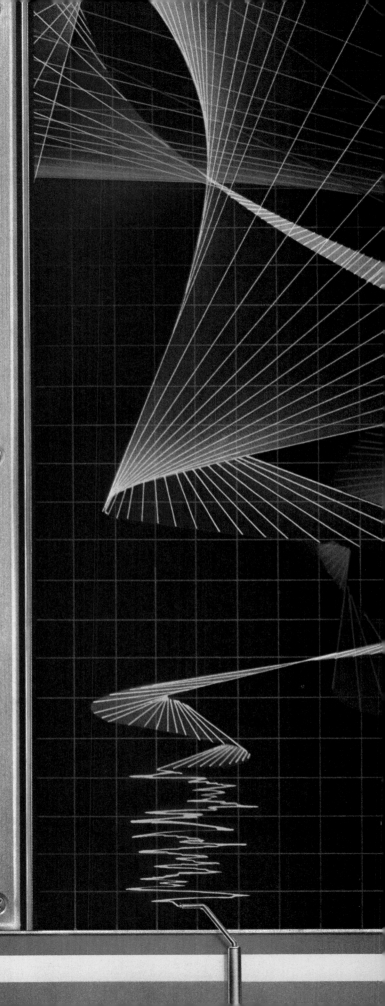

Maps, graphs, designs, animated movies, original art, and pictures from various unseen worlds are a few of the creations of computers that have been taught to draw.

COMPUTER GRAPHICS:
A LENS FOR THE MIND'S EYE
by Melvin L. Prueitt

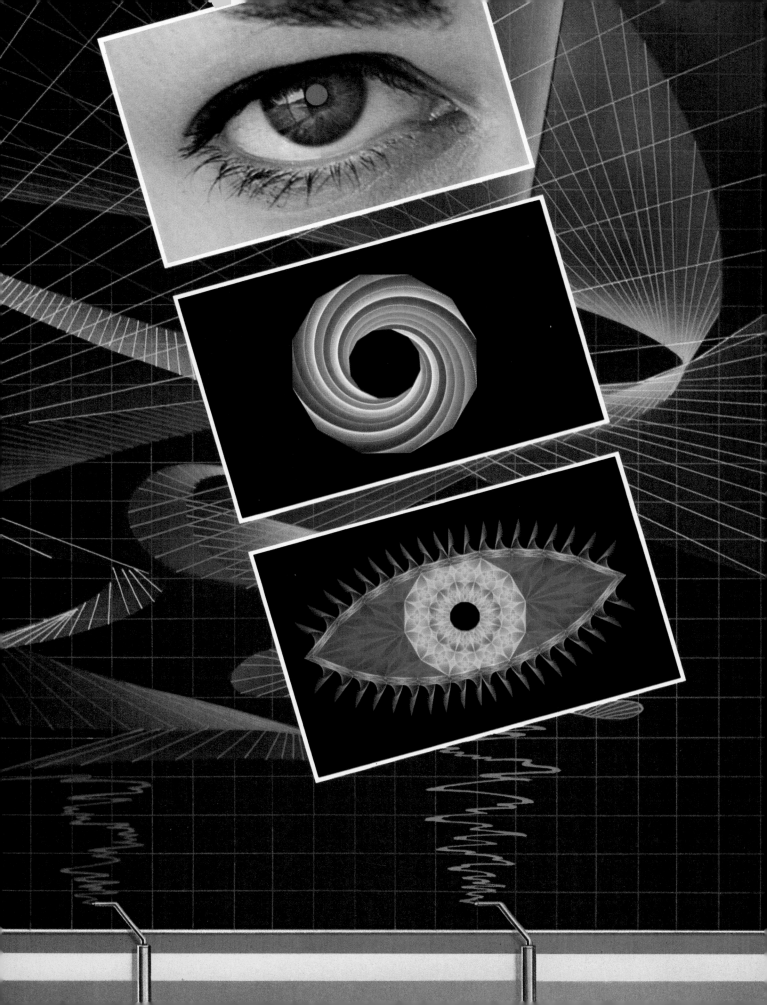

Melvin L. Prueitt, Los Alamos National Laboratory

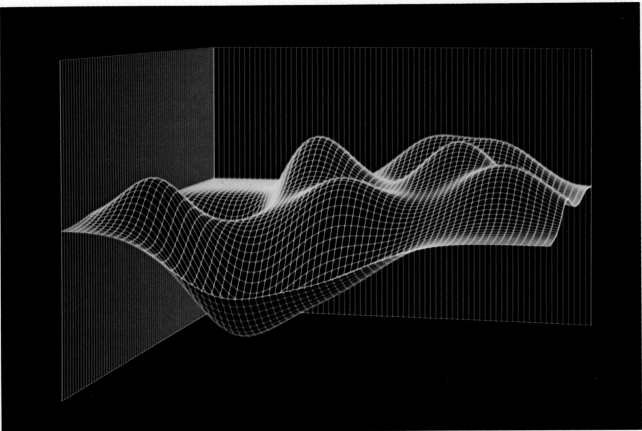

Figure 1: Computer image drawn in three-dimensional perspective is made to seem solid by removing the lines that are normally hidden behind nearer features.

MELVIN L. PRUEITT is a Staff Member of the Los Alamos National Laboratory in New Mexico and President of Orion Computergraphics.

(Overleaf) Illustration by John Youssi; photos, (top) Dan Morrill; (center and bottom) Melvin L. Prueitt, Los Alamos National Laboratory

In the distant future when human exploration of the universe first brings astronauts into contact with other intelligent life, they may find communication with the aliens extremely difficult. Suppose that the beings on another world spoke at a rate equivalent to 10,000 words per second and thought a billion words per second. The creature first encountered might become totally bored with the slow-motion Earthlings a second or two after initial confrontation, while the astronauts' eyebrows were still going up. By the time the astronauts got ready to say "Hi, we come in peace," the alien would have zoomed off to more exciting activities.

For their second visit to that world, what should the astronauts take with them to enable communication with aliens? One answer is graphics. Pictures contain a vast amount of information.

Humans face a somewhat similar situation in communicating with computers. The Cray 1, which in 1981 was one of the two most powerful computers in existence, can calculate 160 million numbers per second. If all those numbers were printed on paper with each page filled solidly, the paper would have to shoot out of the printer at 250,000 miles per hour. Some current high-speed printers can print only about 120 lines per second, but even that is far too fast for the human brain to keep up.

For the first two decades of man's coexistence with the digital computer, most computer output was in the form of printed numbers. Yet people are

10

not equipped by nature to rapidly assimilate and correlate large arrays of numbers. In fact, when they study such numbers, they often try to form geometric mental images in order to comprehend the computer calculations.

What, then, has become the best communication method between man and computer? The answer again is graphics. When the computer speaks with pictures, it not only provides large quantities of information in a compact format but it also displays the information in the form that is easily assimilated through one of the brain's input channels—the eyes. The human visual system consists of a number of complex processors that examine forms, shades, and colors to provide a conscious in-depth analysis of the image. In comprehending the computer's pictures, humans thus begin to understand its "thoughts."

Teaching the computer to draw

The simplest type of computer graphic consists of a single curved line or set of bars representing a variable that changes with time. For example, it could show United States wheat exports for the years 1900 through 1980. Such a plot is easily understood by most people, and the salient features are absorbed more quickly than columns of numbers. Line graphs typically represent less than 100 numbers.

But the computer deals in billions of numbers, and there are many problems in science and technology that embody many thousands of numbers and more than one variable. How does one display so much information graphically? People live in a three-dimensional universe and, by experience, comprehend three-dimensional surfaces. If the computer could be commanded to carve a sinuous surface from a cube of plastic, the surface might represent three variables and as many as 10,000 numbers. But solid blocks would be rather cumbersome to handle.

The solution lies inherent in the human visual system. The visual cortex has the amazing power to create mentally a three-dimensional image simply by observing a perspective picture on a two-dimensional surface. So, if the computer can be taught to draw perspective plots on a sheet of paper, the human user will perceive three dimensions.

It is easy to program a computer to make perspective plots, but the result immediately produces another problem. For example, if one gives the computer all the appropriate coordinates of a mountain, it will obediently draw the whole mountain including the far side, which would normally be invisible to an observer. The result resembles an X-ray photograph. Many workers have spent many years developing elegant algorithms (step-by-step problem-solving computations) for hidden-line and hidden-surface removal with resulting pictures that meet the approval of the decoding networks in the human visual system.

Figure 1 shows a line drawing in perspective from which the computer has removed the hidden lines. How people are able to perceive such a picture as a three-dimensional surface is not completely understood. The image lacks the shading cues that are present in real surfaces. Nevertheless, this type of plot is very useful for displaying computer-generated data, and it can be drawn very quickly.

11

Photos, Melvin L. Prueitt, Los Alamos National Laboratory

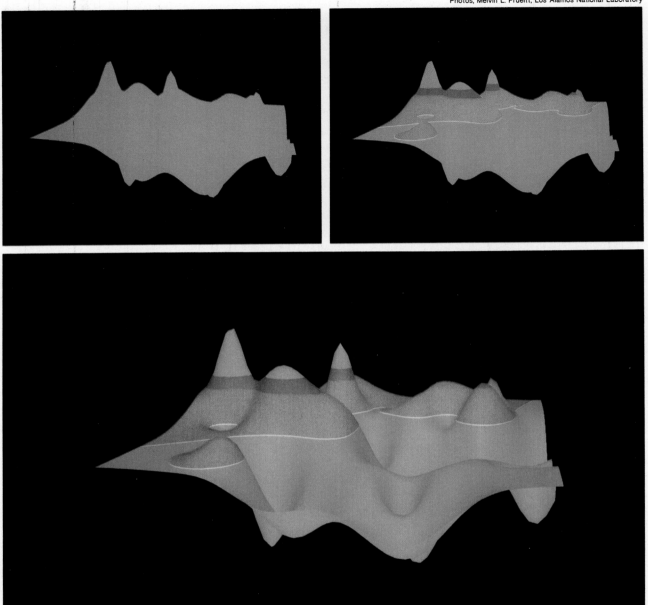

Figures 2a, 2b, 2c (clockwise from top left): Progression in a series of computer images—from a simple featureless outline, to one with added color, and finally to one with color and shading—shows the importance of shading to the perception of depth.

To make the picture more realistic, graphics users resort to shading that resembles realistic lighting situations and use scan lines (similar to lines on a television screen) to portray the surfaces. To illustrate how important shading is, figures 2a, 2b, and 2c have been drawn in perspective and are geometrically identical. Figure 2a has scan lines of constant intensity and constant color. Figure 2b shows that color contour bands give important cues for perceiving the surface, but it is the shading of figure 2c that provides the necessary cues to allow the brain to accept the surface as "real."

Sometimes the scientist is confronted with more variables than can be displayed in a perspective plot. Color can be used to denote an extra variable. For example, in a hydrodynamics problem the height of the surface at a point may represent the pressure at a corresponding point in an experiment, while the color of the surface at that point could represent the temperature—perhaps blue for cool and red for hot. Colors may also be used to delineate various regions of the surface. Thus many complex graphic presentations of scientific data turn out to be not only functional but aesthetically pleasing as well.

Motion may also be used to exhibit an additional variable. By creating a movie from a series of plots, one can watch the surface undulate during the sequence as some parameter is varied. In many cases, that parameter may be time itself.

If, instead of a surface, one wants to display a set of points in space, the problem is more difficult. There are no visual cues to relate one point to another. Some people have programmed computers to produce stereo pairs of plots. These are very effective in allowing the researcher to see the relative positions of the points (which, for example, might represent positions of atoms in a molecule, while colors identify the types of atoms). But the display of stereo pairs is awkward when a scientist is addressing a large audience. In this case, rotation of the points in space via a movie provides the cues for excellent three-dimensional perception. For example, suppose that many points are distributed on all the faces of a perfectly transparent cube. If a perspective projection of these points is shown on a screen, the viewer sees nothing but a two-dimensional agglomeration of points. If, however, the points are rotated about the vertical axis through the center of the cube, the viewer perceives a well-defined cube and can identify all faces. Experiments have shown that when rotation stops, three-dimensional perception is lost and the image instantly goes flat.

Tools of the trade

The creation of perspective computer graphics requires a significant amount of computing power, particularly if hidden lines or hidden surfaces are to be removed. For a picture consisting of 1,000 by 1,000 picture elements (pixels in computer jargon), the color and light intensity for one million points must be calculated. Furthermore, for each point on each object being pictured, the computer must be programmed to determine whether the point is hidden by another object. Hundreds of operations may be performed for each of the million pixels. The need for a computer that can perform 160 million calculations per second now becomes apparent.

General purpose computers can be programmed to execute the operations required to produce excellent pictures. In this case, all of the "intelligence" resides in the program. The computer is a totally ignorant machine that follows the instructions of the program. But there are special-purpose computers in which the equipment itself, the hardware (as opposed to the software program), is designed to make decisions and perform the calculations specif-

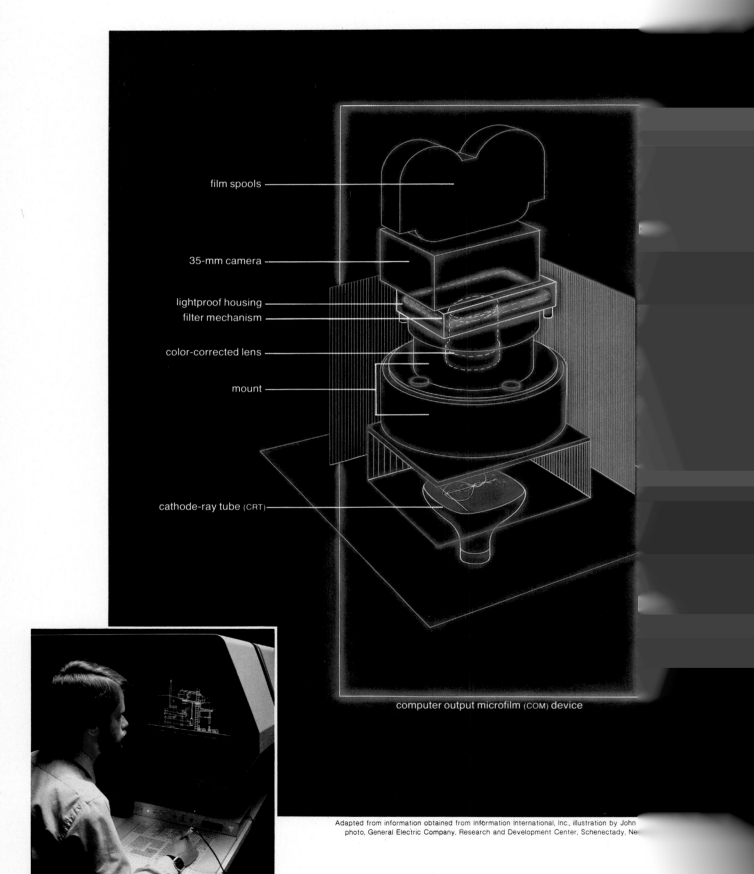

film spools

35-mm camera

lightproof housing
filter mechanism

color-corrected lens

mount

cathode-ray tube (CRT)

computer output microfilm (COM) device

Adapted from information obtained from Information International, Inc., illustration by John
photo, General Electric Company, Research and Development Center, Schenectady, Ne

ically for producing graphics. These machines produce graphics so fast that real-time action can be displayed on a TV monitor.

A suitable computer is only half the equipment required for producing computer graphics. A good-quality plotting device is the other half. These can be mechanically guided pens for such applications as drafting. Cathode-ray tubes (CRT's) are much faster and may be either a television monitor or a computer output microfilm (COM) device. The computer deals with numbers only in the form of electronic pulses. It has no "conception" of images. The plotting device translates those electronic pulses into coordinates for positioning the pen in a pen plotter or the electron beam in a CRT.

Although the TV monitor is fast, highest quality graphics normally require a COM device. The latter is equipped with an automatic camera for recording images that are drawn on a high-resolution, white-phosphor CRT screen. Rather than tracing only horizontal scan lines as in a TV, the COM device draws lines in any direction specified by the computer. Color is supplied by electronically actuated filters placed between the CRT screen and the camera. The shutter of the camera remains open while the image is drawn, since complex pictures may take more than a minute to draw. When all parts of the image are traced and filtered through the proper color filters, the picture is finished, and the computer gives a signal that causes the camera to advance the frame. By changing the image only slightly between frames, a filmstrip results that can be projected as a movie.

A graphics terminal is a useful device that allows an operator to interact with the computer. Usually the quality of the graphics display is not high, but it allows the operator to check his creations before commanding the computer to send the images to a COM device. A light pen for writing directly on the terminal's CRT screen or a graphics tablet, an electronic slate on which images may be drawn, provides an easy way for the user to create and modify the images. He can point to a part of the image and command the computer to move it to his next pen position. He can define colors by pointing to a color "palette" at the edge of the screen. A number of often used commands may be listed in abbreviated form at the side of the screen so that the user can give complex instructions with the touch of his pen.

Home computers are the least expensive of graphics devices and make

Major components of FR-80 computer output microfilm (COM) device are diagramed on the facing page. The filter mechanism consists of arms and drivers that can insert any of four color filters between the generated image and the camera film. Graphics display terminal (facing page, bottom left) features graphics tablet and pen that allow the operator to create and modify images on the screen. These designs can be stored in computer memory or transmitted to a COM device for high-quality records.

"Page" from a teletext electronic magazine (below left) uses computer graphics to present weather forecast and a commercial message. Teletext systems are capable of transmitting hundreds of such pages of news, sports, weather, and business reports and other information directly to the home television set. (Below right) The on-screen graphics incorporated in instructional programs for home computers makes the material more entertaining, attractive, and easier to understand.

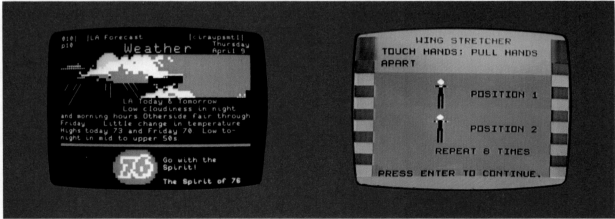

(Left) Courtesy, CBS/Broadcast Group; (right) Dan McCoy—Rainbow

Susan Bunker, Los Alamos National Laboratory

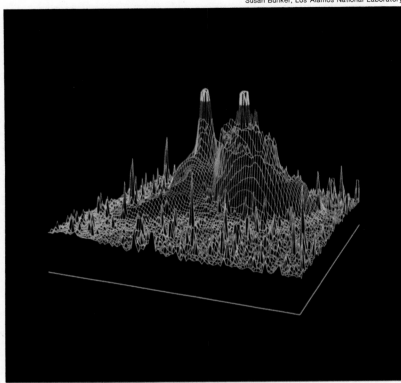

Figure 3 (below): Graphics display represents the strength of a magnetic field across a plane passed through the interior volume of the field. Figure 4 (right): The two most intense regions of light from the double galaxy M51 stand out as high peaks amid a spikelet landscape of individual stars.

possible the creation and enjoyment of colorful plots by the general public. These consist of a computer to generate the numbers and a piece of hardware called a driver that translates the numbers into a format appropriate for an ordinary, horizontally scanning color TV. Without home computers, computer graphics would be reserved for a privileged few who work with expensive equipment.

The graphics churned out by home computers also lie at the heart of a whole new field of entertainment. Sophisticated programs generate colorful images on the TV screen as an integral part of exciting games for one or more participants. The user can even write programs to produce his own games. In yet another application the home computer can be tied into information networks via telephone lines to display on-screen graphics containing a variety of business, cultural, and scientific information.

Pictures from the unseen world

Humans have an overpowering urge to see. At great expense they mounted heavy TV cameras and related electronic equipment on planet-exploring spacecraft. Some had argued that the camera ought to be left home, that lighter instruments could gather all the important physical data. But most people, including the scientists, wanted to see the rocks and hills of Mars and to visually explore the craters of Ganymede.

And now with computer graphics, scientists find that they can see their abstract data displayed in realistic pictures. Mathematicians can see functions, and engineers can observe graphically the stresses in a steel beam.

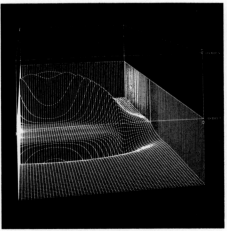

Melvin L. Prueitt, Los Alamos National Laboratory

16

Melvin L. Prueitt, Los Alamos National Laboratory; data supplied by Robert Rowell, University of Massachusetts

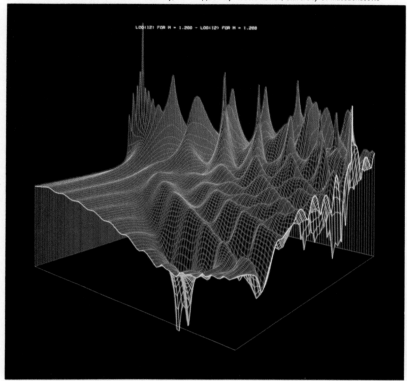

Figure 5: Perspective plot depicts Mie scattering of light by particles in the Earth's atmosphere.

New understandings have been gained as researchers have seen things that would not have been discovered by studying pages of numbers or numerous formulas.

When scientists at the Meson Facility of the Los Alamos National Laboratory in New Mexico built a large hollow magnet to bend a beam of high-energy protons, they wondered how uniform the magnetic field was. Since they could not see, feel, nor smell the magnetic field, they took 25,000 measurements with a magnetic probe throughout the interior volume of the magnet and got 25,000 numbers. They still did not know the shape of the magnetic field. What can a human being do with 25,000 numbers? Physicist Gordon Lind of Utah State University suggested that they plot the numbers in perspective. When they did, they got figure 3. The height of the plotted surface represents the strength of the magnetic field across a "slice" taken through the inside of the magnet's interior volume. They could see not only the shape of the field but something unexpected as well. The faint striations formed by nonparallel horizontal lines across the flat region near the center were immediately obvious to the human visual system. Such features would never have been noticed in an exhaustive study of 25,000 numbers. The scientists knew that something was wrong with the magnet or with the measurements.

Light from a distant double galaxy appears as a charcoal smudge on a long-exposed photographic negative. The astronomer can get very little information by visually studying the negative. The image, however, can be traced with a densitometer, a measuring device that can distinguish among

17

differences in density on a photographic negative far better than the human eye, and the results can be fed to a computer. Figure 4 is the output from a computer for galaxy M51. The height of the surface represents the light intensity of the double galaxy, whose two components stand out unmistakably. The color bands help the astronomer to identify the levels of intensity. The computer even subtracted out the background light from the Earth's atmosphere. The sharp spikes away from the central feature are caused by individual stars in our own Milky Way Galaxy. Now the astronomer can study in detail the characteristics of that celestial marvel. He can have the computer rotate the image and produce pictures from various angles.

The interaction of light with the Earth's atmosphere is very complex. Mie scattering, which is scattering of light from particulate matter in the air, is a good example. The equations that define Mie scattering apply to rainbows, halos around the Sun and Moon, and scattering by dust and air pollutants. Before the advent of computer graphics, scientists could only study the equations and make a few calculations. Now they can study such pictures as figure 5, which plots relative wavelength of light along one horizontal axis and angle of scattering along the other, with the height of the surface representing the magnitude of the scattering. The wealth of detail in just this one plot is striking.

For geological studies a topographical map is useful. The computer can produce such maps in which altitudes are given by color and can print out a color key specifying the altitudes. Although a geologist can go into the field to study the landscape first hand, he cannot see the formations beneath the surface. But he can generate sound waves with explosives and set up instruments to record those sound waves reflected from underground formations. The instruments generate numbers. With the appropriate computer program to interpret the numbers, the geologist can "see" the underground formation in a plot such as figure 6, a location in Nevada. The upper part of the

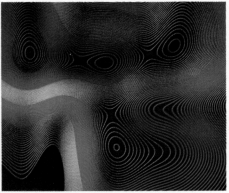

Topographical map made of color-coded contour lines is an easy task for computers. Color-elevation relations plus an accompanying key replace the small numbers printed on the contour lines of conventional maps.

Melvin L. Prueitt, Los Alamos National Laboratory

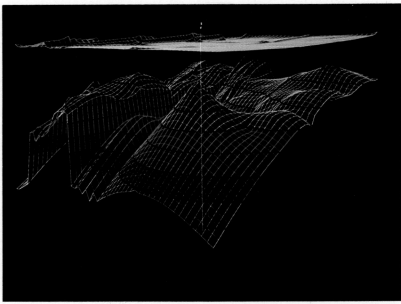

Figure 6: Computer representation of a site in Nevada both above and below ground offers geologists an unusual, highly advantageous view of their subject.

Douglas Lora, Los Alamos National Laboratory

picture is the Earth's surface; the lower one is the formation of interest. Colors denote depth. The Earth's surface is seen to be flattened by erosion and sedimentation, while the underground formation is extremely "mountainous." The vertical line represents the position of a deep well.

There are mountains and valleys that exist only in the mind, but it would be interesting to take them out and look at them occasionally. Computer graphics can represent, for example, the potential electric fields within molecules, with colors defining the regions of influence of different atoms within a molecule. When a scientist has molecular data that are difficult to visualize and even more difficult to explain to colleagues, computer graphics provide a new clarity in scientific communication.

How do biophysicists picture the extremely complex structures in their submicroscopic studies? Some cell components consist of so many molecules that they are impossible to visualize without the help of a picture. Nelson Max at the Lawrence Livermore National Laboratory (LLNL) in California produced one picture, figure 7, representing three subunits of the protein coat of a tomato bushy stunt virus. In another, figure 8, the large spheres represent 90 of the 180 subunits of the viral coat. The yellow side chains are attached to the red subunits and form a framework for the virus within.

Events that occur too rapidly for the human eye and that are invisible or inaccessible to a camera may be calculated and plotted by a computer. The physics department at Brigham Young University, Provo, Utah, calculated the shape of a plasma (extremely hot gas) in an experimental nuclear fusion device. The "archway" of figure 9 shows one half of the plasma a few microseconds after beginning of compression by a magnetic field. The colors define the magnetic pressure exerted on the plasma.

Figure 10 gives an example of the pedagogic value of graphics. Three chemical equations govern a certain chemical reaction. When each of the equations is plotted, it describes a right circular cone. The intersection of the three cones should be the point of equilibrium of the reaction, where opposing reactions go on at equal rates and no net change occurs in the amounts of reactants and products. Question: Is there a unique solution to the set of equations? That is, do the three cones intersect at a single point? The answer is not immediately obvious to most people, but with a computer plot a chemist can quickly show an audience that the answer is affirmative.

When a spacecraft encounters a planet, there is no way of taking a picture of the spacecraft and the planet simultaneously. Computer graphics can incorporate the latest planetary data to provide a motion-picture sequence of spacecraft position and attitude to aid scientists long before the actual flight in their study of trajectory past a planet. When shown on television, such sequences also help the public understand what is happening. James Blinn of NASA's Jet Propulsion Laboratory produced a movie, of which figure 11 is a single frame, showing the U.S. space probe Voyager 2's flyby of Saturn.

Improving on reality

As has been shown, the computer is good at creating a picture where none existed before—from nothing but numbers. In many cases, however, one

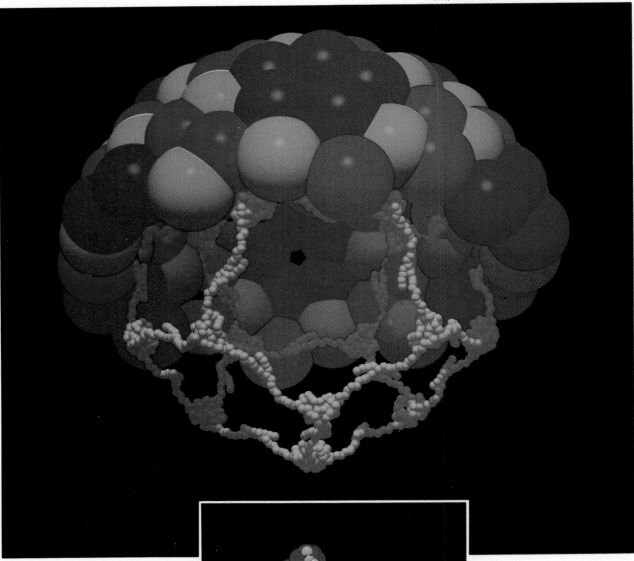

Figure 7 (right): Computer-drawn model of three subunits of the protein coat of a virus helps life scientists comprehend this extremely small yet complex structure. Figure 8 (above): Ninety subunits of the viral coat are represented by large spheres on a framework of side chains.

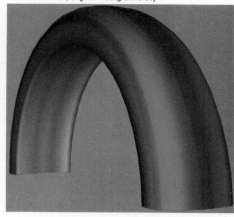

may be presented with a photograph or TV picture from the real world that is of poor quality. If the computer can start with nothing and produce a high-quality picture, surely it could start with a poor picture and yield something satisfactory.

Image enhancement is a very active field in computer graphics. Signals from spacecraft millions of miles from home are processed by computer to remove noise and sharpen the image before producing such startling pictures as those of the thousands of divisions in the rings of Saturn. For a computer it is a simple matter to take slight color variations and then paint a picture with large color variations so that the human observer can easily see subtle details within the turbulent cloud patterns of Jupiter. Scan line by scan line the computer program analyzes the image into spatial frequencies. A sharp edge in a photograph has high-frequency components while a smooth edge has low-frequency components. Upon command the program can boost one component at the expense of another just as sound engineers can boost some frequencies of an old phonograph record to give a better sound.

Suppose someone takes a snapshot of a robber's getaway car, but upon development the image proves too blurred because of motion or an out-of-focus lens to read the license plate. Figure 12 shows what can be done with image enhancement.

Ever since the invention of the X-ray photograph, doctors have worked to refine their abilities to interpret subtle variations in the density of the X-ray negative. Doctors will be the first to admit that man's visual system has not

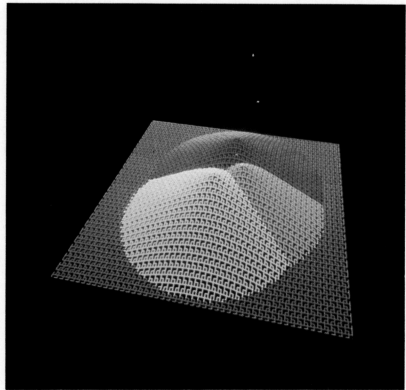

Figure 9 (above): Computer illustration portrays one half of a high-temperature plasma undergoing compression by a magnetic field. Figure 10 (left): Three cones represent three chemical equations that govern a reaction. The cones intersect at only one point, identifying only one point of equilibrium for the reaction.

James F. Blinn, Jet Propulsion Laboratory

Aug. 25, 1981
5:00 PM PDT ERT·

Figure 11: Voyager 2's arrival at Saturn is simulated visually by computer.

evolved to interpret X-rays. When the computer is allowed to translate the image for human sight, the doctor begins to see things with greater clarity, some of which were not visible at all before. Figure 13 shows an X-ray supplied by the Lancaster Cleft Palate Clinic in Pennsylvania and a computer enhanced version produced by Joel Trussell at Los Alamos.

Sculpting for industry

For centuries the tinkerer or modeler has carved in stone, wood, wax, and clay. Often he has wistfully viewed his finished product, wondering how it would appear if it were slightly different. The only way to satisfy that curiosity was to laboriously build another model.

Computers not only draw realistic pictures of models that do not yet exist, but they can control machines to carve out the model from a block of material. But before cutting into actual substance, the human operator first can study various designs visually on a TV monitor. He can have the computer simulate stresses at critical points, study the effects of temperature changes, and estimate the weight of a particular part. If the designer wonders how it would look if it were changed, he simply commands the computer to make the desired change, and in seconds he has the new results. This highly productive, time-saving entry of computer graphics into industry has come to be called computer-aided design, or CAD.

Richard Riesenfeld and colleagues at the University of Utah, Salt Lake

22

City, produced the design of an aircraft bulkhead shown in figure 14. Figure 15 shows how the computer can be commanded to zoom in on part of the model and even cut away a portion of it for close examination. The various colors on the image indicate separate machining tasks guided by numerical control. By having the computer produce pictures that are very realistic, including shading and reflective highlights, rather than line drawings, the designer can judge more accurately whether his design is ready for prototype machining.

With recent advances in theory and algorithms, it is possible to provide accurate graphics and numerically controlled tool-path instructions for good models with free-form "sculptured" surfaces for such objects as telephone handsets, automobiles, airplanes, and household appliances. Moreover, once the model works satisfactorily, the drawings and in-computer testing that were generated during the object's design can serve as instructions for the production machines that will manufacture it or for machining the tools, molds, and other special items needed to make it. Used together with CAD, computer-aided manufacturing (CAM) dramatically reduces the time between conception and the finished product.

Bruce Brown of LLNL produced figure 16, which shows computer-exaggerated bending of a structure. The colors represent the magnitude of the calculated stresses in the structure. The realism and accuracy of computer modeling is evident in figure 17, which compares a computer simulation of the crumpling of a nuclear warhead's nose cone with a one-third scale model that was actually run through an impact test.

A computer for Mickey Mouse

Animation is an obvious application for computer graphics. In traditional animation a storyboard is first produced, consisting of key drawings that outline the progress of the story. The animators and assistants then draw pictures for the movie frames that fill in the action between the key drawings. A computer is not artistic, but a well-designed computer program can create smooth flow from one key frame to the next. It can even dress up and smooth out rough spots in the image itself.

The animator commonly puts his key frames into the computer by enter-

Michael Cannon, Los Alamos National Laboratory

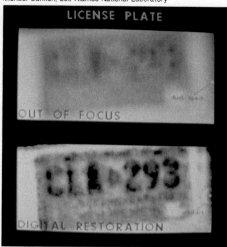

Figure 12 (above): Image enhancement techniques sharpen a blurred photograph of a license plate. Figure 13 (below): Subtle contrast differences in an X-ray plate are emphasized by computer processing.

Photos, Joel Trussell, Los Alamos National Laboratory

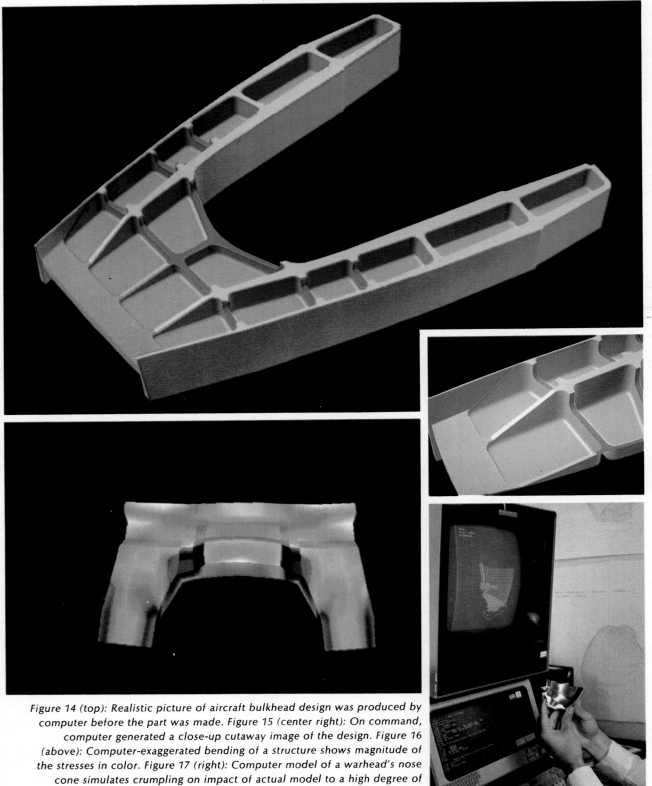

(Top and center right) Richard F. Riesenfeld, Elaine Cohen, Russel D. Fish, Spencer W. Thomas, Elizabeth S. Cobb, and Dino L. Schweitzer, University of Utah; (bottom left) Bruce Eric Brown, Lawrence Livermore National Laboratory; (bottom right) © 1981 Edward L. Miller

Figure 14 (top): Realistic picture of aircraft bulkhead design was produced by computer before the part was made. Figure 15 (center right): On command, computer generated a close-up cutaway image of the design. Figure 16 (above): Computer-exaggerated bending of a structure shows magnitude of the stresses in color. Figure 17 (right): Computer model of a warhead's nose cone simulates crumpling on impact of actual model to a high degree of accuracy.

ing coordinates of individual points around the periphery of an image on a graphics tablet. The points, connected by straight lines, are viewed on the terminal screen. The computer then draws a smooth curve through the points. The animator must flag points at which he wants sharp corners rather than smooth curves. He can move the points around with the graphics tablet until he is satisfied. Upon command the computer fills in the region inside the curve with solid color. Figure 18 shows the sequence of events that produce a key frame.

In order to make an image disappear when it seems to pass behind another image, the images may be defined to exist on different levels. An image on one level will hide an image that passes behind it on a more distant level. The horizon line in figure 18c is assigned a farther level than the cartoon character. The images may be switched from level to level in case the animator wants one image to pass behind another and then move around in front. It seems simple to the animator, but complex program logic is required to remove the hidden portions of images. To create a face, for example, one would define the outline of the head. The eyes, nose, and mouth could be defined as additional images and be assigned to a nearer level than the head. The computer would fill in the region defined as the head with solid color except for those parts that are hidden by the eyes, nose, and mouth, which would be filled in with their own colors.

Once one frame is completed, the animator enters another picture and commands the computer to generate a specified number of intermediate frames. He need change only those parts of the picture that exhibit action. The computer remembers everything else in the previous picture and reproduces it in detail. Many shortcuts are available to the computer animator to ease his workload. He can command the computer to produce rotation,

Figures 18a, 18b, 18c (left to right): To the animator's entry of a few points on a graphics tablet, the computer responds with a crude trace of straight lines, followed by a series of refinements.

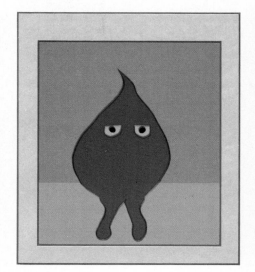

Photos, Melvin L. Prueitt, Los Alamos National Laboratory;
(top) original illustration by Susi Prueitt

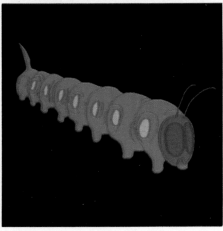

Figures 19a, 19b (bottom to top): Using only two key frames supplied by animator, the computer evolved one into the other to produce a short movie sequence. To create finished butterfly image, artist's sketch was taped to a graphics tablet, and a few points were entered along each important line. The computer filled in the color.

movement from place to place, distortion, and color change of images without having to redraw.

The key frames entered by the animator need not be similar. For instance, in a short movie called *Metamorphosis*, the caterpillar of figure 19a was created on one key frame. The very next key frame was the butterfly of figure 19b. The computer dutifully evolved the one into the other and changed colors on the way.

With considerably more effort on the part of the animator and much more computer time and plotting time, three-dimensional shaded-surface movies can be created with characteristics like those of figure 20. In this case, the separate images are not assigned levels but rather are given coordinates in space. The computer then determines what surfaces must be hidden.

The artist's new brush

Many people have a deep appreciation of beauty in nature and in the artistic creations of others but for various reasons lack the hand/eye coordination and training necessary to produce pleasing art. These "passive artists" may be able to conceive of beautiful designs but not be able to show them to others. With the advent of computer graphics, such people at last have an avenue of expression for their mental creations. But they must first write computer programs that can translate their ideas into pictures.

To make the task simpler, the artist should write a program, called a subroutine, to take care of most of such details as creating a surface, providing shading and color, removing hidden surfaces, and forming perspective projections. Then he can write different driver programs to generate different pictures. The driver programs will use the subroutine to paint the picture.

For example, suppose a person has written a subroutine that can paint surfaces and has decided to create a cave. To avoid defining every point in the cave by hand, he must write a driver program that can make walls, stalactites, and stalagmites and define colors. He can even have it fashion a pool of water in the bottom. He runs the program on the computer and gets figure 21. Once the program is completed, it is easy to make modifications to rearrange the features. Although this cave exists nowhere in nature, one can almost hear the water dripping from its formations.

Although a comprehensive definition of visual beauty is elusive, in physical terms it is simply form and color. In this definition form includes shape, texture, and spatial relationships while color includes hue, saturation, and light intensity. For reasons unknown, people enjoy viewing certain types of forms, and the human visual system is quite adept at perceiving form when given a minimum of visual cues. The computer is an excellent tool with which to study tastes in beauty.

Usually people relate a new visual experience to past experience. Even though an image such as figure 2c may represent some mathematical functions, one can find in it a landscape, albeit somewhat alien. Other computer creations such as figure 22 may not depict surfaces at all, but still the mind assembles the lines into combinations that it perceives as surfaces.

Various forms of symmetry hold a certain fascination. Both bilateral symmetry and top-to-bottom symmetry are easily produced by a computer; the

26

"eye" near the bottom of page 9 is an example of both kinds. Figure 23 has a feeling of symmetry, but the symmetry is broken; the human eye is drawn back to it again and again, trying to solve the mystery of its incompleteness. The curves and colors of figure 22 are pleasing without any symmetry.

No one has yet formulated the relationships among colors that define human preferences. But no one doubts that some color combinations clash while others meld pleasantly. Complementary and contrasting colors can be made to form lovely images. An additional fact that makes the study of color preference more complex is that images which have only slight variations in hue are fascinating to most people.

There are people who prefer photographic realism in art. The scene of everyday objects in figure 24 was synthesized entirely by computer. The objects are not real, nor were they derived from photographs—they were primarily defined as bicubic patches with surface textures. The image was made with about 6,000 pixels across each scan line by Information International, Inc., Culver City, California. Figure 25, by artist David Em, demonstrates a strange realism that one senses may exist somewhere in the universe but not on the Earth.

Figure 20: Realistic computer-animated man is capable of following any motion of a real person as well as of performing feats impossible for a living body.

27

Figures 21, 22, 23 (this page, top to bottom): Ideas for a cave, a pattern of lines, and a construct of surfaces find avenues of expression on the computer display screen. Figure 24 (facing page, top): Texture, shading, opacity, and transparency are qualities of computer-synthesized realism that exist nowhere but as lists of numbers. Figure 25 (facing page, bottom): The computer allows the artist's imagination to paint unearthly yet natural scenes.

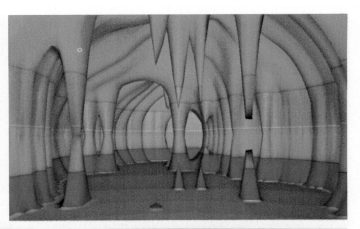

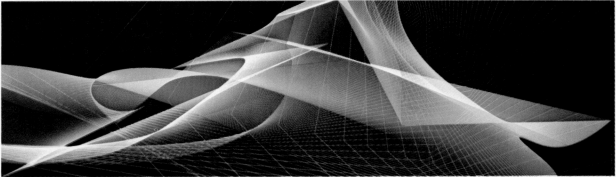

(Top and center) Melvin L. Prueitt, Los Alamos National Laboratory; (bottom) artist, David Em; computer software written by James F. Blinn, © 1980

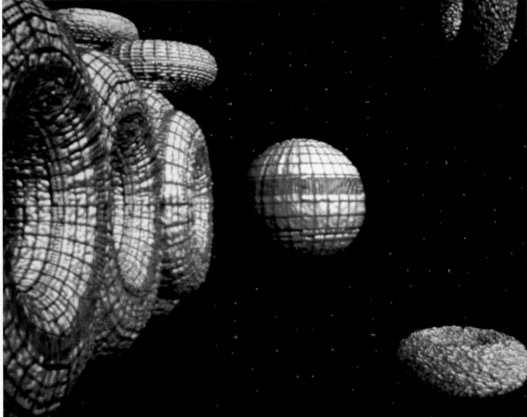

(Bottom) Artist, David Em; computer software written by James F. Blinn, © 1980

Figure 26: The mathematics of fractals did most of the work in producing a landscape not found on Earth.

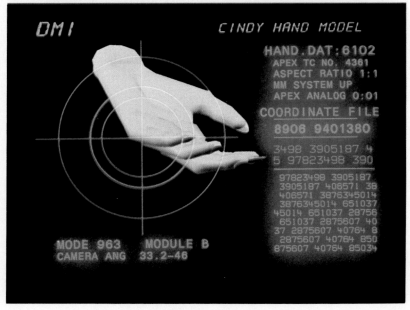

Lifelike, computer-animated models of a hand (right), face, and whole body were used as special effects for a motion picture. In the near future computer-generated performers may act as "stunt" replacements for real actors in hazardous scenes and may even go on to become the featured stars.

Working for the U.S. film industry Loren Carpenter used the mathematics of a family of nature-imitating geometric shapes called fractals to have a computer generate the landscape of figure 26, which otherwise would be extremely difficult to input. Nelson Max produced a computer movie that has shaded surfaces and the movement of ocean waves. Light from the Sun and scattered light from islands were reflected by the water. Figure 27 is a frame from the movie.

Images of the future

Great strides have been taken in computer graphics in the last few years, and the pace seems to be accelerating. Although increased computer speed and

30

Nelson Max, Lawrence Livermore National Laboratory

Figure 27: Frame from a computer movie features waves and reflections all handled by the computer.

higher quality graphics devices are expected, the most significant improvement will probably be made in new software—programs that will be able to do more and better in less time.

The power of computers will be tested in the production of actual three-dimensional moving images. The method of display may be by holography; it may involve coupling of a CRT and a vibrating flexible mirror to produce depth, a technique recently refined by Lawrence Sher of Bolt Beranek and Newman Inc., Cambridge, Massachusetts; or it may be the product of some other technology yet to be discovered. Whatever the method, the amount of information contained in a single three-dimensional image is vast and will require awesome computing power to coordinate the data flow.

With ever greater frequency audiences will see special effects in such movies as *Star Wars* produced by computers and even full-length movies of realistic computer graphics. In the near future, rather than having a stunt man stand in for an actor in dangerous sequences, directors may ask for a computer-generated, animated human figure.

Great artistic creations that would be impossible to form by hand will be produced by interaction between artists and computers. This new era of computer art may inspire a revolution comparable to the Renaissance of Europe. And perhaps there will be works of man and machine to stand the test of time as thoroughly as da Vinci's "Mona Lisa."

See also *1981 Yearbook of Science and the Future* Feature Article: FRACTALS AND THE GEOMETRY OF NATURE.

Industrial robots are unquestionably boosting productivity and product quality in factories around the world. Their long-range effects, however, are far less certain than their performance records.

ROBOTS "MAN" THE ASSEMBLY LINE

by Leonard A. Phillips

Assembly-line robots endlessly repeat their eerie ballet at a Chrysler Corp. plant in St. Louis, Missouri. Retooling for the 1982-model-car production run involved a $75-million plant conversion, including the acquisition of 50 new welding robots. Robots and welding machines automatically place 95% of the 2,500 spot welds needed to assemble each new car body.

LEONARD A. PHILLIPS *is Managing Editor of* Laser Focus *magazine and formerly Senior Editor of* Technology Review, *a publication of the Massachusetts Institute of Technology, Cambridge.*

(Overleaf) Illustration by John Youssi

Robots are here to stay. In the United States, Japan, and several European countries during the past decade these flexible machine tools have escaped the once exclusive purview of science fiction to establish their utility in the workaday world of the assembly line. Increasingly sophisticated models that can see, touch, speak, and react to stimuli—as well as work cooperatively with other robots—are just now beginning to supplant the comparatively crude, typically dumb and senseless ones that constituted virtually the entire robotic work force of the early 1980s.

The common industrial or factory robot is a large, computer-controlled and reprogrammable mechanical arm. It can be equipped with various manipulators to grasp tools or objects (a simple pair of prongs is the most common "hand") and with such specialized devices as spray-paint guns and metal grinders. Some carry sensing devices that can recognize different colors and shapes, others can sense only the presence or absence of a workpiece, and still others have no sensory capability at all. All can perform around the clock and are readily adapted to new tasks. They typically function for years with only minor maintenance; 40,000 hours is a reasonable period to expect from a robot prior to an overhaul.

34

(Left, both photos) Bill Pierce—Rainbow; (right) BBC Hulton Picture Library

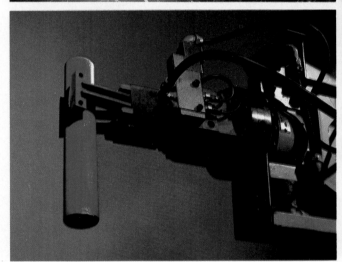

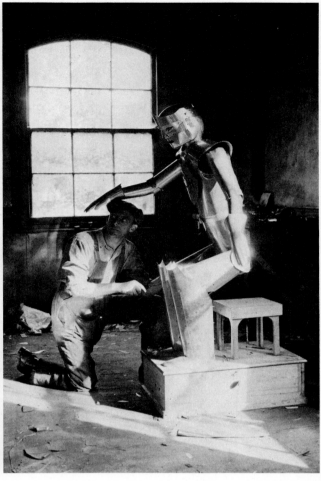

On being robotic

"Consider strapping yourself into a chair with only one arm free. Put blinders on your eyes, plugs in your ears, and a clothespin on your nose. Float in water so you'll feel weightless, put a boxing glove on the one free hand, and try to assemble a mechanical calculator using only chopsticks." Thus did Ken Overton, computer scientist at the University of Massachusetts at Amherst, personify the way many of today's simpler robots meet their daily challenges.

Assembly-line robots are hypnotically fascinating to watch despite, and possibly because of, their sensory limitations. In eerie pantomime of living workers they repeat complex sequences of movements with precision time after time. One waits for a robot to make a false move, to hesitate, to change its routine—in futility. They are the ultimate servants of production. Indeed, the word robot stems from the Czechoslovak *robota,* which means "forced labor," the term having been popularized a half-century ago by Czech author Karel Capek's play *R.U.R.*

Simple robots—that is, those with little or no ability to monitor and react to stimuli—are nonetheless instant learners of routines, typically by being

Robot arms outfitted with various tools or grippers (left, top and bottom) replace human beings in many dangerous, strenuous, or repetitive situations while tirelessly performing their tasks with speed and consistent quality. But "replace" has other implications, as factory workers and labor unions can attest. Robot "Eric" (above), designed in 1928, was inspired by Karel Capek's play R.U.R. Posing imperiously over its builder, it suggests a difficulty that still haunts robot-human relations today—that of making the distinction between master and servant.

· 35

Photos, courtesy, Cincinnati Milacron Marketing Company

Pushing buttons on a hand-held teaching unit (above), an operator leads the robot arm of a manufacturing cell through the series of movements and tasks that the machine is to perform (right). From this guidance the robot-control computer calculates the shortest-path, straight-line motions that the robot will actually follow.

"walked" in slow motion by human operators through each step of a sequence. The skilled hand-eye manipulations performed by a robot's human instructor to move it through a series of lifts, turns, and twists is reminiscent of the strategies of video game players and can even border on fun. Some robots can be taught to execute sequences with as many as 2,000 separate steps.

The robot market

According to one estimate the world population of true industrial robots in 1981 was about 23,000, of which about 14,000 were in Japan, 5,000 in the U.S., and 4,000 in Western Europe. In the U.S. about 80% were being used in the metalworking industries, and about 30% belonged to only six firms, of which three were in the auto industry.

Estimates of robot population from various sources vary because of differences in criteria used to determine what a robot is. In 1980 the Robot Institute of America (RIA), a division of the Society of Manufacturing Engineers headquartered in Dearborn, Michigan, issued their authoritative definition: a robot is a reprogrammable, multifunctional manipulator designed to move material, parts, tools, or specialized devices through variable programmed motions for the performance of a variety of tasks.

More optimistic counts, such as that of the Japan Industrial Robot Association, which has set the Japanese total alone at 50,000, include machines that appear to be robotic but that are able to perform only one kind of task and are not reprogrammable. They are really single-purpose, automatic machines and do not fulfill the RIA definition of robot.

The significance of the robot population is not found in its current size but in the increasing sophistication of its newest members and in the rate at which demand for them is growing. "We are at the bottom of a market explosion," remarked Brian R. Ford, manager of robot systems at ASEA Inc., the U.S. subsidiary of the Swedish firm ASEA AB. Other industry spokesper-

Adapted from "Robots in Modern Industry," Ewald Heer, ASTRONAUTICS & AERONAUTICS, p. 52, September 1981

robot market trends and projections

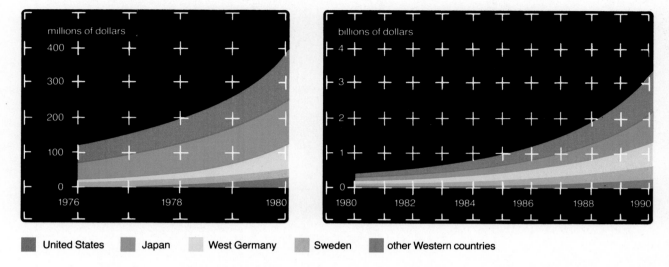

United States Japan West Germany Sweden other Western countries

sons would agree. Even the most limited, pragmatic niches for robots in today's factories are sufficiently numerous to stimulate a burgeoning demand.

Graphs show past performance of the robot market and an estimate of future trends.

While industry clearly is becoming infatuated with robots, workers stand to benefit as well from these machines, which can perform dangerous, repetitious, and difficult tasks in environments ill-suited for humans. For example, robots feed stock into stamping presses, spray-paint auto and truck bodies (advanced models at General Motors recognize different body styles and adjust themselves accordingly), grind metal, sort parts, pick up parts and place them where directed, drill and deburr intricate series of holes, cut gear teeth, and spot-weld sheet metal assemblies. Moreover, they do these tasks much more rapidly than can humans, and with consistent quality. More advanced robots can work several ordinary machine tools in rapid succession, yielding productivity that is beyond human capability. And one robotic system, manufactured by Fujitsu Fanuc, Ltd., in Tokyo, is the first to produce other robots, at a rate of about 100 units per month.

Despite these practical benefits robots are just beginning to enjoy a bull market. The lure of their many potential assets is still mitigated by several countervailing forces. One major holdback is initial cost. Robots can cost from $5,000 or so for simple "pick and place" models to $150,000 and more for sophisticated systems that have sensory and reactive abilities. In the latter, adaptive control, the ability to monitor and modify actions as they are being made, is highly desirable but largely in the experimental stage.

Another hindering force is managerial hesitation. "Managers may be reluctant to deal with the necessary organizational or procedural changes that generally accompany the adoption of a new technology," according to a recent report on the robotization of industry from Arthur D. Little, Inc., a U.S. research and management consulting firm.

Political and social uncertainty adds to the restraint. Robots are certain to displace workers from many blue-collar jobs in manufacturing. Some ob-

37

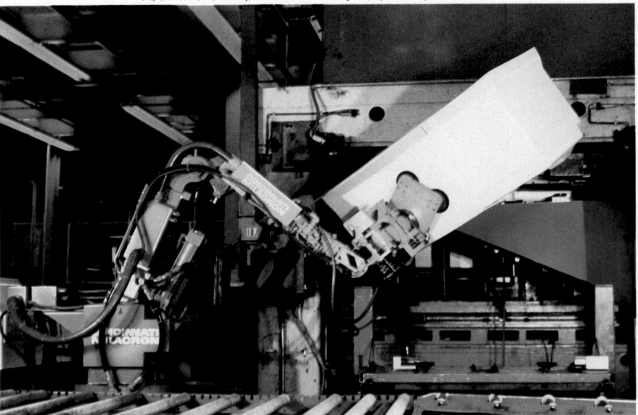

The mixture of strength, delicacy, and precision characteristic of industrial robots makes them adaptable to a broad range of demands. Heavy-duty robot arm (above) lifts cumbersome printing-press roller. Robot fitted with specialized gripper (top) transfers delicate refrigerator liners. Tiny high-speed robot arm (right) wires and bonds hybrid-chip components with ultrasound; the end tool doubles as an ultrasonic feed horn.

servers feel that unions are underestimating the effect that robotization will have on job availability; others argue that technological unemployment has been a common fear throughout history and that robots have created more jobs than they have displaced. In Sweden a strategy emphasizing worker benefits has won over the nation's labor unions, potentially the strongest critics and foes of industrial robotization. Nevertheless, industry has been cautioned against the lure of overautomation. For example, at a recent symposium on robotics computer expert Berthold K. P. Horn of the Massachusetts Institute of Technology (MIT) offered for criticism a scenario in which a complex production robot is surrounded by a few humans who "sweep the floor and orient the parts"—a poor use of human labor.

A continuing role for dedicated, single-purpose machines also may serve to slow acceptance of more flexible industrial robots. These machines perform high-volume, simple, and repetitive tasks most economically, but the advent of cheaper robots could change this picture. General Motors is already planning robotic assembly lines, and its computer scientists are envisioning inexpensive robots supplanting even the high-volume fixed machines that presently turn out engines and transmissions. Robots would enable manufacturers to retool production lines quickly and cheaply to produce variations in such mass-produced assemblies; retooling fixed machines is an extremely costly and time-consuming process. It is reasonable to conclude that although fixed machinery already in operation will continue to be used for some time, replacement machines are likely to be robots.

The robotics industry of the early 1980s has been compared to the computer industry as it was perhaps 30 years earlier, shortly after development of the first successful digital computer. Open speculation about the future of computers was quite conservative at that time, possibly to protect existing grants and contracts, whose limited goals might otherwise have seemed too shortsighted. Today substantively new applications for computers seem to be devised almost daily. Computers smaller than a fingernail (the first successful digital computer filled a large room) animate children's toys, guide cruise missiles, endow automobile safety systems with speech, enable gunnery systems on the newest military tanks to hit the mark during high-speed maneuvers, and permit exploratory spacecraft such as the Viking landers to probe other worlds—unthinkable tasks in the 1950s.

The computer analogy augurs phenomenal growth and profound influence for robots, which after all are the physical extensions of computers. And it also suggests that growth will occur in directions that have not yet been conceived.

The rise of robots

Development of the earliest robots was stimulated by the still-familiar goal of boosting productivity on medium-sized, batch-production lines that might make several hundred or thousand units over a period of a few days or weeks. Such runs generally are too small to justify the use of specialized automatic machines that would be scrapped after production ceased, and yet they are too large to meet time constraints with human workers and non-automatic machines.

Robots were envisioned to meet such needs far longer than they have been technologically possible. Practical robots had to await the development of large-scale integration, or LSI, techniques that would fit many electronic circuitry components onto a tiny chip of substrate. Prior to such microprocessors, computers were too large, expensive, delicate, and unreliable for use under factory conditions. Microprocessors not only reduced the size of computers dramatically but also were cheap and could be made extremely rugged. They swept away the last barrier to the development of practical factory robots.

Before 1964 there were no true robots. In that year Unimation Inc. and AMF-Versatran introduced the first programmable manipulators. Unimation, then a brand-new division of Condec Corp. (Consolidated Diesel Corp.) devoted exclusively to robotics, was destined to become one of the two largest producers of robots in the U.S. Unimation's product was based on principles developed in 1946 by U.S. inventor and engineer George Devol, who had received a patent for his innovation "programmed article transfer" in 1961. In 1974 Cincinnati Milacron Inc., the other of the "big two" U.S. robot makers, introduced a minicomputer-controlled manipulator, thus creating significant competition. Other manufacturers soon entered the fray, including DeVilbiss Co., Prab Conveyor Inc. (which acquired Versatran in 1979), Machine Intelligence Corp., Automatix Inc., and Octek, Inc., in the U.S.; Hitachi Ltd. in Japan; ASEA AB in Sweden; and Keller & Knappich in West Germany.

By 1981 there was roughly one robot for each 3,000 workers throughout all U.S. industry, and one for each 1,300 workers in the U.S. metalworking sector. These figures are based on the March 1981 census of the Bureau of Labor Statistics and the Carnegie-Mellon University Robotics Institute survey of April 1981. Batch production comprises more than 60% of all U.S. manufacturing output, and such proportions of robots to humans are far too small to suit many large manufacturers. To maintain annual productivity increases of 6% General Electric Co. expects robots to take over 15,000 jobs, now performed by its 37,000 production workers, by the turn of the century (2,000 in "relatively short order"). General Motors plans to boost its robot population from several hundred to 14,000 by 1990. Industry giants IBM and Westinghouse have set up entirely new divisions to deal with robots within their own operations.

Such growth is almost certain to accelerate, according to a recent joint report by the Society of Manufacturing Engineers and the University of Michigan. It forecasts that by the 1990s robots equipped with well-developed senses of sight and touch will be able to approximate the results of human workers in batch-assembly work. By 1988 robots and automatic machines will replace half of the current U.S. labor force that assembles small components. And the Carnegie-Mellon survey concludes that by the year 2025 it is conceivable that the sophisticated robots of that time will have replaced almost all operative jobs in manufacturing, which accounted for 8% of the 1981 work force, and in addition will be performing some nonmanufacturing jobs in the retail and office sectors.

The rising cost of labor more than any other single factor has caused the current great interest in robots. One need look no farther than to trends in the relative hourly costs of human and robotic workers to appreciate why such interest was not manifested several years ago. Unimation calculates that the cost of human labor including such fringe benefits as life and health insurance and retirement programs more than quadrupled over the past 21 years, from about $3.50 per hour in 1960 to nearly $17 per hour in 1981. Meanwhile, the hourly cost of operating a robot has remained reasonably constant, between $4 and $4.50 (Cincinnati Milicron sets the figure at $5, including installation, maintenance, overhaul, depreciation over an eight-year period, and cost of power). Because these dollar figures are not corrected to account for the effects of inflation, the real, constant-dollar cost of robots probably has decreased substantially.

Along with attractive operating costs, robots boast performance records that show unarguably striking gains in productivity over levels attained by conventional automatic machinery operated by humans. Japan's Matsushita Electrical Industrial Co. Ltd., for example, reported a 2,900% increase in the productivity of a vacuum cleaner production line on which 120 persons and their machines were replaced with a team of computer-linked robots and four human supervisors. A color-sensing robot system tripled sorting speeds on a telephone-parts assembly line at a plant of Western Electric Co., Inc., in Atlanta, Georgia. And a robot drilling system at General Dynamics Corp. boosted the production rate of aluminum fuselage panels about 400%.

The manufacture of machine tools—the basis of all manufacturing processes—is itself exclusively a batch-production process and a most appropriate candidate for robotization. A round-the-clock robot work force could greatly increase the productivity of machine tool manufacture, which involves metal-cutting and metal-finishing machinery that typically is used only 6–27% of the time it is available. According to the periodical *American Machinist* almost half of the downtime is traceable to the incomplete use of second and third work shifts, periods when humans prefer to be anywhere but at work. Holidays and vacations account for about one-third of the

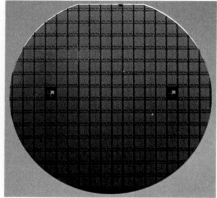

Two hundred microprocessors, each able to handle eight million bits of information per second, reside on a silicon wafer ten centimeters across. The ability to microminiaturize complex electronic circuitry shrank the size and cost of computers, thus clearing the way for the development of practical factory robots.

Factory worker assembles large robot arm, a task still better done by humans at Unimation's plant in Danbury, Connecticut.

downtime in low-volume metal-cutting, and unspecified plant shutdowns account for nearly one-third of the downtime in larger volume operations. Probing the reasons for such losses provided a topic for discussion at a recent National Science Foundation workshop, which concluded that the failure of U.S. manufacturers to apply the latest manufacturing technology—particularly computer-linked robots and other machines—is the fundamental single cause of the nation's productivity problems.

Slow and steady into the future

Thousands of new robots cannot be installed overnight. Such a revolution would overwhelm the infrastructure of a well established industrial complex. There is the need to realize benefits from sizable investments already tied up in today's rigidly automated factories, which themselves may be considered huge, specialized machines. And there is the problem of displacing workers. Labor leaders are becoming more vocal about contractual protections for the job security of the rank and file during hard economic times. Robotics could be perceived as just another thorn in the side of workers already threatened with economically dictated firings.

Industry planners claim that robotics will make life better for workers, who presumably will be retrained and relocated to pursue more interesting occupations than those taken over by robots. But the costs of retraining and relocation are likely to be substantial and to be concentrated geographically. More than half of the unskilled and semiskilled workers destined to be replaced by robots work in a cluster of five states—Indiana, Illinois, Michigan, Ohio, and Wisconsin—plus New York and California. Manufacturing processes involving metalworking comprise much of the statewide employment in these seven states. Surely it would be politically and economically unfeasible for employers there to deal with radical changes in the way their factories operate and at the same time to underwrite the costs of retraining and relocating displaced workers. Thus, from a socioeconomic view it is likely that the conversion of factories in the U.S. to fully robotized, automated facilities will be gradual. It is far more likely that new, automated plants will be built and older plants abandoned or sold.

Furthermore, serious technical barriers stand in the way of the fully automated factory of the future. The capabilities of individual robots continue to be improved by their makers, but routine cooperation among robots promises to be a vexingly unattainable goal in the factory for some time.

Today's stand-alone robots are the vanguard of totally automated factories yet to come. Some may run several machine tools in a configuration called a work cell or manufacturing cell, thus replacing a number of humans who perform solitary operations. Thus engaged, a present-day robot may produce and finish parts or final assemblies.

If human bodies can be said to have analogues in robotic machines, then human social systems have as machine metaphors the "assembly/disassembly networks" that consist of groups of robots working together. The next phase of robotization will be the commercial development of such systems, which will form intelligent automated factories capable of producing a continuous flow of finished products. Limited arrangements of such "flexi-

42

Fujitsu Fanuc Ltd., Tokyo

ble computerized manufacturing systems," or FCMS's, are under study at the Charles Stark Draper Laboratory Inc. and Ingersoll-Rand Co. in the U.S. and exist in the East German "Prisma 2" system and in the Japanese "methodology for unmanned manufacturing," or MUM, system. But before FCMS's become feasible for general use in typically complex manufacturing tasks, improvements will have to be made in robot sensing and reactive capabilities, as well as in the design of communications links among teams of robots.

A fundamental hurdle for those who would implement highly capable FCMS's is the inability of even the most sophisticated of today's commercially available robots to measure and otherwise sense and inspect with precision the parts and assemblies they produce. Metrology, the practice of precision measurement, is beyond all but the most advanced one-of-a-kind laboratory prototypes. Such machines can accommodate unforeseeable variations in materials, monitor their own performance, and make necessary control changes "on the fly."

The basic challenge in designing such machines is to find a reliable diagnostic "handle" for the machine to measure and react to—some variable that is indicative of a quality or characteristic to be controlled. Machines with some adaptive or closed-loop control capability can do jobs that are too complex for reliable prediction, and with minimal waste or error. For example, an automatic welding machine uses the voltage of the welding arc as a diagnostic characteristic of welding quality. An automatic press brake controls the motion of its punch by calculating the point of contact with a work piece as a function of the force expended during penetration; it then reverses the motion at the precise moment to produce a clean hole.

Robot and metal-turning lathe function as a work cell, which in turn forms part of a flexible computerized manufacturing system at the Fujitsu Fanuc plant in Fuji, Japan. Using work cells, automated warehouses, and unmanned carriers, the factory operates a normal day shift and an unattended night shift, producing industrial robots and machine tools.

43

Small robot arm fitted with a mechanical gripper, lens, and solid-state television camera can be directed by its control computer to locate a shape optically, pick it up, and insert it into the appropriate hole in the plastic toy. TV monitor displays the two-dimensional image "seen" by the computer.

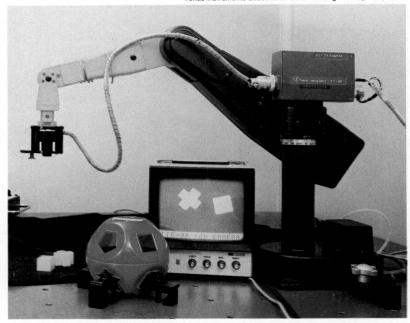

If metrology cannot be included in a routine work-cell function, parts made in antecedent work cells in an FCMS that fail to meet specifications could cause serious foul-ups in subsequent stages of production. Thus, even the prototype machines currently in existence must also be able to certify that their work is "to specification."

Senses uncommon

In order to measure things, robots somehow must be able to examine them critically for such quantities as length, smoothness, roundness, surface regularity, and weight. Neither people nor robots can make such determinations without sophisticated senses. But the present state of robotic sight and touch is far too primitive to do the job on the assembly line.

Today's robots can see in only two dimensions—and that very poorly. This limitation prevents them from doing such simple tasks as picking assortments of parts from bins as well as from making accurate measurements of parts that do not lie in a plane that is exactly parallel to the background. Although they can discriminate among silhouettes and colors of objects, they cannot determine depth. They also cannot tell objects apart if the objects overlap or do not contrast sufficiently with their background, because these robots recognize only "global features" of objects; in other words, complete silhouettes.

A typical robotic vision system consists of one or more television cameras, appropriate lighting, a computer system for processing the TV image, and hardware that connects this equipment with the computer that controls the robot itself. A system might work in the following manner:

1. The camera sends images to the vision system computer. A human operator manually adjusts the image contrast so that only all-white (workpiece) and all-black (background) values reach the computer.

(Facing page, top) Program developed at Stanford University uses light-source information to help computerized vision systems interpret images in three dimensions. Computer first analyzes hand-traced lines that have been superimposed on the edges and shadow boundaries of a photo image (left) for meaningful alignments and coincidences based on knowledge of the direction of the Sun; it then makes a three-dimensional interpretation (top right). Final picture (bottom right) is generated without any further input of information about the object in the photo. Other computer programs can then attempt to identify this generated structure by matching it against models of specific objects.

44

Photos, David Lowe, Artificial Intelligence Laboratory, Stanford University

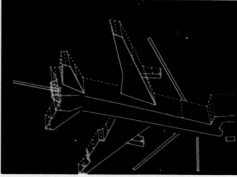

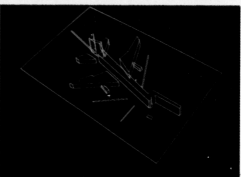

2. The computer then traces the image and determines where the edges of objects are on each scan of the image. It stores in temporary memory lists of points where edges occur. Tracing scans are always made from the top to the bottom of an image, and not until some lists merge at a common point can the computer be sure that it has found the complete outline of an object. As an example, a fork might be positioned with its tines pointed toward the top of the scan. Not until the scan proceeded to the connections of the tines could the lists for the left and right sides of each tine be related, and not until it proceeded to the tip of the handle could the lists for the left and right sides of the fork handle be related and the complete silhouette of the fork be determined.

3. The computer calculates the position and orientation of the silhouettes

Computerized depth-perception system under study at Stanford incorporates automated stereopsis, in which the computer compares stereo pairs of images and determines the depth to every point in the scene by a correlation process. Computer-synthesized stereo pair (below left), which represents an aerial view of a cluster of buildings was analyzed by such a technique and the computed heights used to plot the scene in three-dimensional perspective (below).

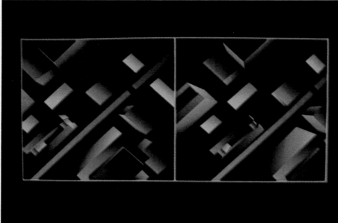

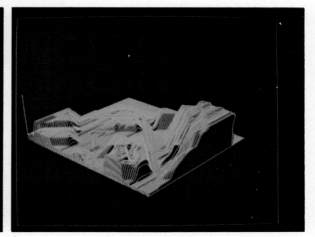

Photos, Harlyn Baker, Artificial Intelligence Laboratory, Stanford University

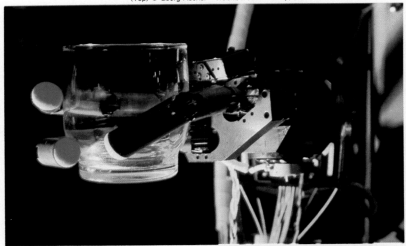

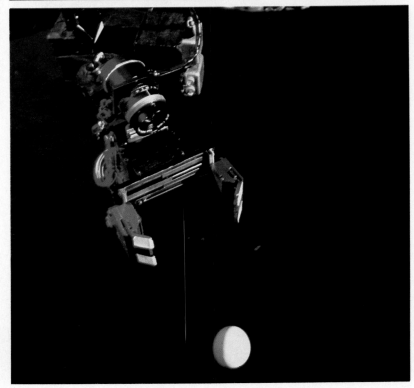

Three-fingered gripper with sensors at the tips (top) resulted from research at the University of Tokyo to give robots a sense of touch. Robot at the U.S. National Bureau of Standards uses a pressure-sensitive claw and TV-camera guidance to grasp an egg without cracking it (bottom).

and searches its permanent memory for similar shapes. When it makes a match, it "recognizes" the image and instructs the robot-control computer how the necessary operation is to be done; for example, it might tell the robot computer the position of the fork, whereupon the robot would be able to pick it up in the proper orientation for a subsequent operation.

This method of visualizing an object is cumbersome and slow. Ways of linking vision microprocessors in parallel, each capable of handling its own lists of edge data, promise to speed up the list-making part of the process. But a two-dimensional image still is the result.

46

(Top, left) Dan McCoy—Rainbow; (top, right) Tadanori Saito—PPS/Photo Researchers; (bottom, left) NASA; (bottom, right) Laski—Sipa Press/Black Star

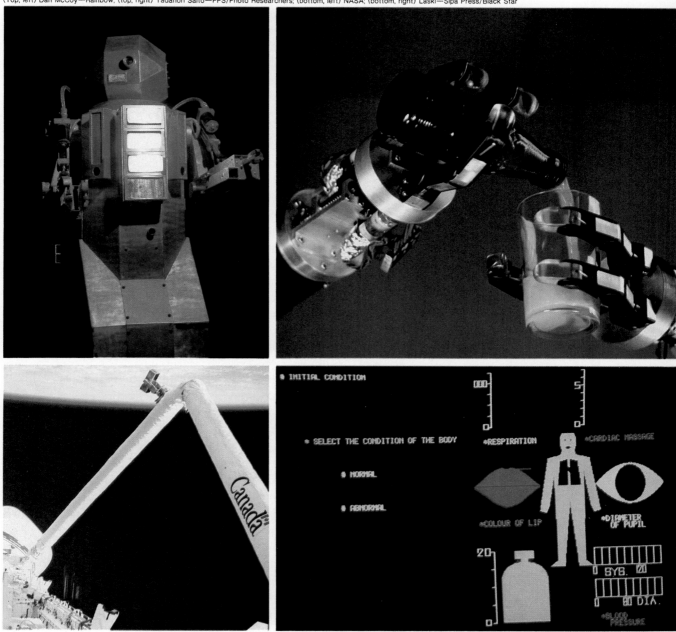

As performance improves and versatility expands, robots can be expected to move out of the factory and into other occupations. Robot sentry (top left) is designed to patrol areas of radioactive contamination and other hazardous environments, shine a light on intruders, and move at a 65-kilometer-per-hour clip. Remote manipulator system of the U.S. space shuttle "Columbia" (bottom left) is a giant, computer-controlled robotic arm and hand for moving objects in and out of the spacecraft. Computer graphic readout (bottom right) reflects various vital signs of a robot "patient" developed to train medical students in emergency cardiopulmonary procedures including heart massage, artificial respiration, and drug injections. Less technical jobs for robots are also foreseen (top right).

Research on three-dimensional robotic vision is being pursued—at Stanford University and at MIT, for example—based on the means by which two-eyed living creatures perceive depth: binocular parallax. Images from each of the two eyes of a human being are somewhat different, varying more with objects that are closer and resembling each other more with objects that are increasingly distant. The brain, and possibly part of the eye, combines and processes these stereo pairs to produce the perception of depth along with the features of the object and perhaps its identification.

But matching stereo pairs is an extremely difficult task for today's robot vision systems. Primitive systems are just now being assembled in research laboratories. A system at MIT uses two TV cameras and a series of microprocessors to produce a stereo image in under four seconds. A system called ACRONYM at Stanford can recognize some objects from only a few of their features (a jet airplane is a frequently used example), but such systems would be prohibitively expensive for use outside the laboratory. Moreover, they have poor fidelity and are too troublesome for industrial use.

A critical sense of touch would be of great use to metrology. But while vision systems, crude as they are, benefit from a technology well developed by the television industry, current attempts at making robotic touch sensors are truly pioneering efforts. A touch sensor under development at the MIT Artificial Intelligence Laboratory consists of a sandwich of silicone rubber, a series of 256 tiny pressure-sensitive switches in a 16-by-16 configuration, and a separating layer of fine nylon mesh; it can discriminate among screws, washers, and cotter pins. It is undeniably a start, but FCMS would require a far better capability.

Further ahead: production and reproduction

Many unquestionably appropriate tasks promise to keep the fires of robotic innovation and improvement burning brightly for years to come. Jobs in space, under the sea, in mines, in radioactive environments, and in warfare are all eminently suitable for robots—and similarly hazardous for people.

Perhaps most intriguing of all robotic capabilities is that of self-replication. The implications of machines that reproduce themselves are profound indeed. The National Aeronautics and Space Administration (NASA) and the American Society for Engineering Education (ASEE) have speculated jointly about a self-replicating robot factory on the Moon, using lunar raw materials. Such an endeavor could yield virtually limitless productivity for a small initial investment, a "seed" factory imported from Earth. They calculate that a self-replicating lunar factory built from 100 tons of hardware would require less than 20 years at a reasonable rate of productivity to manufacture enough photovoltaic cells to produce 500 billion watts of electricity from Earth-orbiting solar power satellites. That compares with 6,000 years for a conventional automated factory to achieve the same goal.

The NASA/ASEE collaboration also speculated that such a factory would be "a stepping-stone to replicating manufacturing complexes on the surfaces of other planets . . . themselves the offspring of automated self-replicating factories. . . ." What would be the role of humans in such a machine-dominated outreach?

48

Norbert Wiener, mathematician and founder of the theoretical study of cybernetics, wrote in *God and Golem, Inc.:* "One of the great future problems which we must face is that of the relation between man and the machine, of the functions which should properly be assigned to these two agencies. On the surface, the machine has certain clear advantages. . . . On the other hand, the human being has certain nonnegligible [mathematicians' jargon for "important"] advantages. . . . Any sensible man would consider the purposes of man as paramount in the relations between man and machine."

And yet Wiener points out in *Cybernetics:* "An animal that multiplies is able to create other animals in its own likeness at least approximately, although not so completely in its own likeness that they cannot vary in the course of time. If this variation is itself inheritable, we have the raw material on which natural selection can work." He thus begs the possibility that a robotic "race" with the vastness of space and time in which to replicate could itself produce progeny that vary from "parent" machines. Does the human race face the science-fiction-like challenge of managing a race of machines that eventually may develop different control strategies than originally intended by their creators?

In light of the etymology of "robot," such a foreboding future would certainly render the term obsolete. Logically it could no longer apply to the mechanical servants that became the masters of their fiefdom in space.

Awesome swarm of toy robots, part of a private collection, bespeaks the fascination that humans long have had for artificial men. It also conveys something of the potential of robots given the ability to reproduce and the freedom of space and time to do so. A technically competent society eventually may be able to build such machines, but only a wise society will feel obliged to consider the effects of cumulative mutations to their programming before turning them loose in the Galaxy.

49

THE ELECTRICITY

ELECTRICITY
OF LIFE AND LIMB

by Richard B. Borgens

Living organisms generate natural electricity during growth and development, tissue regeneration, and wound healing. Real comprehension of this process is just beginning, but already it has been used successfully to repair the human body.

It sometimes confounds the public to read that hundreds of thousands of dollars are being spent by scientists interested in the basic biology of the slime mold, money supposedly targeted for cancer research. The same could be said for funds being used to find links between developing seaweed eggs and regenerating salamander limbs, or between elongating pollen tubes and differentiating nerve fibers. Although common denominators exist in all of the above, they simply are not obvious—and for a good reason. Nature does not willingly give away its secrets. Fundamental insights into such complicated mechanisms as the control of growth are often derived from studies of very basic and simple biological systems. Evolution is very conservative in preserving certain physiological and structural adaptations in cells, tissues, and even whole organisms. At the cellular level similarities often appear between kingdoms. To the cell physiologist there are probably as many likenesses between plant cells and animal cells as there are differences.

This unity among living organisms is well demonstrated by recent advances in developmental biology, which are giving clues about the nature of embryonic development and cell differentiation as well as wound healing and tissue reconstruction. What all of these processes have in common, and what seaweed eggs and salamander limbs share, is a natural flow of electricity, a steady DC electricity similar in principle to the battery-driven current that powers flashlights and automobile electrical systems. The major distinction is that in living organisms current is carried by ions, *i.e.*, electrically charged atoms of sodium, calcium, and other elements, rather than by electrons. It is now becoming apparent that changes in the electrical character of certain cells and tissues are influential factors in growth and development.

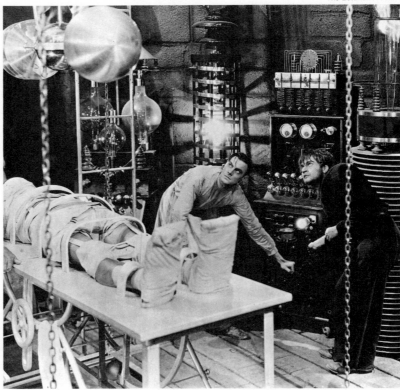

Electrical apparatus features prominently in efforts to return life to the dead in Frankenstein, a 1931 film adaptation of Mary Shelley's 1818 novel. Long before electricity was understood scientifically, people knew of the awesome power of natural lightning to destroy life. Some felt intuitively that electricity also was somehow linked to its creation.

***RICHARD B. BORGENS** is a Staff Scientist with the Institute for Medical Research, San Jose, California.*

(Overleaf) Illustration by John Youssi

Early work

Although the idea of bioelectrical influences may sound novel, it is in reality very old. The fathers of modern physiology and neurophysiology all appreciated the possible role of steady current flow in processes as diverse as wound healing and nerve regeneration. For example, the first person to measure the action potential in nerves—the brief shift in electrical potential across the membrane of a nerve fiber in response to a stimulus—was the 19th-century German physiologist E. Du Bois-Reymond. He also reported measurements of steady current flow in response to wounding human skin as early as 1843. From the early 1900s through the 1960s many scientists toyed with the idea that natural electricity is involved with growth and development. In most cases, however, these investigators lacked either a fundamental understanding of what electricity in living systems really is or the proper instruments to measure and characterize it.

In the 1960s embryologist Lionel F. Jaffe of Purdue University, West Lafayette, Indiana, felt that these older notions of natural electricity may really hold the key to understanding certain mysteries of development. Jaffe began by exploring a simple system, the control mechanisms that help to establish embryological polarity in developing fucus eggs. The eggs of this common marine brown alga are released into eddies and currents of the intertidal zone along rocky seacoasts. Here they are fertilized, in the fashion of animal eggs, by mobile free-swimming sperm. From then on, the egg is sensitive to a variety of environmental cues, which help it to determine a specific polarity at the time of germination some 12 hours later. During germination a bulge on one side of the egg marks the beginnings of the rhizoid, or holdfast, that portion of the seaweed that grips the rocks. As early as the first complete cell division, the egg already has separated into two cells with distinctly different fates: one that will form the rhizoid and the other, the thallus (that portion that will become the shoots and fronds of the seaweed). Jaffe, taking note of developmental physiologist Elmer J. Lund's pioneering work in fucus from the 1920s to the 1940s, felt as Lund did that a difference in electrical potential across the egg may precede and may help to determine the character of the structural changes that become apparent with the first cell divison of the egg.

Jaffe performed a simple, yet elegant experiment to measure the electrical potential across this minute egg, which is only a tenth of a millimeter (0.004 inches) in diameter. He filled a small glass capillary with fucus eggs such that several hundred of the eggs were lined up in a row within the capillary. Knowing that the rhizoid would emerge on the dark side of the cell, he illuminated the eggs with plane-polarized light along the long axis of the capillary tube. Thus, when all of the eggs germinated, their rhizoids were all ordered in the same direction. Then Jaffe measured the electrical potential difference across the capillary tube and divided by the number of eggs in "series." This result gave him an estimate of the total voltage drop across an individual egg. He hypothesized that the polarity of this tiny voltage, which was in fractions of a microvolt, helps determine the developmental polarity of the eggs as they germinate. His next step was to devise an instrument that would measure precisely the minute densities of current traversing the egg, associated with its natural electric field.

In the early 1970s, Jaffe and his student Richard Nuccitelli eventually designed and built such a device. Called the ultrasensitive vibrating probe system, it allowed as much as 1,000 times greater resolution of current entering or leaving a biological source than with conventional measuring techniques. Current that leaves a local area of a cell must be balanced by the same amount entering it. The same amount of total current traversing the cell must also complete the circuit through the medium. The vibrating probe records that component of the current entering or leaving cells or tissues in the medium, without physically penetrating or even touching the cell. The medium can be the natural medium in which cells are found: blood, body fluids, pond water, or seawater in the case of fucus eggs. The probe itself, which is a tiny, rapidly vibrating platinum electrode, oscillates between two points in the medium and detects the minute difference in voltage between these positions produced by the current being studied.

The enormous increase in sensitivity provided by the probe system and its high spatial resolution allowed Jaffe and Nuccitelli to make a detailed examination of changes that occur after fertilization in fucus. Indeed, a few hours after fertilization pulses of current, corresponding to an inward flow of positive ions, begin to enter a local area on the egg. This inflow marks the point of emergence of the rhizoid some 10–12 hours later. Once this event was recognized, it was discovered that techniques which would alter the position of current entry on the egg also altered its axis of development. These early measurements led to many more experiments that helped shape a

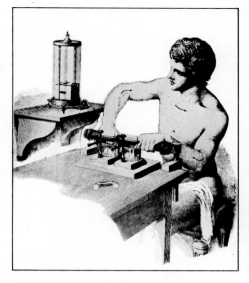

Among pioneering investigators of bioelectrical phenomena was E. Du Bois-Reymond. Cut from mid-19th century illustrates his equipment for investigating wound current. A human subject gripped the bar such that one finger of each hand was dipped in a separate saline bath. When one of the fingers had an injury, the galvanometer registered a difference in potential between the fingers.

(Top) Lionel F. Jaffe, Purdue University;
(bottom) G. I. Bernard—Oxford Scientific Films

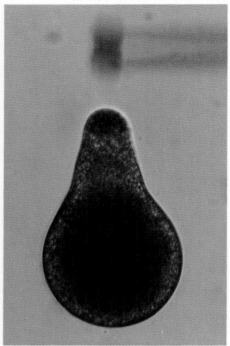

more complete understanding of the early events leading to the establishment of polarity in fucus. Moreover, when the probe system was applied to a variety of other elongating cells, both plant and animal, a unique picture began to unfold: small, steady electric currents enter the growing tips of barley root hairs and elongating pollen tubes as well as the tip of an extending ameoba's pseudopod. Endogenous currents were also measured traversing developing systems in amphibians and insects, and in many cases current flow was found to vary with certain pageants in their development.

Amphibian regeneration

These new insights in developmental physiology prompted Jaffe, Joseph W. Vanable, Jr., and Richard B. Borgens at Purdue to reinvestigate the role of current produced by injury in the ability of newts and other salamanders to regenerate their limbs. Limb regeneration in these creatures is essentially an embryonic process played over again in the adult. After amputation, undamaged cells making up bone, cartilage, muscle, and other tissues at the stump end undergo a process called dedifferentiation, in which they transform to a mass of unspecialized cells resembling embryonic tissue. This bulbous aggregation, called a blastema, enlarges and then redifferentiates, reorganizing into specialized tissue and eventually forming the new limb of the animal.

It had long been suggested that electrical changes occur along the stumps of salamander limbs after amputation and that these changes may be involved with the regeneration of the limb. The Italian embryologist Alberto Monroy was the first to perform electrical measurements on regenerating salamander limbs, reporting his studies in 1941. Since the 1960s a number of other investigators have done similar studies. Essentially they all detected a change in potential difference across the limb in response to amputation. This voltage drop was measured between the stump end and some other point on the body of the animal. These voltage readings gave a crude indication that current was leaving the wound. By convention, the direction of current flow is defined as that direction in which positive charge would move. Thus, if the stump end is electrically positive with respect to undamaged areas, then it can be inferred that current leaves the stump end and reenters elsewhere along the body. For a variety of technical reasons, however, the magnitude of these externally measured voltages as well as details of their oscillations are biologically insignificant. Moreover, these measurements did not address the electrical changes occurring inside the stump, where regenerative processes are begun. Thus, although these external measurements were good clues that something was happening electrically, they offered little else. By contrast, the vibrating probe system would precisely measure current should it leave or enter the wound and would allow inferences to be made about the electrical environment inside the stump.

In experiments conducted during the mid-1970s Borgens, Vanable, and Jaffe scanned the surface of salamander stumps with the vibrating probe system and found that a large density of current, 50–100 microamperes per square centimeter, does indeed leave the stump end, returning to the undamaged portions of the limb and body. Moreover, the current persists for

54

more than a week after amputation while steadily declining in strength, and its disappearance coincides with the first appearance of the blastema. This density of current would produce a weak electric field within the soft tissues of the stump on the order of ten millivolts per millimeter.

The next task for the investigators was to isolate the source of this large stump current. They tested the two most likely candidates: nerve and skin. Surgically removing the major nerve supply to the limb stump had little effect on the stump current; thus, nerves were not the source of the current. The skin of most animals supports a large difference in potential across itself: it is electrically positive on its inner surface with respect to the outside. Furthermore, in most amphibians maintenance of the skin's potential difference is very dependent on the presence of sodium in the pond water (or other form of moisture) on the skin's surface. The skin of amphibians possesses a sodium transport system, which moves sodium ions from the skin's surface into the body. If one could either remove sodium from the artificial pond water used to maintain the animals in the laboratory or inhibit the access of sodium through the skin, one theoretically could "turn off" the stump current. In fact, such treatments did just that. When salamanders were placed in sodium-free water or the exterior of their skin treated with a drug that blocked the uptake of sodium from the pond water, current leaving their limb stumps was radically reduced or abolished.

These tests produced two important results. First, it was demonstrated that skin surrounding the limb stump was indeed the source of the currents driven out of its end. Second, by finding a way to turn off the flow of current from the stump, the investigators could then test the relevance of the current to limb regeneration. Stated another way, if one could chronically keep the stump currents low, would the animal regenerate normally? To find out Borgens, Vanable, and Jaffe treated tiger salamanders and newts to chronically inhibit or reduce their stump currents. In many cases these efforts greatly retarded limb regeneration, caused it to be abnormal, or completely inhibited it.

Another known way to inhibit limb regeneration in salamanders is to sew a flap of whole skin over the stump end in place of the membranous tissue called epithelium that normally grows to cover the wound. Studies of normally healing stumps have shown that the current density leaving the stump is highest in areas covered by wound epithelium and is greatly reduced in areas where whole skin begins to encroach on the stump end. Thus, a flap of skin completely covering the wound surface would be expected to prevent the efflux of current. It is well known that such treatment also inhibits limb regeneration. In this light it is interesting to point out that children can regrow the tips of their fingers after an accidental amputation. If the finger is severed somewhere between the last joint and the nail, a nearly perfect replacement will regrow within a few months, often complete with nail and fingerprint. The only prerequisite is that the attending doctor leave the tip of the finger alone and not sew it closed. If the fingertip is surgically closed, no regrowth will occur. Significantly, natural flows of current have been measured leaving the finger stumps of children, current similar in most respects to that leaving salamander limb stumps.

Germinating fucus egg (facing page, top), about a tenth of a millimeter across, shows elongated bulge that marks the beginning of its anchoring holdfast. The end opposite the bulge will develop into the system of bladderlike floats and flat blades (bottom; Fucus spiralis shown) that is common to members of this genus of marine algae. Some 10–12 hours before the bulge appears, an influx of electric current locates the region of emergence. The rapidly oscillating tip of the vibrating probe system that was used to map the electric currents around the egg can be seen as a faint blur at the top of the upper photo.

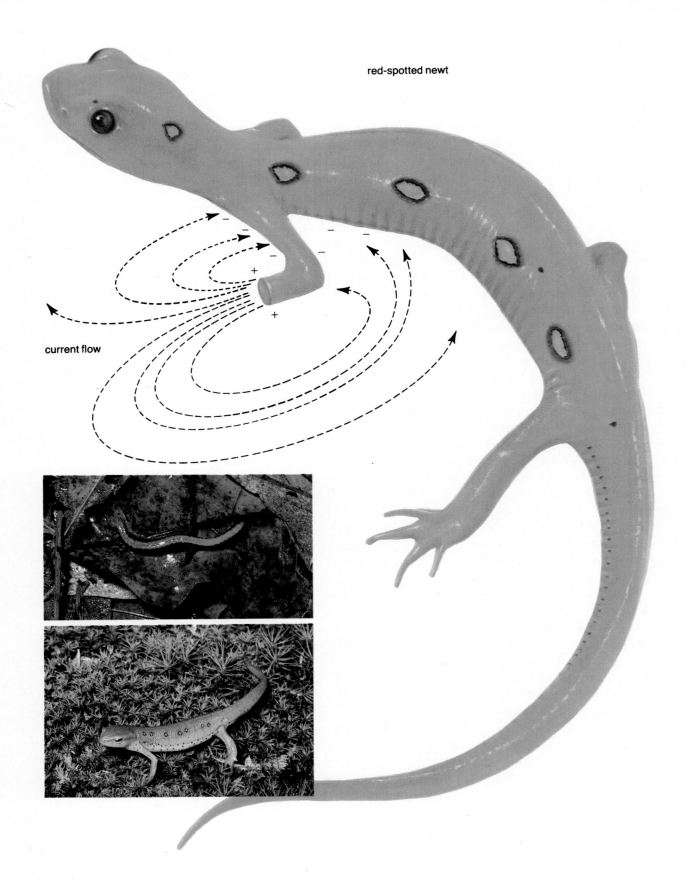

red-spotted newt

current flow

Borgens, Vanable, and Jaffe also mapped the topography of currents leaving the limb stumps of adult frogs, which are amphibians that do not regenerate their limbs. Frogs possess as potent a "skin battery" as salamanders, so current was expected to leave their stumps as well. The pathway of the current, however, proved to be different between the two types of animals. In the salamander stump current density is high in the core tissues, the tissues that give rise to a major portion (if not all) of the regenerated limb. In adult frogs the great majority of current is shunted beneath their skin, resulting in very little current traversing the core tissues. This effect occurs because frogs have subdermal lymph spaces, large sinuses full of conductive body fluids that effectively short-circuit the current. Salamanders do not possess this type of lymphatic channel, nor do tadpoles, who do regenerate their limbs. Tadpoles lose their regenerative ability as they metamorphose into adult frogs; interestingly, the exact area on their limbs where the loss occurs is also the area where the subdermal lymph spaces begin to appear.

Artificially stimulated regeneration

Given these demonstrable differences in the electrical behavior of regenerating and nonregenerating limbs in amphibians, it was natural for the investigators to see if a nonregenerating species could be stimulated to grow new tissue. Earlier work had shown that a variety of treatments could reawaken regenerative ability in frogs. Increasing the sodium concentration of a medium topically applied to frog stumps has this effect. Borgens, Vanable, and Jaffe found that such a treatment also increases the output of the natural skin battery in amphibians, just as sodium deprivation shuts it down. The investigators also repeated earlier experiments in which the application of a weak electric current had stimulated regeneration in frogs, but they performed these experiments in such a way as to know that electricity really was the stimulus.

Small, suitably insulated batteries were placed under the skin on the backs of a number of common leopard frogs with amputated limbs. The electrodes were positioned within each animal such that they produced a flow of current through the frog stump that was similar in direction, magnitude, duration, and locality to the natural flow of current through a salamander stump. Current was kept flowing for 3½ weeks. Dead battery units were used in other animals to form a control group. As early as six weeks after amputation it was obvious that something was happening in many of the current-treated stumps. They had bulbous swollen tips indicative of blastemas. In contrast the six-week-old control stumps had almost healed completely. Over the next 6–9 months the electrically treated limbs regenerated to varying degrees, although all were very abnormal structures. Nevertheless, careful examination of these tissues proved that new bone, muscle, nerve, and cartilaginous precursors of new bone were all present past the point of amputation. The control stumps showed only varying degrees of fracture callus and scar tissue between the cut end of the bone and the skin. In frogs in which the direction of the artificially applied current had been reversed, there was no sign of limb regeneration.

Photos, C. M. Illingworth, F.R.C.P.,
Consultant in Accident & Emergency Department,
The Children's Hospital, Sheffield

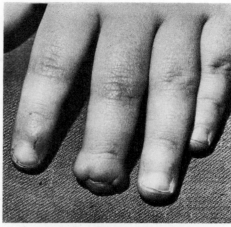

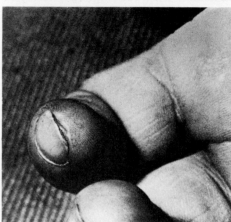

Healing fingertips in two three-year-old children with accidental amputations are compared. Four months after an accident, tip that was surgically sewn closed has grown into blunt stump (top). Tip given simple cleaning and bandaging and five months' time (above) has regrown both nail and fingerprint.

(Facing page) Its tail lost to a predator or by accident, red-backed salamander (top inset) begins growing a new one from the end of its stump. Vibrating probe studies of the red-spotted newt (bottom inset) and other salamanders indicate that a large density of current leaves the end of an animal's stump and returns to the undamaged parts of the body. Illustration diagrams current flow leaving the limb stump of a newt.

57

Tadpoles can regenerate lost limbs, but they lose this ability during metamorphosis to adult frogs. Both photos are of the leopard frog.

These results posed major questions: How did a very weak dose of electric current (0.0000002 amperes) delivered for less than four weeks initiate limb regeneration? What was the target tissue or tissues for the current? The appearance of gross amounts of regenerated nerve within the frog stumps offered a clue that nerve tissue was at least very responsive to the applied electric field; indeed it actually may prove to be the pertinent target tissue. This notion also fit very nicely with what was already known about nerve and its role in limb regeneration, much of which had been discovered by Marcus Singer of Case Western Reserve University in Cleveland, Ohio. Singer found a higher density of nerves within stumps of salamanders and newts than in stumps of their nonregenerating cousins, adult leopard frogs.

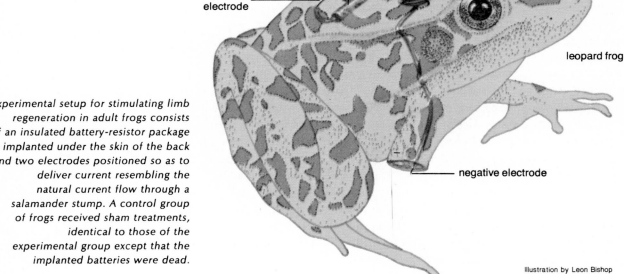

Experimental setup for stimulating limb regeneration in adult frogs consists of an insulated battery-resistor package implanted under the skin of the back and two electrodes positioned so as to deliver current resembling the natural current flow through a salamander stump. A control group of frogs received sham treatments, identical to those of the experimental group except that the implanted batteries were dead.

If the ratio of nerve tissue area to stump cross-sectional area is reduced in newts and salamanders, they lose their regenerative ability.

In one particularly celebrated experiment published in 1954, Singer surgically rerouted a large bundle of nerves, the sciatic nerve, from the frog's leg to its forearm stump. This addition of nerve within the stump increased the ratio of nerve area to stump-surface area. Singer hypothesized that if this ratio was increased to the level of salamanders and newts, then limb regeneration could be initiated. He was right. His experiment, concluded some 20 years previous to the electrical treatments done at Purdue, had resulted in similar regenerated tissue. Jaffe, Vanable, and Borgens theorized that, although nerves are certainly not the source of the natural current leaving the salamander stump, they probably are the target. Similarly the applied electric field enhanced the regeneration of nerves within the frog stump, increased the ratio of nerve to stump tissue, and thus initiated limb regeneration.

These experiments into the electrical control of limb regeneration in amphibians certainly produced useful clues about the similarities and dissimilarities between regenerating and nonregenerating animals. Moreover, the observations of a strikingly enhanced regeneration of nerves was in itself most significant.

Regeneration of nerve tissue

There had been many older reports that an applied electric field will direct or enhance nerve growth. But once again, these early experiments did not benefit from a thoughtful approach and for this reason had always been controversial. In the past few years, however, it has become apparent that if one carefully applies fields to nerve tissue in culture and carefully monitors the responses, striking effects can be observed.

This can best be demonstrated by recent experiments on embryonic tissue performed by Kenneth Robinson, Colin McCaig, and Laura Hinkle. (Robinson is now at the University of Connecticut Health Center in Farmington.) Robinson's group grew individual embryonic nerve cells in culture that had been isolated from very early embryos of the African clawed frog, *Xenopus*. The cells were maintained on the bottom of plastic chambers, to which they adhered, and were kept immersed in a proper culture medium. In such an environment the nerve cells differentiated much as they would in the embryo, sending out one or more long extensions called neurites. When weak electric fields were applied across the cells, the neurites sometimes bent through great arcs to grow toward the negative pole, or cathode, of the applied field. Moreover, the rate of growth was enhanced in neurites that grow out normally toward the cathode. (This situation conforms to the natural electrical environment that exists within the limb stumps of salamanders or the artificial environment imposed within the stumps of adult frogs.) Sometimes embryonic muscle cells contaminated Robinson's nerve cell cultures. Incredibly, while the neurites elongated parallel to the long axis of the applied electric field, the muscle cells lined up perpendicular to the field axis. In fact, with this arrangement, nerve-muscle contacts were even established in culture.

59

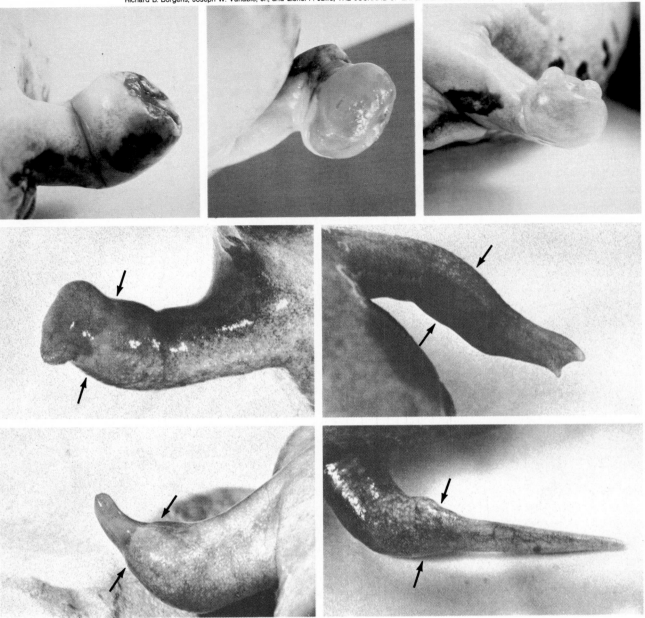

(Top, all photos) Richard B. Borgens; (center and bottom, all photos) From "Small Artificial Currents Enhance Xenopus Limb Regeneration," Richard B. Borgens, Joseph W. Vanable, Jr., and Lionel F. Jaffe, THE JOURNAL OF EXPERIMENTAL ZOOLOGY, vol. 207, no. 2, pp. 217–225, February 1979

Electrically stimulated and sham-treated stumps of adult frogs are compared. Sham-treated leopard frog (top left) shows no regeneration six weeks after amputation. By contrast, six-week-old current-stimulated stump (top center) has developed a blastema of embryonic-like cells. By six months the stimulated limb has regenerated a very abnormal and deficient structure (top right). Current-treated limb stump of African clawed frog eight weeks after amputation (center left) possesses a paddle-shaped mass of regenerating tissue extending beyond the plane of amputation (arrows); 18 weeks later—the new limb (center right). Sham-treated stump 8 and 26 weeks after amputation (bottom, left and right) has grown only a narrow, tapering rod.

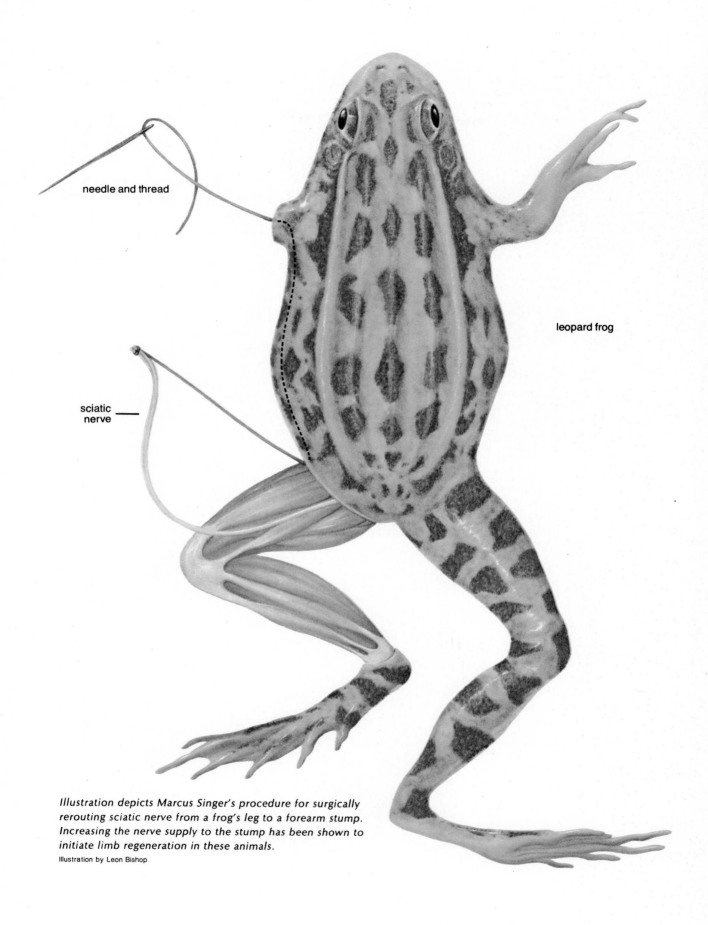

needle and thread

leopard frog

sciatic nerve

Illustration depicts Marcus Singer's procedure for surgically rerouting sciatic nerve from a frog's leg to a forearm stump. Increasing the nerve supply to the stump has been shown to initiate limb regeneration in these animals.

Illustration by Leon Bishop

Kenneth Robinson, University of Connecticut
Health Center, Farmington

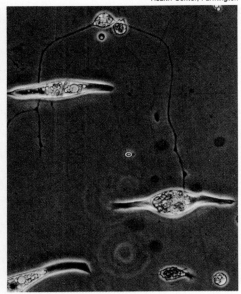

Cultured embryonic nerve cell (rounded body at top) of African clawed frog sends out long extensions that bend toward the negative pole of an applied electric field (current flow is from top to bottom). Whereas these neurites align parallel to the field axis, spindle-shaped embryonic muscle cells align perpendicular to it. Under such conditions nerve-muscle contacts have even been established.

Using the vibrating probe system Robinson also measured natural steady current flow traversing the developing neural tube, the precursor of the brain and spinal cord, of *Xenopus* embryos. He speculated that this natural electric field may help guide embryonic nerves from the developing spinal cord to their destination in developing muscle. This research comes close to offering a physical basis for the "morphogenic fields" that have been postulated by embryologists for more than a century. The concept of morphogenic fields arose to fill the need for describing in some way the guiding forces that underlie morphogenesis—the cellular movements and aggregations, the growth, bending, and folding of tissues, and the other processes that form and pattern the embryo into a complex organism. Just what these fields actually are is a controversial and much-explored topic of embryological research. Robinson's work suggested that, at least in certain cases, they may be endogenous electric fields.

In the late 1970s Borgens moved to Yale University to conduct work supported by the National Spinal Cord Injury Foundation. His aim was to test if either naturally produced or artificially applied electricity could be involved with nerve regeneration (or the lack of it) within the spinal cord of a primitive vertebrate. Melvin J. Cohen at Yale had already spent some years studying the central nervous system of the larval lamprey, a very primitive parasite of fish but a true chordate nonetheless. It was on the simply organized central nervous system of this animal that Cohen and Borgens decided to test some of the theories developed earlier at Purdue.

The lamprey possesses giant nerve cells that can be identified easily at various locations within the brain and spinal cord. In addition, the entire central nervous system of this animal can be removed and placed in simple organ culture where it lives remarkably well for a week or more; this makes it an ideal preparation for vibrating probe studies. Another advantage is that blood vessels are only found at the surface of the lamprey's spinal cord.

The lamprey, a primitive vertebrate, possesses giant, easily identifiable nerve cells in its brain and spinal cord, a limited capacity to regenerate nerve tissue of the central nervous system (CNS), and an easily cultured brain and spinal cord. These assets have made it a good subject for electrophysiologists and students of CNS regeneration in vertebrates.

John Paling—Oxford Scientific Films

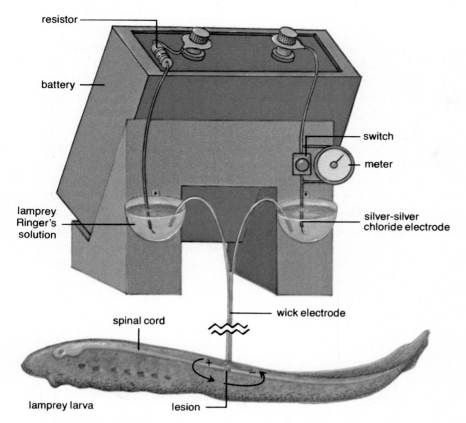

resistor

battery

switch

meter

lamprey Ringer's solution

silver-silver chloride electrode

wick electrode

spinal cord

lamprey larva

lesion

Cutting the spinal cord does not produce the severe vascular damage seen after traumatic injury to mammalian spinal cords. Thus the lamprey's spinal cord presented an ideal simple system.

The first question to be answered was whether natural currents are induced by injury to the cord. Borgens studied completely transected spinal cords with the vibrating probe system and found that immense densities of current enter the end of the severed cord and enter the severed nerves within as well. This current flow was sometimes as great as ten times that leaving an entire salamander limb stump. It declined with time after the lesion was made but reached a much reduced, yet steady, level by two days after injury. This stable low-level current persisted for the next four days until measurements were discontinued.

It is interesting to speculate on the many possible consequences to severed nerve endings experiencing this transcellular flow of charge. One thing was certain: if current entered the lesion, then the polarity of the electric field that existed about the cells within the spinal cord would be negative near the injury and more positive in undamaged areas. It should be recalled that the electrically enhanced nerve growth and the orientation of nerves in previous experiments were all mediated by fields that were externally negative in the regions of the growing tips. This common factor suggests that the unique behavior of regenerating nerves in artificially applied electric fields may be related to their natural physiological responses to injury.

In the lamprey the giant identifiable nerves within the central nervous system (called Müller and Mauthner cells) already possess a limited ability to regenerate. Borgens, Cohen, and Ernesto Roederer at Yale next explored

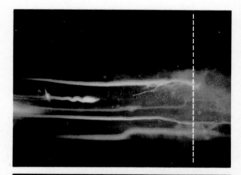

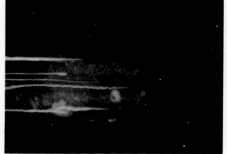

Photos, Richard B. Borgens

63

whether these regenerative properties could be enhanced by increasing the level of current that already flows in response to injury. For these experiments two small electrodes were positioned within larval lampreys, next to the spinal cord and about four to five centimeters (roughly two inches) apart. The spinal cord of each animal was completely severed between these electrodes. About ten microamperes of steady current was delivered to the leads by a voltage source located outside the animal's chamber. The spinal cord was stimulated for five to six days, the electrodes were removed, and about 50 days later the extent of regeneration was compared with that of animals treated in an identical manner except that no current was delivered to the lesion. The investigators analyzed the extent of nerve regeneration by a variety of techniques, including precisely identifying the extent of regeneration in individual nerves by filling them with fluorescent dye and observing them under a fluorescence microscope, electronically measuring the propagation of action potentials along nerves across the lesion, and correlating these measurements with the morphology of individual cells. The results were quite conclusive: the application of the artificial electric field greatly enhanced the regeneration of spinal cord nerves.

This work, together with a growing body of other findings, demonstrates that nerve growth and regeneration can be greatly influenced by applied electric fields. Moreover, the basic biology of apparently unrelated organisms, tissues, and cells strongly suggests this influence is due to the role that naturally produced electricity plays in biological development.

Happenings at the cellular level

Scientists investigating bioelectrical phenomena are also intensely interested in the ways in which a natural or an artificially applied electric field might actually affect target cells and tissues. In general two kinds of effects are known, ionic effects and voltage-mediated effects. Ionic effects are in reality biochemical effects, caused by the very ions that carry the charge through cells. The individual cellular response depends on what ion or ions are carrying the current. For example, a major component of the injury current in damaged nerves is calcium. When calcium concentration is increased within a nerve (where normally it is found in only minute quantities), it causes local disassembly of various fibers that form the internal structural framework, or cytoskeleton, of these specialized cells. Change in cytoplasmic calcium also has been implicated in cellular elongation in a variety of other cells.

The steady voltage gradient that is associated with the continuous flow of current through or around cells also has its effects. Negatively charged cell components will move toward the positive pole of the voltage gradient, and positively charged components will move toward the negative pole. These components may be large molecules floating in the membranes of cells exposed to the voltage gradient surrounding the cell. Thus, these membrane constituents may be condensed on the surface of a cell in response to steady current flow. Many such molecules are implicated in cellular recognition, cellular aggregation, and other important developmental events, and others are important hormone receptors.

64

When a cell drives current through itself, the electric field within the cell will also move some components about, perhaps even whole organelles. Such effects may help explain the rapid movement of vesicles and mitochondria to the end of a damaged nerve soon after injury.

It is important to note that formal proof does exist for the electrically induced movement of large membrane-bound molecules and for the ability of endogenous electric fields to move charged components within the cytoplasm of certain cells. Nevertheless, the exact identity of the developmentally important cellular constituents remains to be discovered.

Implications for medicine

Taken as a whole the observations discussed above suggest that electricity may be used clinically to enhance the regenerative properties of various tissues in human beings. Indeed, as one outgrowth of such research, electricity already has begun to be used in the clinic for treating chronic nonunions. Nonunions are bone fractures that for a variety of reasons never heal properly. If several bone grafts fail to produce a cure, then sometimes that portion of the extremity has to be amputated. Two different types of stimulating devices, both approved by the U.S. Food and Drug Administration, are dramatically increasing the success rate in treating such cases, sometimes as high as 85%. In one type, pioneered by Carl Brighton and Z. B. Friedenberg of the University of Pennsylvania School of Medicine, surgically implanted electrodes connected to an external power supply deliver weak levels of steady DC current to the fracture (a recent variation is totally implantable, power source and all). In the other, developed by C. A. L. Bassett of Columbia University, New York City, electromagnetic coils secured to the cast produce pulsing electric fields within the affected member. It is important to note that bone is an electrically dynamic tissue. It produces short-lived potential differences when it is stressed, and it drives steady electric currents into the site of injury after a fracture. Thus the healing potential of artificially applied electric currents once again probably resides in their action on natural electrical mechanisms already present in growing or healing bone.

One might ask if the next application for electrotherapy may be in the treatment of nerve injuries, even acute spinal trauma. Damaged nerves of the human central nervous system normally do not repair themselves. At present it can be said only that this idea certainly bears promise. Most workers in the field now regard spinal cord injury as far from the clinically hopeless situation that it once seemed to be. One approach might be to use electrotherapy to initiate and enhance nerve growth and orient damaged nerves within the spinal cord, coupled with other therapy to repair the orthopedic and vascular damage caused by the injury. Such a regimen has not yet been properly tested in primates, and it should be. Overall, indications are that a more complete investigation of the basic electrical controls of development in cells and tissues will pave the way for useful clinical applications in the future.

C. Andrew Bassett, Orthopedic Research Laboratories, College of Physicians & Surgeons of Columbia University, New York

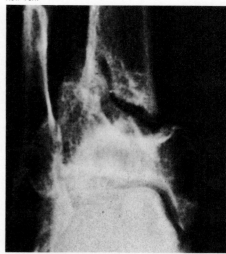

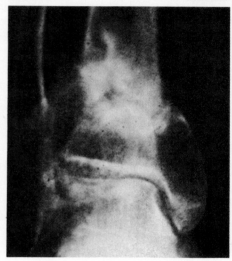

X-ray (top) of 66-year-old person reveals fractured tibia (the larger of the two lower leg bones), which had failed to heal two years after treatment with pins and a cast. Taken two months after electrical treatment, a second X-ray (above) shows the beginnings of bone formation across the fracture gap. After one year the tibia had formed a solid, pain-free union.

TWINS–NATURE'S TWICE-TOLD TALE

by Thomas J. Bouchard, Jr.

From ancient times twins have been extolled, persecuted, or otherwise distinguished by society. Today they are the center of scientific studies of the influence of heredity and environment.

In form and feature, face and limb,
I grew so like my brother,
That folks got taking me for him,
And each for one another.
It puzzled all our kith and kin,
It reached a fearful pitch;
For one of us was born a twin,
Yet not a soul knew which.

—Henry Sambrooke Leigh, from "The Twins"

About three or four human births out of every thousand produce a set of identical twins, a rate that is much the same the world over. Births of three or more identical infants are much rarer. By comparison, fraternal twin births are about twice as frequent, but the rate varies from one ethnic group to another.

Identical twins are also called monozygotic, or MZ, twins because both members of the pair develop from the same zygote, or fertilized egg. Such twins are genetically identical and are thus always of the same sex. In fraternal twins, two separate sperm fertilize two separate eggs to produce two zygotes; consequently fraternal twins are termed dizygotic, or DZ, twins. Fraternal twins are no more genetically alike than a pair of siblings born successively, and they have the same 50% chance of being of opposite sexes.

The relative rarity of identical twins and their remarkable similarity have combined to create a universal fascination for twins. Throughout history and in all parts of the world, twins have been regarded as special. Twin legends abound. The Huron and Iroquois Indians, for example, speak of the twins who they believe founded their tribes. The mythical twins Romulus and Remus are given credit for founding the city of Rome. In other myths one twin is considered good and the other evil. In some aboriginal societies twins were thought to have supernatural powers; consequently in some societies they were venerated and in others they were slain.

How twins are studied

Twins do have a special power. They are an experiment of nature that provides a unique opportunity to observe the relative influence of genetic and environmental factors—of nature and nurture—on human characteristics. Before ways were developed to probe the biochemistry of the cell directly, as well as its chromosomes and individual genes, twin studies played an important role in the study of human genetics. In the field of human behavior genetics, the study of the contribution of heredity to behavior, they remain the most powerful method of investigation.

Twin-study designs follow from a simple line of reasoning. Identical twins who are raised together in the same household not only share all of their genes in common but grow up in closely similar environments as well. Consequently any differences between such twins are assumed to be due to specific environmental factors; i.e., experiences, sometimes even events within the womb itself, that for some reason were not quite the same for both twins. In the case of stature, for example, the correlation (a measure of similarity) for identical twins reared together (frequently abbreviated MZT twins) is 0.94. Because perfect similarity would yield a correlation of 1.00,

Figure 1 (facing page), which illustrates the degree of similarity in intelligence between selected relatives reared apart and together, is described in text on pages 76–77.

THOMAS J. BOUCHARD, JR., is Professor of Psychology at the University of Minnesota and Director of the Minnesota Study of Twins Reared Apart.

Illustrations by John Craig

68

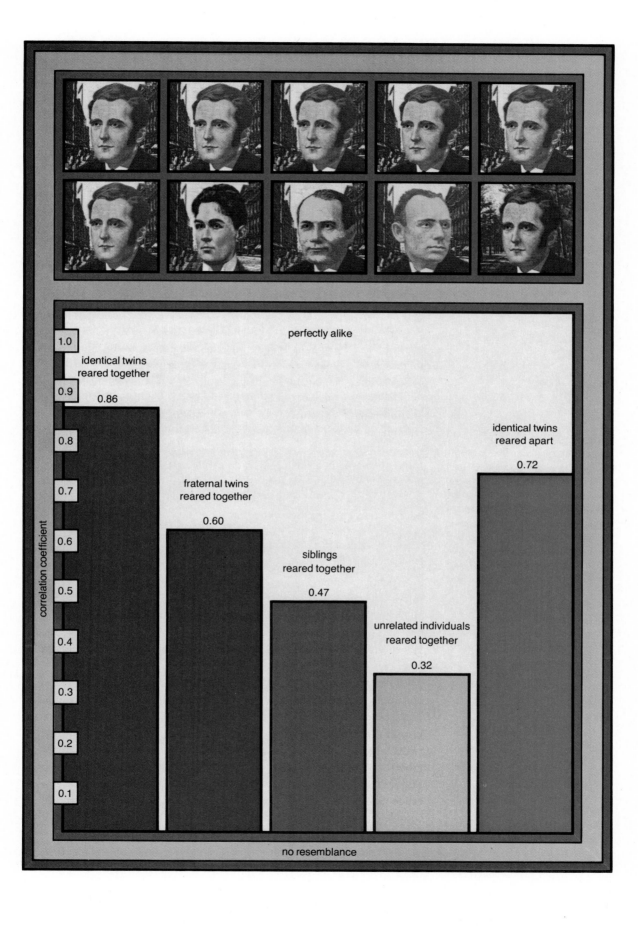

about 6% of the variance among MZT twins in stature must be due to specific environmental differences.

Sometimes, although less often now than formerly, identical twins put up for adoption are separated in infancy and reared apart in different adoptive homes (MZA twins). To the extent that these homes are chosen at random, one can say that any similarity between identical twins reared apart must be due to their identical genetic structure. The correlation for stature among MZA twins is about 0.90, slightly less than for MZT twins. Therefore, one can estimate that about 4% (0.94 minus 0.90) of the variance in stature is due to shared environment, to such things as the similarity of diets provided in the home. But the important point is that the correlation among identical twins reared apart provides at once an estimate of the extent to which variation in a given trait is genetically determined (*i.e.*, about 90% in the case of stature).

It should be emphasized that these "heritability" estimates are generalizations. Very deviant environments can radically alter the expression of any trait in individual cases. A child who in an average environment would be expected to become six feet tall might suffer a crippling accident or disease or be reared during a period of famine and therefore never reach his or her expected stature. Again, hormone injections or a tumor of the pituitary gland might cause the person to grow much taller than six feet.

This finding can be checked using another twin-study method. Fraternal twins reared together (DZT twins) share half their genes and a common environment. Their correlation for stature is 0.50, which when subtracted from the correlation for MZT twins ($0.94 - 0.50 = 0.44$) gives an estimate of half the genetic effect. Since the additional similarity in identical twins comes about by their having all, rather than half, of their genes in common, one should be able to estimate the total genetic influence by doubling 0.44. Indeed, 0.88 is very close to the value of 0.90 found for MZA twins. This agreement reinforces the notion that about 90% of the variation in stature is genetic in origin.

Because the correlation of identical twins reared apart offers a direct estimate of the relative influence of heredity, their study provides a powerful investigative technique. Such twins are extremely rare, however, and only four studies have ever been conducted. In terms of sample size, the smallest study involved 12 sets of identical twins reared apart and the largest involved 44. One study, an ongoing project at the University of Minnesota, is occasionally cited below; by early 1982 it had collected information from 30 sets of MZA twins.

Using correlations of genetic and environmental relatedness among various family relatives, investigators can obtain additional checks on estimates of the relative influence of heredity and environment. This model-fitting approach to the nature-nurture question is now being widely used. Although twins typically contribute more information to the analysis than any other group of relatives, it is important to cross-check the results on other types of families. Adopted siblings make a good contrast since they are the opposite of identical twins reared apart: they share a common environment but are completely unrelated genetically. Barring placement bias (efforts by an agency to place children with similar characteristics in similar homes) the

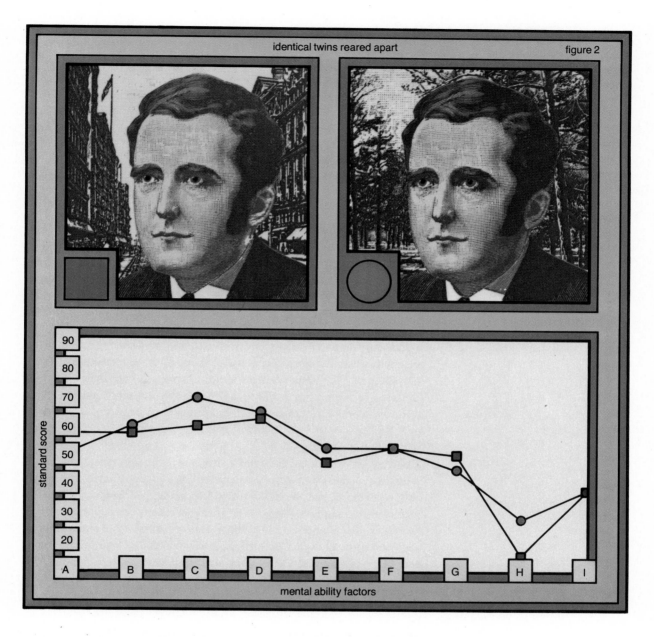

only reason adopted siblings should be alike is because they share a common environment.

The first scientific study of twins took place little more than a century ago. In a paper published in 1875 entitled "The History of Twins, as a Criterion of the Relative Powers of Nature and Nurture," British anthropologist and eugenicist Francis Galton introduced the classic twin-study method, which involves a comparison of identical and fraternal twins reared together. Although he studied only a small number of twin pairs, Galton knew he had a problem. He wrote:

There is no escape from the conclusion that nature prevails enormously over nurture when the differences of nurture do not exceed what is commonly to be found among

Figure 2 presents a special mental ability profile, reflecting performance in tasks involving nine separate factors (A–I), for a set of identical twins reared apart. In order the factors are verbal comprehension; word fluency; induction; spatial orientation, two dimensions; spatial orientation, three dimensions; flexibility of closure; spatial scanning; visual memory, immediate; visual memory, delayed. See text, page 78.

persons of the same rank of society and in the same country. My only fear is that my evidence seems to prove too much and may be discredited on that account, as it seems contrary to all experience that nurture should go for so little.

Human behavior geneticists continue to face the same problem encountered by Galton. Although the influence of heredity is not as great as he purported it to be, it is large and does seem contrary to experience. Contemporary twin research has gone a step further. It suggests that common family environmental influences are often much less important than psychologists previously believed and that the environmental determinants of such important traits as personality and vocational interests remain largely a mystery.

Personality and interests

The domain in which human beings are at their most individual is that of personality. Although some psychological theories have emphasized the biological origins of human drives as the fundamental sources of variation in personality, most psychological research has focused on the social environment, particularly the family. The following quote is from the 1981 edition of one of the most widely used textbooks on personality: "Genes and glands are obviously important, but social learning also has a dramatic role. Imagine the enormous differences that would be found in the personalities of twins with identical genetic endowments if they were raised apart in two different families—or, even more striking, in two totally different cultures." This observation probably represents the opinion of a majority of U.S. psychologists, who believe that the family is by far the most important influence on personality development.

Early work with identical twins reared apart focused mostly on intelligence and medical conditions. But results based on the study of two major personality traits, extroversion-introversion and neuroticism, suggested that such twins might be even more similar in measured personality than twins reared together. In her review of the world literature on twins reared apart U.S. clinical psychologist Susan Farber concluded, "As a group the more time MZ (monozygotic) twins spend with no contact with each other, the more similar they seem to become." None of the early work, however, allowed for a careful quantitative assessment of similarity. Preliminary quantitative results from the Minnesota Study of Twins Reared Apart, headed by Thomas Bouchard, Jr., suggest that across a broad array of traits—aggression, introversion-extroversion, impulse control, and neuroticism—identical twins reared apart are just as alike as identical twins reared in the same families. Both types of identical twins are also twice as similar as fraternal twins reared in the same families. These results, contrary to the conventional wisdom, show that the expected enormous differences do not materialize in identical twins reared in different families. They also refute the commonly heard argument that subtle environmental similarities are the primary cause of identical-twin similarities in personality.

Surprising as the results with MZA twins are, they are completely compatible with the large body of work on identical and fraternal twins raised together. John Loehlin of the University of Texas at Austin and Robert Nichols

72

Separated at birth, the Mallifert twins meet accidentally.

of the State University of New York at Buffalo, on the basis of their work with 850 sets of twins, concluded that heredity accounts for about half the variation in personality among individuals and environment accounts for the other half. Their own words are worth quoting. "Thus, a consistent—though perplexing—pattern is emerging from the data (and it is not purely idiosyncratic to our study). Environment carries substantial weight in determining personality—it appears to account for at least half the variance—but that environment is one for which twin pairs are correlated close to zero. . . . In short, in the personality domain we seem to see environmental effects that operate almost randomly with respect to the sorts of variables that psychologists (and other people) have traditionally deemed important in personality development. . . . If we have made life more difficult for the authors of elementary textbooks on personality by stirring up those paradoxes, we apologize."

Although there has been much less research on vocational interests than on personality, the twin research that has been done suggests a remarkably similar pattern of results. Heredity appears to account for about half the variation between people in scores on vocational interest measures (one popular test, for example, groups vocational interests into six themes: realistic, investigative, artistic, social, enterprising, and conventional). There also appears to be very little influence from a common family environment.

The findings in both vocational and personality studies imply a much smaller degree of similarity between parents and their children than most people, including psychologists, expect. They also predict a very small degree of similarity between parents and adopted children and between adopted siblings. These predictions recently were confirmed in the large Minnesota Adoption Study conducted by Sandra Scarr and Richard Weinberg at the University of Minnesota. Preliminary results from the Minnesota Study of Twins Reared Apart are entirely consistent with the adoption study. Identi-

73

Adapted from "Synchronies in Mental Development: An Epigenetic Perspective," Ronald S. Wilson, SCIENCE, vol. 202, pp. 939–948, December 1, 1978, © AAAS

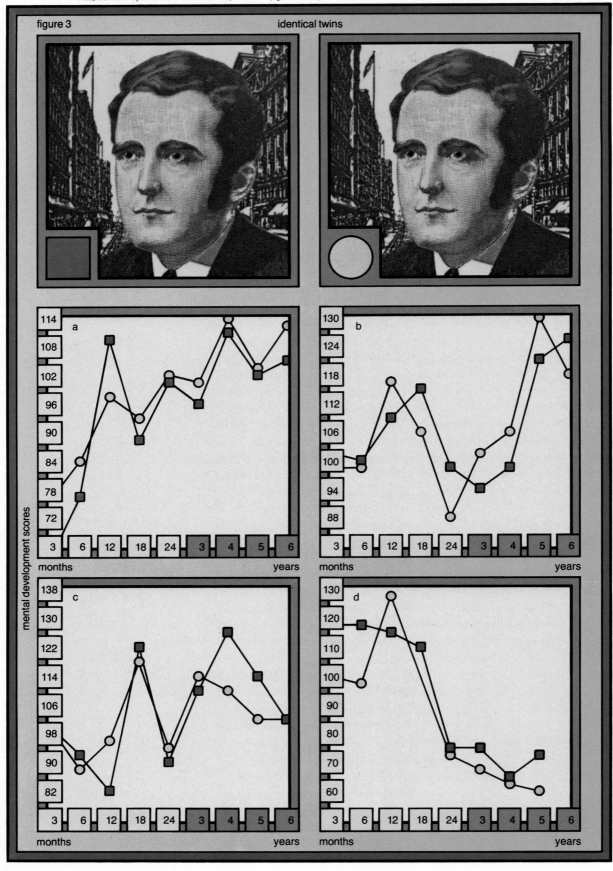

figure 3

identical twins

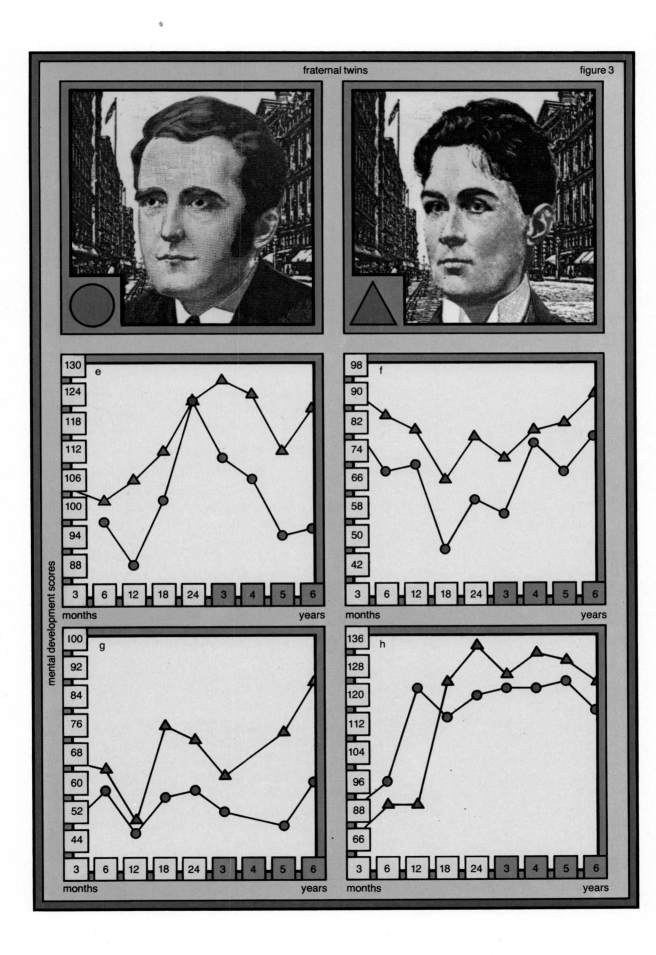

Figure 3 (pages 74–75) presents mental development curves for four sets of identical twins (a–d) and four sets of fraternal twins (e–h) from three months to six years of age. See text, page 79.

cal twins reared apart are four to five times more similar than genetically unrelated individuals (parents compared with adopted offspring or adopted siblings compared) who are reared in the same home, and twice as similar as related individuals who share half their genes (parents compared with offspring or siblings compared).

Thus, the studies of twins reared apart, twins reared together, and adopted children converge on a set of findings which suggest that scientists know much less about the important environmental determinants of personality and vocational interests than they thought. This is not a conclusion that needs an apology. A primary goal of scientific inquiry is to scrutinize accepted theory and common beliefs with the objective of replacing them, if not with the truth, then with a theory that at least is closer to the truth.

In summing up the results of the personality and interest studies one could say that the major finding is one of differences—differences due to different genes and different environments. As Scarr put it, "Upper middle class brothers who attend the same school and whose parents take them to the same plays, sporting events, music lessons, and therapists and use similar child rearing practices on them are little more similar in personality measures than they are to working class or farm boys, whose lives are totally different. Now, perhaps this is an exaggeration of the known facts, but not by much." Only when individuals share all of their genes do striking degrees of similarity (but not identity) appear, and then it does not matter whether they are raised in the same family or not.

Mental abilities

Psychologists do not agree on how to conceptualize human mental ability. A common and useful model is that of a general factor called intelligence plus supplemental mental abilities of narrower scope and independent of intelligence called special mental abilities. Examples of special mental abilities are perceptual speed and accuracy, the ability to quickly spot small differences in complex configurations; spatial visualization, the ability to mentally rotate three-dimensional objects; and verbal fluency, the ability to rapidly generate words and ideas.

Over the last 50 years a large body of evidence has accumulated to show that identical twins are much more similar than fraternal twins in intelligence. In addition identical twins reared apart have been shown to be far more similar than fraternal twins or ordinary siblings and remarkably more similar than adopted children reared in the same home. (*See* figure 1.)

Like fraternal twins, siblings also share half their genes as well as the same family environment, yet they are less similar in intelligence than fraternal twins. This suggests that, as it affects intelligence, fraternal twins are treated more similarly by their family (and perhaps others) than ordinary siblings. Critics of heredity as a strong determinant of intelligence have pushed this line of reasoning one step further and argued that identical twins are so remarkably similar in intelligence because they are treated even more alike than fraternal twins. As in the domain of personality, this line of reasoning can be best checked by looking at the similarity in intelligence between identical twins reared apart.

76

Adapted from THE STRATEGY OF THE GENES, C. H. Waddington, London: Allen & Unwin, 1957

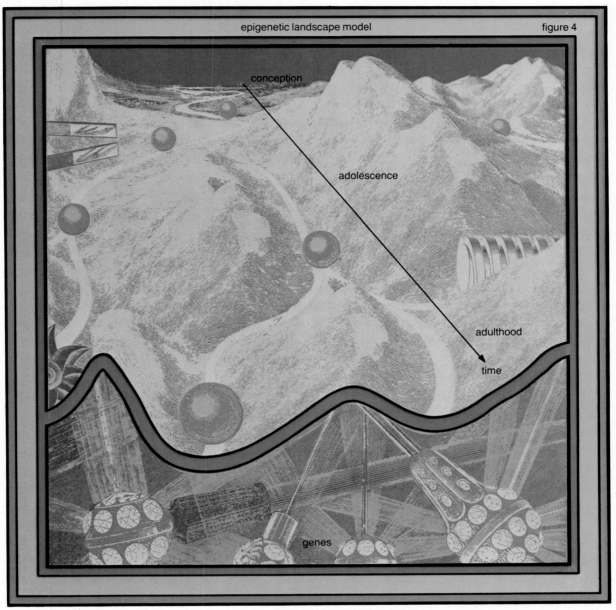

epigenetic landscape model   figure 4

conception

adolescence

adulthood

time

genes

It is seen in figure 1 that identical twins reared apart are also very similar—more similar than fraternal twins but not quite as similar as identical twins reared together. Thus, the high correlation among identical twins reared together is due only in small part to the fact that they are raised in the same family and treated as twins. Notice also that unrelated individuals reared in the same family are far less similar than identical twins reared apart. These results as well as other lines of evidence suggest that approximately 70% of the variation in intelligence among individuals is due to genetic factors and 30% to environmental factors and error of measurement. In contrast to the work on personality and interests, intelligence

Figure 4 illustrates the epigenetic landscape model for conceptualizing genetic and environmental influences on individual development. See text, page 80.

appears to be more influenced by both genes and common environment.

Little twin work has been done on special mental abilities. Existing evidence suggests that special abilities are somewhat more responsive to environmental variation than general intelligence, but that heredity is still very important. Figure 2 shows a selected special mental ability profile for a set of identical twins reared apart recently studied at the University of Minnesota. The overall profiles are remarkably similar. Indeed, they could have come from the same person taking the battery of tests on two occasions reasonably close in time. Both twins show the same pattern of strengths and weaknesses. Not all identical twins reared apart are this similar, but many are.

Mental illness

Twin studies have been used many times over the years to better understand psychiatric disorders. The earliest twin study of schizophrenia goes back to 1928. The most recent careful and comprehensive study was carried out in the Maudsley-Bethlehem study by Irving Gottesman of Washington University, St. Louis, Mo., and the late James Shields of the University of London and published in 1972. Their results were remarkably similar to previous studies. Taken together they all show that over the risk period for developing the disorder, if one identical twin has schizophrenia, the chances are about 50% that the other twin will develop it. If one fraternal twin has schizophrenia, the chances are only about 17% that the other will develop it also. These studies, in conjunction with a long series of adoption studies, conclusively implicate both heredity and environment as important contributors to the disorder. If heredity were the only important factor, all of the identical twins would have been concordant; that is, both members of the pairs would show the disorder. This conclusion is reinforced by findings with twins reared apart. Of 16 pairs of identical twins reared apart of which at least one member had schizophrenia, only 10 pairs were concordant.

A recent large and comprehensive twin study of the manic-depressive disorders was carried out in Denmark by B. Bertelsen of the Institute of Psychiatric Demography in Aarhus and Bent Harvald and Mogens Hauge of the University of Odense. The findings of these investigators were also highly consistent with previous research. As in the case of schizophrenia, hereditary factors were shown to be very important. But again, identical twins were far from perfectly concordant, thus solidly confirming the role of environmental factors.

Developmental behavior genetics

Until recently one of the most underappreciated features of genetic influence was its dynamic nature. Psychologists in particular have tended to equate genetic influence with stability. It has become increasingly apparent, however, that the total influence of genes is not manifested at any one time. Human development is continually subject to both environmental and genetic influence. Genetic mechanisms turn on and off over the course of a lifetime. Common phenomena that reflect such genetic clockworks are the age of onset of puberty and menopause. Identical twins are highly concordant for both events whether reared apart or together. A more dramatic

78

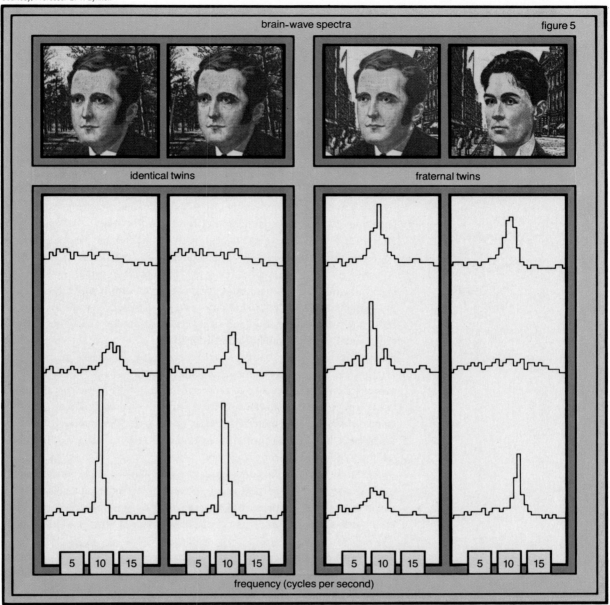

brain-wave spectra

figure 5

identical twins

fraternal twins

frequency (cycles per second)

example is Huntington's chorea, a degenerative disorder of the central nervous system caused by a dominant gene. Age of onset varies from under 5 to over 75, but family studies show that it is under strong genetic control.

Longitudinal twin research follows and compares changes in sets of twins as they age. Such work by Ronald Wilson at the University of Louisville in Kentucky has strongly highlighted the importance of genetic influence on the developmental spurts and lags so characteristic of young children. Figure 3 graphs mental development for four identical and four fraternal twins from the age of three months to six years. Identical pairs a and d show dramatically similar upward and downward trends. Pairs b and c show

Figure 5, which shows EEG spectra for three sets of identical twins (left) and three sets of fraternal twins (right), is discussed in text on page 80.

79

similarity for rather complex configurations. The fraternal pairs show some similarity, as expected, but are not nearly as similar as the identical twins.

A number of models have been proposed to explain these synchronous developments. The most general is the "epigenetic landscape" proposed by British geneticist C. H. Waddington. This model, shown in figure 4, is a three-dimensional physical model. The position of a ball represents an individual at a given time and the landscape the possible developmental paths. The structure of the landscape is determined by the individual's genetic background and is represented by the supports provided by genes to the landscape. Each individual has a somewhat different landscape. There is a most probable path down a given landscape, but the individual's development, determined by the ball as it moves down and across the landscape, can be influenced by external events. If the ball is pushed off course early in life, development will proceed along a different course than if it is pushed off later in life. The valleys get deeper with advancing age, and a change in course is much less likely and more difficult to accomplish.

Notice that this model does not imply what is often called "strict genetic determinism." There are many possibilities, some simply much more probable than others. Identical twins reared apart or together would have essentially identical epigenetic landscapes. Reared under reasonably similar environments they should develop in much the same way. The similarity for many traits of identical twins reared apart suggests that the concept of "reasonably similar environments" probably encompasses a wider range of events than psychologists have been comfortable with in the past. Fraternal twins would share only about half the features of their landscapes and develop differently. One should be careful not to generalize a model of this sort too broadly, but it does capture the essential results of these twin studies in a parsimonious and illuminating way.

The study of age-linked developmental phenomena in human behavior is in its infancy, and much more about the biological clocks underlying human psychological development will emerge in the near future. Longitudinal twin studies will be the primary source of much of this new information.

The computer that manipulates

Brain-wave patterns, or electroencephalogram (EEG) spectra, are recordings of the minute electrical currents generated at the surface of the living brain. Although every person has a unique characteristic brain-wave pattern, the brain waves of identical twins are very similar, much more so than those of fraternal twins. Figure 5 shows pairs of brain-wave spectra from both types of twins. The brain waves of identical twins reared apart are just as similar as identical twins reared together, suggesting that the "hardware" of the brain is determined primarily by genetic processes. These findings supplement the remarkable behavioral similarity seen in twins reared together and apart, but they do not explain it. Two computers with identical hardware may contain entirely different programs and content. The same probably is true of the human brain. Psychological measures draw very heavily on specific content of the brain, and it is this commonality of content that must be explained.

80

Part of the explanation may lie in the fact that, unlike the computer, the human organism is an active manipulator of its environment. Consequently identical twins reared apart as well as together, because they have the same "hardware," will shape their environments by the way they respond to them. For example, a child who enjoys having stories read to him or her and responds positively is likely to hear more stories. A child who is bored by story reading and cries or fusses probably will hear fewer stories. As an adolescent the first child may spend a great deal of time in libraries, whereas the second child may prefer playing with friends. Given a wide array of such propensities it is not difficult to see how two identical twins raised in different families might come to be very much alike mentally and behaviorally. Numerous similarities in the lives of identical twins reared apart are explained easily by such a mechanism. The validity of this explanation, however, remains to be demonstrated.

Some implications of twin research

When genes are shown to be a predominant determinant of individual differences in a trait, it is easy to jump to the conclusion that environment is unimportant. Environment is unimportant in the limited sense that differences in existing environments are not the primary cause of the trait differences. Nevertheless, an adequate environment is necessary for the development of any trait. This assertion appears trivial on its face, but it raises the important question: what is an adequate environment?

Consider the trait of stature. By the use of ordinary twin-study methods, stature can be shown to be influenced predominantly by genetic factors. Yet there has been an almost consistent increase in stature in developed countries over the last century. In Europe the increase was arrested only briefly after each world war. The increase is still occurring even in the privileged classes and is linked with numerous factors that characterize a good physical environment. Thus, the trait is being influenced by trends in the environment that affect almost everyone.

The evidence is quite strong that human intelligence is influenced by many environmental factors, none of which is predominant in its own right. It may be that the intellectual competence of modern populations is increasing in the same way as height. Such an influence, of course, could be countered by other forces; for example, differential reproduction (any tendency for numbers of offspring to vary with the parents' intelligence, social class, or some other characteristic). Scientists simply do not know what is happening since they cannot measure intelligence on an absolute scale in the way one measures height.

It is important to recognize, however, that as the quality of the environment gets better and its features are more equitably distributed, differences between individuals will reflect genetic influences more and environmental influences less. In that event every pair of identical twins who have been raised either apart or together, even such twins already as maddeningly indistinguishable as the brothers of Henry Sambrooke Leigh's poem, could well become even more alike.

THE
SHAPES
OF
DREAMS

by Rosalind D. Cartwright

*New research is shedding light on the nature
of dreams as scientists seek to understand
how dreams are formed and how their
content can be understood.*

ROSALIND D. CARTWRIGHT is the
Director of the Sleep Disorder
Service and Research Center and
Professor and Chairman of the
Department of Psychology and Social
Sciences at Rush-Presbyterian-St.
Luke's Medical Center, Chicago.

Throughout recorded history people have been intrigued by their dreams and have speculated about their source and meaning. Now the two questions of how dreams are formed and how their content can be understood are being taken out of the realm of the mystic and pursued as areas of scientific inquiry.

As psychology enlarged its study of the mind, one class of cognitive experience characteristic of all humans, and probably also of all mammals, got left behind: dreams. As a young field, psychology was cautious about the objectivity and verifiability of the observations on which statements explaining human behavior were based. Since no one can observe the dreams of another directly, they appear to be outside of the scope of the scientific method. But with the development of laboratory techniques for the study of sleep, this situation changed dramatically.

While monitoring the electrical activity of the brain (EEG) during the change from waking into sleep, observers noted other changes throughout the night. Periods of light sleep were seen to occur with some regularity approximately every hour and a half. During these light sleep episodes the EEG resembled the rhythms of drowsy wakefulness except for a profound reduction of muscle tonus and accompanying bursts of darting movements of the eyes. This set of events, the high level of brain activity while the closed eyes seemed to be "looking" and the body acted as if paralyzed, conformed so closely to the subjective reports of dream experience that it seemed reasonable to the experimenters to wake sleepers at those times to ask if they had been dreaming. During this early research (1953–65) many laboratories confirmed that the sleep associated with rapid eye movements (REMS) and reduced muscle tonus is accompanied by dreaming. Approximately 85% of the time that subjects were awakened from this stage of sleep they were able to report a dream in progress and recall it in some detail.

Dream cycles

Typically, a night's sleep for a young adult alternates between nondreaming (NREM) sleep and dreaming (REM) sleep on a regular 90-minute cycle. In this way three to five cycles are completed each night. If awakened during each REM period and asked for a report, a person usually can retrieve three or four dreams from the night. The first rapid eye movement period is normally the shortest, approximately only ten minutes long, with the fewest eye movements and the lowest percentage of dream recall. Only 50% of the times that subjects are awakened during this REM period can they recall a dream. It is usually a short, reality-oriented statement of some recent or current event. This often is like a preview of the night's dreams. Each succeeding REM period is somewhat longer and has more rapid eye movements per minute of sleep. The ability to recall a dream also increases as the night proceeds. There is a better than 95% chance that an awakening from the last REM period, which may be as long as 45 minutes, will yield a long, detailed account of a dream—a full-length feature.

These early laboratory studies established that dreaming is both regular and plentiful in the normal human mind asleep. It is highly predictable on the basis of the associated brain waves, eye movements, and muscle patterns. It is present when they are present and absent when they are absent. Waking persons between dreams, in the NREM stages of sleep, and asking them to report their mental activity proved that the ongoing cognitive activity at these times is distinctly different. The reports from NREM sleep are vaguer, less storylike, less sensory in character, and less emotional. These differences helped to define the distinctive properties of a dream. It is a perceptual (usually visual) experience that seems to be really occurring and that has an interconnected plotlike structure. The reports following awakenings from NREM sleep were rarely visual and more often thoughtlike. Very often these reports were that no mental activity at all was going on.

The three to five dreams of a night not only increase in the length at which they are reported as morning approaches but also increase in the brightness of the colors experienced and in the intensity of the feelings. For example, a female medical student had the following three dreams on her first night in the laboratory:

1. I was dreaming about a test (female name) and I were taking a physiology test together, I think it was a physiology test, it was some medically related test. I think it was a physiology test. And we were discussing the results of it; it was a hard test and we weren't really sure we had done too well. We had done pretty well up to that point, but that was a harder test than normal and we weren't sure whether we had done well on that test. It was also slightly different than any test we had had before. And we'd been sitting there in the test and the test was O.K. I remember taking the test, walking out and talking to (female name) about the test and we were both pretty worried. It was something like physiology or something that involved a lot of remembering, a lot of terminology, and a lot of thinking, and we both remarked to each other that we had to learn a lot for the next test.

2. I was dreaming about going back to the undergrad college I went to. It was during the summer and I went to visit a professor that I was very fond of when I went there and who I worked for, for a while over the summer, doing chemistry research. As I talked to him, I talked quite a bit about another student who worked for him who got married this summer. And I was her bridesmaid, and he also went to the wedding. And we talked about how she was doing and she was doing very well, but we talked about that a little. And then we talked about whether he wanted me to work for him again this next coming summer or something like that and, no, I guess it was the summer we are in now. He was talking about whether I could possibly work for him then because she had left to go away to get married, and he was very nice to me in the dream. It wasn't an unhappy dream at all. He was in his lab and he had all these test tubes all around him, and there was a lot more glass and test tubes than there actually was in his lab. He's a very small person and he was, like, sitting up on a chair and was much taller than me and there were test tubes all around him. I think it was his lab but it was kind of distorted and not normal looking, but I assume it was the same lab that I had seen before.

3. There were a bunch of medical students together, me and about three other people. I don't think I knew the other medical students really well, they were people I knew but they weren't like close friends of mine. I don't think they were distinctly people I knew but were like combinations. I'm not sure where we were but I don't think we were in Chicago or right around the school or something, but we were in a smaller town. We were all together and we all decided to walk down into the center of town and it was a small town then. So we all did that and then we had to go back to school again. I asked the other people, oh, I know what it was, we all walked downtown and, for some reason, we were getting into a red car and they were going out and eat some dinner, no, lunch, that was it. Then we all had to go back to school again. I asked them if I could go with them and they said, they looked at each other and they said, no,

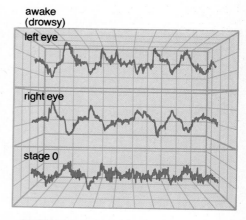

awake (drowsy)
left eye
right eye
stage 0

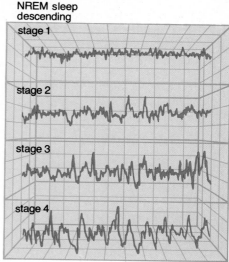

NREM sleep descending
stage 1
stage 2
stage 3
stage 4

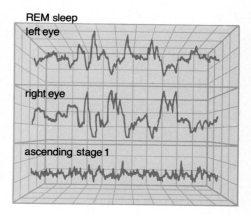

REM sleep
left eye
right eye
ascending stage 1

we are not going back to school after lunch, which for some reason I got the distinct impression that that wasn't why. I just knew that that isn't why, really, that they didn't want me. It wasn't that they weren't going back to school again, they were. They were people who just didn't want me there with them. They didn't go to school a lot either, they, they didn't go to many classes, whereas I tend to go to a lot of classes. So I walked back, although I wasn't walking back to school, I think I was walking back home or something to my apartment or something like that. So I walked back all this way, and it was in a pretty dingy neighborhood and the streets were very dirty, everything was gray, and the store fronts were all boarded up, and I was walking down that street. When I was walking back, it looked sort of like some of the places I've walked around here. I recognized some of the stores as being stores I've been by around here.

This early descriptive laboratory work established that the impression that dreams are occasional events is false. The ability to recall dreams is variable from person to person and an individual's recall varies somewhat from night to night. But dreaming itself is invariable in its occurrence and duration.

Once a method of identifying when and for how long a dream takes place had been established, researchers moved forward to compare home dreams to laboratory dreams, dreams of the young with those of the old, and dreams of the normal with those of persons in various psychiatric conditions before and after taking certain prescribed medications. Along with this map work came questions of the role of dreaming in the total 24-hour psychic economy. Are dreams entertainment to keep people at rest? Do they foretell the future, act as warnings? Do they process information of the day into long-term memory? Do they solve problems or are they only a by-product of the periodic endogenous activity of the brain, nonsensical at their inception and interpretable only through association of the random images to the current concerns of the sleeper? In other words, are dreams originally not meaningful but organized only after the fact? Once the heightened brain stimulation of REM sleep has produced visual activity, are those images that express some ongoing theme from waking life then selected for story production, or do the themes active from the day stimulate the production of specific images? This basic question led to research attempting to discover how dreams are constructed.

Dream formation

One approach to the production question has been to manipulate the pre-sleep condition, that is, to put persons into some specific state of deprivation or satiation. Subjects were made thirsty, socially deprived, physically exhausted, and even sexually aroused prior to bedtime in order to study the effect of those states on their dreams. The person was then sleep-monitored and the dreams collected by interrupting each REM period for a report for one or more nights following the experimental conditions.

For the most part these studies have not been able to show strong evidence of an association between presleep experimentally induced states and subsequent dream themes or images. One reason for this may be because people in studies of this kind do not take these conditions as seriously as they would if they were "really" happening. They assume that everything is really all right and that the experimenter can be trusted not to involve them in any

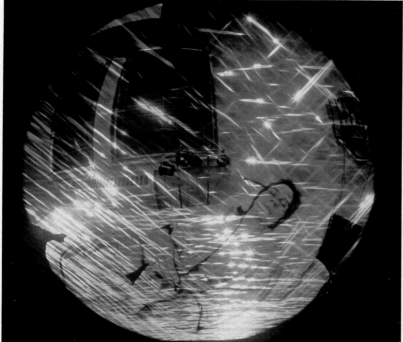

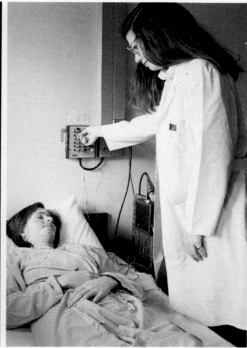

real danger. They do not appear to "need to dream" of the event at all. The other possible explanation for the failure to find any relationship is that subjects do dream about the experimental situations when they arouse real feelings in them but that these events are so transformed into dream images that they are difficult to identify.

The manipulation of the presleep period to change the subject's state did not lead to a clear picture of how dreams are formed and whether they are preprogrammed. Thus the question remains as to whether the images of REM sleep are inherently meaningful and selected to respond to the presleep state or are random and acquire meaning only as they are seen through the perspectives of prevailing interests.

Changing an individual's state experimentally is not the only way this question can be pursued. Other studies have exposed subjects to movies in an attempt to track the carry-over into dreams of specific strong visual stimuli. These studies have usually reported that the laboratory itself and the real people present during the study are incorporated more into the dreams than are the fictional movie characters or images. The stimuli that are effective in influencing dreams are those personally important to the subjects. This made such good sense that a series of studies picked up this clue to look at the dreams of people in some real-life crisis, such as a study of dreams on the night before surgery. Again, results were suggestive but not clear-cut. Without doubt more is going on in the forming of a dream than can be accounted for by knowing the person's presleep need state, visual context, or even current emotional problems.

Two other factors have to be taken into account: the coping style of individuals—that is, do they face problems directly and try to master them,

In the sleep research laboratory at Rush-Presbyterian-St. Luke's Medical Center in Chicago, a technician plugs in a subject's electrodes (above) so that she can be monitored during sleep (above left).

87

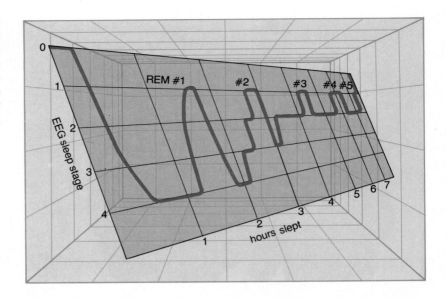

A typical night's sleep for a young adult alternates between NREM and REM stages on an approximately 90-minute basis. The dreaming episodes of REM sleep become longer as the night goes on, while the deep-sleep stages of NREM become shorter and eventually disappear.

or do they avoid or deny problems—and the dream language accumulated up to that point for representing important persons, feelings, places, and actions. Not only must the immediate states of subjects be known but also the manner in which they typically handle their emotional experiences and how they have coded them visually in the past.

It would be convenient if there were a standard dream dictionary in which the various meanings associated with each image were spelled out. But, alas, dream language appears to be a rather private one. It is not meant for social communicative purposes, and so it is idiosyncratic in character. However, since to be human is to share certain common problems, it is possible that some of them may be expressed in dreams through common forms. If this is true, it may follow that if the same anxiety is repeated at several points in a lifetime, it may be "phrased" in the same way in the accompanying dreams. If dreams are repeated under similar circumstances, and if many people have the same or similar dreams, it would be difficult to consider these as random events.

Repetitive dreams

A first approach to this attack on the dream formation problem is to discover whether people are aware of having the same dream repeatedly. The aim in this case is to discover whether dreaming is responsive to heightened states of emotion and, if these emotions and the circumstances that induce them recur, whether there is a characteristic dream response.

In a survey questionnaire study 167 women aged 18 through 55 were asked if they ever had the same dream more than once. One hundred thirty-three replied yes. Overall, 65% of the sample could report one or more repetitive dreams, how long they had been having them, and how often they were aware of these occurring. Most of these dreams (46%) were unpleasant. Another 43% began as unpleasant but eventually ended satisfactorily. Only 8% were purely pleasant, and 3% were neutral in feeling. A repetitive dream

88

thus is most likely to be a dream dealing with a problem and accompanied by uncomfortable feelings of fear, panic, embarrassment, or anxiety.

The repetitive dreams reported by these women can be classified into three general categories: physical, psychological, and social. A repetitive dream of the physical type most often dealt with fears of death and/or physical vulnerability to accident or illness. Often in such dreams the dreamer struggled to talk, scream, or run and experienced difficulty commanding her own body. The prototype of this category is the commonest dream of all, that of falling. The few pleasant physical dreams involved pleasure in body mastery such as flying. The psychological dreams also were largely negative, such as the familiar dreams of being to blame for one's own incompetence — being unprepared for an exam, late for a train, or unrehearsed for a performance. The positive psychological dreams were those in which the dreamer took pride in some extraordinary competency; for example, being a particularly able surgeon or spy. The negative repetitive social dreams involved being harmed, abandoned, or socially embarrassed, whereas the positive involved giving or receiving love, affection, or admiration.

When did the subjects have such dreams? Their own responses indicated that they were aware of having more of them following stressful events that generated upset emotional states. When things were going well, they remembered fewer dreams.

When the presleep state is one of high emotional arousal, the dream sequence that night may include one or more familiar dreams from the past. These are often not identical to previous dreams but share enough common features so that the subject says, "I had a familiar dream, one I recognize from before." When the presleep state is one of only moderate emotional level, the subsequent dreams seem more unique, often developing variations on a single theme from dream to dream across the night. Reading through these dreams in sequence, one can see a pattern of several ways of looking at the

Dan Morrill

EEG *brain wave patterns of sleeping subjects are recorded in the sleep research laboratory at Rush-Presbyterian-St. Luke's Medical Center. A subject can be viewed on the television screen at the upper right.*

same problem. When life circumstances are peaceful, the dream themes appear to vary across the night with no observable regular sequence.

The fact that repetitive dreams are associated with periods of strong emotion makes it likely that there is a threshold that needs to be reached before particular familiar dreams are triggered. Since some of these dreams are so common among different individuals (24 of the adult women subjects reported a repetitive dream of being chased), it seems likely that all people have a repertoire of key dreams that represent their major problems and methods of coping with them. However, life is not all problems, and not all dreams are recognizably purposeful. Many appear to be incidental and playful, and some are bland and even dull. Perhaps woolgathering takes place at night as well as by day when there is nothing much to demand one's attention.

Dreaming and life crises

Under normal circumstances the percentage of sleep spent in the rapid eye movement state is fairly well fixed unless some REM-suppressing drugs are taken. Even if the amount of REM sleep is reduced experimentally by waking the sleeper whenever the signs of REM sleep begin, at the next uninterrupted sleep opportunity the amount of REM will be increased as if to make up for the loss. It appears as if the balance between the proportions of REM to NREM sleep must be kept within a fairly narrow range if people are to feel and function well. What happens when there is an emotional crisis is not an increase in the total amount of REM sleep but two other changes in dreaming: a reduction of the time before the first REM period begins, and more dreamlike mental activity during NREM sleep.

It has been established that persons who are experiencing a depression differ consistently in their REM sleep from the normal. REM sleep begins earlier in the night, after as little as 40 minutes of NREM sleep, instead of the usual 90 minutes of NREM sleep. For these people the first REM period of the night is not short with few eye movements as it is in the nondepressed, but may be as long as 45 minutes during which the rapid eye movements are profuse such as are usually characteristic of the last REM period of the night. The sleep of depressed persons appears as though they cannot wait to begin dreaming, and the restful NREM sleep gives way quickly to the highly active REM state. When such subjects were awakened for reports during NREM sleep, they reported that it was infused with dreamlike mental activity. Depressed persons reported more imaging and less thinking in NREM periods than did normal subjects. This raises the question as to whether this extra and early dreaming helps such people work through their emotional crises. When emotional levels are high prior to sleep, does dreaming become engaged in a process of "working through" which serves to reduce the level by morning? This question has not yet been answered. However, there is evidence that as depression is resolved and functioning during the day improves, the first REM period of the night moves back in time toward its accustomed place of one and a half hours after sleep onset. Also, its length shortens and the accompanying eye movements subside from storms to more occasional single bursts. As this happens, the sleep of the night deepens and appears to be more restful. However, this does not always occur, and some persons may recover from their depression without their REM sleep becoming normal.

Several recent studies report that the dreams of the depressed deal with the past more often than with the present or future and that they are masochistic in nature, the outside world being viewed as hostile; this hostility is generally viewed as the dreamer's own fault. Peter Hauri reported that these dream characteristics tend to persist for as long as two years after the waking mood has improved. This is also true of the intrusion of dreaming into NREM sleep. In a study by Rosalind Cartwright of the sleep and dreaming of a group of women undergoing marital separation and divorce, those who were most depressed at the time still had early first REM periods and abnormal REM patterns throughout the night when retested two years later. The frequency of the eye movements did not increase in a regular fashion across the night from few in the first REM period to many eye movements at the end of the night. Instead, the sequence was irregular.

All of these findings suggest that not only may dreaming be responsive to emotional upsets but that persons prone to incapacitating emotional responses to life events may have chronically "defective" dream mechanisms. The suggestion is that their dreaming may be sensitized to react to even normal emotional levels as if these signaled an emergency.

In an early study Paul Verdone showed that the normal time orientation of the night's dreams moves from the present in the first dream to the recent past in the second and to the remote past in the third. Then the time often moves into the future before there is a return to the present at the night's end. If this work is confirmed as typical of the usual healthy person, it contrasts sharply with the persistent past-oriented dreams of depressed individuals.

Treatment possibilities

Treatment of dream disturbances is one area of application of dream research for the future. Perhaps in the normal person the heightened intensity and early dreaming during emotional upsets is a real help in their resolution. The return of familiar dreams of the past may indicate that the present feelings have triggered the memory system to reproduce the dreams dealing with similar problems that were successfully handled earlier in life; these dreams, in turn, channel dream production to deal with possible future choices and their application to the present problem. However, those people with severe and repeating depressions may not have developed adequate dream scripts to move from the past to future to present. They repeat the past problem over and over. A test of this hypothesis is under way in several current studies. In Cartwright's study of women being divorced, one group was not depressed. They were looking forward to the end of the bad marriage and to the future. Another group treated the change as a personal failure, which created a major depressive episode. The dreams of these two groups are clearly different.

Those who were depressed had more present-time-oriented, unpleasant dreams, whereas those who were going through the divorce with little or no upset showed more variation in the mood of the dreams and in the time orientation, which included dreams set in the past, present, and future. This group also expanded in their dream story lengths well beyond the normal and beyond the length reported by the depressed group. It appears that dreaming expands in amount and kind in response to a life change, but if this change is seriously distressing, the dreams can become limited to the immediate problem.

Can dream patterns be changed directly, reshaped to deal with the future? The idea of controlling dreams is at first blush absurd. Dreams have proved difficult to manipulate by experimenters and not to be a matter of choice by the subjects either. For example, highly motivated subjects have been asked to preselect a topic for the following night's dreams and to try hard consciously to dream about it. However, in repeated studies they have not been able to do so.

A different approach to dream control and shaping that is now being tried appears to have more promise of success. The first step is to teach motivated subjects with some dysfunctional dream pattern, such as upsetting nightmares or past-oriented depressing dreams, to indicate when these are occurring by making a deliberate signal. One such signal is the closing of a microswitch taped to the palm of the preferred hand, while other researchers have instructed their subjects to clench their fists. Several such studies have established that subjects can learn in one night to make a preselected response while remaining asleep and to be correct in identifying that they are experiencing a dream at that time.

That many people can monitor external events while asleep and can discriminate between those which require an active response and those which do not has been known for some time. Mothers routinely awaken when their infants first whimper but sleep through other much louder sounds. Many persons of both sexes can wake up at a preset time even though it may be different from their accustomed time to do so. This requires some internal monitoring of the amount of time that has elapsed. The observation of one's own dreaming is not something that is usually attempted unless a person is in psychoanalysis and required by the therapist to report the dreams at daily sessions. This typically results in greatly increased dream recall in response to the motivation to be productive in treatment.

The next step in dream control work is to attempt to induce dream changes in depressed persons whose REM patterns appear disrupted. This is done by cuing them to make a change in the ongoing dream. Once they signal that they are aware that a disturbing dream is in process, the experimenter signals to them by means of a tone or a touch that they should make a dream change. Based on the findings that depressed persons are past-oriented and masochistic in their dreams, subjects will be instructed before sleep that at the signal they are to add a new future-oriented ending to the dream and/or to be assertive in handling the hostility of others. Pilot studies of this kind in normal subjects appear promising. If such direct self-control can change dream content from its depressed characteristics, maybe the REM periods will be normalized. It remains to be seen if this intervention helps to shorten the episodes of depression and prevents recurrences.

92

Dan Morrill

Future prospects

Other areas of dream research for the future include further work on understanding the dream formation process as a skilled cognitive, nonrandom act using the model of language production. Studies are also needed to test the many hypothesized dream functions, such as assimilation of anxiety, gratification of forbidden impulses, rehearsal for future events, and mastery of new information.

The research to date has revealed that part of the mind is regularly at work throughout the night producing a series of curious short stories, inventive in their combination of familiar, half-familiar, and strange images. Dreams appear to have regular patterns within the night, and there seem to be associations between these patterns and the emotional state of the individual prior to sleep. Careful experimental designs and hard work are required to push forward the understanding of the functions of this mental activity.

Dream research in the future is expected to focus on understanding the dream formation process as a skilled cognitive, nonrandom act using the model of language production. Hypothesized dream functions such as assimilation of anxiety and rehearsal for future events also need to be tested.

FOR ADDITIONAL READING

Arthur M. Arkin and others (eds.), *The Mind in Sleep* (Lawrence Erlbaum Assoc., 1978).

Rosalind D. Cartwright, *Night Life: Explorations in Dreaming* (Prentice-Hall, 1977).

Rosalind D. Cartwright, *A Primer on Sleep and Dreaming* (Addison-Wesley, 1978).

David B. Cohen, *Sleep and Dreaming* (Pergamon Press, 1979).

William Fishbein (ed.), *Sleep, Dreams, and Memory* (Spectrum Publications, 1981).

Montague Ullman and Nan Zimmerman, *Working with Dreams* (Delacorte Press, 1979).

WHAT MAN HAS DONE TO DOGS

by
Simon Wolfensohn

Selective breeding for desired characteristics has sometimes led to physical and emotional problems for many kinds of dogs. Efforts are now being made to eradicate these unwelcome changes.

In May 1981 the British Veterinary Association and the Kennel Club of England issued a preliminary report on the subject of breed standards for pedigree dogs. The report concluded that some breed standards can encourage inherited defects, and the standards for the short-nosed breeds in particular were criticized as encouraging an unacceptable degree of exaggeration. Descriptions of eye characteristics were also cited as especially likely to cause trouble. The report ended by urging breed clubs to study their standards in an attempt to eliminate inherited abnormalities.

The following discussion reviews some of the problems found in pedigree dogs and how they are established and perpetuated. It describes the

Dachshund: susceptibility to
back injury due to overlong
back; calcification of disks in
old age and slipped disks

Pug: protruding eyes;
respiratory problems; dental
problems resulting from
short nose

Chow: eyelid problems, with
eyelids turning either inward
or outward

Boxer: respiratory problems
and dental problems due to
short nose and jaw; higher
than normal incidence of
cancer

Chihuahua: susceptibility to
eye injury due to protruding
eyes; difficulties in pregnancy
due to small size; retention
of immature features such
as milk teeth and open
fontanelles (gaps between
bones of the skull); higher
than normal incidence of
hydrocephalus

Pekingese: excessive
protrusion of eyeballs leading
to drying of the cornea and
susceptibility to injury;
respiratory problems due to
short nose; dental problems
due to short jaw; corneal
ulceration and conjunctivitis
due to folds of skin rubbing on
the eye

Basset hound: eye and eyelid
problems including glaucoma;
arthritis due to bent legs and
distorted feet; susceptibility to
back injuries; slipped disks;
ear problems due to overlong
and floppy ears

Terriers: avascular necrosis
of the head of the femur, *i.e.*,
death of bone tissue due to
failure of the blood supply;
storage diseases in some
breeds (due to failure to
produce enzymes important
in metabolism)

extent of the trouble and attempts to demonstrate the dangers inherent in
the system of breeding dogs by pedigree when the aim is primarily appearance rather than performance.

The long-suffering friend

The dog may be called man's best friend, but over the course of history man
has developed some strange ideas about the appearance of his dogs, and it is
doubtful that he deserves the same compliment from them. Dogs have lived
side by side with humans for thousands of years, and the process of domestication has a long history. There is evidence that as long as 12,000 years ago
the Natufian people, hunter-gatherers occupying what is now northern
Israel, had achieved a certain amount of selective breeding in their dogs. It
also appears that these people had developed a pet–owner relationship with
their dogs; a puppy was found buried with human remains at a place called

*SIMON WOLFENSOHN is a veterinary
surgeon in general practice in Essex,
England.*

(Overleaf) Illustration by Karel Haviček

Adapted from " The Things We Do to Dogs," Simon Wolfensohn, NEW SCIENTIST, vol. 90, no. 1253, pp. 404–407, May 14, 1981

German shepherd: dwarfism due to failure of the pituitary gland to develop normally; higher than normal incidence of epilepsy; hip dysplasia

Bloodhound: eyelid problems leading to sore eyes and conjunctivitis; acromegaly (excessively heavy bone structure)

Great Dane: short life span; bone problems; arthritis; curvature of the leg bones

St. Bernard: eyelid deformations, leading to sore eyes and conjunctivitis; giant size, possibly leading to short life span; acromegaly; hip dislocation

Cocker spaniel: distiachiasis (extra eyelashes on the inside of the eyelid) causing sore eyes; chronic ear infections resulting from floppy, hairy ears; higher than normal incidence of epilepsy

Shetland sheepdog: excessively heavy coats

Collies: collie eye anomaly, which includes a variety of eye defects; progressive retinal atrophy; heavy coats in some breeds,

English bulldog: respiratory problems due to short nose; dental problems due to short jaw; protrusion of upper or lower jaw; skin infections due to bacteria trapped in folds of skin; problems giving birth

Mallaha in a manner suggesting that the dog was a companion rather than some kind of sacrificial offering. It is only in the last few hundred years, however, that pedigree breeding has really become established. In that time a great deal of change has been achieved, some of it good but some of it giving rise to a wide range of problems.

One well-documented example of changes made in a breed—in this instance relatively minor ones—is the case of the Shetland sheepdog or Sheltie. In the last century the Sheltie was a small but robust, rough-coated, working sheep dog, far removed from the present-day version, which is a small, slight dog with an immensely fluffy coat. The contemporary animal is not too bad a dog, but all too often the characteristics bred into dogs are such as to cause them considerable inconvenience; from time to time they are so extreme that they require veterinary attention. Not content with breeding dogs into peculiar shapes and sizes, people have also adopted the practice of

97

snipping off bits of their anatomy to make them conform further to arbitrary ideals.

Pets and their owners

Clearly, the responsibility for perpetuating these abnormalities rests not only with the breeders but also with the people who buy the dogs. What, then, is the nature of the relationship between a dog and its owner? In the last 20 years or so a substantial amount of research has been carried out on this subject, and the motives for owning a pet have been classified in various ways. Essentially, there are three main classes of pet dogs, although these can be subdivided into many other categories. First is the straightforward family pet which provides an educational experience for children, a means of recreation and exercise, a source of physical security, friendship for children or the elderly, and, often, especially for the latter, a means of establishing social contacts. Second are dogs that serve as a source of prestige or pride for the owner, including in some cases guard-dog types kept as a kind of virility symbol. Third are the dogs that are kept for companionship but are treated as child substitutes by their owners.

Any breed can fit into any of these groups, but on the whole the family pets tend to be the most common types, mongrels or breeds that were originally working types, such as Labradors and spaniels. The status-symbol dogs frequently belong to the larger breeds, and the child substitutes are most often the miniatures and the small, short-nosed breeds. In addition to these categories, there are the genuine working dogs—gundogs, guard dogs, collies, huskies, and so forth—representing a further wide range of types, mainly with strong characteristics based on various instincts as well as on physical features.

Most breeds of pedigree dogs have problems that probably have been bred into them, either by accident or by design, but on the whole it seems to be the status-symbol dogs and the child substitutes that collectively have the most trouble. To the average family looking for a pet to keep the children company, physical factors are relatively unimportant. Usually the most important characteristic is the temperament of the dog, and owners also look for a pet that will require only the minimum number of visits to the veterinarian. Unfortunately, these factors do not seem to be the main ones in the minds of the judges at dog shows, although a dog that attacks the judges or has an obvious deformity is unlikely to win many prizes.

Dog shows and the pedigree system

To be a successful breeder, one must have dogs that win prizes at dog shows. Consequently, the shows are taken very seriously. Thus the breeder's aim is to produce dogs that conform to the standards laid down for the breed, often a century or so ago; but these standards refer only to visible characteristics, without regard for the health of the dog or its temperament.

This system is a mixed blessing. When it tends to consolidate a preference for a characteristic that really should be considered an abnormality, the results for the breed can be detrimental and long-lasting. Even when the champion selected by the judges is apparently a thoroughly good, all-round

98

Bulldog of 1820 (top) contrasts markedly with the present-day version of the breed (bottom). Selective breeding for the heavy, exaggerated muzzle has contributed to respiratory and dental problems. Also, bacteria become trapped in the many skin folds of the modern dog and cause skin infections.

specimen, the effect on the breed as a whole may be distinctly retrogressive. In many cases the original stock of dogs introduced to establish a breed was very small, or the forebears of the breed came from a restricted geographic area. Thus, the gene pool tends to be small in the first place. Because show champions are in great demand for their services at stud, their genes flood the market. Add the fact that highly incestuous matings over several generations are commonplace, and it is easy to see how an undesirable characteristic that is in fashion for a time can become deeply established within a breed.

Because champions tend to be chosen for their visible, fashionable characteristics, and because standard agricultural techniques such as progeny testing (in which the parents are assessed solely on the merits of their offspring) have never been used seriously in dog breeding, it is likely that many recessive characteristics have been incorporated into breeds by accident. It is also quite possible that in some breeds the available gene pool has become so restricted that it would be almost impossible to backtrack and reestablish healthier genes within the population.

Fortunately for those breeds that retain a reasonable degree of genetic flexibility, there is now a more general awareness of the dangers of inbreeding, and some of the more extreme examples of bizarre physical features are becoming less common. Nevertheless, there is still a lengthy catalog of physical peculiarities perpetuated by breeders, often at the expense of more desirable characteristics. It would be impossible to give an exhaustive list of abnormalities found in dogs that are attributable to their breeding, but plenty of interesting examples are to be found.

Physical trouble spots

To begin with the head, many troubles stem from standards that affect the shape of the face and the facial expression. The obvious inference is that breeds with these problems are often the child substitutes. The shape and position of the eyes are specified in many breed standards, and the shape of the head, weight of the dewlaps, and so forth also affect the eyes. Thus a bloodhound puppy or a basset hound may have a very appealing expression, but, along with Saint Bernards and others, these are typical examples of dogs that may have severe eyelid problems. These breeds often suffer from a deformation of the eyelids known as ectropion, in which part of the eyelid is turned outward, resulting in an unpleasant appearance and a continuous overflow of tears. In many cases these dogs have permanently sore eyes and a constant low-grade conjunctivitis. Often the condition requires surgery.

Surgery may also be required in the opposite condition, entropion, in which the eyelid turns inward. This deformity is most common in chows, but it is not unusual in Labradors and several other breeds. It causes such obvious symptoms that it is regarded as a fault, and since it is known to be inherited, most breeders are careful to avoid it. The commonest condition affecting the eyes is distichiasis, in which there are extra eyelashes on the inside of the lid margin. These lashes tend to be short bristles, and their constant movement against the eye can produce very sore eyes and may lead to secondary entropion. Distichiasis is common in many breeds but is found especially in cocker spaniels.

To win prizes at dog shows breeders must meet standards that often were established more than a century ago. Unfortunately, these criteria sometimes have caused the incorporation of abnormal and detrimental characteristics into a breed. On the opposite page, top, an Old English sheep dog is prepared for the judge's ring at a show in London in 1913. At bottom is a present-day show in Arizona.

101

In the Pekingese and many other short-nosed breeds the face is so squashed that the eyeballs protrude excessively, exposing the eyes to drying and corneal injury. In some cases the protrusion is so pronounced that the dog has difficulty closing its eyes properly, even when asleep. In others the eyes are permanently on the verge of popping clean out of their sockets, and even moderate physical trauma is enough to make this happen. The flattening of the Peke's face also produces extremely deep folds in the facial skin around the nose, and these folds may rub the surface of the eye, producing ulceration and conjunctivitis. The depths of the folds provide such good conditions for bacteria that skin infections are common, often necessitating surgical removal of the folds. Similar folds around the mouth in many breeds tend to trap saliva and debris, leading to a foul smell at the very least and sometimes to dermatitis.

The shortening of the jaw and the anterior part of the skull in short-nosed breeds has the effect of distorting the airway; the soft palate is prolonged to the point that it interferes with breathing, especially when the dog is asleep, and the nasal sinuses are shortened, giving rise to chronic sinusitis and more serious respiratory infections. The gasping, snoring, and wheezing that result are especially familiar to owners of Pekes, pugs, and English and French bulldogs. In addition, most of these breeds suffer dental problems because the upper and lower jaws are not equal in length and the jaw is so short that the teeth are overcrowded; the latter condition is especially common in Pekes. Yorkshire terriers, Chihuahuas, and miniature poodles also tend to have poor teeth, but it is unclear whether this is caused by dietary factors, by some factor directly associated with miniaturization, or by the fact that the jaw has become too small to accommodate the teeth.

Many of the short-nosed breeds have difficulty getting born at all. The size of the pups' heads and the stockiness of their bodies result in a disproportionate need for delivery by cesarean section. This is also a problem in the very small breeds, such as Yorkshire terriers and Chihuahuas, raising the question of whether miniaturization has stunted the growth of the adult without producing a comparable reduction in the size of the fetus.

There are many breeds in which the legs are small and out of proportion to the rest of the body. In basset hounds, for example, the legs are so bent that the joints have to work at peculiar angles, considerably increasing the wear and tear on the load-bearing surfaces. As a result these dogs almost invariably develop some degree of arthritis. At the best of times they have an awkward, shuffling gait that is a terrible mockery of the grace and power of a dog like the greyhound. Bassets, and more especially dachshunds, also have absurdly long backs and are highly vulnerable to back injuries. In old age almost all of them develop calcification of the intervertebral disks, and slipped disks are much more common in these breeds than in others.

Unfortunately for the basset, its problems do not end there. The thick, heavy, low-set ears cut off the circulation of air in the ear canal, thus providing a breeding ground for bacteria and yeasts that cause chronic ear infections. It is the cocker spaniel, however, that may be the worst example of this fault. Not only is the anatomy of its ear similar to that of the basset but it also invariably has a very hairy ear canal that further restricts air

102

Several breeds of dog suffer from inherited disorders of the eye. At the left, the shar-pei has a high incidence of congenital entropion, in which the eyelid turns inward. Below left, basset hounds are sometimes afflicted with ectropion, a turning outward of the eyelid which results in soreness and a continuous overflow of tears. The eye of an English bulldog, below, has entropion of the lower eyelid and mild entropion with trichiasis of the upper lid; in trichiasis the lashes grow inward toward the eye, causing considerable pain and irritation.

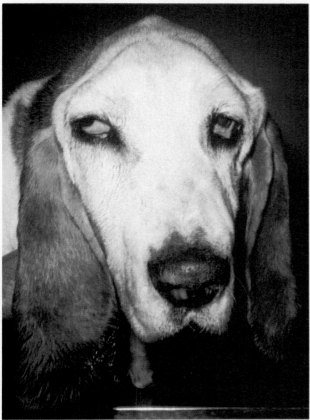

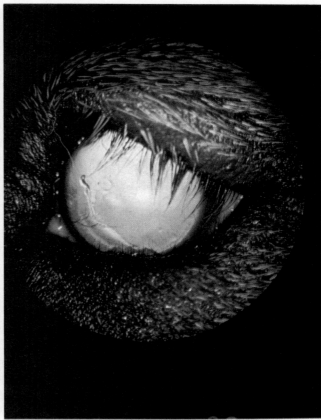

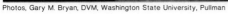

Photos, Gary M. Bryan, DVM, Washington State University, Pullman

Eye problems occur in dogs that have been bred for short noses and a squashed facial appearance. The Boston terrier puppy (above) suffers from outward turning of the eyes, making it difficult to achieve binocular vision, and from protrusion of the eyeballs; even moderate physical trauma can cause such eyes to pop out of their sockets. The pug (above right) has shortened nasal passages, resulting in chronic sinusitis and other respiratory infections.

circulation. Ear infections are extremely common in cockers. Surprisingly, perhaps, hair in the ear canal is not a feature mentioned in any breed standard.

Even the shape of the chest and abdomen may cause difficulties. In the bloodhound, for example, the requirement that the loins be deep and slightly arched is probably responsible for the very high incidence of torsion of the stomach, an often fatal condition.

Big dog—little dog

So much for a brief look at some of the physical trouble spots in pedigree dogs. Anyone familiar with dogs can add many other examples to the list. More interesting in many ways are the general health problems found in pedigree breeds. For example, why is it common for poodles and Labradors to reach 16 years of age or even more, while Saint Bernards, Great Danes, and some of the other giant breeds are lucky to live 10 years? For that matter, how can the species *Canis familiaris* vary so much as to include both the tiny Chihuahua and the giant Irish wolfhound?

There is no simple explanation for the shorter life-span of the giant breeds. They do not seem to be more predisposed to disease in middle life than other breeds, and apart from those that are destroyed because of bone problems early in life (usually due to faulty development of the growth plates of the bones or defects in bone mineralization) or because of severe arthritis, they seem to die of as varied a range of diseases as any other breed. Research is currently under way into cardiac failure in the giant dogs, and it may be that this is a significant factor in many cases. Or it may be that the hormonal mechanisms or other factors responsible for the giant size and heavy bone development of these breeds are intimately related to the aging

104

Courtesy, Patricia Frost, University of Illinois, College of Veterinary Medicine

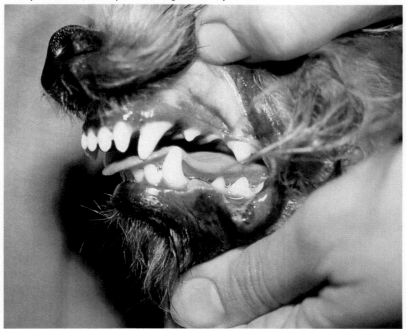

process. It is still too soon to say definitely, but intuitively one may suspect that these dogs have simply become too big.

Little is known about the factors that affect a dog's size. Obviously, part of the answer must lie in a straightforward selection process favoring the large or the small, but it seems likely that this has been combined over the years with selection for distortions produced by hormonal mechanisms. Thus it is very likely that Saint Bernards and bloodhounds have a strong inherited tendency to acromegaly, a condition caused by excess production of growth hormone in the adult, which leads to heavier than normal bone structure, especially in the feet.

At the other end of the scale are the very small breeds, and in their case a number of mechanisms may be involved. First, there is an autosomal (not sex-linked) recessive gene that occurs in the Alaskan Malamute, among others, and produces defective growth of the long bones. Second, there is dwarfism caused by failure of the pituitary gland to produce growth hormone, leading to dwarf size but with normal proportions and with retention of the temporary teeth, puppy-type coat, and an immature, high-pitched bark. A severe form, with complete failure of the pituitary to develop normally (panhypopituitarism), is seen in German shepherds, and in this case it is known to be a recessive characteristic inherited through an autosomal gene. Finally, there is cretinism caused by congenital hypothyroidism. Animals with this condition are also dwarves but have broad skulls, short thick legs, and a short spine. Often they also have a hunched back and/or excessive curvature of the forehead. Although there is no substantial hard evidence implicating these mechanisms in the small size of certain breeds, it seems reasonable to suggest that they may operate in various combinations to produce the effects seen.

Yorkshire terrier exhibits an overshot jaw in which the top jaw is longer than the lower one. This condition is a result of breeding for a short nose and the general miniaturization of the dog.

105

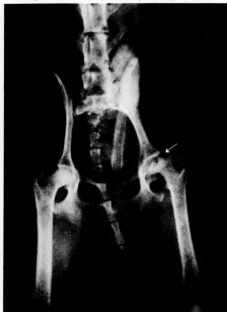

X-ray reveals presence in a miniature poodle of Legg-Calvé-Perthes syndrome, indicated by the dark gray area at the head of the right femur. This condition, which leads to secondary arthritic changes in the hip joint, is found only in small breeds.

Very large dogs such as the Saint Bernard (below) usually die at earlier ages than do smaller breeds. The hormonal mechanisms responsible for the giant size of the dogs may be intimately related to the aging process.

Breed-related diseases

Another area where there is little solid documentation concerns medical oddities found in specific breeds. Again, there is a long list of conditions that might be mentioned, but a few examples will serve to illustrate the problem. Heart failure in giant dogs has been mentioned, and it is of particular interest because it is similar in many respects to a syndrome occurring in humans. It is caused by a disease of the heart muscle of unknown etiology that occurs primarily in adult male Great Danes and Irish wolfhounds around four years of age. Still on the subject of heart conditions, it is well known that white miniature poodles seem to have an unusually high incidence of heart murmurs, but again the reason is unknown.

Hydrocephalus (accumulation of cerebrospinal fluid in the cranial cavities) is disproportionately prevalent among Chihuahuas, while dislocation of the lens of the eye has recently been recognized as a common problem in Tibetan terriers (which are not actually true terriers). Several of the small breeds of terriers are susceptible to avascular necrosis of the head of the femur, a painful and disabling condition with close similarities to Legg-Calvé-Perthes syndrome in children. Boxers are unusually prone to various forms of cancer, and epilepsy is more common in German shepherds and cocker spaniels than in other breeds. German shepherds also tend to be deficient in the digestive enzyme trypsin, lack of which leads to diarrhea and weight loss. Dalmatians are unique among dogs in that they excrete purines as uric acid rather than in the more soluble form of allantoin, and as a result they are susceptible to gout and the formation of ammonium urate bladder stones. Basset hounds are relatively more susceptible to glaucoma than other breeds, while clumber spaniels may suffer muscle weakness caused by a specific deficiency of one of the mitochondrial enzymes responsible for energy metabolism.

There are many other examples of conditions with strong breed affinities, although few are well documented in print. Several are interesting because of their close analogies with human problems, one of the most notable in this respect being Legg-Calvé-Perthes syndrome. In this condition the bone of the head of the femur is deprived of its blood supply and dies, causing pain and leading to secondary arthritic changes in the hip joint. In children there is little evidence that the disease is inherited, but in dogs (in which the condition is very similar) it is found only in some of the smaller breeds—especially terriers and miniature poodles—clear evidence for some hereditary influence. Children affected with the disease are usually skeletally immature, often coming from poor homes, but the condition is rare among black children. This suggests that both environmental and hereditary factors are involved and also that the condition in dogs may be related to reduced size.

In humans Perthes syndrome occurs at an age when the blood supply to the head of the femur depends on blood vessels that run outside the bone itself and hence are more vulnerable to injury. A similar situation exists in those breeds of dog that are affected. Mongrels, in which the blood vessels run in the bone itself, are resistant to the disease. Although it is known that development of the disease is linked to the anatomy of the blood supply, the actual cause of the damage remains obscure. It may be a transient inflam-

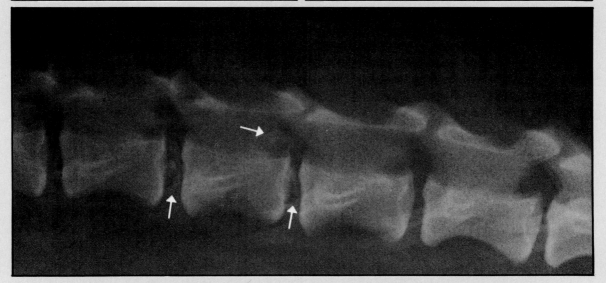

An Alaskan Malamute litter produced a normal dog (top right) and a dwarf (top left). The dwarfism is caused by a recessive gene. Above is a radiograph of the spine of a five-year-old dachshund. The lower and upper arrows indicate mineralized disk material between lumbar vertebrae and extending into the spinal canal; dachshunds have a high incidence of disk problems.

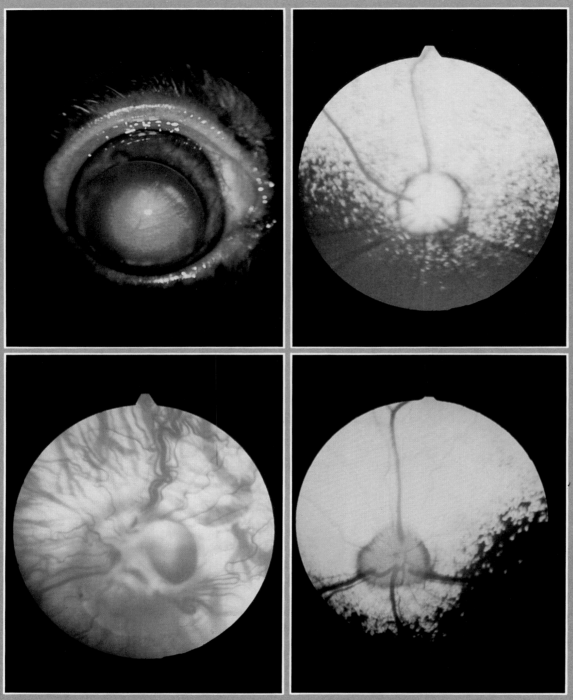

Lens luxation, displacement of the lens of the eye into the anterior chamber, occurs in a wirehaired fox terrier (top left) and other terrier breeds. Another visual ailment, progressive retinal atrophy, is found in a Brittany spaniel (top right). Collie with eye anomaly (bottom left), a defect common to the breed, is contrasted with a normal collie ocular fundus (bottom right).

mation of the joint, but evidence of this can be found only in some cases. Further work on the subject is needed, and a comparative approach may well help to provide the answers.

An inherited condition that is well understood is lens luxation in the Tibetan terrier. Quite recently it was found that this condition is related to an autosomal recessive gene, and analysis of 27 pedigrees demonstrated that all the cases could be traced back to one or more of three animals born in the mid-1950s, all champions of their breed. This is only one of several inherited eye defects found in dogs. Others include cataracts in several breeds and a common condition, known as collie eye anomaly, which is found in various types of collie and may have an incidence as high as 85% in the United States. Collie eye anomaly includes a variety of defects such as chorioretinal hypoplasia, colobomas (localized structural defects), detachment of the retina, and intraocular hemorrhage. The hereditary mechanism for this disease is probably complex, and although the signs appear before breeding age, no scheme has yet been introduced to control its spread.

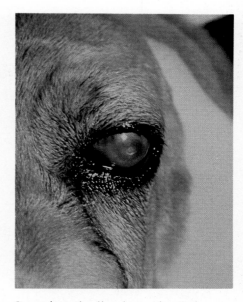

Basset hound suffers from advanced glaucoma and is irreparably blind in the greatly enlarged right eye.

Efforts at control

A scheme does exist for the control of progressive retinal atrophy (PRA), a condition found in several breeds. In most cases the genetic basis of the disease is known. In border collies it is thought to be regulated by a dominant gene that does not always express itself. Every border collie entered in the United Kingdom national sheep dog trials must have a compulsory eye examination, and entry to the stud book is restricted to dogs that are free of the disease. The scheme has met with a fair degree of success, and in recent years the incidence in the U.K. has been reduced from around 12% or more to about 2%. Since PRA is untreatable and progresses to complete blindness, this result is encouraging.

Unfortunately, the same degree of success has not been achieved in the case of the hip dysplasia scheme of the British Veterinary Association and the Kennel Club. Hip dysplasia involves a flattening of the head of the femur and the acetabulum, the socket of the hip joint. Left untreated, it progresses to severe osteoarthritis, and it can often be disabling. Like PRA, it affects several breeds, though it appears to be especially common in German shepherds and Labradors. The condition is about 62% due to inheritance in the German shepherd, and is transmitted through a combination of genes. Development of the disease is substantially modified by environmental influences.

Although the hip-dysplasia-control scheme has been in existence for some time, it has met with relatively little success, and incidence of the disease remains high. Until the hereditary and environmental factors involved are better understood, this is likely to remain the case. However, the fact that the breeders are at least trying to control the problem provides considerable stimulus for substantial research if money becomes available.

Cosmetic surgery

Apart from the problems that have been bred into dogs, either by accident or by design, there remains the practice of surgically altering the animal by removal of the dewclaws, tail docking, and, in some countries, ear cropping.

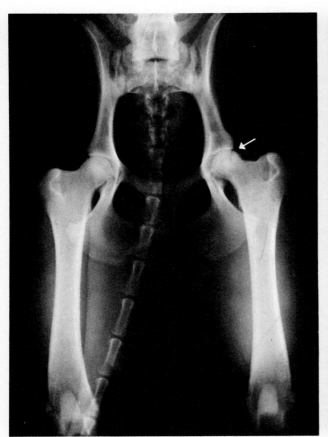 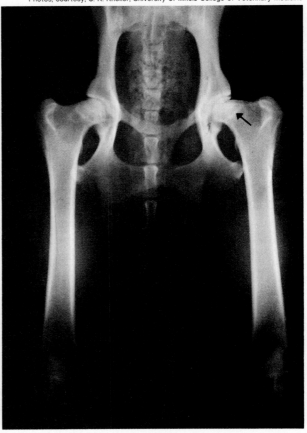

Labrador with normal hip joint (above) contrasts with one suffering from hip dysplasia (above right), the flattening of the head of the femur and the socket of the hip joint. A common disability of Labradors, hip dysplasia if left untreated progresses to severe osteoarthritis.

There may be some slight justification for removal of the dewclaws because they occasionally cause trouble, but the other procedures are done purely for the sake of appearance. In some countries it is still common practice to cut the ears of certain breeds such as boxers and Doberman pinschers (admittedly under anesthesia) and strap them up so as to make them stand upright. Although these practices are required by the breed standards and hence perpetuated by breeders, the power to stop them is in the hands of the veterinary profession. In Britain the Council of the Royal College of Veterinary Surgeons (the statutory body of the profession) has said that "the Council believes that it cannot be ethically correct for a veterinary surgeon to carry out the docking of a dog's tail except in cases of disease or injury. The Council considers that legislation should be sought which would ban the docking of the tails of dogs except in cases of disease or injury to the tail, and then only by veterinary surgeons." (At present the law permits tail docking by lay persons under certain circumstances, usually on their own animals before the pups' eyes are open.)

Despite the official disapproval by the profession, veterinarians are in a difficult position with respect to this practice and will be until legislation is enacted to prevent it. If a vet refuses to perform the operation, clients may go elsewhere, taking their otherwise valuable business with them. Or they may attempt to dock the tails themselves, in which case their crude methods and lack of expertise may produce even worse mutilations and cause the pups a great deal of pain. Feeling on the subject runs so high in the U.K. that a woman who tried to exhibit her undocked weimaraner in a show in 1980 made the front page of at least one national newspaper. A few brave breeders who have ignored the demands of breed standards—and of course forfeited the prizes at shows—have actually found it easier to sell their pups with the tails on. Nonetheless, most continue to have their dogs' tails docked, even though they often admit to disliking the practice, because they dare not risk losing in the show ring.

Conclusion

To sum up briefly, there are basically two types of problems afflicting pedigree dogs. One concerns the physical problems that result directly from overzealous interpretation of poorly defined breed standards, without sufficient regard for the comfort of the animal (and this includes the docking of tails). The other involves the more subtle problems of conditions affecting various body systems, established, mainly by accident, in certain breeds or lines. These are essentially the fault of a pedigree system of breeding that is obsessed with appearances and pays insufficient attention to considerations of general health.

In both cases the root cause is human greed. Breed standards were originally set for people who bred dogs as a hobby, but now breeding has become a business. People will pay relatively enormous sums for a pedigree pup ($500 or more in some cases), and so breeders adhere slavishly to the standards and breed widely from champion stock, despite the dangers of the pedigree system, because of the need to win shows and thus make their pups more salable. Clearly, until the system is changed by modifying the breed standards when necessary, the situation will not improve.

Spinal problems afflict the basset hound because of its long back, a consequence of breeding for appearance without sufficient regard for general health.

Elizabeth Crews—Stock, Boston

CONSERVATION BY THE ANCIENTS

by Robert M. Alison

Preservation of wildlife and other natural resources originated at least with the ancient Egyptians and possibly earlier.

Sarcophagus for an ibis was made in Egypt about 330 BC. The ibis was considered an incarnation of the god Thoth and therefore was protected from being hunted.

ROBERT M. ALISON *is an author and journalist.*

(Overleaf) Illustration by Bill Peterson

About 12,000 years ago there began a partial breakdown in the self-regulating mechanisms that had previously maintained a delicate balance among the Earth's many life forms. Human selection began to supersede natural selection. Humans began to inflict their standards on all other living things, to master all nonhuman elements. As they strove to attain that mastery, countless species fell victim to human progress and human greed.

But, remarkably early in their advancement, humans discovered that they were not entirely above the selective process but rather a product of it. In order to be the most successful species they realized that it was their task to master the art of prudent manipulation of renewable and nonrenewable resources. Even before that realization came the first traces of what would eventually blossom into a large-scale conservation movement. When human beings first recognized that the stability of their life-styles was at stake, they acted quickly—in the name of self-interest.

The earliest hints of conservation were the tribal taboos spawned by circumstances of time and place and passed along from the founding generations to those following. None were written, and their details are unknown. But there is ample evidence for their existence. The first written conservation laws were likely the formalization of already deeply entrenched principles. They testify to an early realization of the concept that the presence of humans on the Earth was beginning to pose a threat to certain species of animals and plants.

114

Egypt and Assyria

Among the first conservation steps were those taken by the ancient Egyptians. To them, some animals had special religious significance. Protection from indiscriminate killing was necessary for creatures that enjoyed such an elevated status, and more than half the Egyptian wildlife species were protected for that reason alone.

On the other hand game animals received almost no protection. In some districts they were immune to hunting by all but the pharaoh, but the concept of game laws was for the most part unknown. Duck hunting was a favorite pastime, and the marshes of the Nile Delta at times overflowed with sportsmen. By 1198 BC officials were forced to do something about the congestion. They issued "marsh tickets," possibly the first hunting licenses.

Most of the pharaohs were avid sportsmen. Although they did not appear to have been anxious to pass laws regulating hunting activities, some of them clearly saw the value of habitat improvement as a means of stimulating game production. Such practices had an early origin, but it was not until the time of Ramses II the Great (1304–1237 BC) that they were widespread. Among the most common of the practices was tree planting.

Ramses II took great pride in his habitat programs. Hieroglyphic inscriptions dedicated to his work refer to the "sweet and fragrant woods" and "the many gardens" for which he was responsible. By the time of Cleopatra in the first century BC, it was mandatory to plant a quota of trees on all crown

Duck hunting was popular in ancient Egypt as indicated by the painting found in a tomb of about 1425 BC. The marshes of the Nile Delta became so congested with hunters that in 1198 BC officials began issuing "marsh tickets," perhaps the first hunting licenses.

115

Wall engraving reveals Ashurnasirpal II (883–859 BC), a king of Assyria, hunting a lion. On the opposite page another Assyrian engraving, a lion-hunt relief from the reign of Ashurbanipal (668–627 BC), shows a herd of gazelles. The Assyrian kings established game laws that applied to all except the king and his servants. Violators faced severe penalties, including dismemberment.

lands. Unauthorized tree cutting was severely punished. Among Egyptian fishery laws was a prohibition on the netting of certain valuable species, dating from April 17, AD 46.

Throughout the period of Babylonian and Assyrian dominance, the conservation movement seems to have been largely limited to the widespread construction of great lavish pleasure parks called "pairidaeza," from which the word "paradise" was derived. They were enclosed places rich in trees and shrubs and stocked with all manner of wild birds and mammals. A few of them were hunted by the park owners.

In the seventh century BC King Sennacherib of Assyria constructed a mammoth park at Nineveh. Contemporary clay tablets recorded that below the city he "laid out many parks" but that the central one was the greatest of all. It was planted in "cypress and mulberry, all kinds of trees . . . (and) the birds of heaven . . . wild swine and beasts of the forest brought forth their young in abundance."

All the Assyrian kings were fond of hunting. They were responsible for establishing game laws in their region dating from the time of Tiglath-pileser I (c. 1100 BC). The laws dealt with closed seasons, falconry practices, and captive game mammals and birds. All but the king and his servants were bound by them, and severe penalties, including dismemberment, were meted out to violators. Also, anyone who removed trees from any park was subject to a heavy fine.

Of Assyrian origin and unknown date, the Mosaic Law as related in Deuteronomy 22:6 decreed that, although it was permissible to take eggs and young birds from nests, the adult females should always be spared. This was probably the earliest formal recognition of the value of conserving wildlife breeding stock.

116

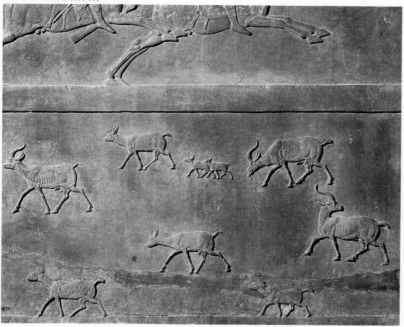

India and China

The notion of conservation arose early in the development of the Indian civilization, starting in the twelfth century BC with the Hindu precept of ahimsa, nonviolence to all living creatures. It culminated under the guidance of Emperor Asoka (265–238 BC), who, in order to propagate his version of the Buddhist dharma, issued a number of edicts etched on pillars and stones. One pillar edict dealt almost exclusively with wildlife conservation. In it Asoka ordered the complete protection of "parrots, mynas, the aruna, ruddy geese, wild geese, the nandimukha, cranes, bats, queen ants, terrapins, boneless fish . . . tortoises and porcupines, squirrels, twelve-antler stags . . . rhinoceroses, white pigeons . . . and all quadrupeds which are useful." He went on to ban the burning of forests in any case where wildlife might be adversely affected.

Subsequent Indian emperors reaffirmed Asoka's prohibitions. Their combined efforts have been credited with substantially reducing the destruction of some of India's useful and colorful wildlife species. This was one of the first known attempts to conserve wild animals other than those valued by sport hunters.

In China the practice of constructing hunting parks and zoological gardens was already firmly established by the time of the Chou (Zhou) dynasty (began 1122 BC). The activity was intensified early in the Han dynasty (began 206 BC) when a huge park was built near Ch'ang-an (modern Xian). Another had a five-kilometer (three-mile) periphery.

The Chinese developed conservation practices long before they were described in writing. The first to be formally recorded appeared in the Code of Ch'in (Qin), dating from the third century BC. In the Chou period imperial orders prescribed hunting and angling methods, some of which dated to the

117

time of Confucius (551–479 BC). They concerned mainly ethical practices, such as prohibitions on fishing with nets and shooting at roosting fowl.

In 62 BC under Hsiao-hsüan (Xiaoxuan) it was ordered that "in the three capital commanderies people shall not be allowed in the spring and summer to remove nests, or try to find eggs, or to shoot pellets or arrows at flying birds." The ordinance applied to all birds. Public hunting areas fell under the supervision of the chief commandant of waters and parks or the privy treasurer. It was their task to prevent violation of the various applicable game laws. There were similar officials who were responsible for overseeing hunting activities in royal parks.

By 7 BC restrictions were placed on the practice of capturing wild animals for public display. Under Hsiao-ai (Xiaoai) subject states were no longer permitted to present wildlife as gifts to the imperial court.

Crown land was inviolate. But, to that general rule, there was one exception. During periods of famine, the public was allowed to collect "birds, beasts, fish, turtles, or the various insects . . . leaves, silk worms . . . and other products" there. Those activities were always conducted under the eyes of the forester of the mountains or the forester of the marshes. The idea was that conservation was a luxury, to be afforded in times of plenty but to be abandoned temporarily in times of need.

Greece and Rome

In the Greco-Roman world the conservation movement never fully matched accomplishments in other fields of endeavor. However, some efforts were made. According to Xenophon (c. 360 BC) sport hunting had always been a passion among the Greeks. They shared the Assyrian taste for large hunting parks and zoological gardens. From the time of Aristotle falconry was a popular Greek pastime, and there was also local interest in sport fishing.

Naturally in a society in which sport hunting and angling played so prominent a role, the first conservation practices focused on game species. Indeed, Greek conservation laws rarely contemplated any matter not directly related to hunting or fishing. In Plato's time, about 375 BC, Greek laws prohibited poaching with nets or snares. Fowlers were not permitted to hunt on "cultivated or holy ground," and anglers were excluded from "harbors and sacred rivers, ponds and lakes." Angling methods could not include the use of "noxious juices that make the water turbid."

Closed seasons were established on certain game animals, and hunting was forbidden on certain special days. There does not appear to have been any Greek law in regard to hunting at night. But Xenophon advised that the practice should be banned near cities in order "not to rob the young lads of their game."

The Romans were not very active in formulating protective legislation. They too had their hunting parks, including one owned by Tiberius Pompeius in Gaul that measured some 40 square kilometers (15 square miles). There were also many zoological gardens to which general access was not permitted. But in much of the Roman Empire wildlife could be taken by anyone at any time; there were no restrictions on habitat destruction. Furthermore, hundreds of thousands of wild animals were captured for display and

118

eventual killing in the Circus Maximus at Rome; 9,000 were sacrificed to celebrate the opening of the Colosseum and another 11,000 to celebrate the Emperor Trajan's victory over the Dacians.

The first Roman game preserve was built about 100 BC by Fulvius Lippinus in the Tarquinii area. Lucius Lucinius Lucullus and Quintus Hortensius followed his example. More elaborate versions of the Egyptian and Assyrian pleasure gardens, these game preserves were lavish landscaped enclosures containing boar, deer, and other big-game mammals and a variety of colorful birds. In common with their predecessors, their main purpose was to enhance the owner's pleasure. Any contribution to conservation was secondary.

Quintus Hortensius was not the father of aquaculture, but he practiced it on a large scale. Near Bauli he constructed great fish tanks that housed all manner of salt- and freshwater species. He kept fish for his personal enjoyment and probably had no idea that his techniques would bloom into a widespread fishery management activity in the centuries to come.

Actual Roman laws on conservation were few. Most of them dealt with ownership of game animals and rights of landowners with respect to game. In the first century BC, however, the Roman Senate passed a resolution calling for a stop to the capturing of wild animals for public killing. This growing practice had caused game stocks to be depleted.

Mongolia and the Americas

Long before most Europeans focused on conservation as a matter worthy of their attention, the leaders of the newly emerged Mongol Empire had seen fit to do so. Under Genghis Khan (1206–27) the Mongols conducted great hunts lasting several months and involving hundreds of thousands of huntsmen. In order to protect game animals so as to ensure maximum success on such expeditions, the khan set forth a law forbidding "any man of the Empire to kill from the month of March to October, deer, bucks, roe-bucks, hares, wild ass and some birds." It was a small step, but its significance for the conservation of some wildlife was unmistakable.

Kublai Khan (1260–94) went even farther. He instituted a large-scale wildlife feeding program in which corn and other grains were planted along public roads. Nobody was permitted to harvest the grain. It was for the sole use of wild game birds. Game management officers were stationed along the roads to protect the birds.

All of Kublai Khan's efforts were made to enhance stocks of game species, for, like his grandfather, Genghis, he was an ardent hunter. But regardless of the motives, the manipulation of food-producing habitats to increase wildlife populations locally was a novel approach at the time and one that would be used often in the years to come.

Curiously, about the time Kublai Khan was putting in place his game management program, a similar operation was being instituted in Peru by the Inca Indians. Like the Mongols, the Inca lords conducted great hunts involving many thousands of participants. In order to ensure an adequate quantity of game for those hunts appropriate wildlife conservation practices were necessary. In Huamachuco Province wild animal preserves were created in

120

which hunting by ordinary Indians was forbidden under pain of death. As a result alpacas, pumas, bears, foxes, deer, and other animals flourished there. The first such preserve was established under the emperor Pachacutec. The Lord Inca alone was permitted to hunt in such preserves.

Any Inca could hunt in some regions. However, even there hunts were normally conducted in a rotating manner, with three years of closed season for every one that was open. In many cases only harmful animals were killed. Alpacas were captured alive, shorn, and set free. Females of all useful species were never killed. Hummingbirds, eagles, vultures, and some ducks were protected owing to their religious significance. Habitat management programs were also undertaken on a grand scale. They included tree- and shrub-planting operations.

Among the Maya Indians (*c.* 200–1500) of Central America sport hunting was not a common activity. It is, therefore, not surprising that Mayan conservation laws were few. There was a strict prohibition against the killing of the quetzal because its feathers were used as money, but there do not appear to have been any other protected species. The Maya were highly superstitious. Their conservation practices were to a great degree not controlled by precise laws but rather by a firm belief in lucky and unlucky hunting activities. The sale of certain parts of a deer was unlucky, as was hunting on Tuesday or Thursday. Naturally, the Maya avoided doing anything unlucky, and the indirect result was a certain degree of wildlife conservation.

Among the Aztec Indians (*c.* 1250–1519) of Mexico sport hunting was

Ancient Roman mosaic at the Piazza Armerina in Sicily depicts three stags driven into a net by Roman hunters in North Africa. Although the Romans established some game preserves with limited hunting, they captured hundreds of thousands of animals throughout their empire for display and eventual killing in the Circus Maximus at Rome.

121

The Mongol emperor Kublai Khan (1260–94) leads a hunting party in this painting on silk. An ardent hunter, Kublai Khan began a wildlife feeding program in which corn and other grains were planted along public roads in an effort to increase the numbers of game birds.

primarily an aristocratic pursuit. Common folk were permitted to hunt peccary and deer for food on certain public lands. They could snare rabbits and capture ducks, but they were excluded from crown land. Only the Aztec emperor and his chief officials could hunt there. To that extent crown lands functioned as wildlife preserves because sport hunting in those areas was conducted by few individuals.

The Aztecs shared the Roman liking for extensive game parks, one of the largest of which was near the city of Tenochtitlán. It was enclosed by a canal and contained several species of the most popular game animals. During the time of Montezuma II (c. 1516) no one was allowed to hunt in the several zoological gardens that had been constructed throughout the empire.

Specific laws provided for the complete protection of quetzals, flamingos, and several other birds whose feathers could be worn exclusively by the ruling class. Furthermore, by custom the Aztecs avoided taking certain wild animals considered to be unclean. There was also a prohibition against unauthorized destruction of trees.

Britain

In most of the preceding cases the record is so incomplete, or the society in question so short-lived that no long-term conservation trend can be fully described. Measures were adopted sporadically, and no specific evolutionary development can be traced. But in the case of Britain that is not so. There re-

122

mains a continuous record of a conservation movement that began with the earliest Saxon kings and has continued more or less uninterrupted to the present.

At first, conservation measures in Britain, as in many other parts of Europe, were generated by a self-indulgent aristocracy intent on excluding commoners from what was considered to be the noble pursuit of sport hunting. Conservation, thus, meant the act of restricting access to wildlife to a select few. As time passed, however, it came to mean a great deal more.

At the end of the seventh century Britain was a mosaic of great woods: the forests of Dean, Wyre, Kinver, Sherwood, and Rockingham. Some measured more than 13,000 square kilometers (5,000 square miles). They were striking features of the landscape. More than that, they hosted the king's game.

The first known English conservation law was promulgated by King Ine (688–726) of Wessex. It prescribed a heavy fine for cutting down or burning any tree; the fine increased in proportion to the size of the tree. Under a law of Wihtred of Kent (c. 695) domestic animals were not allowed to graze in forests to the detriment of the lush ground vegetation used extensively by the king's deer.

Canute the Great (1016–35) was a dedicated hunter. As king it was his divine right to hunt anywhere and at any time in Britain. But among other Englishmen hunting opportunity depended on whether or not they owned land; those who did not could not hunt. By the time of Henry I (1100–35) vast royal forests had been established in which the king had an exclusive right to hunt. Forest Courts administered the Forest Law, which prescribed death or dismemberment to anyone who molested the king's wildlife.

Aristocrats could hunt on their own landholdings. Some built lavish game parks and stocked them with deer and boar. They could hunt in the royal forests only by permission. Even on their own lands they were forced to observe certain customary closed seasons that had generally been established by 1080. There was a closed season on red deer from Holy-Rood Day (September 14) to the the Nativity of St. John the Baptist (June 24). The season on fallow deer was closed from Candlemas (February 2) to Holy-Rood Day. Roe deer could only be hunted from Holy-Rood Day to Michaelmas Day (September 29). The open seasons reflected those periods in which the flesh of the animals in question was in prime condition.

During the twelfth century there was a bitter struggle between the king, who wanted to preserve the royal forests intact, and the nobles, who wanted to chip away at the forests in order to expand the lands upon which they could lawfully hunt without permission. It was a seesaw battle. The Charters of Liberties (1100) established certain royal forests, and the Charter of the Forest (1217) expanded them. However, a revision of Magna Carta in 1225 reduced their number. Later, under Edward III (1327–77) more royal forests were created. Regardless of their extent they served to restrict access to vast tracts of land, thereby ultimately serving in the interest of conservation even though that was not necessarily their original intent.

The Assize of the Forest (1184) was the first comprehensive English conservation document. It prohibited access to royal forests and established heavy penalties for unauthorized destruction of trees. Royal foresters looked

123

Stela of the Maya Indians of Central America (above) shows a priest wearing a headdress adorned with quetzal feathers. Because the Maya used quetzal feathers both for adornment and money, these birds were never killed. At the right, alpacas roam in the Andes Mountains in Peru. During the time of the Inca Empire, from about 1000 to the Spanish conquest in 1532, alpacas, prized for their wool, were captured and shorn but not killed.

after the king's wildlife. Every male over the age of 12 years was required to take an oath to protect the king's game. Unleashed dogs were forbidden in the forests. Night hunting was outlawed on pain of one year's imprisonment. In each county a council of 12 knights was created to act as "custodians of the game." The assize was a monumental step, the first formal statement of the Forest Law. It set the stage for many future improvements.

Under the terms of the 1225 revision of Magna Carta, some of the strict forest laws were made less severe. The penalties of death or dismemberment for the taking of the king's deer were discontinued. Any archbishop, bishop, earl, or baron passing through a forest could lawfully take "one or two deer" under the watchful eyes of a forester.

Conservation of trees was a steady theme in Britain. Under Henry III (1216–72) no one was allowed to waste trees. Similar provisions were enacted by a dozen subsequent sovereigns. Beginning at the time of Edward III fur-bearing animals were protected, not because of any intent to conserve them but only to restrict access to them because the wearing of fur was a privilege enjoyed by a chosen few. The era of wetland preservation dawned in 1427 when Henry VI put in place a statute securing certain coastal marshes that had become badly eroded over time.

Falconry was extremely popular in Britain from the earliest times. During the reign of Edward III it was deemed appropriate to restrict that activity to the upper classes. That was the beginning of a steady stream of falconry legislation that culminated in the time of Henry VIII (1509–47) with the imposition of the death penalty for unauthorized possession of any bird of prey. Hawks, including their nests and young, were protected to one degree or another from 1360 onward.

Swans received full protection in 1482, and restrictions on hare-hunting

124

were enacted by 1522. The first closed season on waterfowl, from May 1 to August 31, was in effect in 1533. In that same year wild bird eggs were protected for the first time. A closed season on pheasants and partridge was established in 1581. Nets, traps, and snares for taking birds were outlawed at the same time.

In the 1600s there was a great deal of legislation on deer; most of it focused on poaching. In 1692 the first British fishery legislation was enacted. It dealt with the unauthorized use of nets and other commercial gear.

More than 30 statutes on wildlife were enacted in Britain between 1700 and 1831. Only one, a ban on the burning of black grouse range, touched on habitat preservation. None dealt with nongame animals. The British left consideration for nongame animals to the last. Such legislation was regarded as superfluous. Thus, it was not until 1869 under Queen Victoria that the first nongame law came into being. Its aim was to preserve seabirds. Most other wild birds were protected 11 years later.

A persistent trend

Regardless of time or place there has been a persistent trend throughout history toward conserving natural resources, particularly wildlife. The actual motives in doing so have varied widely. In the early times they were mostly self-serving, but wildlife benefited anyway. Later they were more altruistic. In conclusion, it appears that religion, mythology, and social pressures—along with a genuine desire to conserve—all influenced the development of conservation practices in early times.

FOR ADDITIONAL READING

F. L. Attenborough, *The Laws of the Earliest English Kings* (Cambridge University Press, 1922).

J. H. Breasted, *Ancient Records of Egypt* (Russell and Russell, 1906).

Edward, Duke of York, *Master of Game* (Ballantyne, Hanson and Co., 1904).

J. B. Pritchard, *Ancient Near Eastern Texts* (Princeton University Press, 1955).

H. Rackman (trans.), *Naturalis historia* (Harvard University Press, 1940).

M. Rugoff, *The Travels of Marco Polo* (New American Library, 1961).

Medieval illustration depicts an English king hunting in a royal forest. By 1100 there were throughout England huge tracts of woodland in which the king had an exclusive right to hunt.

SEA OF SALT SEA OF LIFE

by Christopher Riley

Despite its reputation for sterility the Dead Sea is neither biologically lifeless nor a useless geological curiosity. Its joint owners, Jordan and Israel, are racing to exploit the sea's varied resources.

(Above) © Nathan Benn–Woodfin Camp; (right) © Werner Braun

(Left) Zev Radovan; (right) U.S. Geological Survey, EROS Data Center

Stone marker (above) near the shore of the Dead Sea proclaims the uniqueness of the site. False-color image of the Dead Sea depression and surrounding topography (right) was taken by the U.S. Landsat satellite from an altitude of 920 kilometers (570 miles). The Jordan River valley, Lisan Peninsula, and man-made evaporation flats at the southern end of the sea are prominent features.

CHRISTOPHER RILEY *is a Producer for BBC Television in London.*

Take the winding, rock-faced road east from 'Arad, down the tortuous, plunging descent through the southern Judaean wilderness, past the Crusader fortress of Metzad Zohar, lying in its ravine like a child's sand castle ruined by the tide, and on past the sign announcing that the height above sea level is zero. Finally drop another 400 meters to Newe Zohar at the southern end of the Dead Sea, the site of the most unlikely museum in the world. Its guide, Shlomo Drori, formerly of the Israeli potash works at Sedom, will relate the tale of the extraordinary geological aberration that the world now knows as the Dead Sea.

For Drori the Dead Sea and its potential have become a passion, just as they were for pioneering Zionist leader Theodor Herzl nearly a century earlier. Herzl's statue stands by the Zohar museum door, together with the text

128

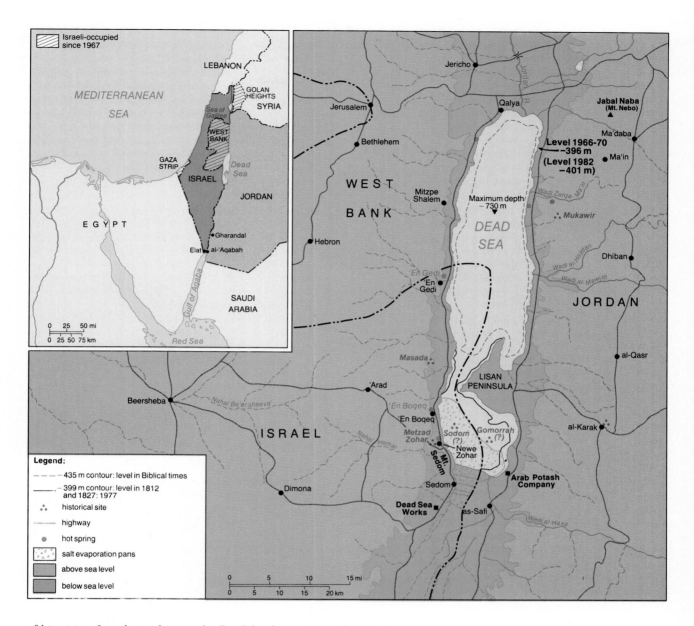

of his vision. In a dream he saw the Dead Sea humming with industry, providing natural riches for the people around its shores.

The sea of antiquity

Strictly not a sea at all but a landlocked salt lake, the Dead Sea lies between Israel and Jordan. Physiographically it is situated in a deep depression along the Great Rift, the extensive African-Middle Eastern rift valley system, and is the result of a sinking of the Earth's surface between shifting blocks of crust. About 75 kilometers (45 miles) long by 15 kilometers (9 miles) wide, the Dead Sea at 400 meters (a quarter of a mile) below sea level is the lowest body of water on the Earth.

Neither Drori nor Herzl before him would think of this natural chemical

Entry of the Jordan River into the Dead Sea is shown in a detail of the Ma'daba map, a 6th-century mosaic set into the floor of an early Christian church as a guide for pilgrims. One fish in the river appears to be traveling downstream while a second battles against the current to escape the intense saltiness of the sea. A salt-laden boat floats in the sea, but the images of the sailors aboard are tiled-in patches, having been defaced by Iconoclasts in the 8th century.

reservoir as "dead." "Dead Sea" is the English, not the local, name. The Hebrew name is Yam ha-Melah, the "Salt Sea," a title used by both Jews of the Old Testament and modern Israelis. The 14th chapter of Genesis contains the first biblical reference: Bera, King of Sodom, and Birsha, King of Gomorrah, together with the rulers of the other Cities of the Plain, waged war against their neighbors "in the Vale of Siddim, which is the salt sea." Bera and Birsha lost the battle, "and the Vale of Siddim was full of slimepits; and the Kings of Sodom and Gomorrah fled, and fell there."

By the 1st century AD the sea had earned yet another name. The historians Diodorus Siculus and Flavius Josephus had come to call it Lacus Asphaltitis, the "Asphalt Lake." Periodically the sea has spewed up huge floating blocks of asphalt, used by ancient shipwrights for caulking their vessels. Both the saline and the asphalt-bearing descriptions are more appropriate than "Dead Sea," for this body of water has little to do with death. Nevertheless, whatever writers and locals actually called the place, it gained an early reputation for sterility. Aristotle, three centuries before Christ, pronounced that the waters were so saline and bitter that no fish could survive. Diodorus was puzzled at the lack of life in view of the "great rivers [particularly the Jordan] of remarkable sweetness that empty into it." He concluded that "the lake gets the better of them by its evil smell."

In the biblical city of Ma'daba, a few miles from the northern end of the Dead Sea on the eastern (Jordanian) side, archaeologists have uncovered the earliest known map of the sea. The colored mosaic, dating from the 6th

130

century AD, is a work of art as well as of geography. On it fish are seen swimming up and down the Jordan. One fish is moving hopefully toward the sea, while two others are swimming desperately back upriver with pained expressions. The main features on the sea itself are two boats laden with piles of salt. By the 6th century the salt trade was well established, and in modern times remnants of small trading posts have been found near the water's edge.

But a flourishing salt trade was not enough to prevent the myths and legends that began to enshroud this strange place. The heat, the salinity, and the low-lying remoteness of the sea combined to give it a fearsome reputation. Despite the evidence of the Ma'daba map, it was believed that boats would sink mysteriously and that any bird attempting to fly over the water would die immediately. Travelers during the Middle Ages believed devoutly in the accounts of the Old Testament and went looking for biblical monuments. Here, Lot's wife had been petrified for eternity after the apocalyptic destruction of Sodom and Gomorrah as recounted in the 19th chapter of Genesis. "The sun was risen upon the earth when Lot entered into Zoar. Then the Lord rained upon Sodom and upon Gomorrah brimstone and fire from the Lord out of heaven; and he overthrew those cities, and all the plain,

From THE HOLY BIBLE, illustration by Gustave Doré, 1866

Biblical illustration by Gustave Doré depicts Lot's wife's fatal glimpse of the destruction of Sodom and Gomorrah.

a

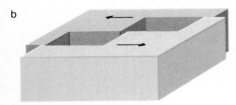

b

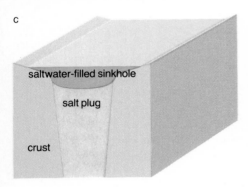

c

saltwater-filled sinkhole

salt plug

crust

The deep basin of the Dead Sea is generally believed to have been formed as the result of the oppositely directed motion of parallel, irregularly shaped edges of rifting crust. As the edges shifted positions, crustal blocks called graben sank between them, creating depressions (a). With continued motion several graben coalesced to produce a larger, composite depression (b). An alternate theory supposes the preexistence of a salt plug in the region (c), which was dissolved out to form the northern basin following a large influx of fresh water. Left behind was a large sinkhole, now filled with the salt water of the Dead Sea.

and all the inhabitants of the cities, and that which grew upon the ground. But [Lot's] wife looked back from behind him, and she became a pillar of salt." Modern tourists arrive in busloads to stare at "Lot's Wife" between the Newe Zohar museum and Sedom. But on Mount Sedom, which is solid salt to a great depth, winter rains keep eroding one salt pillar and erecting another. Lot has had many "wives" over the centuries.

Science takes a hand

Such biblical stories and the general unwholesomeness of the Dead Sea easily led to a belief that it was an accursed place, a home of the devil, the very entrance to hell itself. It was not until the 19th century, when scientists turned inquiring eyes toward the sea, that the myths and legends began to evaporate. The formation of the sea at last emerged as scientific theory supported by geological evidence, which interestingly has also served to reinforce its link with Bible stories. For instance, science has shown that the sea's basin, which drops to a maximum depth of 730 meters (2,395 feet) below sea level, was formed by seismic convulsions on the scale of those that once rocked Sodom and Gomorrah. Earthquakes continually shake this area of the turbulent Great Rift, and tremors of magnitude 3 on the Richter scale occur annually. Today in the Dead Sea mud near the former Jordanian resort of Qalya, on the Israeli-held West Bank, strange parallel furrows run out into the water. Near Jericho there are deep splits in the ground, testimony to the magnitude-4–6 earthquakes of 1927 that killed 1,000 people. It seems quite likely that an earthquake, and not Joshua's heroic trumpets, flattened the walls of the biblical city some 4,500 years ago.

The Dead Sea basin resulted primarily from so-called strike-slip motion along parallel edges of rifting crust at the site. As they pulled apart, crustal blocks called graben sank between them, becoming flanked by high ground heaved upward. Ocean water filled the whole area at the end of the Pliocene Epoch, about 2½ million years ago, flowing in across the low Plain of Esdraelon, from what is now the Mediterranean. Over a million years later, as the graben steadily sank and the salt water evaporated from the shallows, only the deepest, salt-concentrated basins remained and connection with the ocean was severed. During this time the climate changed several times from dry to wet and back again. Beginning about 60,000 years ago, during one of the rainy periods, a large expanse of water called the Lake of Lisan built up to cover the eastern rift valley from near Elat in the south to Galilee in the north. Remnants of this predecessor to the Dead Sea can be seen today, notably the terraces of so-called Lisan marl on the hook-shaped Lisan Peninsula (Arabic al-Lisan, "the tongue") on the Jordanian side. This promontory divides the deep and extensive northern basin from the shallow and much smaller southern basin.

There is another theory of the Dead Sea's birth, its proponent an eminent scientist who has lived and worked by the sea all his life, Rudolf Bloch. In 1970 he astonished traditionalists by suggesting that the deep northern basin of the present sea was not created primarily by fault movements but by the formation of a "salt sinkhole." Bloch argued that, during the time of the Lake of Lisan, which was shallow, brackish, and six times longer than today's Dead Sea, a kind of salt plug existed in the seabed, similar to today's Mount Sedom. With the inflow of large amounts of fresh water the lake gradually dissolved the upper surface of this plug. When eventually the early lake receded, the plug was left, dissolved out like some massive hollow tooth.

Whatever its origins, it was the salty remoteness of the Dead Sea that made it forbidding to explorers, and it is not surprising that only in the 19th century was any serious exploration attempted. The first two recorded surveys ended in tragedy. An adventurous Irishman, Christopher Costigan, came to grief in 1835 from a fever he caught while exploring the Dead Sea in an open boat. Found half-dead on the northern shore, he was carried by some "good samaritan" more than 32 kilometers (20 miles) up through the Judaean hills to the Franciscans in Jerusalem, where he died. A gravestone erected to his memory by his mother was discovered and preserved by Israeli forces when they stormed Jerusalem's Old City in 1967.

Twelve years later a more serious attempt to survey the sea was made by an Englishman, Lieutenant A. G. C. Molyneux of the Royal Navy. Molyneux, too, succumbed to a fever and died, but the flimsy boat in which he rowed and sailed around the sea has come to rest outside Drori's museum at Newe Zohar. The British officer who had sent young Molyneux on his fatal trip was full of remorse and transported the boat home with him from Palestine to England. There for a century it adorned his estate near Torquay in Devon

Predecessor to the Dead Sea, the Lake of Lisan (right) stretched from almost 30 kilometers south of the present southern basin to the Sea of Galilee. At its maximum extent it reached 220 meters above the present-day level of the Dead Sea. Graph (below) plots climatic fluctuations for the past 20,000 years, as deduced from evidence of variations in the extent of the Lake of Lisan and in the chemical and physical properties of the lake's bottom sediments. About 10,000 years ago the Dead Sea appears to have dried up almost completely.

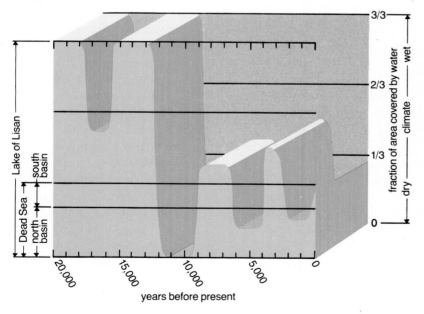

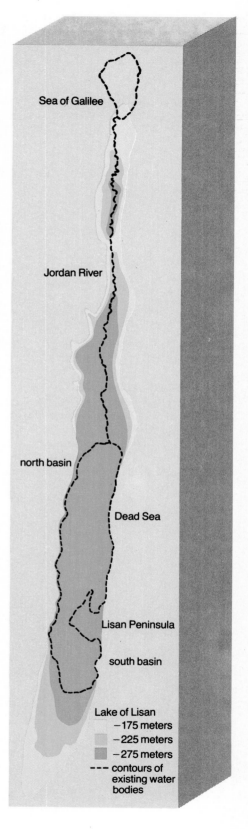

Sea of Galilee

Jordan River

north basin

Dead Sea

Lisan Peninsula

south basin

Lake of Lisan
- −175 meters
- −225 meters
- −275 meters
- - - - contours of existing water bodies

Nineteenth-century illustration depicts W. F. Lynch's overland trek by caravan from the Mediterranean to the Sea of Galilee in 1848. The U.S. naval lieutenant used two boats to travel down the Jordan to the Dead Sea. His report and survey stood as the final word on the sea for more than a hundred years.

as the roof to his summer house. The vessel was finally brought back to the shores of the Dead Sea by Zev Vilnay, an archaeologist from the Hebrew University of Jerusalem.

By 1847 a proper Dead Sea survey still had not been completed. The expedition that finally succeeded set out in that same year from Philadelphia, led by another naval lieutenant, W. F. Lynch of the United States. It was Lynch's team who wrote the report and drew up the survey that were used as the official records for well over a hundred years.

With amazing endurance Lynch had his boats, the "Fanny Mason" and the "Fanny Skinner," towed overland to the Sea of Galilee and then sailed down the Jordan to the Dead Sea itself. The sea's water, he wrote, is "a nauseous compound of bitters and salts. There's a tradition that no one can venture upon this sea and live. Repeatedly the fates of Costigan and Molyneux had been cited to deter us." But Lynch battled on heroically, past the hot springs of 'En Gedi to the Lisan Peninsula, whose extremities he named Point Costigan and Point Molyneux. The southern basin was at that time still navigable and Lynch sailed into it, the first explorer to do so. He may have known the story about the Roman emperor Vespasian who, doubting tales of the Dead Sea's buoyancy, had bound slaves thrown in to prove the point. Eighteen centuries later Lynch carried out a similarly crude scientific experiment. He dropped two eggs into the brine and found that they floated. In the Mediterranean, some eight times less salty, they certainly would have sunk.

The saltiest water on Earth

The water of the Dead Sea is odd indeed. The sea has no outlet and depends solely on evaporation to counter the inflow from the Jordan and other

134

streams. In 1959 David Neev of the Geological Survey of Israel and Kenneth Emery of the Woods Hole Oceanographic Institution in Massachusetts carried out a definitive new survey and found that the water level has shifted considerably over the centuries. Horizontal terraces high above the present shoreline show the limits of previous levels. The ancient Lake of Lisan was about 220 meters (720 feet) deeper than the present northern basin of the Dead Sea. As the rainy climatic period of 20,000 years ago gave way to a dry spell, evaporation increased, dropping the surface level to 700 meters (2,300 feet) below sea level, or about 300 meters (985 feet) lower than its present level.

From this time until about the 8th century AD there was probably no southern basin of the Dead Sea. Biblical tales of Ruth and Naomi refer to easy access between the eastern and western shores, probably by way of a land route across the present-day Lisan Straits. Archaeologists have found traces of a Roman road joining present-day Jordan with Judaea by way of the Lisan. When the annual rainfall increased once again, the roadway was flooded and the southern basin was formed, probably no more than 200 years ago. At the start of the 20th century, as the latest wet cycle reached its peak, levels rose to about ten meters higher than at present. Then once again another drought period set in, and the level has been falling ever since by half a meter every year. Today the southern basin has no "natural" waters of its own. Its area is covered by man-made evaporation ponds of the potash

Past water levels of the Dead Sea and Lake of Lisan are etched in the terraced escarpments near Masada.

Zev Radovan

Adapted from "The Dead Sea," David Neev and Kenneth O. Emery, SCIENCE JOURNAL, pp. 2–7, December 1966

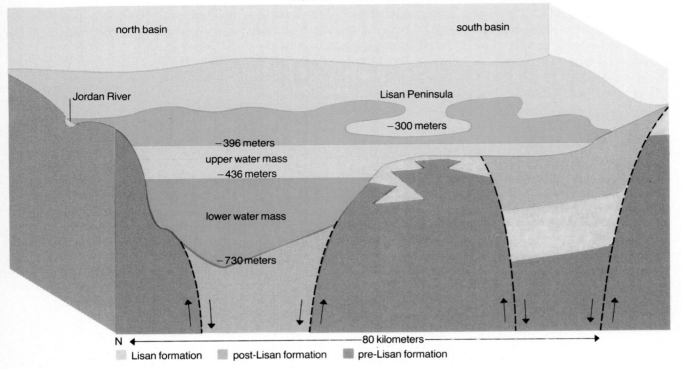

north basin

south basin

Jordan River

Lisan Peninsula

−300 meters

−396 meters

upper water mass

−436 meters

lower water mass

−730 meters

N ◄—————————— 80 kilometers ——————————►

◼ Lisan formation   ◼ post-Lisan formation   ◼ pre-Lisan formation

Cross-sectional diagram through the long axis of the Dead Sea reveals the stratification that existed in the sea's northern basin before 1979. The upper 40 meters of water, only slightly less dense than the water below, overlaid almost 300 meters of oxygenless "fossil" water, which had remained undisturbed for perhaps thousands of years. Following gradual depletion of the insulating upper layer, in 1979 the Dead Sea "turned over"; the two layers merged and the entire water body became homogenized and oxygenated. Diagram also shows the geologic faulting that produced the sea's two basins.

works on the Israeli side; in the early 1980s these extraction beds were being matched by similar ones in Jordan.

Probably the most well-known peculiarity of the Dead Sea is its salinity, which has arisen during the thousands of years of evaporation of its source waters. Not only is the Dead Sea the lowest body of water on Earth, it is also the saltiest and densest, with as much as 33% by weight of dissolved solids. By contrast, Utah's Great Salt Lake has a salinity of 28%.

For centuries, until the late 1970s, one of the most bizarre features of the water of the northern basin was that it had lain in two distinct blocks or layers. Down to about 40 meters (130 feet) depth the water temperature, salinity, and density varied with the seasons and with freshwater inflow. Below that depth they remained unchanged throughout the year. Near the surface the temperature ranged from 19° to 37° C (66°–98° F), and salinity was a little less than 30%; at 290 meters (950 feet) the water remained a constant 22° C (72° F), and salinity was 33.2%. The upper layer was rich in chloride with lesser concentrations of bromide, sulfate, and bicarbonate. Below the 40-meter mark, magnesium, potassium, chloride, and bromide rose rapidly in concentration, and the deepest waters of the basin were saturated with sodium chloride, which formed salt crystals and sank to the bottom. In their studies Neev and Emery concluded that the lower water mass was probably "fossil" water from which sodium chloride had been precipitated for many thousands of years. This fossil layer had lain oxygenless (anoxic) and insulated from the atmosphere by the steady inflow of lower density fresh water above it.

Recently the steady state of the Dead Sea has been disrupted. The Jordan

River has been reduced to a muddy trickle, as both Israel and Jordan have used its waters extensively for irrigation and industry, and as a result the insulating layer of fresh water steadily diminished. Finally in February 1979 the whole northern basin became homogenized, and the lower fossil layer merged with the screening upper layer. In the words of Joel Gat of Israel's Weizmann Institute of Science, "The Dead Sea has turned over." Gat has been working with Neev and scientists from the Rensselaer Polytechnic Institute, Troy, New York, the University of Heidelberg in West Germany, and the Scripps Institution of Oceanography in California to trace the course of this turnover. For earth scientists like them, it is without doubt the Dead Sea's event of the century, maybe even of the millennium. The layered structure has disappeared, water temperatures except right at the surface are now uniform, and concentrations of trace metals like iron, manganese, and lead occur throughout the water mass. One immediate effect has been the disappearance of the world-renowned bad-egg smell that clung around the Dead Sea basin. Hydrogen sulfide from the lower layer precipitated out as oxygen from the atmosphere filtered down to the fossilized depths. This influx of oxygen, in fact, has formed an entirely new chemical soup in the Dead Sea deeps.

The sea's varied wealth

Paradoxically, elimination of the foul odor may come as unhappy news for the sea's longest established modern industry—tourism. Today the smell clings only locally at the sites of sulfur springs around the sea. The more general odor had been convincing "evidence" of therapeutic powers for the hundreds of thousands of clients who swarm to the beaches and mud baths run by Israel's prosperous Dead Sea hotels. Ever since ancient times bathers

Visitor to the Dead Sea (left) smears her body with its black mud, which is rich in mineral salts. Some people take the treatment for beauty; others claim relief from rheumatism and skin ailments like psoriasis. Bobbing high in the water, a bather (below) demonstrates the Dead Sea's extraordinary buoyancy.

(Left) Dan Porges—Peter Arnold, Inc.; (right) Bonnie Geller—Peter Arnold, Inc.

Solar pond at 'En Boqeq traps the Sun's heat under 7,000 square meters (about 1.7 acres) of water from the Dead Sea to produce 150 kilowatts of electricity. Heat exchanger and turbine house are visible at the left.

have been urged to suffer a little in the stinging, tacky waters for the sake of health and beauty. The black mud around its mineral springs was meant to invigorate the skin, and Cleopatra herself is said to have sent specially for consignments of it. 'En Boqeq on the sea's southern basin has become an international spa. A seaside clinic treats skin diseases like eczema and psoriasis for patients from around the world, and some health services including those in Sweden and West Germany contribute to the cost of patients' visits. Psoriasis sufferers claim at least six months' relief from their disfiguring ailment. In the early 1980s there were half a dozen hotels whose residents returned year after year to find solace at perhaps the strangest lido in the world.

Alongside the luxury hotels of 'En Boqeq lies another source of Dead Sea promise, the promise of energy. Oil is scarce in Israel. Under the Egyptian-Israeli treaty of 1979 the Israelis handed back the captured Egyptian oil fields of Sinai. A desperate oil search has been centered on the Dead Sea, for surely the bituminous "Asphalt Lake" of history must be secreting oil somewhere. So far, however, finds have been meager, mainly confined to the discovery of oil shales around the sea. According to some scientists the asphalt may be a decomposition product of oil leaked from the shales and later released into the sea during crustal movements.

But if oil is rare, another energy source is abundant. By 1981 solar power already was heating the water in 25% of Israeli homes. Harry Tabor of the Hebrew University is the father of his country's solar policy and has taken the lead in a solar enterprise that could close Israel's energy deficit in a dramatically simple way. Tabor has built a large, reinforced, rubber-lined

138

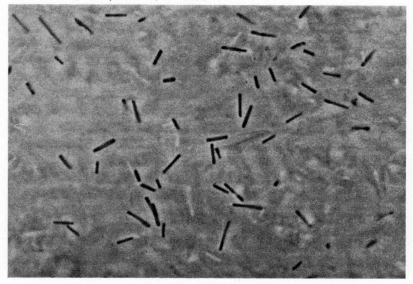

Halobacterium halobium, *a salt-loving relative of bacteria found in the Dead Sea, carries an extraordinary system in its cell membrane for trapping and storing the energy in sunlight. Scientists are studying ways of adapting this system to man's energy needs.*

Electron micrograph showing a section through the salt-tolerant green alga Dunaliella bardawil reveals the presence of massive amounts of beta-carotene, visible as small dark globules around the periphery of the organism. D. bardawil also produces high amounts of glycerol and protein and, together with other members of the genus, is regarded as an attractive biological system for investigating the conversion of solar energy into chemical products of commercial interest.

pond alongside 'En Boqeq's bathing beaches. The pond is filled with Dead Sea water, which separates into layers, the very salty mass settling toward the bottom and the less salty remaining on top. Sunlight penetrates the upper layer and becomes trapped as heat in the denser solution below, which approaches the boiling point. The hot water is then pumped to a turbine house where it passes through a heat exchanger and vaporizes a special low-boiling liquefied gas. The vapor drives a turbine and so generates electricity. Once the vapor has done its work, it is condensed into liquid again by cooler water taken from the pond's surface. This water is then returned to the pond.

Tabor's solar pond is an elegant and inexpensive example of recycling and can be scaled up easily. It also resembles an enormous battery; its saline water can store heat for delivery at night or during sunless periods. The 'En Boqeq pilot pond generates only 150 kilowatts, but Tabor foresees huge ponds to meet about 20% of Israel's electricity needs by the year 2000. He even envisages the Dead Sea's surface transformed by giant floating solar ponds, which would not need shore-based installation. For something long considered "dead," the sea is showing a lot of energy.

Even in the biological sense the Dead Sea has never been "dead" at all. Nevertheless, the stigma of sterility inherited from medieval legend and seemingly borne out by fruitless searches for indigenous life persisted well into the 20th century. In the 1940s bacteriologist Benjamin Elazari-Volcani pronounced the Dead Sea to be indeed alive and well, for he had discovered bacteria and algae in the sea's chemically saturated brines. The bacteria are specially adapted to the hostile conditions in which they thrive; among them are halophilic (salt-loving) bacteria that not only tolerate the Dead Sea environment but positively demand such conditions. If these bacteria are placed in water with a salt concentration of less than 15%, they quickly expire. Several species of halophilic bacteria are known, many of them found in highly saline waters other than those of the Dead Sea.

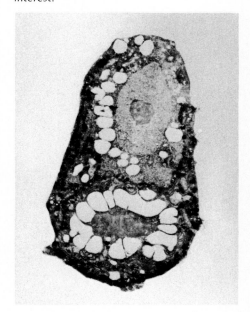

139

Perhaps the most exciting modern development of work with halophilic bacteria has come from *Halobacterium halobium*, a close relative of Elazari-Volcani's Dead Sea discovery. The cell membrane of this salt-loving microorganism is covered with patches of a purple pigment, called bacterio-rhodopsin, that harnesses the Sun's energy for the organism in a quite extraordinary manner. When light strikes these pigmented patches it drives certain physical and chemical changes in the pigment such that protons (positively charged hydrogen ions) are transported or "pumped" from one side of the membrane to the other. In the case of the living bacterium, protons are transported from the cellular interior to the outside medium. As protons collect on the second side they build up both a chemical and an electrical difference in potential across the membrane. This difference represents a form of stored energy, which the bacterium itself taps as needed. *H. halobium*'s proton pump has been studied extensively in recent years and has provided powerful evidence for British biochemist Peter Mitchell's "chemiosmotic" explanation of the way in which living cells chemically convert the energy in oxygen and sunlight, a theory that won for Mitchell the 1978 Nobel Prize for Chemistry.

In the early 1980s Mitchell, S. Roy Caplan of the Weizmann Institute, and other scientists were asking if this proton transport mechanism can be applied to man's energy needs. One highly encouraging fact is that the pumping action continues in pigmented membranes even after the cells are destroyed and the membranes separated and collected from the other cellular components. Nevertheless, the task of constructing an efficient solar cell containing a supported barrier of isolated membranes that pump protons from one compartment into another poses many formidable challenges for the future.

Back in the 1940s Elazari-Volcani also announced that he had discovered a number of different species of cyanobacteria (blue-green algae) in the Dead Sea, both in the surface shallows and at the greatest depths, as well as a green alga. His green alga belongs to the genus *Dunaliella*, a group of single-celled plants that show a remarkable degree of environmental adaptation to salt. To help regulate their internal pressure in briny conditions species of *Dunaliella* produce large amounts of an energy-rich compound called glycerol (glycerin), a combustible alcohol that can itself be burned as a fuel or serve as a raw material for producing natural gas or even gasoline. Glycerol is already an important ingredient in lubricants, pharmaceuticals, cosmetics, and foods. And all these undemanding algae need in order to flourish is salt water, plenty of sunlight, and carbon dioxide from the air.

In the 1970s Mordhay Avron of the Weizmann Institute built algae ponds for *D. parva* and found that the organism could produce 40% of its dry weight as glycerol. Later Avron identified another species, *D. bardawil*, that in addition yields a plant pigment, called beta-carotene, widely used by the food industry as coloring. Beta-carotene gives carrots their bright color and belongs to a family of compounds in the human diet that are converted by the liver to vitamin A. In addition, it was discovered that extraction of glycerol and beta-carotene from the alga leaves a high-protein meal similar to that obtained from soybeans. By the early 1980s a major Israeli company

Scenes of Israel's Dead Sea Works at Sedom include part of overall view of the installation (top), potash storage shed (left), and rotating kilns for drying the chemical harvest (center right). Plastic-covered heaps of potash fertilizer await shipment at Sedom (bottom right).

Arab Potash Company's chemical extraction plant (top and above, shown under construction) is situated in full view of its Israeli counterpart across the Dead Sea's southern basin. The Jordanian plant was formally opened in March 1982, with production to start six months later.

had completed commercial-sized algae ponds near Elat and was harvesting *Dunaliella* as fast as it could reproduce itself.

The chemical harvest

Algae, bacteria, and solar power are new scientific potentials from the Dead Sea. The sea's chemical wealth is much older and has been exploited since salt traders set sail along its coasts centuries ago. Sedom today is as full of salt, heat, and noise as was its biblical namesake in the days of devastation. Israel's Dead Sea Works at the southern extremity of the now largely man-made southern basin is a grim place. The 1,000-strong work force is bused in daily from 'Arad or Beersheba. Blistering temperatures are increased by the clanking kilns that roast the chemical products amid constant bedlam.

Dating from the 1930s, the Dead Sea Works is Israel's biggest exporter, selling over a million metric tons a year of the sea's chemicals, especially potash as fertilizer to the world's farmers. Its operation uses the Sun to evaporate fluids and extract the chemicals from vast salt pans that cover the Israeli half of the southern basin. Billions of tons of concentrated chlorides are there for the taking. Lavoisier, the great French chemist of the 18th century, was first to examine the Dead Sea's chemicals, and his analysis remains accurate today: sodium chloride (common salt) and potassium chloride (potash), as well as magnesium chloride and magnesium bromide. Israel, together with the U.S., Canada, the U.S.S.R., and East Germany, belongs to an exclusive club of potash producers. With the substance selling at around $100 a metric ton it is a profitable business.

Nevertheless, the Israeli potash company has problems. First, the Dead Sea is slowly drying out. The Sedom works has to draw its raw material, brine, from the northern basin through 16 kilometers (10 miles) of pumps and canals. And there is a new and urgent commercial consideration. Across in Jordan, a few hundred meters away, the Arab Potash Company has set up in business, building its own salt pans and dikes in the already crowded southern basin. This part of the Dead Sea seems destined to be shared by commercial rivals as well as by political enemies.

Jordan's Arab Potash Company, backed by the World Bank, U.S. AID, OPEC, and special Arab funds, is the biggest commercial enterprise ever attempted in the country. U.S. and British companies won the major engineering contracts for the $425-million project. Visitors to the new township—complete with supermarkets and squash courts—that the Jordanians are building in the parched mud and rock of the eastern shore hear scarcely a reference to the Israeli plant visible so clearly across the sea. British and U.S. contractors may vaguely mention "the other side," while the Jordanian management speaks distantly of "our cousins." The fact is that the cousins do not recognize one another, let alone cooperate. The Israeli and Jordanian managing directors do not even know one another's names.

More dream than future?

At Shlomo Drori's museum in Newe Zohar, young Israelis stare across the Dead Sea toward the Arab earthworks and then glance down at the Katyusha rocket fragments mounted as a museum exhibit. The rockets had been fired

142

at the Sedom works by PLO gunners near as-Safi, where the Arab Potash Company presently stands.

Drori still clings to his Dead Sea dream, though the odds must be massively against the vision becoming reality. Israel and Jordan must cooperate, he insists, to prevent the Dead Sea from drying up. Now that the Jordan River has been extravagantly drained by both sides, the only possible new source of water can be a canal. Drori sees the canal coming from the Mediterranean, as Zionists have planned it for more than a century, and there has been a multitude of projected routes. All would use the drop to the Dead Sea to generate hydroelectricity with power stations en route. A southern route from Katif in the Gaza Strip to the ancient Jewish fortress of Masada has been approved in principle by the Israeli government, but it would cost several hundred million dollars and ten years of labor to build. Dan Weiner, Head of the Dead Sea Canal Project Authority, says the plan is unique in that power capacity would be determined by the downstream reservoir, the Dead Sea, rather than its upstream reservoir, the Mediterranean. The canal would generate 570 megawatts of electrical power, or about 6% of Israel's requirements. It could replenish the Dead Sea's steadily falling water level and might even restratify the sea into upper and lower water bodies. This plan would also benefit the solar energy project, as the canal waters could be used to stock further solar ponds.

But—and it is a monumental "but"—there are what the Project Authority calls "drawbacks, questions concerning the economic feasibility" of the idea. In other words, can Israel afford such a canal? There is also Arab opposition to the plan. Egypt objects to the canal originating in Gaza, and Jordan fears possible ill effects on its new potash works. Moreover, the Jordanians have talked of a canal of their own, running from al-'Aqabah on the Red Sea northward to the Dead Sea near as-Safi. Water would be pumped 85 kilometers (53 miles) to Gharandal and then would flow downhill to the Dead Sea, generating 330 megawatts on the way. Israeli scientists have expressed their concern that the Jordanian canal would seriously affect Israel's own canal plans. The additional water would force Israel to cut back the flow from the Mediterranean or risk flooding both Jordanian and Israeli potash works, along with Israel's Dead Sea hotels.

Around the Dead Sea today, the Israelis have more to lose than their Arab neighbors. According to Drori, "as long as in Jordan there are nothing but swamps and deserts, there is no security for Israeli industry. What we need is Arab interest in peace in the area. While they have nothing to lose, they might be tempted to destroy us. But if Jordan will base its economy, like Israel, on exploitation of the Dead Sea, they can't afford another war."

In the 1980s however, Drori's dream for the Dead Sea, like Herzl's before him, seemed further removed from reality with each fresh political spasm of the Middle East. Unhappily, his is a voice crying out in the Dead Sea wilderness.

Alternately suggesting an expanding vista or a receding dream, this view of the Dead Sea evokes something of the uncertainty surrounding the commercial future of the region.

SURPRISING NEW USES FOR
SULFUR

by Marion D. Barnes

Because of the increased cost of petroleum-based asphalt scientists and engineers are looking to sulfur, in its plasticized form, as a substitute. In addition, elemental sulfur is showing promise as a useful building material.

In recent years the discovery of new sources of sulfur, primarily from fossil fuels (natural gas, sour crude oils, and some coal) has resulted in the production of large amounts of this element. The consumption of fossil fuels is expected to increase, indicating that a much larger amount of sulfur will be produced than has been derived in the past. Thus, there has arisen interest in research to develop new uses of sulfur.

Historically, the greatest single use of sulfur has been for the manufacture of sulfuric acid, which has largely been employed in the phosphatic fertilizer industry and for the pickling of steels. One of the most important applications has been in the vulcanization of rubber, though in total tonnage this represents only a small percentage of the sulfur produced.

The proposed new applications of sulfur generally utilize its unusual physical properties as an element in contrast to the earlier uses, which capitalized on its chemical properties. The physical properties of greatest interest are sulfur's extreme weather resistance (it has been exposed to the atmosphere in geological deposits for thousands of years and has remained largely unchanged), its great compressive strength and hardness, its capability of conversion into a polymeric form having plastic properties, and its readily attainable melting point, conveniently located above ambient atmospheric temperatures. Such a melting point makes it possible to work with the element in either a solid or liquid form. Conventional mining operations involve melting the solid sulfur that occurs in subterranean deposits with superheated water and bringing it to the surface. It may then be shipped either as a liquid or solid.

Sulfur, although quite hard, is very brittle. Various modifiers used in small amounts largely eliminate this problem. Though insoluble in water, sulfur can be dissolved in a limited number of other materials. Its solubility in and compatibility with asphalt is of great practical significance.

Opposite page, liquid sulfur is sprayed into vats in Louisiana.

144

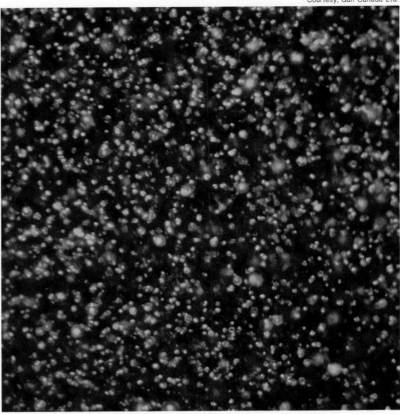

Photomicrograph reveals dispersion of sulfur in asphalt with sulfur particle sizes averaging about 4–5 micrometers (1 micrometer equals one millionth of a meter). The useful range of proportions of sulfur to asphalt in such a mix extends from 20–50%. Pavement made from a sulfur-asphalt combination resists high temperatures better than does regular asphalt concrete.

MARION D. BARNES *is the Chancellor of Covenant College at Lookout Mountain, Tennessee, and was formerly Director of Industrial Research at The Sulphur Institute in Washington, D.C.*

(Overleaf) Farrell Grehan—Photo Researchers

Sulfur and asphalt

The search for new and expanded uses of sulfur has involved seeking existing uses of other materials for which sulfur, possibly by modification of its properties, could be either an addition or a substitute. One such promising prospect is to use sulfur with or in place of asphalt for highway paving. In the United States approximately 30 million tons of asphalt binder are used annually. If sulfur could be used either instead of or with asphalt, a valuable application of the material would be established. Recent research results have shown that sulfur properly introduced into asphalt substantially improves the properties of the latter in road paving.

Sulfur in asphalt is a simple mixture of the two materials in which the proportion of sulfur may reach 50%. The product may be prepared by mixing hot asphalt with molten sulfur at a temperature between 120° C (248° F) and 150° C (302° F). When these two liquids are blended, some of the sulfur reacts to produce polysulfides and renders the resultant mixture softer and more fluid at hot mix temperatures. The remainder of the sulfur is dispersed as fine droplets, generally of the size of five micrometers, in the asphalt. (One micrometer equals one-millionth of a meter.) On cooling, the unreacted sulfur solidifies, and the mixture of asphalt and polysulfide remains very viscous. The useful range of proportions of sulfur to asphalt extends from 20 to 50%. Up to 20% of the sulfur reacts with asphalt, and the remainder is dispersed in the mixture as an emulsion.

146

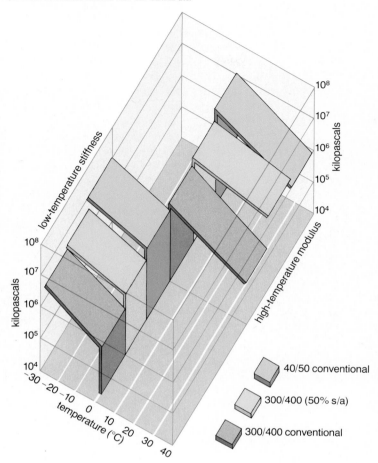

40/50 conventional

300/400 (50% s/a)

300/400 conventional

Figure 1. Sulfur-asphalt mix of 300/400 penetration asphalt containing 50% sulfur by weight demonstrates both the excellent low-temperature characteristics of conventional 300/400 penetration asphalt and the advantageous high-temperature qualities of the 40/50 asphalt.

As a consequence of the inclusion of the sulfur in the mixture, the viscosity of the asphalt is changed. The extent of the change depends upon the temperature, the asphalt grade, and the sulfur content. For a mixture of 20 parts sulfur with 80 parts of sulfur-asphalt 40/50 penetration asphalt the viscosity of the mixture is greater than that of untreated asphalt above 43° C (110° F), whereas below this temperature the viscosity is less than that of untreated asphalt. For some grades of asphalt the "crossover" temperature shifts to larger values. The density of the sulfur asphalt binder is substantially greater than that of the asphalt binder alone.

Sulfur asphalt mixture makes an excellent binder for use in asphalt concrete, having superior properties to the regular asphalt binder. The sulfur asphalt binder may be used in the same way as regular asphalt binders, employing the same mixing equipment and the same paving equipment for laying the mixture on the road. The temperature of the mixture should range between 130° C (266° F) and 150° C in order to provide appropriate viscosities of blends and mixes for processing through conventional mixing and paving equipment; temperatures above 160° C (320° F) will cause a reaction between the sulfur and asphalt that will generate hydrogen sulfide.

In the paving operation less compacting and rolling of the mix is required

Sulphur Development Institute of Canada (SUDIC)

Sulfur-asphalt paving mix is compacted on a highway using conventional equipment and procedures.

than with regular asphalt concrete, and the properties of the resulting pavement are superior. They show no greater amount of low-temperature cracking than does regular asphalt concrete, and they do demonstrate an improved performance at higher ambient atmospheric temperatures, thereby reducing the amount of rutting and deforming that normally occurs in the asphalt products.

Modern paving design technology involves the concept of the ideal pavement. With asphalt concretes one composition must be formulated for high ambient temperature conditions and another for low-temperature conditions. Sulfur asphalt concretes achieve this result with one formulation that has excellent performance at both high and low temperatures. This remarkable achievement is illustrated more quantitatively in figure 1.

Tensile strength, the modulus of elasticity (the ratio of stress in a body to the corresponding strain), and fatigue life are all improved in the sulfur asphalt pavement. It also provides improved resistance to water and to spillage of fuels on the surface. Furthermore, this improved binder is more compatible with lower quality aggregates than is asphalt. For example, in many cases it is possible to use ungraded sand or other low-grade aggregate. Careful studies have shown that the blending, mixing, and paving operations can be carried out without generating hydrogen sulfide, sulfur dioxide, or other undesirable sulfur compounds.

In recent years the price of asphalt has increased substantially due to the increasing cost of petroleum and to depletion of available supplies. Sulfur, however, being produced "involuntarily" from fossil fuels, should be readily

148

and widely available at a relatively stable price. Other factors favorable to the use of sulfur asphalt binder are the possibility of using cheap low-grade aggregates and the comparatively low energy requirement for heating the aggregate to the desired mixing temperature.

Other types of sulfur asphalt mixes have been prepared by utilizing different proportions of sulfur and asphalt and by observing particular sequences in mixing the ingredients; these have varying properties. Recently a formulation was developed, studied, and patented under the name of Thermopave. Preparation of this product involves loading a machine called a pug mill with sand at a temperature ranging from 130°–150° C, mixing for 30 seconds with hot asphalt, and subsequently mixing for another 30 seconds with molten sulfur at approximately the same temperature. A typical sample for this product consists of 81% sand, 6% asphalt, and 13% sulfur. During the mixing operation the asphalt coats the grains of sand; the sulfur introduced thereafter reacts somewhat with the asphalt, and the excess sulfur solidifies to fill the interstices between the asphalt-coated grains of sand. The resulting product has a high compressive strength and can be handled in a very fluid condition. The temperature required to keep the mix fluid requires that the trucks for hauling it be heated, and when the product is laid, the leveling device of the paving machine must be modified because the fluid material does not require the same type of handling as conventional asphalt concrete. No subsequent packing or rolling is required.

A distinctive feature of Thermopave is its capability for producing a high-strength pavement utilizing ungraded sand as an aggregate. In many areas

Old pavement is removed from a road, after which it is mixed with aggregate and sulfur-asphalt binder to make the material for the new surface.

149

Sulphlex is laid down on a road surface using ordinary equipment. A product of heating a mixture of sulfur and certain hydrocarbons to temperatures of 150°–165° C, sulphlex has performed well in tests as a highway pavement. It contains no asphalt and thus requires no petroleum.

around the world such as southern Louisiana, eastern Texas, and the Middle East, sand is plentiful, but a good quality of aggregate is hard to find. Thus, this product has particular interest for road paving in such regions.

Several tests of the sulfur-asphalt-sand mixture have been made in various locations. Environmental investigations during the process of mixing and paving have demonstrated that when the temperature is maintained between 130°–150° C, any generation of hydrogen sulfide and sulfur dioxide is well below the maximum allowable concentrations at all locations where personnel would be exposed.

Sulphlex

When sulfur is heated above approximately 163° C (325° F), the viscosity increases sharply due to the formation of a highly viscous liquid mass consisting of high-molecular-weight polymers. If this material is allowed to cool, it reverts completely to liquid monomeric sulfur of very low viscosity. If, while the mass of polymeric material is still hot, it is chilled quickly, a rubbery, elastic product is produced that has several potentially useful properties. Unfortunately, the cooled product quickly reverts to hard, brittle sulfur. Many investigators have tried unsuccessfully to stabilize the polymeric material and thus produce plasticized sulfur.

Recently it was discovered that if sulfur is heated with appropriate olefinic compounds to a level approaching its polymerization temperature, the result is a stable polymeric material which has properties that can be varied widely. (An olefin is an unsaturated open-chain hydrocarbon containing at least one double bond.) A family of such products consisting of heavy oils having some properties similar to asphalt were recently produced and given the name sulphlex.

In contrast to the mixtures of sulfur and asphalt binders previously discussed sulphlex contains no asphalt, yet by proper formulation it can be made to duplicate the viscosity properties of widely differing asphalt products. Thus, instead of replacing a part of the asphalt in a pavement binder with sulfur, a road builder can use sulphlex and eliminate completely the need for asphalt. Potentially, therefore, sulphlex frees the paving industry from dependence on petroleum-derived raw materials.

Useful sulphlex products are made by heating together in a closed vessel 60–70 parts of sulfur with 30–40 parts of such olefinic modifiers, in approximately equal proportions, as divinylbenzene and dipentene. One of these modifiers produces linear polymers, and the other produces branched or crosslinked products. The viscosity of the mixes can be varied widely by changing the proportions of the modifiers. Reaction time normally takes an hour or more depending upon the quantities of material. Temperature control is important in order to produce polymerized sulfur, and yet it must not be exceptionally high because that would cause the generation of hydrogen sulfide. Usable temperatures are in the range of 150°–165° C.

The use of chemical modifiers and heat radically modifies the viscosity of sulfur so that it approaches that of various asphalt mixtures. Figure 2 shows the variation of the viscosity of sulfur, sulphlex, and asphalt with temperature. It can be seen that the viscosity of sulfur when temperatures are increased to above 120° C produces a reduction in viscosity, after which further elevation of temperature, particularly in the region of 160°–177° C (320°–350° F), causes a very sharp increase in viscosity. By way of contrast the viscosity of two different asphalt varieties, AC-10 and AC-20, decreases continuously when the temperature is raised from 65° C to 177° C.

Two different sulphlex formulations are shown in figure 2. Sulphlex 233 corresponds closely to the viscosity curve for AC-10, while the viscosity curve for sulphlex 230 approximates that of AC-20. In comparing binder properties of the various formulations, one discovers that the penetration, ductility, and softening point of sulphlex 233 are very close to those of AC-20. Sulphlex 233 has a greater specific gravity and a lower flash point than that of AC-20, but neither of these differences limits the utilization of sulphlex 233 in place of AC-20 for asphalt binders. In comparing typical mixture properties of sulphlex 233 and AC-20, the major differences between the two include compressive strength and tensile strength. The higher values for these properties for sulphlex 233 are considered preferable to the lower values for AC-20.

The family of sulphlexes perform well as pavement binders. After sulfur and the proposed modifiers react at a temperature of 155° C (310° F) under a confined atmosphere for an appropriate time depending upon the amounts of material involved, the material can subsequently be handled completely as a regular asphalt binder using the same hot mix equipment, aggregates, and paving equipment as for asphalt, without change of leveling device. The sulphlex concrete can be laid almost exactly as an asphalt concrete and re-

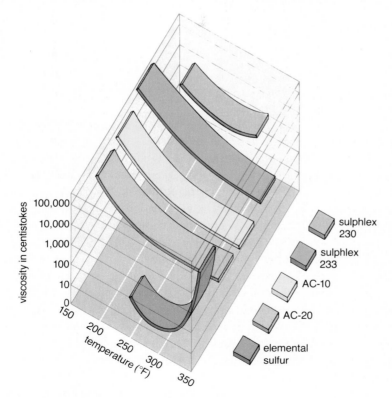

Figure 2. Variations in the viscosity of sulfur, two varieties of sulphlex, and two types of asphalt are shown. Sulphlex 230 approximates asphalt AC-20, while sulphlex 233 is similar to asphalt AC-10. Elemental sulfur differs markedly from asphalt and sulphlex in its reaction to increased heat.

Adapted from information obtained from the Southwest Research Institute

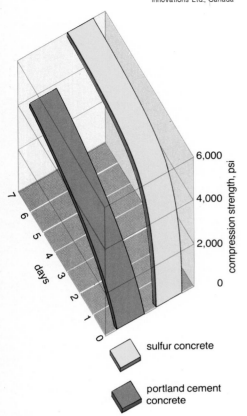

sulfur concrete

portland cement concrete

Figure 3. Sulfur concrete develops compressive strength much more rapidly than does portland cement concrete. It is also resistant to the acids and sulfates that attack the portland cement product.

quires approximately the same amount of compacting and rolling. Careful tests have shown that the amounts of hydrogen sulfide and other noxious sulfur compounds are present, if at all, only at such levels that are completely within established safety requirements at all personnel exposure points.

Tests of performance of asphalt concrete and sulphlex concrete pavement have shown superior performance of the latter at several locations in the United States. Wear characteristics are outstanding, and summertime temperatures that cause asphalt concretes to "bleed" asphalt to the surface of the pavement cause no observable change in the sulphlex pavement. Furthermore, sulphlex does not become too slick under wet conditions and shows no softening from spillage of fuel and/or lubricating oils on its surface. For these reasons sulphlex is expected to find application not only in paving concrete, where it is the sole binder, but also as a seal coat for asphalt pavements in order to prevent water penetration, softening from fuel and oil spills, and bleeding in hot weather.

Sulfur concrete

Sulfur's properties of hardness, stability to weather, and low melting point have suggested the possibility of making a cheap and useful concrete analogous in many ways to portland cement concrete but having superior resistance to acids and to electrolytes. Such a sulfur concrete has been prepared by mixing approximately 84% of an aggregate with about 16% of molten sulfur. This sulfur performs best when modified by reacting it with 2–5% of a cycloparaffin such as dicyclopentadiene. In the preparation of the material sulfur and dicyclopentadiene should be heated to a temperature of approximately 130°–160° C. Aggregate is then added, and complete mixing should be achieved. The material may be poured into any appropriate form and allowed to set. While the product is still hot and the sulfur is in a liquid form, the material may be compacted by the use of a vibrator and its surface may be appropriately prepared by the use of a leveling device or by heat treatment after the product has set.

The properties of sulfur concrete differ in several ways from those of portland cement concrete. The high compressive strength of sulfur concrete is produced within a matter of a few minutes to a few days, whereas portland cement concrete does not develop its maximum strength for approximately a month. Figure 3 shows that sulfur concrete develops a strength of approximately 4,000 pounds per square inch (280 kilograms per square centimeter) in a matter of 30 minutes and achieves a maximum strength, which may be as high as 8,000 or 9,000 pounds per square inch (560 or 630 kilograms per square centimeter) depending upon the type of aggregate used, within a maximum of four or five days. This behavior contrasts with the slower increase in compressive strength of portland cement concrete.

Sulfur concrete has demonstrated a high fatigue resistance compared with portland cement concrete. The latter is attacked readily by acids, sulfates, and other dissolved electrolytes. Sulfur concrete, however, was impervious to these substances over long periods of time regardless of the strength of the attacking agent; it is also impervious to water. Sulfur concrete can be made with a great variety of aggregates, such as crushed quartz, crushed limestone, various kinds of sand, and such residues as cinders. About the only kind of aggregate that cannot be satisfactorily used is clay, and care should be taken that all aggregates are free of this material.

Sulfur concrete is not attacked by bacterial action or by atmospheric oxidation. Fire, however, can be a problem. The concrete can be melted by continued heating at a high temperature. The sulfur also burns, producing sulfur dioxide gas, when it is heated at a high temperature with a blowtorch or some similar device. When the external source of heat is removed, the sulfur flame is self-extinguishing and does not propagate across the surface of the sulfur concrete.

The density of sulfur concrete is slightly greater than that of portland cement concrete, being approximately 150 to 153 pounds per cubic foot (2,400 to 2,450 kilograms per cubic meter) when a limestone aggregate is used. The linear coefficient of expansion is very close to that of portland cement concrete that is made with the same aggregate. The hardness of sulfur concrete can be modified somewhat by varying the aggregates and the types and amounts of modifiers used with the sulfur as well as the total amount of modified sulfur used to bind the aggregate. In general, the more modifier used with the sulfur the greater the decrease in hardness compared to the unmodified sulfur.

Sulfur concrete has found application in acid storage tanks and other similar structures in chemical and metallurgical processing plants. In such plants portland cement concrete is readily destroyed by the action of an electrolyte environment, whereas the sulfur concrete lasts indefinitely. Sulfur concrete also is used as precast curbs, highway dividers, and related structures for highway construction as well as in quick repair materials for existing pavement. It has been recently shown that it can replace portland cement concrete or asphalt concrete as an overall pavement.

Another unusual feature of sulfur concrete as a paving material is in its ease of recycling. Broken and crushed sulfur concrete can be remelted and repoured, regenerating a product that is equal in quality to the original structure involved.

Existing porous portland cement concrete structures, such as sewer pipes, that will be exposed to soil or water can be impregnated with modified molten sulfur. Such treatment greatly increases the strength of the concrete and protects it from electrolytes and acids. The sulfur is not attacked by bacteria when it is reacted with a modifier before impregnation. Thus, the service life of the sewer pipes is greatly extended.

Surface bonding with modified sulfur

As the temperature of sulfur is increased above a point slightly higher than its melting point, the liquid becomes increasingly viscous. When such a hot, slightly viscous melt is spread on a porous surface, it becomes more fluid as it cools (in contrast to asphalt which becomes more viscous as it cools). This maximum fluidity permits efficient penetration of porous structures just prior to solidification of the sulfur.

An interesting formulation used for bonding purposes consists of sulfur modified with dicyclopentadiene to eliminate brittleness and with a small

153

Courtesy, The Sulphur Institute

amount of chopped strand glass fibers to provide tensile strength. The mixture is prepared by heating approximately 2% dicyclopentadiene in sulfur until the reaction is complete. Chopped strand glass fibers comprising 1–2% of the mixture are then stirred in, after which the product is painted on concrete blocks. It solidifies quickly and provides tensile strength and water-proofing to the resulting structures.

An application of such bonding material is in the construction of concrete block walls. The blocks are stacked without any mortar, and the sulfur formulation is painted on both sides of the wall. The coating dries within 5 minutes, and its maximum strength is developed within 15 minutes. The resulting wall is waterproof and has such great tensile strength that panels of blocks can be prefabricated and placed in position if one so desires.

This method of construction is vulnerable to fire in that at temperatures higher than the melting point of sulfur the coating melts. But the flame spreads slowly on the surface, and it is also low-lying and easy to control. The coating is not susceptible to atmospheric oxidation or bacterial attack and is therefore particularly useful in structures exposed to soil.

Sulfur in construction

Portland cement concrete blocks are widely used in construction in spite of such shortcomings as their imprecise dimensions and their requirements of water for their manufacture and mortar for their use. Furthermore, in wall construction for residential purposes, painting or plastering or some other appropriate form of finishing is necessary. Thus, a great improvement could

Alvaro Ortega

be made in construction by an improved block with precise dimensions; no requirement for water; no need for mortar during construction; and no requirement for paint, plastering, or finishing.

Sulfur concrete blocks meet all of the above requirements. They may be prepared by heating 23 parts of sulfur and 2 parts of dicyclopentadiene in a concrete mixer to a temperature of 130°–150° C. Seventy-five parts of aggregate are then added, and the heating and mixing are continued in order to produce a thoroughly reacted product. The material is then poured into oil-coated steel molds of dimensions 40 cm (15.7 in) by 20 cm (7.9 in) by 20 cm. The molds are particularly designed to produce a tongue-and-groove joining surface and a smooth exposed surface. The material is allowed to set in the molds for ten minutes, after which it is carefully removed because the fresh blocks are quite brittle. After one hour of cooling the block has become tough, hard, resistant to packing, and ready for use. The blocks have a precise dimension; are resistant to oil, electrolytes, water, and air; and have good insulating characteristics. They may be used for a variety of purposes in construction. Any blocks broken at any stage in the process may be recycled back through the concrete mixer.

In constructing a house of sulfur concrete blocks the walls are made by simply stacking the interlocking blocks without any need for mortar or other binder. The stacking operation can be carried out quickly and satisfactorily with relatively unskilled labor. After the wall is erected, there is no further requirement for waterproofing or decoration such as plaster or painting. The wall has a marblelike appearance, may be cleaned by washing, has good insulation characteristics, and is particularly resistant to aggressive environments such as one finds in the Arabian desert, where portland cement concrete structures fail comparatively readily.

Sulfur concrete block structures are susceptible to fire and on burning produce sulfur dioxide. The flames, however, do not spread nearly as rapidly nor leap nearly as high in the air as do the flames from burning wood or oil. A comparatively small amount of heat is generated, and the flame itself never reaches more than approximately one-half to one centimeter above the surface of the burning material.

Future prospects

Asphalt is expected to increase in price and become more scarce. Sulfur, on the other hand, is expected to be readily available in increasing amounts as a result of its production during the processing of fossil fuels. Modifiers to produce sulphlex from sulfur are comparatively cheap chemicals derivable from coal. It is clear that as a result of recent sulfur research one can produce a group of pavements varying in properties from the flexible asphalt types to a rigid product closely resembling portland cement concrete simply by varying proportions of asphalt to sulfur in sulfur asphalt binders or the proportions of the appropriate modifiers for sulfur in sulphlex.

Portland cement has the disadvantage of requiring fossil fuels in its manufacture and, as mentioned above, is vulnerable to attack by dissolved electrolytes. Thus as a replacement or additive to portland cement in construction requiring concrete, sulfur also appears to have a bright future.

Sulfur concrete blocks (opposite page, top and bottom) can be made with precise dimensions and require no water in their manufacture and no mortar when used in construction (top). The blocks in the bottom photograph are products of the world's first commercial-scale sulfur concrete plant, located in the United Arab Emirates. Sulfur is an especially desirable building material in the Persian Gulf area because it is abundant there and the materials for making cement are not.

155

A GIANT FLOWER
FOR THE FARMER

Sunflower, the sleeping beauty of native American crops, awoke in the 1970s to the kiss of a devoted court of plant breeders. Now her princes are promising her a very lively future.

by Benjamin H. Beard

Small-headed, branched wild sunflower (above) contrasts with field of a single-headed cultivated variety (right). Both are the same species, Helianthus annuus.

BENJAMIN H. BEARD *is a Research Geneticist with the U.S. Department of Agriculture and a Lecturer at the University of California at Davis.*

(Overleaf) Illustration by Eraldo Carugati

Vincent van Gogh captured the beauty of sunflowers on canvas, but he lived too early to see the stunning brilliance of a large field of hybrid sunflowers in full bloom. Even the weedy sunflowers, close relatives of the crop plant, can be extremely showy. Yet beauty is not the only attribute of the sunflower. It is the world's second most important oilseed crop.

Sunflower was a crop in North America when Columbus landed in the West Indies in 1492. American Indians probably first grew it in what is now the southwestern United States. Yet as late as 30 years ago U.S. agricultural interest in the plant was virtually nonexistent. The U.S. Department of Agriculture's 1950–51 *Yearbook of Agriculture* devotes only 16 lines to sunflower, compared with 28 lines for rice oil, 41 lines for castor oil, two entire chapters on flax, and four chapters on soybean. In 1947 U.S. production was only 1,200 tons of seed; this figure rose to 10,000 tons in 1948 and dropped to 5,000 tons the year after. Production continued at about this level for the next two decades. Then in the 1970s interest increased so rapidly that by 1978 seed production was 1.8 million tons. Since 1978 U.S. production has varied between 1.8 million and 3.4 million tons and world production between 12.9 million and 15.5 million tons. Most of the demand has been for the oil in its seeds, commonly called sunoil.

158

(Top, left and right) John H. Gerard—DPI; (bottom, left) Sylvia J. and Lloyd R. Brockus III—DPI; (bottom, right) Richard Parker—Photo Researchers

Form and reproduction

The common sunflower (*Helianthus annuus*) belongs to the Asteraceae (*Compositae*) family, the largest family of higher plants. Asters, dandelions, dahlias, lettuce, and ragweed also number among the 15,000–20,000 species of this family. The *Helianthus* genus contains about 100 species. There are two types of *H. annuus* plants, the domestic and the wild.

The domestic sunflower is 1.2–3.6 meters (4–12 feet) tall, has a single stem, and usually has a single head. The head varies in diameter from 10 to more than 30 centimeters (4–12 inches). Some domestic types cultivated solely as ornamentals have additional heads on short branches near the top of the main stem. The seeds, 10–15 millimeters (about a half inch) long, are large compared with those of the wild species and are of various colors and color patterns.

The wild sunflower is found along roadsides and in abandoned areas throughout North America. It ranges from less than one meter to five meters (3.3–16.4 feet) in height and has many branches from the bottom to the top of the primary stem. The seeds are small, three to six millimeters (less than a quarter inch) in length, and usually are gray without stripes or color patterns.

Relatives of the common sunflower include (clockwise from top left) the Jerusalem artichoke (Helianthus tuberosus), the stiff sunflower (H. rigidus), Maximilian's sunflower (H. maximiliani), and the prairie sunflower (H. petiolaris). The Jerusalem artichoke is valued both as an ornamental and for its edible fleshy tubers; the others are cultivated primarily as ornamentals. These and other species of Helianthus constitute an important reserve of genetic traits for keeping sunflower a competitive crop.

159

Sunflower seed production in various countries and the world is given for 1978–81 and projected for the 1981–82 season. Figures are in 1,000 metric tons.

country	1978–79	1979–80	1980–81	1981–82 (estimated)
U.S.S.R.	5,333	5,414	4,650	5,000
U.S.	1,823	3,484	1,816	2,640
Argentina	1,430	1,650	1,300	1,650
Eastern Europe	1,962	2,270	1,822	2,215
Western Europe	603	744	764	692
Turkey	485	550	630	625
South Africa	312	329	488	450
China	280	340	900	945
Australia	186	142	147	131
India	165	150	170	160
Canada	120	218	166	150
Africa, excluding South Africa	95	103	86	90
Uruguay	51	30	60	60
Brazil	5	20	90	125
Chile	30	33	38	6
Mexico	10	20	25	28
other	22	13	12	11
world total	12,912	15,510	13,164	14,978

Like the flower heads of other family members the sunflower head is made up of numerous small flowers, or florets. Large yellow ray florets circle the outside of the head, and smaller disk florets lie within. The ray florets are thought to consist of five petals fused into one structure; they are nearly flat and usually play no role in reproduction except to attract bees or other pollinating insects. The disk florets also have five fused petals, which are formed into a tube that surrounds the reproductive organs. When the ray florets have completely opened in a ring around the outside of the head, a band of disk florets about 0.5–2 centimeters (0.2–0.8 inches) wide and adjacent to the ray florets begins to mature in a process called anthesis. The next day, a similar band inside and adjacent to the previous band begins to mature.

Each disk floret has a tubular ring of five fused anthers, the pollen-bearing structures of the floret's male organ, or stamen. Early in the morning when a floret begins anthesis the filaments that support the anthers elongate rapidly, thus carrying the anthers above the petal tube. Pollen is released inside and at the top of the anthers. A short time later the stigma, the tip of the floret's female organ, or pistil, rises through the anther ring. The two parts of the stigma spread apart and move downward, exposing sticky, pollen-catching inner surfaces. Under natural conditions insects gather pollen and transfer it to other plants to bring about a high degree of cross-pollination and fertilization.

The seed, botanically a dry fruit called an achene, is pointed at the base and rounded at the top. In cross section it appears to be four-sided. The outer portion, usually called the hull but more correctly the pericarp, consists of a layer of epidermal cells. Below these are several layers of structurally supportive cells, and below these cells is the kernel, which consists of a seed coat, endosperm, and embryo. The seed coat, or testa, is a white, papery layer of compressed cells. The underlying endosperm serves as the first food of the new plant and is only one or two cells thick as most of it is consumed dur-

(Top) Grant Heilman; (bottom) Spence McConnell—
Bruce Coleman Inc.

ing the growth of the embryo. The embryo itself, the young plant of the next generation, consists of two tiny leaves called cotyledons attached to a radicle, the embryonic root. Achene colors may be white, gray, black, brown, or purple. They are often gray or white with brown or black stripes in varying amounts. Commercially, completely black seeds of domestic sunflowers are classified as oilseeds, whereas striped seeds are considered nonoil or confectionery types. A mature sunflower head contains 200–1,500 seeds arrayed in a complex spiral pattern.

The sunflower's characteristic of tracking the Sun throughout the day and facing east again in the morning accounts for its Latin name *Helianthus* (from the Greek *helios*, "Sun," and *anthus*, "flower"). *Girasol* and *tournesol*, which are common names in other languages, are also combinations of words meaning flower and Sun. The heliotropic movement of the sunflower plant is due to a bending of the stem and is properly called nutation. This movement ceases before or during sexual maturation, and the heads then permanently face east. Because of this behavior, if the plants are to be harvested by hand, the rows are usually planted in a north-south direction to make harvesting much easier.

Early interest

Remains of wild and cultivated sunflower have been found at archaeological sites in North America, and evidence of cultivation dates from about 3000 BC. The best accounts of early cultivation of sunflower by native Americans are found in journals and reports of early European explorers. Some tribes gathered seeds from wild plants; others grew cultivated or wild-type plants in gardens and harvested the seeds by beating the heads with a stick while holding a basket in position to catch the falling seeds. The Indians recognized the value of the domestic type with its larger seeds, and many tribes maintained a supply of planting seed. Seeds presumably from the original stocks of some tribes are preserved today by means of cold storage and periodic plantings in the collection maintained by the North Central Regional

Sunflower head (top) displays concentric bands of tiny disk florets in various developmental stages surrounded by a halo of large petallike ray florets. Close-up of fully opened disk florets (above) shows their corollas of fused petals, dark tubular rings of anthers, and pollen-catching stigmas. Under natural conditions foraging bees (left) and other insects cross-pollinate sunflower plants to a high degree.

Camilla Smith—Rainbow

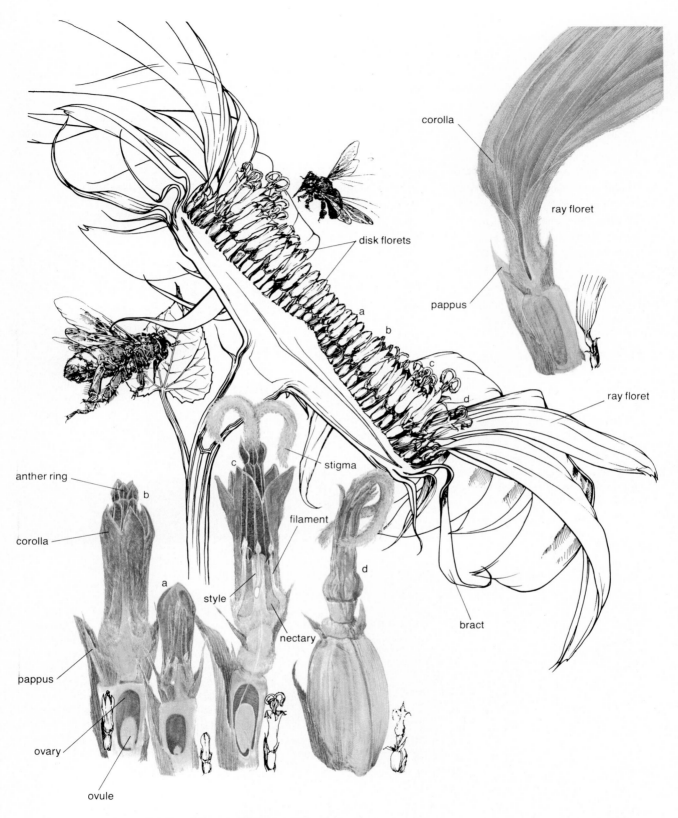

corolla

ray floret

pappus

ray floret

disk florets

a

b

c

d

stigma

filament

style

nectary

bract

anther ring

b

corolla

a

pappus

ovary

ovule

disk floret in four developmental stages

Sunflower oilseeds (far left) and confectionery seeds (left) are compared. Oilseeds produced by modern hybrids contain as much as 45% oil; after oil extraction and removal of hull material, protein content of the residue may reach 44%. Confectionery seeds serve as a popular health and snack food for humans and as feed for birds and poultry. Color and striping in confectionery types reflect consumer preferences.

Plant Introduction Station of the U.S. Department of Agriculture (USDA) at Ames, Iowa.

The earliest published description of the sunflower is in a herbal written by a Belgian, Rembert Dodoens, and dated 1568. Seeds were taken to Spain in 1581 where sunflower was grown as an ornamental plant or as a novelty in gardens. It spread across Europe to Russia where it attracted particular attention, probably because it was an oilseed crop that could mature that far north. It also may have received impetus from the church in Russia, which restricted nearly all foods rich in oil but overlooked the sunflower because of its recent introduction. As the crop became increasingly important in Russia, efforts to improve yield and plant characteristics were begun. Interest in the sunflower in North America brought about its reintroduction there, and by 1880 a "Mammoth Russian" cultivar (*i.e.*, cultivated variety) was offered for sale in the U.S.

20th-century research

The sunflower's recent spread throughout the rest of the world is indebted to the cooperative efforts of plant breeders in several countries. V. S. Pustovoit in the U.S.S.R. began improvement in the 1920s by crossing wild species with the domestic type to obtain genetic resistance to broomrape, a parasitic plant that grows on the roots of sunflower. (Broomrape is not a pest in North America.) Some of the progeny from that cross were found to have a much higher oil content in the seeds than was known prior to that time: 40–50% oil rather than 30–35%. His open-pollinated cultivars (plants allowed to cross-pollinate freely and naturally) with 40–45% oil eventually appeared on the market and were grown in many countries.

In 1942 Eric D. Putt of the Canadian Department of Agriculture developed a shorter variety with high seed-oil concentration that was moderately successful from 1943 to 1948, but unfavorable weather plus a fungal dis-

Illustration (facing page) shows details of a sunflower head in cross section and of its component florets. Disk florets are portrayed at four successive stages of sexual maturity: (a) unopened; (b) after the anthers have protruded above the corolla, or petal tube, to shed pollen; (c) a day or two later, when the stigma has risen through the ring of anthers and spread apart; and (d) about two days after pollination. Within the ovary of each disk floret is the ovule, the structure that will develop into the seed after fertilization.

163

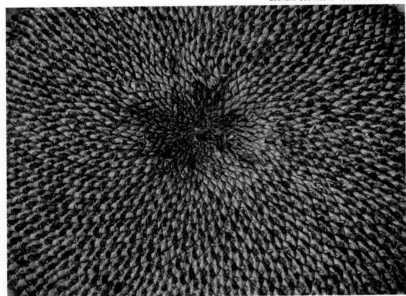

Head of a large cultivated sunflower may be more than 30 centimeters (one foot) in diameter and is capable of producing many hundreds of seeds. On a ripened disk, after the florets have dried up and fallen away, the complex spiral pattern of seeds is clearly visible.

Seeds from wild sunflowers show much variation in size, shape, and coloration. The largest seeds pictured actually measure less than a centimeter in length. Remains of wild and cultivated sunflowers have been unearthed at several archaeological sites in North America, and evidence of cultivation extends back some 5,000 years.

ease called rust discouraged growers, and interest faded. By 1955 Waldemar E. Sackston working with Putt had discovered genes for resistance to rust in some wild species. New shorter cultivars incorporating these genes made sunflower crops attractive once again, and farmers in Canada and other countries began to grow them on a larger scale. Even so, the cultivars were extremely variable. For example, plants in the same field would mature as much as a month apart, causing a corresponding delay in harvest. Before the late plants were ready for harvest, the early plants would be damaged by birds or their seeds would fall from the heads. Extra time also meant extending pest and disease control measures, which increased total production costs.

The outstanding success that plant breeders had experienced with hybrid varieties of corn (maize; *Zea mays*) suggested that hybrid sunflower crops would have fewer problems of variability. In addition, Putt had shown experimentally that hybrid sunflowers produced 20–25% higher yields than the best open-pollinated cultivars. With corn, hybrid varieties were developed by selecting superior plants and then inbreeding each selection for several generations to produce pure and highly uniform lines. Two of these inbred strains were then crossed, resulting in hybrid seed that grew into vigorous plants with nearly identical characteristics. Because corn bears its male and female parts as separate flowers—tassels and ears—it was quite easy to plant two inbred lines together in an isolated field and then cut off the immature male flowers of one line so that only pollen from the other line was available. Consequently the emasculated plants yielded mostly hybrid seed and could be harvested separately from the second line. With sunflower, however, the close association of its tiny male and female organs made it impossible to emasculate the plant except on a small experimental scale.

In the early 1960s Murray L. Kinman of the USDA tried to develop two sunflower lines having high degrees of self-incompatibility, a characteristic

164

Len Gallagher—Commonwealth Scientific and Industrial Research Organization,
Division of Irrigation Research, Griffith, New South Wales

Sunflowers photographed sequentially over a one-day period (above) reveal
their Sun-tracking movement, called nutation. After midnight (2400 hours) the
unopened, west-facing heads turn to the east, anticipating another dawn.
Accessions of sunflower seeds from four American Indian tribes (below left)
number among seed samples collected from all over the world and maintained
at the USDA North Central Regional Plant Introduction Station at Ames, Iowa.
The seeds are stored in glass jars (below right) in a room kept at 4° C (40° F)
and about 40% relative humidity.

Purple-stemmed sunflower seedlings contain a gene for the plant pigment anthocyanin and can be distinguished easily from seedlings with green stems. Linking this gene with the gene that determines male fertility allows male-sterile and male-fertile plants to be identified in the crossing field before flowering.

Schematic illustration (facing page) outlines the genetic male-sterility procedure used in the early 1970s to produce hybrid sunflower. Text description is on this page. Plants that possess a gene for anthocyanin are shown in purple.

of some plants that prevents pollen from functioning properly on the stigmas of the same plant. An inbred line of such plants could not pollinate itself, and two such lines planted together in an isolated field would produce mostly hybrid seed. Unfortunately this plan did not work. A large proportion of the seed was hybrid, but many were self-fertilized and did not meet legal requirements to be labeled hybrid.

In eastern and western Europe in the 1960s several researchers investigated a way of producing hybrid plants by means of a recessive genetic change that resulted in male sterility. Plants inheriting one gene for this change (symbolized ms) from each parent lacked the male function. The use of genetic male sterility to produce hybrids required two separate operations. The first was the maintenance and increase of the male-sterile, or female, parent ($ms\ ms$). The maintainer line had to comprise heterozygous, male-fertile plants ($Ms\ ms$); that is, plants possessing one gene determining fertility (Ms) and one determining sterility (ms). When crossed with the female ($ms\ ms$), this line produced 50% fertile ($Ms\ ms$) plants and 50% sterile ($ms\ ms$) plants. The fertile plants had to be removed from the crossing field prior to the second operation, the production of hybrid seed. Patrice Leclercq of France found that the gene determining fertility (Ms) was closely linked with a gene for plant pigment, called anthocyanin, that causes a distinctive purplish color in seedlings. Used in the proper combination, the fertile gene and the anthocyanin gene allowed male-fertile seedlings to be identified by their color and thereby removed from the crossing field. Of the seedlings that remained, most would be male-sterile, and at flowering these were crossed with the desired male parent ($Ms\ Ms$) to produce 100% hybrid seed ($Ms\ ms$). Because of genetic crossover, a few fertile plants could not be detected in the seedling stage and had to be removed (rogued) at flowering. (The entire procedure is outlined in the figure on the facing page.) Leclercq, A. V. Vranceanu in Romania, and others produced hybrid seed using the genetic male-sterile system, and seed was offered for sale throughout the world in the early 1970s.

A development of great significance for commercial sunflower production occurred in 1969: Leclercq announced discovery of an effective method for producing a female parent that was virtually 100% male-sterile, thus requiring less labor and breeding effort. In this system the cause of male sterility involves the interaction of genetic factors with the cell cytoplasm, the protoplasm outside the cell nucleus. A male-sterile plant possesses a sterile cytoplasm (symbolized Ⓢ) and two recessive fertility-restorer genes ($rf\ rf$). The maintainer differs from the sterile only in that it has normal cytoplasm (Ⓝ $rf\ rf$) and thus is male-fertile. In the operation for increasing the female parent, the cross between the male-sterile, or female, with the maintainer results in 100% male-sterile plants. In the subsequent operation for producing hybrid seed, the male parent possesses dominant genes ($Rf\ Rf$) for restoring fertility, and when it is crossed with the female, hybrid (Ⓢ $Rf\ rf$) seed is produced. This seed is then sold and planted by the farmer, and all plants are fertile. (*See* the figure on page 169.) Kinman and others discovered the dominant genetic restorer genes soon after the sterility source had been widely distributed. The first hybrids produced by this system were

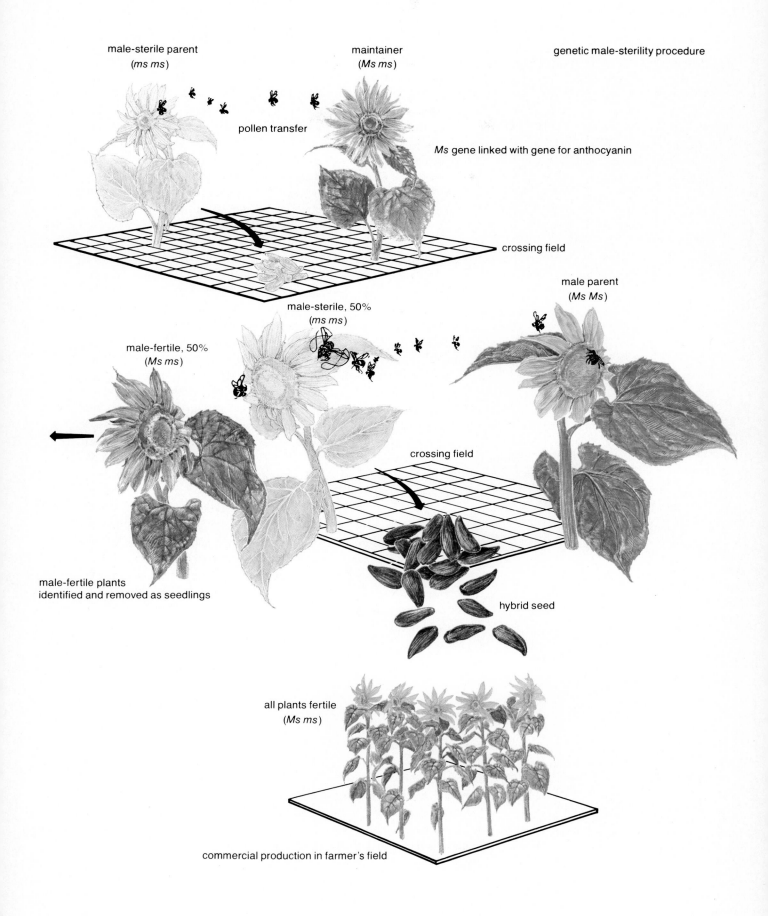

male-sterile parent
(*ms ms*)

maintainer
(*Ms ms*)

genetic male-sterility procedure

pollen transfer

Ms gene linked with gene for anthocyanin

crossing field

male-sterile, 50%
(*ms ms*)

male parent
(*Ms Ms*)

male-fertile, 50%
(*Ms ms*)

crossing field

male-fertile plants
identified and removed as seedlings

hybrid seed

all plants fertile
(*Ms ms*)

commercial production in farmer's field

A severe rust infection in the early 1950s discouraged commercial interest in sunflower growing until plant scientists succeeded in transferring genes for rust resistance from wild Helianthus species to domestic cultivars.

Illustration (facing page) outlines the cytoplasmic male-sterility system discussed in text on page 166. Plants with sterile cytoplasm are sterile if dominant fertility-restorer gene (Rf) is absent. Plants with normal cytoplasm are fertile whether Rf gene is absent or present.

made available for commercial production in the U.S. in 1972; by 1976, hybrids were estimated to account for more than 80% of U.S. sunflower production. Their use has had a significant effect worldwide in countries that previously had used only open-pollinated varieties.

With modern hybrids, yields are 20–25% above open-pollinated cultivars, oil concentration of the seed is about 45%, and plants are very uniform. These attractions have helped make sunflower the second most important oilseed crop in the world. Certain problems still vex farmers, including diseases that sometimes cause widespread damage. Such insects as the head moth and the midge cause crop failures, and birds take a big toll each year.

Farming practices

By the early 1980s sunflower crops were being grown on some 1.6 million hectares (4 million acres) in virtually every state in the U.S. Most seed production came from about a dozen states, from North Dakota to Texas and from Ohio to Oregon, with heaviest plantings in the Red River Valley of North Dakota and Minnesota. On the modern farm sunflower is grown with methods similar to those used for other row crops like corn and soybeans. The crop is planted in the spring in rows spaced 76–95 centimeters (30–37 inches) apart. Herbicides and cultivation are used to control weeds. In the fall the crop is harvested with a grain combine equipped with a special attachment consisting of long trays that stick out in front of the cutter bar. The attachment guides the stalks into the cutters such that only the head and a short piece of stalk are removed; the trays also catch seeds knocked loose by the oncoming combine before they fall to the ground. The sunflower heads then pass into the threshing cylinder of the machine where seeds are removed and cleaned. In the U.S. the seed is usually sold to local grain elevators. If destined for Europe, it most likely will be shipped through the St. Lawrence Seaway. About 90% of U.S. sunflower oilseeds are exported.

Farming practices for oilseed and confectionery sunflowers are similar, except that confectionery types are grown less densely to encourage large heads and thus large seeds, which command a better price. Nonoil hybrids usually are planted at a density of 40,000–45,000 per hectare (16,000–18,000 per acre) and oilseed hybrids at 45,000–60,000 per hectare (18,000–24,000 per acre). Selective breeding accounts for the difference in the coloration of the various varieties of commercial seed. Marketers can distinguish among the varieties more easily by their color, and the public seems to prefer eating light-colored, striped confectionery seeds.

Present and future uses

The seeds of oilseed sunflower usually are processed through a screw press to remove most of the oil and then treated with a solvent to extract the rest. The solvent is later separated from the oil and meal and reused. Oil destined for human dietary use is degummed, refined, deodorized, and winterized, resulting in a high-quality product that is clear and light in color, bland in taste, high in polyunsaturated fats, and free of toxic substances. Sunoil serves as a premium vegetable oil in making salad dressings, mayonnaise, and margarine. It is also used for household cooking and for frying potato

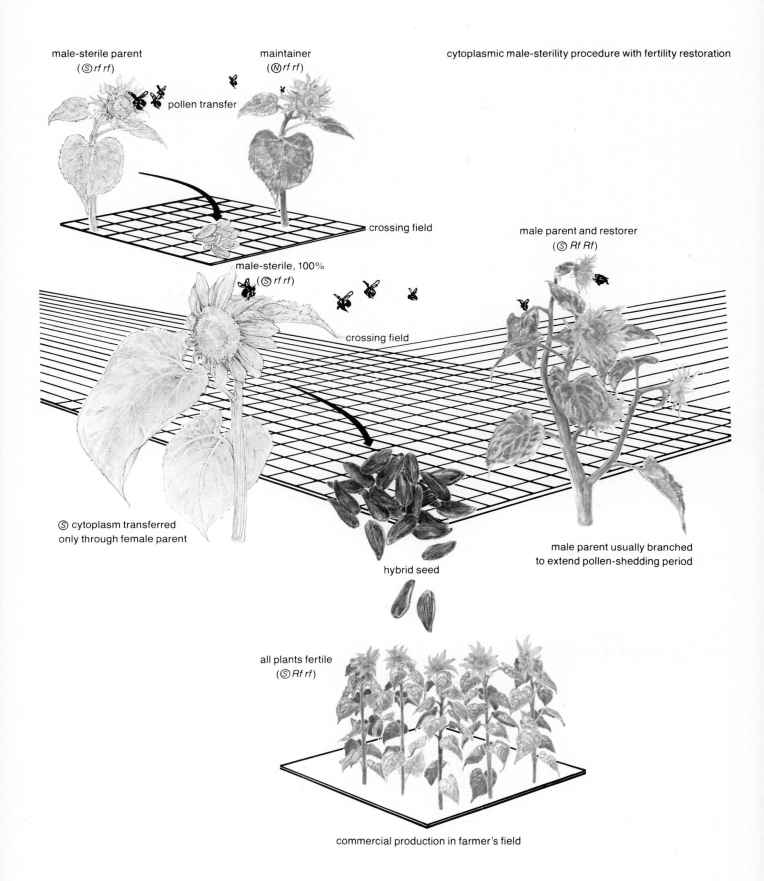

male-sterile parent
(⑤ *rf rf*)

pollen transfer

maintainer
(Ⓝ *rf rf*)

cytoplasmic male-sterility procedure with fertility restoration

crossing field

male-sterile, 100%
(⑤ *rf rf*)

male parent and restorer
(⑤ *Rf Rf*)

crossing field

⑤ cytoplasm transferred
only through female parent

male parent usually branched
to extend pollen-shedding period

hybrid seed

all plants fertile
(⑤ *Rf rf*)

commercial production in farmer's field

(Top, right) North Dakota State University, Ag Communications from Extension Bulletin 25; (top, left) A. Schneiter, Dept. of Agronomy, North Dakota State University; (bottom, left and right) W. E. Sackston, Plant Science, McGill University

Damage to sunflower heads from head moths (top left) and birds (top right) may mean serious production losses for the farmer. Downy mildew, a fungus that stunts plant growth (above right), also takes its toll. Scanning electron micrograph of a sunflower leaf infected with downy mildew (above) reveals clusters of fungal spore bodies.

chips, french fries, and other commercially prepared foods. Europeans, in fact, prefer sunoil to all other oils for household use, thus accounting for the European outlet for most of the U.S. crop. If the American public comes to prefer it, the market would expand considerably. Sunflower plantings in the U.S. conceivably could expand to 5 million hectares (12 million acres) to meet the demand.

In industry sunoil serves well in the manufacture of paints, varnishes, and plastic. In the future, however, its greatest industrial use may prove to be as diesel fuel, either alone or mixed with conventional fuel. Research groups in Australia and South Africa have been conducting field tests for several years, and some U.S. makers of agricultural diesel equipment also have shown interest in sunoil as well as other seed oils. Small-scale studies with dewaxed, degummed, and filtered crude sunoil mixed with diesel fuel to reduce sunoil viscosity have given especially promising results, although good long-term performance may require some chemical modification of the oil or redesign of the engine. At present diesel fuel is somewhat cheaper than sunoil, but if petroleum prices continue to rise and if breeders and farmers can improve the oil yield of sunflowers still further, sunoil may become a practical form of renewable energy.

170

Compiled from information in the 1981 "Sunflower Crop Quality Report," National Sunflower Association, Bismarck, North Dakota

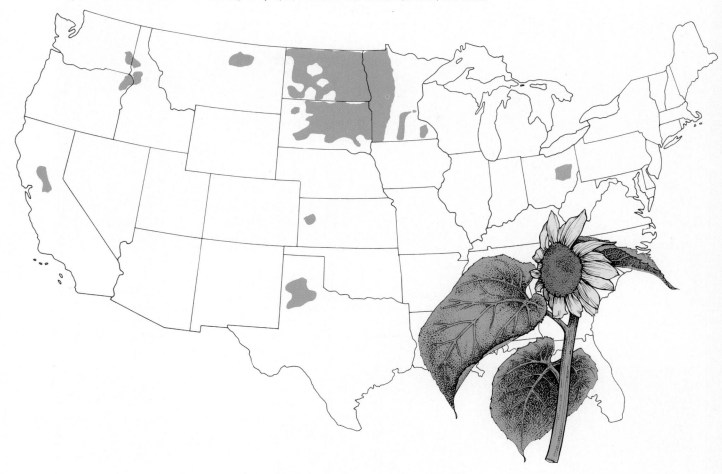

Sunflower seed residue after oil extraction is a crude meal that contains about 18–23% protein if the seeds are crushed with the hulls. It may have as much as 44% protein if all hull material is first screened out. The low-protein meal can be used as a protein supplement in cattle feed, and the higher quality meal is suitable for swine and poultry feed. The meal can be processed for human consumption, but this use has not been well explored.

In contrast with the growing oilseed market, the demand for confectionery sunflower seed remained constant in the U.S. during the 1970s. In the early 1980s, however, exports were beginning to increase as other countries discovered the nutritional advantages and versatility of the confectionery product. Larger confectionery seeds are roasted and sold as snack and health food, both hulled and in the hull. The smaller seeds become bird feed or are used as a poultry feed ingredient. A sunflower-meal product similar to peanut butter but with a different taste recently became available for limited distribution. Because it is high in polyunsaturated fatty acids, especially linoleic acid, it may become a popular health food.

Researchers also have found uses for the hulls themselves as combustible fuel in seed-processing plants, in compressed form as fireplace "logs," and as a roughage ingredient in cattle feed. Both hulls and the deseeded flower

Map locates major sunflower production regions in the U.S. Growing areas in California are crossing fields devoted to the production of hybrid seed for planting.

171

(Left) Grant Heilman; (right) Hugh E. Whitted III

Growing sunflowers (above left), planted in rows about a yard apart, bask in a Kansas field. Sunflower harvesting is done with a specially equipped combine (above right); the projecting trays catch seeds knocked loose by the oncoming machine and guide the heads into the combine's cutters. Small screw press (below left) and filter press (bottom left) extract and filter sunoil for experimental use in diesel engines. Oilseeds bound for export are loaded aboard ship (below right) at Duluth, Minnesota, on Lake Superior.

(Left, both photos) Daniel Ruud, North Dakota State University; (right) "The Sunflower" magazine

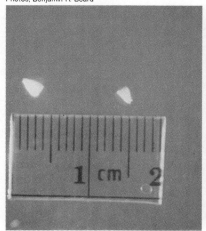
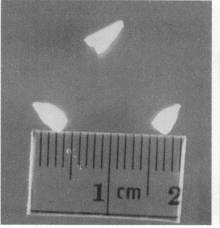

heads yield pectin, which is used in jams and jellies, and sunflower stalks have been made into construction-grade fiberboard. In Europe fermentation of the entire plant to produce livestock silage is popular.

Research and cooperation needed

Keeping sunflower a competitive crop depends on continued improvements to meet changing conditions. Genetic variability is the key ingredient for attaining and maintaining competitiveness of any crop. Wild sunflower species have been important sources of new characters in the past and will no doubt be important in the future. Even today none of the wild *Helianthus* species have been thoroughly investigated. Each small population of a wild species may possess germ plasm that is different from all other populations. To be sure this valuable source of potentially desirable traits is preserved, it is important to collect and maintain accessions of as many species as possible. Several collections are available at present; probably the largest is the USDA collection at Bushland, Texas.

One barrier to crossing different species of sunflower has been a natural phenomenon called embryo abortion, in which for some reason the endosperm fails to nourish the embryonic hybrid in the seed. In hybridization work with plants other than sunflower, plant scientists have circumvented this problem by removing the immature embryo from the seed and nurturing it in an artificial medium, a technique called embryo culture. In 1981 B. H. Beard of the USDA and John Chandler, a graduate student at the University of California, Davis, extended this method to sunflowers, finding that if the sunflower embryo is first cultured on a medium high in sugar, its germination is delayed, allowing it time to develop and grow larger. Later the embryo is transferred to a low-sugar medium where it germinates and grows into a seedling capable of flourishing in soil. Using this procedure they have produced 17 interspecific hybrids not previously reported.

With more such research, together with continued cooperation among plant breeders plus the collection, maintenance, and use of a broad genetic reserve of wild species, sunflower can help alleviate the oil and protein shortage throughout the world.

Freshly excised from the seed for embryo culture, embryos of interspecific sunflower hybrids (left) are almost microscopically small. After a few days on a medium of high-sugar agar in a petri dish, the embryos have become larger and more mature (center) while germination has been delayed. Mature embryos are placed in a test tube with a low-sugar medium, where they germinate into young plants capable of growing in soil (right).

173

OUR FUTURE FOODS

by Kendrick Frazier

By the year 2000 food production must be tripled to feed adequately the expected world population. To accomplish this scientists are attempting to create new foods and to render edible some products that formerly were discarded.

Noel D. Vietmeyer

The winged bean, long known in New Guinea and parts of Southeast Asia as a source of protein, has recently been introduced into many other tropical countries, where more protein is needed. Some believe that it may eventually join the soybean as one of the most important new crops of the 20th century.

KENDRICK FRAZIER, former editor of Science News, is a freelance science writer, editor of The Skeptical Inquirer, and author of Our Turbulent Sun (1982).

(Overleaf) Illustration by John Zielinski

Future decades pose many uncertainties, but two things are as sure as death and taxes: we will all have to eat and there will be more of us to be fed than ever before. What will we be eating? What is the future of food?

Some science fiction writers would have us all popping protein pills in lieu of real meals in the future. Food forecasters and food technologists are cool to that concept. Foods in the early twenty-first century may not *be* exactly the same as today's, but they probably will *look* much the same. Taste and public acceptance will still be important. Foods by then may come from some novel sources not widely tapped today. They will be "engineered" to a far greater degree than they are now, but their ultimate source will still be nature (given some innovative boosts by science). The process of eating is not likely to change radically; human taste buds, palates, and stomachs are not soon destined for the evolutionary scrap heap.

Within these broad constraints many new kinds of foods seem sure to take their place on the future dinner table. Now-popular items, such as steak and pure-beef hamburger, are likely to make up a diminishing portion of the diet. Two decades from now food industry analysts expect that people will be eating fewer steaks and roasts, fewer chops and hamburgers, about the same amount of cheese, butter, and milk, more fish, about the same amount of chicken and eggs, and more grain and vegetable products.

Even within these kinds of existing foods many changes can be expected. As the cost of producing meat continues to rise, more hamburger will be a mixture of meat and vegetable protein analogues. Real, mouth-watering steak will still be around, but there will also be processed, blended meats molded into the shape and texture of steak.

Genuine aged cheese will still be available in gourmet shops, but more than half of all our cheese will be "imitation," made from vegetable protein and fats. Seafood lovers will still be able to sit down to a meal of filet of sole, but much of the increased consumption of fish will be in the form of fish sticks and other molded forms made of minced fish of all kinds blended with vegetable analogues. Poultry products will change little, but egg farms will have even greater production per hen than today and frying chickens will be bred larger, some nearly as big as turkeys. More vegetables will be grown hydroponically or in other indoor controlled-environment situations. Grains will come from genetically altered plants of vastly increased productivity.

Thus, the future of food will be shaped by developments in several areas. They include new crops and the wider use of exotic natural sources, new food-industry processes, and new technologies.

New crops

Of the estimated 80,000 species of edible plants in the world, mankind historically has used no more than 3,000 for food. And 95% of all calories and protein from plants comes from just 30 species. To some botanists this is a dangerous and unwise concentration on so few varieties. Greater diversity can protect against epidemics of plant disease, exploit land and environments now only marginally useful to food production, and provide rich and much-needed new sources of protein.

Many exotic plants are available. The winged bean is one example. It is

tasty and edible, and contains up to 37% protein. Long a source of high protein to New Guineans and some other Southeast Asians, the winged bean was little known elsewhere until the 1970s. Then the U.S. National Academy of Sciences did a report in 1975 touting it as a new high-protein crop for the tropics. The response was enormous, and the winged bean has now been introduced into more than 70 countries. Many believe it is at about the same stage now as the soybean was in the 1930s when it vaulted into agricultural prominence and soon became the most important new crop of the century.

Fifty-four potential new crops for the United States have been identified in a study by the National Science Foundation. Twenty were considered most promising. Not all of their names come tripping off the tongue. They include the pigeon pea, the buffalo gourd, the tepary bean, the pummelo, and grain amaranths. Also the black walnut, the Chinese water chestnut, and the pinyon pine nut. The buffalo gourd, also called the prairie gourd, grows wild in the U.S. Southwest, thriving on semiarid and other marginal lands. Its seeds contain up to 35% protein. It is now being cultivated in Lebanon and Mexico and is considered a significant potential source of protein.

Amaranths were important grain crops for the Indians of the tropical highlands of Mexico and Central America, but the Spaniards suppressed them because they played a role in religious practices. Amaranth grains contain more protein than cereal grains and are especially rich in the key amino acid lysine. The plants can thrive in adverse conditions. (*See* Feature Article: AMARANTH: RETURN OF THE AZTEC MYSTERY CROP.)

Other exotic plants have potential as food sources in parts of the world far from their place of origin. The marama bean, native to Africa's Kalahari Desert, tastes like cashews or almonds when roasted. It contains as much protein as soybeans and as much nutritional energy as the peanut. Its roots make a sweet-tasting vegetable. Botanists believe that it could easily become

The buffalo gourd (left), pinyon pine nut (center), and black walnut (right) are among the most promising new crops for the United States according to a study by the National Science Foundation.

177

Mushrooms, according to a food protein scientist, "represent one of the world's greatest untapped resources of nutritious foods." Rich in proteins, minerals, and vitamins, they can be grown on agricultural and industrial waste materials.

an important new crop. Cocoyam, a potatolike plant, is a possible commercial-scale crop for the world's tropical regions.

Other plants, already well known as ingredients or complements to various dishes, are severely underutilized as food sources themselves. Mushrooms, for example, "represent one of the world's greatest untapped resources of nutritious foods," says Hong Kong biologist and food protein researcher S. T. Chang. They can be grown on various agricultural and industrial waste materials and are rich in protein, minerals, and vitamins, as well as containing an abundance of lysine.

Animal sources

Not all the newly exploited kinds of natural foods will come from the plant kingdom. Animal scientists searching for underused sources of protein are taking a good look at rabbits. Rabbit stew and roasted rabbit are hardly uncommon food to rural people and Indians in the Southwest, but they are not the usual dinner fare for others. That could change.

Rabbits reproduce quickly and can be raised in small areas. They are also an excellent food. Rabbits, in fact, rank highest in protein and lowest in fat content of all meat-producing animals, yielding 20% edible protein per pound compared with 12% for beef. "Rabbits are an excellent protein source and one which has not been tapped in this country," points out University of Illinois animal scientist and physiologist Janice Bahr. The U.S. government has begun funding research into small-scale production of rabbits for meat.

Species of fish and other sea animals so far unexploited for food may find their way into future diets. Pacific hake, the Great Lakes drumfish, and the ocean pout, abundant in New England waters in winter, are all gaining new attention from food protein researchers. Ocean pout, they hope, will follow in the fin trails of flounder. Flounder was once considered a trash fish and thrown over the side when caught by fishing boats. Now it is a popular food.

The icy waters surrounding Antarctica may help supply future food needs with the phenomenally abundant planktonic crustaceans known as krill. Scientific estimates of the amount of krill in Antarctic waters range from 183 million to 1,350,000,000 metric tons, with annual natural production ranging from 200 million to 330 million tons. Biologists report that krill are a potentially valuable, high-quality food, rich in essential amino acids, vitamins, and minerals. Various krill products have been produced experimentally, including whole meats, coagulated paste, and protein concentrates. The technology, economics, and marketing of krill as a food source are not yet well understood, but it seems possible that Antarctic krill might be a part of the U.S. diet by the year 2000.

Fish can convert food into body tissues more efficiently than can farm animals. As a result the percentage of edible lean meat in fish is much greater than in beef, pork, or poultry, and the costs per amount of protein are lower too. Aquaculture, or fish farming, is expected to help supply the additional quantities of fish that food forecasters are certain will be consumed in the future. The practice of fish culture began thousands of years ago in China. But even there it is considered to have become a science only during the past 25 years, when carp were first injected with hormones to induce them to

Krill (left) are planktonic crustaceans that are greatly abundant in the cold waters surrounding Antarctica. Containing essential amino acids, vitamins, and minerals, they may become a part of the U.S. diet within the next 20 years. The rabbit (below) might also find its way to the dinner table. Ranking highest in protein and lowest in fat content of all meat-producing animals, it reproduces quickly and can be raised in small areas.

spawn in stillwater ponds. In the 1970s Chinese biochemists developed a synthetic analogue to this luteinizing-releasing hormone, and enough is being produced to supply all of China's aquaculture centers. The hope is that aquaculture will contribute significantly toward feeding China's population of more than one billion. Already it supplies one-third of the total fish tonnage consumed in that nation. Israel, Japan, Taiwan, and Mexico are also leaders in aquaculture. Though fish has never been as popular a food in the U.S. as it is in many other nations, Richard T. Lovell of Auburn (Alabama) University's Department of Fisheries and Allied Aquacultures believes that if fish were farmed on a major scale in the U.S., it would provide red meat with healthy competition for the protein dollar.

Even without a large increase in fish consumption in the U.S. aquaculture must play a larger role in supplying food fish, Lovell believes. Ocean stocks are declining, and the U.S. spends more dollars on importing fish than on anything else except petroleum. Thus, surprisingly, fish imports contribute significantly to the nation's balance-of-trade deficit.

The Mississippi River floodplain is already the site of a major catfish-farming enterprise because large ponds can be built there easily. Aggressive marketing may in the future overcome the stigma attached to catfish that limits its consumption in many parts of the nation. Rainbow trout is the second-leading cultured food fish in the U.S.

179

Fabricated foods

Even if the source of food in the future remains nature, the form that food will take may, in many cases, be radically different. Familiar foods will be produced in new forms, and new foods will be produced in familiar forms. There will also be many changes in the way food is processed and sold.

One example is beefsteak. The engineered steak has already arrived and is likely to become far more prominent in the future. The idea is to reduce the enormous amount of wasted meat left behind in packing plants and butcher shops. Methods of restructuring meat can now make use of 72% of the steer's carcass instead of the measly 30% that has been traditional. A process called flaking takes knuckles, heels, bottoms, flanks, and other such secondary portions and transforms them into the shapes of familiar cuts of meat. Chunks of meat, gristle, and connective tissue are all shaved into three-quarter-inch-long flakes, blended and folded into each other, salted to help bind them together, frozen, and then extruded into long metal casings. These meat logs are pressed under pressure of 500 pounds per square inch and then sliced with precision blades. The resulting cuts can be made to look exactly like New York strips, filet mignon, boneless rib eyes, or whatever else a customer might want. The meat has the appearance and texture of unprocessed steak.

The U.S. Army Natick Research and Development Command in Massachusetts, in charge of developing new items for the military, has been active in this effort. No-waste flaked veal restructured into the shape of veal cutlets has been served to the military for about five years. Engineered lamb is a newer innovation, and no-waste pork cutlets and fish are next on the drawing boards. The Natick researchers reported that their surveys showed that military personnel rated the restructured veal cutlets superior to the real item. As a result the purchase of standard veal roasts, cutlets, and ground veal was being phased out in favor of restructured veal.

The concept of "fabricated foods" need not be negative and unpalatable. Food technologists believe that in significant ways they often are improvements on the real thing. Ideal simulated foods would be more healthful, less expensive, and easier to use than natural, unprocessed fare. Fabricated foods such as margarine, artificial bacon bits, and coffee whiteners are lower in both calories and saturated fats and generally are cheaper and more convenient to serve than the foods they emulate.

Taste and texture, two closely related characteristics, pose many challenges to food technologists. Such appealing attributes as the flavor and tender chewiness of steak, the crunch of fresh lettuce, and the juicy taste of garden-grown tomatoes remain mysteries. The engineering of them into fabricated foods presents specific problems for science, engineering, and psychology.

Fabricated foods already constitute an $11 billion industry. Their share of total food sales is sure to continue upward in the coming decades, as researchers find new ways to produce them. For instance, research in food-process engineering at the Massachusetts Institute of Technology has found that the pulpy residue left over from squeezing cranberries for juice can be used to make an edible "sponge." The cranberry cells in this sponge can soak

180

John Colwell—Grant Heilman

Channel catfish are harvested in Mississippi. Fish farming on a large scale could provide consumers with a readily available source of protein and could help counterbalance the decline in stocks of ocean fish.

up flavored liquids added to the material and release the flavor during chewing, thus serving as a base for many new succulent foods. This research has also produced an edible sponge from chitosan, the structural material found in lobster and clam shells. It can be used to encapsulate starch or fruit juice and thus simulate bread or fruit products.

Just as flaked beef will be made into restructured steaks to reduce wasted protein from land animals, fish- and poultry-processing companies will continue to develop new ways to get more flesh off the bones of fish and chicken. These scraps will be used in combination with beef for beef-fish burgers. Minced-fish technology also will come to the fore. Minced fish offers a practical use for many small-sized species of fish that are not easily marketed. It will probably be added to sausage and other meat products. A government-industry collaboration has produced experimental fish/meat frankfurters in which Alaskan pollack made up 10–40% percent of the protein. Cornell University researchers formulated a canned minced-fish product that essentially duplicates tuna; it has been favorably received by consumers.

Soybean protein will become a commonplace addition to ground beef, fish, poultry, and other foods. Soybeans that have been extruded and machine-spun into strands are an ideal textured vegetable protein extender. Soybeans have already found their way into cookies, crackers, doughnuts, cereals, candy, nut meat extenders, marshmallows, and baby food as well as frankfurters, beef patties, and simulated bacon. Though there seems little limit to their use as a nutrient-rich extender, soybeans are nevertheless now used mainly for animal feed. But they are such a cost-effective source of protein for human consumption in comparison with their use in the production of meat that the amount directly consumed in foods for people in the future seems likely to increase considerably.

181

Retort pouch food, originally developed for astronauts and the military, will enter the civilian market. Advocates are touting such pouches as the most significant packaging advance since the can. They need no refrigeration and only have to be placed in boiling water for cooking.

Milk in the future may not need refrigeration either. Already, ultra-high-temperature milk is available. It is made by heating raw milk to very high temperatures. Because bacteria do not readily grow in the resulting milk, refrigeration is not necessary. Expected further increases in the cost of refrigerated transportation and in-store refrigeration as well as improvements to rid the milk of a slightly "cooked" flavor may make it a widely used food in the future.

The cows that make milk may also be the targets of some improvements. For example, the polyunsaturated cow may not be far away. The U.S. Department of Agriculture's Animal Research Center in Beltsville, Maryland, has raised cattle whose meat and milk contain lessened amounts of the saturated fats that may contribute to heart disease. Embryo transplants will be used routinely in the breeding of cattle and other farm animals. The sex ratios will be controlled, and the number of offspring per birth increased.

Microbiology and genetic engineering

The most revolutionary advances in the production of the foods of the future are likely to come in microbiology laboratories. Several dozen of them are seeking ways to use microbiological techniques to design new microorganisms useful to agriculture or to manipulate plants genetically in previously impossible ways.

One of the most exciting aspects of this research focuses on making nitrogen-fixing bacteria more efficient in converting molecular nitrogen from the atmosphere into nitrogen compounds usable by plants. The nitrogen compounds, primarily ammonia, are essential for the growth, protein synthesis, and high yields of plants. This natural nitrogen-fixing process is a symbiotic relationship. *Rhizobium* or other nitrogen-fixing bacteria infect the roots of legumes such as beans, alfalfa, soybeans, peas, and clover. The bacteria obtain their nourishment from the plant and in turn supply the plant with nitrogen in the form the plant can use.

One method to identify more efficient nitrogen-fixing bacteria is to expose bacterial colonies to mutagenic substances or to ionizing radiation in order to produce mutant forms. These are then injected into plants, and the amount of nitrogen fixed by the plants is measured. In this way mutant strains capable of significantly higher levels of nitrogen fixation can be identified.

A more sophisticated technique is to use genetic engineering, specifically recombinant DNA microtechnology. Superior nitrogen-fixing strains of bacteria will be created by the manipulation of particular genes involved in the complex chemical process. For instance, a particular chemical side reaction that wastes energy and benefits neither the bacteria nor the plant might be "switched off" by gene-modification technology. This entire area of agricultural biotechnology is a rapidly advancing field of research.

The advantages of practical success in improving nitrogen-fixing capabilities will be enormous. Soybean yields, for instance, could improve immedi-

The cow in the photograph produced all the calves shown with her from one ovulation. Fertility drugs were administered so that the cow would ovulate at an accelerated rate. The fertilized eggs were removed from the cow seven days after it was bred, a process requiring three inseminations within 36 hours. After being bathed in antibiotics and sheltered from contamination, each egg was transplanted into a recipient cow. In this way a cow with desirable characteristics can produce many more offspring than she could normally.

ately by 15%. The benefits would be double: all food industries that use soybeans would profit from the increased yields, and world fertilizer use could be reduced. There is also hope that a better understanding of the details of the symbiotic relationships of several nitrogen-fixing bacteria that work in cooperation with legumes may lead to the engineering of microorganisms that fix nitrogen for cereal crops as well.

An even more exotic, but more difficult, enterprise would be to insert nitrogen-fixing genes directly into cereal plants. No crop plants currently have their own direct nitrogen-fixing abilities. If this could be accomplished and the plants made to function in nature, the practical benefits to food production would be almost without limit.

The 17 nitrogen-fixing genes of one particular bacterium have been introduced successfully into yeast. Yeasts are much more closely related to the higher plants than they are to bacteria, and so this is an important advance. Unfortunately, so far the yeasts have not been able to express the nitrogen-fixing capability; that is, they have not been able to fix nitrogen from the atmosphere. Nevertheless, it seems likely that there will be advances in this area in the future.

Workers at Washington University in St. Louis, Missouri, are attempting to insert the protein-forming gene from the soybean into tobacco, a common laboratory research plant. This is an important step in increasing the protein content of future food crop strains through genetic engineering. Research at Stanford University seeks to alter the protein-storage genes in corn to make

183

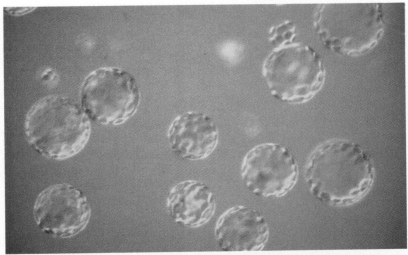

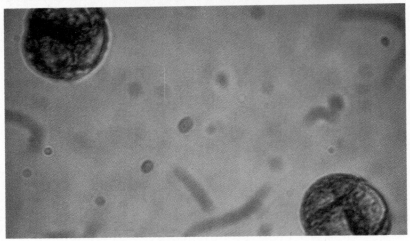

Single potato cells stripped of their cell walls (top) are called protoplasts. Without the walls such cells can be more easily fused with one another (bottom). Such fusion allows the creation of potentially useful hybrids that generally cannot be produced through natural sexual recombination.

that important crop more nutritious. It appears that significant improvements in the overall quality of the stored protein of crop plants will require individual modification of many genes rather than merely one. Thus, this work becomes more complicated, but the difficulties do not appear to be insurmountable.

Microbiology research may also lead to entirely new sources of food for humankind—microbes. Single-celled microbes (algae, yeasts, fungi, and bacteria) are already essential in many food-production processes. Bacteria are consumed by the trillions in fermented milks and yogurts. When bread is eaten, the yeasts used to leaven it are also consumed as are the molds in bleu cheese. Important meat substitutes also depend upon microbes. The typical meatlike flavor of soy sauce is produced after soaked, cooked, and wheat-coated soybeans become overgrown with the mold *Aspergillus oryzae*. When this mixture is covered with salt brine, enzymes in the mold make soluble the proteins, lipids, and other components in the soybeans and give the filtered soy sauce its distinctive, meaty flavor. The traditional Indonesian meat analogue tempeh is another example. Tempeh is made by soaking dehulled

(Left) B. Ben Bohlool, Department of Microbiology, University of Hawaii, Honolulu; (right) E. I. du Pont de Nemours & Company

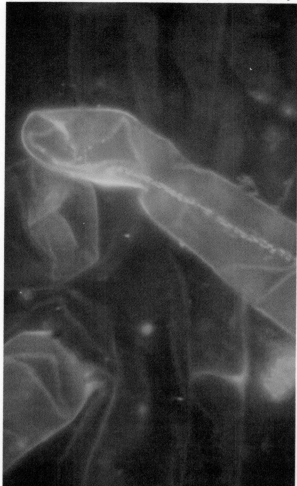

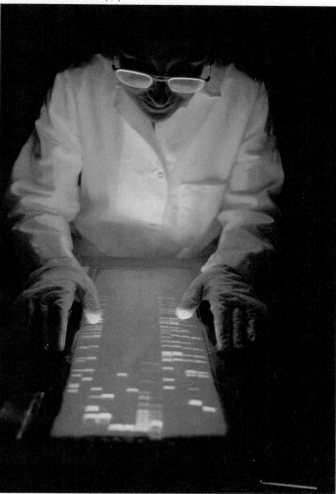

and partially cooked soybeans which then become overgrown with the edible mold *Rhizopus oligosporus*. This mold knits the soybeans into a nutritious, compact cake that can be cut into chunks and used in soups or sliced and fried in deep fat.

Consumption of microbial cells as foods in themselves has historically been limited to mushrooms and certain forms of algae eaten in parts of Africa and Mexico, but that could change. Food from microbes may become a significant source of protein for humans in the future, in the view of scientists such as Keith H. Steinkraus, a microbiologist and food scientist at Cornell University. Microbes can double their cell mass in 20 minutes to two hours. Bacteria can contain as much as 80% protein, compared with 40–45% for soybeans. Steinkraus and Carol Waslien of the League for International Food Education in Washington, D.C., believe that microbial cells grown in mass quantities could be consumed in some form directly by man as a major protein source in the diet.

A research institute in Great Britain developed a process in which fibrous mold mycelium is grown and used to provide the protein and texture for

Rhizobium *bacteria (above left) infect the root hair of a clover plant. Rhizobium and certain other bacteria enter the roots of legumes and obtain nourishment from the plant; in return they convert molecular nitrogen from the atmosphere into nitrogen compounds usable by the plants. Research is under way to make these nitrogen-fixing bacteria more efficient. Above right, a scientist uses a gene-splicing technique in an effort to find better methods for producing nitrogenase, an enzyme important in the nitrogen-fixing process.*

185

Varieties of corn will undergo implantation of new genes in an attempt to increase yields, improve resistance to disease, and augment nutritional value.

meat substitutes. Problems of flavor, color (algae, for instance, tend to be bitter and dark green), and texture as well as psychological matters (one scientist refers to the need for overcoming the "gag factor" when contemplating algae for dinner) will all have to be solved before microbes can become an attractive food source. The best processing route is probably to rupture the cells in order to release their contents, concentrate and isolate the proteins, and spin the isolated proteins into fibers to make meat substitutes, just as soybean protein is processed today. The costs and difficulties of these procedures make it unlikely that the first algae cheeseburger will be consumed in the near future.

Fungus burgers may be another matter. A British firm developing a mold from a microscopic fungus (it calls the product "mycoprotein") has been producing foods with it. The company's chefs have prepared it to taste like fried chicken, breaded shrimp, and other delicacies. They have had good results in taste tests with students in Britain and the U.S., and the company plans to construct a fermenter capable of producing 20,000 tons of mycoprotein a year.

Hydroponics

Even where the food crops of the future remain the same as today, the methods of growing them may change. Indoor, controlled-environment farming is on the increase, and that trend seems certain to continue. Large corporations are becoming interested in hydroponics, the raising of crops, usually vegetables, in fertilized water rather than soil. This is done indoors, where temperature, light, humidity, and the carbon dioxide content of the air can be carefully controlled. Hydroponics will not do away with the wheat farm, but it will become more popular for raising vegetables that can be

186

Grant Heilman

Tomatoes are grown hydroponically, in fertilized water rather than soil. Temperature, light, humidity, and the carbon dioxide level of the air are carefully controlled in this indoor method of farming, which seems likely to prove most useful for vegetables that can be grown abundantly in limited space.

grown abundantly in limited space. The risks of bad weather are removed, and the "growing season" can be greatly speeded up. Hydroponics allows vegetables to be raised close to their points of consumption, and thus eliminates the need to truck them expensively for long distances.

Hydroponics also will be useful if future generations decide to colonize space. Some of our descendants will probably live in such permanent colonies. They will manufacture most of their own food and grow the rest in hydroponic or other controlled-environment conditions. Whether they will produce surpluses enough to provide their less adventurous relatives on Earth with samples of their culinary wares remains to be seen.

Future outlook

Food has always been many things to many people. To a large part of the world it is solely a matter of survival. To those more fortunate, mealtime is a welcome occasion of pleasure. The foods of the future—a time of vastly increased world population—must continue to fulfill both kinds of roles. Some of these foods will be the same as today. Others will only appear to be. Novel sources and processes will be tapped. Genetic capabilities for plant protein production will be cleverly bolstered. And although nature will remain the ultimate source, future foods will be far more likely than those of today to be manufactured, fabricated, restructured, and reconstituted rather than merely "grown" or "raised."

"Blessings on him who invented . . . the food that satisfies hunger," wrote Cervantes. That was almost four centuries ago. But in the future "invent" will be far more than a metaphor in regard to food. To satisfy the hunger of future multitudes, nature and human ingenuity will collaborate in mutual resourcefulness as never before.

187

AMARANTH:
RETURN OF THE AZTEC MYSTERY CROP

After 400 years of obscurity amaranth, once one of the most important food crops of the Americas, may regain its former prominence.

Amaranth is perhaps the oldest food crop of the Americas. First cultivated by cave dwellers, it had become as important as corn and beans by the time of the Aztec and Inca Indians 500 years ago. In more modern times, however, its existence was known only to a few dozen scientists and historians—that is, until the last ten years. In the 1970s amaranth began to attract research attention. By 1982 such impressive advances had been made that the crop was on the threshold of commercial production in the United States, and limited quantities of the grain and flour were available by mail order. It should not be long before amaranth products will be available over the counter, probably at first in health food stores and later in supermarkets. Eventually, amaranth may prove to be one of the Aztecs' richest legacies.

Of the 60 species found in the genus *Amaranthus* three produce large seedheads loaded with white or cream-colored seeds that are promising food grains. Two, *Amaranthus hypochondriacus* and *Amaranthus cruentus*, are native to Mexico; one, *Amaranthus caudatus*, is native to Peru and other Andean countries.

Cereals such as wheat, rice, and corn are grasses. Amaranths, however, are broad-leaved plants and are one of the few nongrasses that produce significant amounts of grain. (Buckwheat is another.) They grow easily, resisting drought, heat, and pests and readily adapting to new environments, including some that are inhospitable to conventional cereal crops.

There's not a prettier plant on Earth. Amaranth leaves, stems, and flowers are usually brilliantly colored with purple, red, and gold, and they glow with almost incandescent radiance. The seedheads, a foot or more long and six inches or so across, are somewhat like those of sorghum. Although the seeds are barely bigger than a grain of sand, they occur in massive numbers—sometimes more than half a million to a plant.

Destruction and rediscovery

By the time of Columbus these seeds were one of the great basic foods of Mexico. Tens of thousands of acres of Aztec farmland were planted to the tall, leafy, purplish crop. Each year farmers brought 200,000 bushels of amaranth grain from the 20 Aztec

by Noel D. Vietmeyer

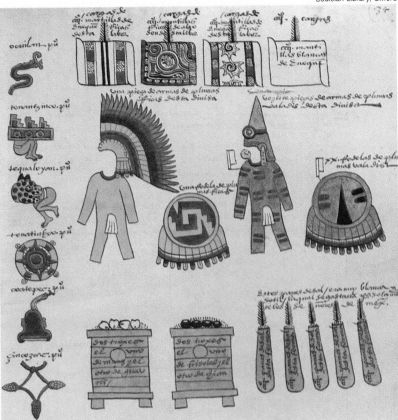

The Codex Mendoza, commissioned by the Spanish viceroy Antonio de Mendoza in about 1541, reveals that for two-thirds of the towns of the Aztec empire amaranth was a required part of the annual tribute paid to the emperor Montezuma II. The drawing depicts six towns, shown in the left column, and their tribute. Bins of corn and amaranth are in the bottom row.

***NOEL D. VIETMEYER** is a Professional Associate at the National Academy of Sciences in Washington, D.C.*

(Overleaf) Rodale Press, Inc.

provinces to the palace in Tenochtitlán (now Mexico City) in tribute to their king Montezuma II. (They brought that much corn too, but it takes many more of the minute amaranth seeds to make up a bushel, and meeting the amaranth quota put a much heavier burden on the farmers.)

Because the intense pigments in amaranth flowers were coveted for religious rites the crop had acquired mystical properties. Held in awe by the Aztecs, it was planted for protection against evil spirits and was interwoven with their legend and pagan ritual. For example, on various days set by the religious calendar women ground the seed, dyed it red with coloring from amaranth flowers, and mixed it with honey or even human blood. This dough—shaped into figurines of dogs, snakes, birds, mountains, and gods—was eaten during ceremonies in which the faithful tithed part of their amaranth crop to the temple.

On arriving in Mexico in 1519 Hernán Cortés immediately began eradicating the Aztec ceremonies and culture. Amaranth was a prime target. To destroy the culture and to expunge what he considered the barbaric rituals he banned its cultivation. He and his conquistadores roamed the countryside, trampling and burning thousands of fields. People who continued eating amaranth had their hands cut off or were even put to death. Almost overnight one of the most important and revered foods of the Americas fell into disuse and obscurity.

But the plant survived. It never regained its past prominence, but in

190

Adapted from information obtained from Jonathan Sauer, Department of Geography, University of California, Los Angeles

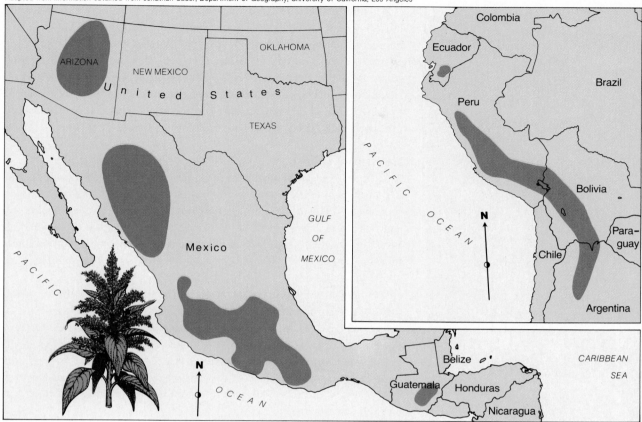

isolated mountain valleys in the highlands of Central and South America pockets of tenacious farmers continued carrying on the tradition of cultivating it. Even today in remote areas of Mexico, Guatemala, and Peru one can find a few farmers growing amaranth as their ancestors did before the Spanish conquest. They still mix the popped grain with honey, not to make idols but to make a confection known in Spanish as *alegría*.

Although it all but disappeared from the American landscape, where it had been a fixture for thousands of years, amaranth flourished in China, the Himalayas, and in parts of Africa. How it got there is not known. But farmers in Asia and Africa still grow the same species that Cortés tried to wipe out 460 years ago. Strangely, few of them know that the seed is a good food; most raise amaranth only for its leaves. When picked young, the leaves make a green vegetable.

In 1972 Australian plant physiologist John Downton, then at Australian National University, made a remarkable discovery that has since focused international interest on the plant. He found that amaranth seeds contain an unusually high percentage of protein. The protein was exceptional for the amount of the amino acid lysine it contained. Wheat, rice, corn, and other cereal grains are considered "incomplete" because they lack sufficient lysine for optimum human health. Amaranth protein, on the other hand, has nearly twice the lysine of wheat, three times that of corn, and very close to that found in milk—the standard of nutritional excellence.

Grain amaranths are distributed throughout Mexico and extend into Guatemala and the southwestern United States. In South America (inset) they are found in a band stretching south and east from southern Ecuador through Peru, Bolivia, and into northern Argentina.

191

Amaranthus hypochondriacus, a
potentially valuable food grain,
grows in a garden in Mexico (top).
Above, the new crops coordinator at
the Rodale research center in
Pennsylvania prepares selected
amaranth plants for cross-pollination.

Downton's discoveries have since been confirmed, and the staggering implications of Cortés's decision have become more apparent. The Spaniard may have believed that he had saved the Aztecs' souls, but it was at the expense of their nutrition. He had destroyed amaranth as the great food staple of Mexico and had halted its probable spread into North American agriculture. His actions—mandated by intolerance, politics, and religion rather than by technical or humanitarian considerations—had caused the eclipse of a potentially global crop of outstanding food value.

Nutritional value

Amaranth is indeed a nutritional treasure. At a rating of 75 it comes closer than any grain to the perfect balance of essential amino acids, which theoretically would score 100 on the nutritionists' scale of protein quality. By contrast, corn scores about 44, wheat 60, soybean 68, and cow's milk 72. When amaranth flour is mixed with wheat flour, the combination almost reaches the perfect 100 score because the amino acids that each lacks are abundant in the other.

It is no wonder that enthusiasm is resurfacing for amaranth. The grain can be used in breakfast cereals, granola, pablum, or as an ingredient in confections. It also can be cooked into gruel or parched and milled to produce flour that is suitable for cookies, breads, cakes, and other baked goods. When heated, the grains pop. The result is a crunchy product tasting like a nutty flavored popcorn. The popped seeds are light and crisp and can be used as a snack, as a cold cereal with milk and honey, and as a "breading" on chicken or other meat.

Not only the seeds are nutritious. Amaranth leaves also are rich in protein, as well as in vitamins and minerals. They have a mild flavor and can be cooked much like spinach into such dishes as amaranth au gratin and amaranth quiche. In addition, tender new leaves may be used as salad greens. In recent taste tests at the United States Department of Agriculture in Beltsville, Maryland, most of the 60 participants said that cooked amaranth tasted at least as good as spinach. Some likened the flavor to that of artichoke.

Research and future prospects

Despite the growing wealth of evidence for amaranth's excellence much research needs to be done before the crop can be widely grown commercially. Amaranth is still essentially a protein-packed semi-domesticated plant, but agronomists are now "taming" it by breeding plants of uniform height with sturdy wind-resistant stalks and high-yielding seedheads that hold onto their seeds until they are harvested. The responses of these plants to a variety of climates, soil conditions, pests, and diseases are also under investigation.

Leading amaranth research is the Rodale Press, a publisher of literature on organic gardening and health. In 1977 it hired an internationally renowned agronomist, Richard Harwood, and a team of nutritionists and plant scientists to develop the crop. At the Organic Gardening and Farming Research Center near Emmaus, Pennsylvania, Harwood and his researchers grew, evaluated, and crossbred hundreds of different amaranth varieties.

Left, amaranth seedhead is wrapped in cotton and covered with a gelatin capsule to prevent contamination after breeding. Cultivated fields of amaranth at the Rodale center are compared below. At the left is one of the earliest fields, in 1974, showing a great variety in plant size and maturation. After years of research and experimentation a field in 1981, right, reveals a plant with uniform height, sturdy stalks, and high-yielding seedheads.

In four years the Rodale team worked on problems of field preparation, precision seeding, timing of planting, spacing between plants, weed and insect control, harvesting, and seed cleaning. In doing this they laid much of the groundwork for amaranth's introduction as a large-scale crop. The Rodale test kitchen also developed many amaranth recipes. Staff and visitors regularly dine on salads, soups, breads, and desserts made of amaranth leaves or seeds. Using the flour or the popped seeds, the test kitchen has served such unlikely dishes as amaranth crepes and amaranth foo yong.

Universities and other scientific institutions have become interested in the Rodale work. Research teams began studying amaranth at the University of California at Davis, Pennsylvania State University, Iowa State University, Cornell University, and Michigan State University as well as at the

193

Amaranth is cultivated (above left) and harvested by combine (above right). Below at left from top to bottom are flour from grain, popped amaranth, the grain itself, and flour from popped amaranth. Amaranth grown for use of its leaves as a vegetable is shown below right.

Photos, Rodale Press, Inc.

Cereals Research Unit of the U.S. Department of Agriculture, and at several food processing firms.

In 1977, using 13,500 readers of one of its magazines, the Rodale group conducted a nationwide test to see where amaranth could be grown in the United States. The answer was almost everywhere. The plant adapts to many environments, grows vigorously, and tolerates adversity because it uses an especially efficient type of photosynthesis to convert the raw materials of soil, sunlight, and water into plant tissues. Known technically as the C4 carbon-fixation pathway, this process is used by only a few other fast growing plants, including sorghum, corn, and sugarcane. The major photosynthetic products initially formed in the C4 pathway are organic acids with four carbon atoms. (Most plants use the C3 pathway and produce organic acids with three carbon atoms.)

Amaranth is the only C4 crop yet found that is not a grass. The C4 pathway is especially efficient at high temperature, in bright sunlight, and under dry conditions. In comparison with C3 it uses light more efficiently and requires only half the water. For this reason amaranth is a promising resource for hot and dry regions. Drought and poor soils make the major cereal crops difficult to grow in those areas, but amaranth should make better use of such poor land and thereby help to feed the world's hungry.

As with any crop there are some production uncertainties. Problems being reported in the various research locations include the lygus bug (an insect that sucks nutrients out of the immature seeds), fast-growing weeds that overwhelm the slow-starting amaranth plants in the first few weeks, and strains of amaranth that produce seedheads so heavy that they flop over when a summer thunderstorm blows through. These should not be insurmountable difficulties.

Skeptics initially predicted that the tall plants and tiny seed would make machine harvesting impossible. But the Rodale group bred short plants and modified a combine to harvest amaranth. In 1980 a one-hectare amaranth field in Pennsylvania was combine-harvested. (One hectare equals 2.47 acres.) The machinery had to move slowly, and improvements are needed in technique, but it proved that mechanical harvesting is feasible. As a result farmers in the Middle West began slowly producing amaranth grain on a commercial scale in 1981.

Amaranth's rediscovery by a hungry world may have been just in time. The U.S. National Academy of Sciences selected amaranth as one of the 36 most underexploited tropical plants. Robin Saunders of the U.S. Department of Agriculture, predicted that it would become valuable as a commercial crop in the western United States as irrigation decreases due to the high cost of fueling the pumps. Thus, the height of amaranth's popularity may not have occurred during the reign of the Aztecs; it may be yet to come.

One should not, however, expect amaranth to be on the dinner table next week. It took the U.S. public and farmers a century to accept the soybean and many decades to accept sunflower and safflower. Nevertheless, within a few years the oldest grain of the Americas, the crop whose cultivation Cortés tried to crush four centuries ago, should have popped back to face the modern age. Amaranth, it seems, is a survivor.

SCARCITY AMIDST PLENTY: THE PROBLEM OF WATER

by John Opie

In recent years water supplies in many parts of the United States have been severely depleted, while other areas have more than enough. Providing adequate amounts of fresh water in the future poses a major challenge.

Several myths about water supplies need to be corrected by the facts. Myth: Large amounts of new water can be produced. Fact: Water can only be provided by precipitation as rain, snow, or hail, controlled by the climate. Myth: There are vast underground rivers and pools of water to be tapped. Fact: Water is stored only in the soil and in aquifers made of permeable layers of rock. Myth: Fresh water will soon be available from large-scale seeding of clouds, desalination of seawater, and even from polar icebergs.

Harald Sund

Fact: Such sources of water would be utilized only at unacceptably high costs or with less-than-acceptable certainty. Myth: Water is constantly self-purifying. Fact: Water cleans itself only in a limited way in fast-flowing streams. Once contaminated, most water resources remain contaminated indefinitely. Myth: Water supplies are quickly restored after depletion. Fact: While water is a renewable resource, the speed at which it is used is not always matched by the pace of renewal.

Water consumption on a grand scale is part of the American way of life. By 1981 urban and suburban dwellers, making up 90% of the population of the United States, were using approximately 160 gallons (one gallon = 3.79 liters) of water a day. This is almost triple the 60 gallons a person used in the typical urban home or electrified farm in 1955. In 1900, when most homes were without running water, the rate was only 10 gallons per day. Earlier, the American frontier homestead, like the peasant village in Europe or the prehistoric Middle Eastern settlement, consumed 3 to 5 gallons a person daily in order to sustain life, prepare food, and wash bodies and clothes. Even today most Americans would have few serious difficulties at the minimum comfort level of 5 gallons a day. The remaining 155 gallons are used for conveniences, including air conditioning, running water in the kitchen and bathroom, the flush toilet, and washing machines for clothing.

One of the historic but largely unheralded engineering triumphs since the Civil War—the water mains and sewers underlying the cities of the U.S.—made urban life healthier, more comfortable, and more convenient. Metropolitan water systems eradicated major epidemics of typhoid and dysentery. They also led to an unprecedented consumption of fresh water. Even more significant are the vast irrigation projects of the U.S. Southwest, intended to "make the desert bloom" and provide an abundance of food for the entire nation. Such projects account for more than 80% of the water consumed in the U.S. each year. Since the 1930s the obvious benefits of rural electrification have led to increased water use in agriculture and on farmsteads, severely straining limited well-water supplies.

This unprecedented water consumption also results from the demands of an industrialized society. Some 60,000 gallons of water are needed to make a ton of steel, 250 tons of water to make one ton of wood pulp, and as many as 1,000 tons per ton of coal in a steam power plant; 18 gallons of water are needed to refine a gallon of oil, and 10 more gallons to process a gallon of gasoline. Approximately 3,500 gallons of water are needed to provide the beef for a family dinner for four. Nine gallons are required to make a gallon of beer. In contrast, Europeans produce a gallon of beer with half the water. Recently, by conservation and recycling, a California brewery reduced its water consumption to one-third of its 1972 level.

European nations, including the Soviet Union, function on half the U.S. water consumption. In less developed countries per capita water consumption is about ten gallons a day, including personal, agricultural, and industrial use. On the average in 1975 Americans used about 1,900 gallons per person per day, out of about 3,100 gallons available. On this basis there was a surplus of 1,200 gallons a day for every person in the U.S. But between 1970 and 1975 U.S consumption rose at the rate of 2.3% a year, which would

JOHN OPIE is Professor of History and Editor of the Environmental Review at Duquesne University, Pittsburgh, Pennsylvania.

198

A paper mill in full production uses as much water per day as a city of 50,000.

swallow up that surplus before the next century. A realistic assessment of current water supplies and the increase in the consumption of those supplies cannot be computed, however, on the basis of averages. Water is not spread evenly in the U.S., nor are water problems distributed equally.

Supplies and demand

Geographically, the United States includes more than 20 major river drainage basins, such as the Colorado Basin, California's Central Valley, the Missouri River Valley, and the Columbia Basin. Most controversy over water supplies arises in the arid West, where water demands exceed supplies. The issues become more complex when water is transferred by pipelines or aqueducts from one basin to another, as from the Colorado to southern California. These river basins are formally organized into 21 Water Resource Regions (including Alaska, Hawaii, and Puerto Rico), the major hydrological units established by the U.S. Water Resources Council. In these regions water resources vary enormously, depending upon rainfall, river drainage patterns, surface reservoirs, and underground aquifers.

The significance of such water supplies, and the degree and kind of controversy, also depends upon competition for water between growing metropolitan populations, agricultural priorities, and industrial needs, as well as upon energy production requirements, recreational interests, and wilderness preservation. For example, a middle-sized 2,000-acre (810-hectare) irrigated farm in the West, or the day's production of a large paper mill, uses as much water daily as a city of 50,000. The major debates of the late 20th century will focus on losses of groundwater so enormous that it may become unavailable, and on contamination problems of water that may make it unusable.

To provide the beef for a dinner of four approximately 3,500 gallons of water are required.

199

Aqueduct carries water from the Owens Valley in the Sierra Nevada approximately 240 miles (385 kilometers) southwest to Los Angeles.

The key to understanding the water supplies and needs of the U.S. lies in the "hydrologic cycle," the means by which water is moved, stored, or renewed. Water reaches the Earth by precipitation; there is enough rain, hail, and snow each year to cover the entire U.S. 30 inches (75 centimeters) deep. Two-thirds of this precipitation is immediately returned to the atmosphere through evaporation or transpiration from plant life. Another large part is lost through runoff, water moving through streams and rivers into the oceans. Significant amounts of water are also kept in storage, on the surface in lakes and reservoirs, and in snow and ice. Underground storage is in aquifers or simply in soil moisture. Only about 16% of the annual precipitation is actually available for human consumption. But a large part of this supply can be reused time and again. Furthermore, water is a constantly renewable resource as the land is resupplied by rain and snow. Nevertheless, there are no other sources of water, and scientists cannot invent new supplies or alternatives; unlike synfuels, there is no such thing as "synwater."

Water supplies are not usually a problem in the humid eastern half of the United States, where rainfall far exceeds the minimum 25 to 30 inches (65 to 75 centimeters) required for successful farming. East of the 98th meridian, which divides the nation into almost equal east-west halves, water is usually abundant for urban populations and industrial centers.

One of the most remarkable examples of water use in the East is New York City's water system. Some 6,100 miles (9,800 kilometers) of pipeline service 800,000 buildings. Farsighted city policy in the late 19th century gave New York City major upstate water rights. By the early 1980s approximately 1.5 billion gallons were carried daily to the city from as far as 125 miles (200 kilometers) away. The adequacy of this supply was severely challenged in the drought of the mid-1960s. Today the city's 18 reservoirs and 4 man-made lakes provide a "safe-yield" capacity of 1,290,000,000 gallons a day. But New York City by 1982 was consuming 1.5 billion gallons daily, a per capita consumption of 190 gallons. During the deep 1981 drought conservation measures lowered consumption to 1.3 billion gallons (160 gallons a day per person), which allowed the city to cope with temporary scarcity.

Based on rainfall patterns of the past 100 years New York City now has sufficient resources even for occasional short-term droughts, which are predicted to occur every 15 years or so. But longer droughts could cause debilitating shortages. Such problems could be alleviated, at considerable cost, by reducing the 8–15% leakage in New York. Boston's leakage, by comparison, soars as high as 25%. The safe-yield cushion could be raised by building more reservoirs, by developing interconnecting water system "grids" (as in New Jersey), and by more intensive conservation. In the Northeast, thus, the issue is less one of scarcity of water than it is of its efficient management.

The problems of the dry West can be seen most vividly in southern California. The rapid population growth during the last 25 years in that area created the same water demands as in the northeastern cities but with different results. Los Angeles had already overshot its local water supplies early in the century, when its population exceeded 200,000. The city's search

200

for water is as representative for an arid geography as is New York City's experience in a humid zone.

Los Angeles turned for water to the Owens Valley, some 240 miles (385 kilometers) to the northeast in the Sierra Nevada. The city began acquiring water rights in the valley as early as 1904 and built an aqueduct into it in 1913. Owens Valley farmers began complaining about worsening local water supplies in the 1920s; the lack of response to their complaints led to aqueduct bombings. Los Angeles's grip on water in the valley extended north to the Mono Lake basin in the 1940s. And in 1970 a second aqueduct began to deplete the valley's groundwater seriously, leading to a bitter local reaction, the risk of more violence, and statewide and national attention to the issues. By 1982 more than 60% of Los Angeles's water was supplied by Owens Valley. But valley residents, despite the city's legal entitlements, claimed a moral right to set limits on this water outflow since it had significantly lowered the water table, driven up water rates, devastated the local economy, and affected environmental quality, including drying up historic and scenic Lake Mono, north of Owens Valley and 350 miles (565 kilometers) from Los Angeles.

Los Angeles's needs also determined the controversial and innovative Colorado River Compact of 1922, which guaranteed the city a specified amount of Colorado River water from 450 miles (725 kilometers) away, to be piped and raised at ever higher energy costs over mountains. Southern California's water troubles will be more complicated in the near future. It

Pumping station (above left) and trough through the desert (above) are parts of the Central Arizona Project, designed to carry water from the Colorado River to Phoenix and Tucson.

201

Prolonged lack of rain in the 1930s created the Dust Bowl in the plains states of the U.S., resulting in financial ruin for many farmers and the abandonment of much land.

has been able in the past to draw substantially more water than it was entitled to from the Colorado. But the Central Arizona Project, intended to carry water to the parched cities of Tucson and Phoenix, will consume all of Arizona's previously unused allotment. Furthermore, the allotments were designated during the Colorado River's highest historic flow, hardly matched since. By the year 2000 the upper basin states, Colorado and Utah, will increase their own consumption to 84% of the river's average flow. Already commitments cannot be fulfilled in dry years.

Thus, water previously available to southern California will simply not exist, with the potential for serious scarcities, legal entanglements, policy confusion, and a major regional "water war." Arguments have been made that the U.S. could be "balkanized" by bitter and intense conflicts over this basic commodity. "Free trade" regions could include the Southwest and High Plains country, while "protectionist" zones would include most of the East, the Rocky Mountains, and the Pacific Northwest.

Agriculture and aquifers

Major agricultural regions in the western United States depend upon historically scarce water supplies. Only parts of the Pacific Northwest and northern California have a surplus of water. When early pioneer explorers and settlers crossed the Mississippi River and entered the High Plains just before the Civil War, they recognized that the climate changed at mid-continent from humid to dry. The High Plains were quickly labeled "The Great American Desert." At this point historic settlement leapfrogged across these

202

plains to the West Coast. The arid region was left unsettled for more than 40 years, until an unusual decade of heavy rains in the 1880s drew settlers there. Temporary moisture created a mistaken impression of the essentially arid region. Dry times returned. Settlers were left stranded and tried to exist with less water. One result was the Dust Bowl of the 1930s.

Farmers quickly learned that the region was an unworkable desert if they depended upon rainfall alone for water. One of the unacknowledged turning points in U.S. history was the discovery of a vast body of rockbound water lying under the High Plains of Nebraska, western Kansas, eastern Colorado, Oklahoma, northeastern New Mexico, and upper west Texas. The great 165,000-square-mile (430,000-square-kilometer) Ogallala aquifer, three times the size of New York state, contained a water supply equivalent to Lake Ontario. The aquifer was easily tapped by hundreds and then thousands of artesian wells, where water pressure alone created water "gushers." Windmills also changed the landscape, and in the 20th century the aquifer was pumped electrically. The result was the most intensive, widespread, and efficient production of grains and corn in history, which led to the unprecedented food surpluses after World War II. The U.S. became a leading food exporter, the potential rescuer of impoverished or drought-stricken nations. Center-pivot irrigation, which decorates the High Plains in rows of circles in squares when seen from the air, resulted in the rise in feed-grain production from 129 million bushels in 1954 to 386 million in 1973.

But the Ogallala aquifer, for all its abundance, is vulnerable to depletion. Water levels are decreasing, pumping costs are rising, and water quality is declining. In the High Plains Kansas is the state most dependent upon groundwater, drawing more than 80% of its annual use from the Ogallala and other aquifers. Aquifer levels declined more than 100 feet (30 meters) in the 150 square miles (390 square kilometers) of Scott County, Kansas, between 1940 and 1975. In Chase County, Nebraska, the flow of water from wells declined 30% between 1967 and 1975; by the year 2000 water from Chase County's wells may be only 10% of 1975 production. Replenishment of the aquifer through recharging by rain and flooding is unlikely, since, at best, recovery would be only a few inches a year at a time when the water levels of the Ogallala are falling two to five feet (a half to one and a half meters) a year. Predictions of usable supplies from the aquifer range from 50 more years to 10 more years. Largely because of the loss of water, the High Plains economy in the next generation will almost certainly be very different from that of 1983.

Nothing puts as much strain on water supplies as does farming, because the water is not reusable as it is in personal and industrial use. With poor planning, inefficient management, and simple bad luck because of a series of extended droughts, extreme water scarcity in selected food supply regions could trigger a national emergency. The Central Valley of California, once a barren region, by 1960 supplied 80% of the nation's grapes, one-third of its fruit, and one-quarter of its vegetables. But such concentrations, no matter how efficient, make national resources vulnerable. For more than half a century the availability of inexpensive water for irrigating the Central Valley has profoundly influenced nationwide eating habits. Cheap water was made

The Ogallala aquifer is a vast body of rockbound water lying under some 165,000 square miles (430,000 square kilometers) of the High Plains. Tapped by thousands of artesian wells since the 19th century, the aquifer has been used to irrigate the plains. This has resulted in large agricultural production gains for the region, but it has also depleted the aquifer. Between 1940 and 1975 aquifer levels declined more than 100 feet (30 meters) in the 150 square miles (390 square kilometers) of Scott County, Kansas.

203

Grant Heilman

Center-pivot irrigation, made possible by tapping the water in the Ogallala aquifer, resulted in a tripling of feed-grain production in the High Plains after 1954. Sprinklers are mounted on long lateral arms that sweep across the fields in circular patterns.

possible by the 1902 Land Reclamation Act, which guaranteed irrigation subsidies, often at one-tenth of real costs.

Over the ensuing years the Central Valley experienced an entire agricultural system, economic structure, and consumption pattern based on irrigation subsidies. The result is contradictory: on the one hand, irrigation led to the desirable development of large-scale, multiple-crop, intensive food production; on the other hand, it created widespread dependence upon a deceptively cheap and artificially supported water supply. The result is that as demand increases water tables are declining and water costs are rising. Existing conditions in the Sacramento Valley and the San Joaquin Valley can only be stabilized by further human intervention, including controversial and expensive massive water imports from as far north as Canada or the Columbia Basin.

Adapting to shortages

Americans cannot expect more water in the future, but less. In the past farmers learned how to cope with drought following the disastrous Dust Bowl experience of the 1930s, but not until 500,000 inhabitants had fled the plains. The farmers learned to compensate at least partially for less water by adopting new farming techniques, growing new crops, and externally capitalizing "agribusiness." For these reasons the negative impacts of the "Little Dust Bowl" of 1952–56 and of the droughts of the mid-1970s and of 1981 were significantly reduced. Adaptation to changing circumstances is again occurring. As water disappears and costs rise, farmers in western Texas

204

have already returned to the less productive "drylands" farming that had been commonplace at the turn of the century. Also, plant geneticists are working to develop less water-intensive crops, including a new strain of corn announced in late 1981.

In the long run less rainfall might also result from the human-induced "greenhouse effect" of increased carbon dioxide in the upper atmosphere, caused by intensive burning of coal. At worst, computer-run predictions of a 3° C (5° F) rise in global temperatures by the year 2020 would make the High Plains into a rainfall-free desert and move wheat and corn production into Canada. The result of the greenhouse effect would be a severe decline in U.S. water supplies, with virtually no opportunity to restore the Ogallala aquifer or allow alternative means of production. Some climatologists also argue for a continued global warming trend based on the end of the most recent ice age. Such gradual warming, and the global "desertification" tied to it, would further reduce national water resources. Such long-term speculation aside, many experts have accepted "drought cycles" of 20 to 22 years as the basis for planning and development in the High Plains.

Western water demands also escalate with new water-intensive and strategically important oil shale and synthetic fuel technologies. The debate over their water consumption in arid regions such as western Colorado, where so much competition for water already exists, has become the source of new conflicts. As of 1982 in the Southwest, the Mountain states, and the High Plains there was not enough water to encourage population growth, expand agricultural production, and develop energy resources simultaneously. The major source of water in these areas is the Colorado River; its water services ten million people and irrigates farms that supply 15% of the nation's crops. Yet the Colorado has only about one-fifth the flow of the Columbia, half the flow of the Missouri, and less than either the Arkansas or Red rivers.

Conservation and transportation

The inevitable scarcity of water in the future will severely test U.S. ingenuity. Less water in the western food-producing regions could challenge the greatest success story in American history—food abundance. In addition, a lack of water in the southwestern Sunbelt could effectively restrict population movement and deny the classic American "birthright" to personal geographical mobility.

Technological or scientific "fixes" are not likely to increase the supply of water enough to solve major shortages. These shortages will grow in the future. Important contributions, however, can be made to reduce water losses by reforestation of water-holding regions and by genetic research into less water-consuming crops. There can be a 15–25% reduction in High Plains consumption by "irrigation scheduling." More storage reservoirs on the scale of those on the Colorado, the Missouri, and in the Tennessee Valley could be built, but increased losses through evaporation would reduce their value. Attempts to increase local water supplies still center on cloud-seeding, which has not fulfilled its promise, and on costly desalination techniques, which would be cost-effective only if water prices multiplied significantly.

Among the most controversial solutions are major water transporting

Grapes are harvested in the Central Valley of California. Once a barren region, the valley has been extensively irrigated and by 1960 supplied 80% of the grapes for the U.S. as well as many other fruits and vegetables. Water tables in the region are declining, however, and water imports from as far north as Canada may become necessary.

205

Farmers in western Texas are returning to "dry farming" as water supplies in the area diminish and costs rise. Dry farming consists of making the best use of a limited water supply by storing as much moisture in the soil as possible and by choosing crops (such as sorghum) and growing methods that make the best possible use of the existing moisture.

projects, including the relatively modest "Texas Water Plan" to pipe water from the Mississippi River to western Texas and New Mexico. The larger "R. W. Beck Plan" would divert water from the upper Missouri, reverse the course of the Niobrara River for 200 miles (320 kilometers) in northern Nebraska, and send water down the middle of the High Plains as far south as New Mexico. Largest of all is the overwhelmingly massive North American Water and Power Alliance, which would use major mountain valleys as well as canals and aqueducts to move water from Canada's Yukon into most of the American West. Ranging in cost from the tens of billions to the hundreds of billions of dollars, these projects would be the greatest ever attempted by the U.S. They have been sidetracked in recent years, however, by rising energy costs. Because water is so heavy, one gallon weighing 8.34 pounds (3.79 kilograms), considerable energy is required to lift and move it.

Increased water costs are certain by the end of the 1980s. Already in northern Texas the cost of pumping water has forced farmers into dry farming; soon the same effect will be felt in Kansas and Nebraska. In California and Arizona the extension of existing aqueducts, the development of new pipeline systems, and desalination could cost more than local economies could absorb. Yet the pressures are extremely strong to guarantee agricultural and population growth. Eastern metropolitan water systems, from Cleveland and Pittsburgh to Philadelphia, New York City, and Boston, are old and creaky and will demand investments reaching into the hundreds of billions of dollars before the year 2000. A ten-year project to replace water mains in Manhattan alone is estimated at $90.5 billion. Waste and breakdowns are already endemic in these neglected public services.

Ultimately, rising water costs may be the most effective inducement to conservation. But the result could change the way Americans produce goods, feed themselves, and live their daily lives. The water-intensive society of the U.S. could be transformed into a water-conserving society, but only with significant changes in quantity and quality. Even cost figures lead to compli-

206

cated decisions. For example, water use for recreation could return five times more profit than it can for food production, but agricultural production must be maintained. Historically in the United States water has not been associated with the marketplace. "Water futures" are not sold on the commodities market. Water has been cheap, often offered through public subsidies at less than the cost of production and delivery. However, such cheap water has encouraged waste and inefficiency, and basic changes in how water is priced and marketed can be anticipated.

Americans must now, somewhat belatedly, regard their water supplies with concern. The problem of how much water is available is intensified by high levels of waste, mismanagement, pollution, and government policies that may actually discourage conservation and encourage excesses rather than efficiency. Federal planning depends upon coordinated efforts by the U.S. Department of Agriculture, the U.S. Department of the Interior, the Council on Environmental Quality, and the Water Resources Council. State and regional bodies are badly fragmented or virtually nonexistent. Important early steps toward consolidation have been taken with the operations of the Colorado River Compact, California state water agencies, and the Kansas groundwater management districts. But more typical are the 47 independent water districts of Nassau County, on Long Island (New York), adjoined by the 110 similar agencies in Suffolk County; their numbers make it impossible to develop a common policy to protect their common aquifer from severe chemical pollution. There are more than 600 independent water supply companies in New Jersey, making it difficult to act upon serious pollution and supply problems in that state.

The pollution problem

The quantity of fresh water is also controlled by its quality. Water can be naturally contaminated by harmful bacteria, poisons, and sediments. Groundwater is often preferable to surface water because of its purity. Yet

Desalination plants have been built on or near seacoasts in many parts of the world. They are expensive to operate, however, and will be cost-effective only if water prices increase considerably.

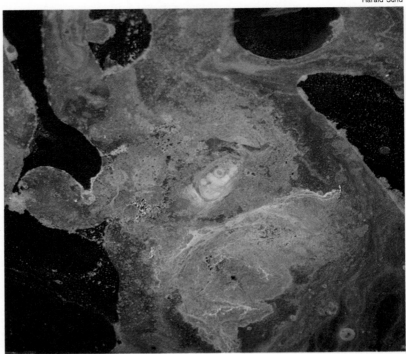

Water pollution is severe in the Duwamish River near Seattle, Washington. The river is lined with logging, shipbuilding, and cement plants. Industrial pollution significantly decreases the supply of usable fresh water.

between 1979 and 1981 more than 600 wells were closed in the New York City area because of chemical contamination of groundwater reservoirs. By 1982 major areas of Long Island were threatened with chemical contamination of their only water sources; $1.5 million were spent in Suffolk County alone to replace polluted wells. Groundwater contamination is particularly difficult to control or correct.

An even greater problem is the increased human and industrial pollution of previously fresh water. This is especially true of surface water in rivers and lakes, which tends to be used and reused many times. Natural cleansing processes cannot eliminate all wastes, particularly the tens of thousands of synthetic chemical compounds, many of which are toxic and not biodegradable. Improved techniques for detection and treatment to remove such hazards are expensive. Even so industrial and municipal pollution is coming under increasing control, but agricultural (pesticides) and urban (salt) run-off are becoming major sources of contamination.

Water contamination results from many sources. These include natural salinity and the effects of saltwater intrusion as freshwater tables decline along coastlines. Wastes that consume oxygen threaten fish and plants, but an even greater problem exists with excessive nitrogen and phosphorus concentrates which stimulate too much plant growth (eutrophication) and clog rivers and lakes. Acid rain, a result of industrial air pollution, also contributes significantly to water contamination.

The most serious attention has been given to persistent industrial chemicals such as PCB (polychlorinated biphenyl) and heavy metals such as mercury. These accumulate in ever increasing doses in the flesh of fish and shellfish, creating a significant public health hazard. Although the detection

of such hazards has become more sophisticated, the more than 30,000 chemical compounds in use today, increasing at the rate of about 1,000 a year, has made their monitoring and treatment a major problem. Water quality in significant parts of the Great Lakes and in many of the states is degraded by PCBs, pesticides, and other industrial chemicals.

Future prospects

The U.S. is not running out of water, but it will become dramatically more expensive. This will increase water reuse and encourage conservation. Moving water long distances will remain a last resort, largely due to high costs. Water will also be saved through the expensive but effective repair and proper maintenance of existing water distribution systems. Costs will also increase as chemically contaminated water is more intensively purified.

Other factors affecting water supplies will be population growth and migration, patterns of agricultural and industrial development, and water-use technologies. The nation will be challenged to resolve and reconcile vastly different and contradictory water laws and institutions in order to encourage economically efficient water allocation and management. Yet, despite best intentions some regions of the U.S. will continue to experience severe water shortages. Whether these are debilitating may well depend upon natural forces, particularly long-term drought. The future is filled with uncertainty, as was the past. The task of modern society is to reduce the potential harm.

Rising costs may eventually be the most effective inducement to conserve water in the U.S. Such conservation could change the ways Americans work and play.

209

THE PHANTOM

NEUTRINO

BY JAMES S. TREFIL

FROM THE *NUCLEAR HEARTS* OF THE *UNIVERSE* THEY CAME...

THEY SEEMED TO WEIGH *NOTHING* AND TO MOVE AT *LIGHT SPEED*...

IRON *METEORS*, GIANT *PLANETS*, EVEN THE BURNED-OUT *CORES* OF DEAD *STARS* COULD NOT *STOP* THEM...

VILLANI & CEGIELSKI

JAMES S. TREFIL, a particle physicist, is Professor of Physics at the University of Virginia, Charlottesville.

(Overleaf) Illustration by Ron Villani; script by Charles Cegielski

There are few things in the array of elementary particles that excite more curiosity than the neutrino. It seems to have no mass, so scientists cannot weigh it. It has no electric charge, so they cannot detect it easily. It shuns interaction with more familiar types of matter: indeed, a typical neutrino could travel through a rod of solid lead stretching from the Earth to the nearest star without leaving a single disturbed atom in its wake. Yet this particle, mysterious as it is, plays a central role in mankind's understanding of nature, and if some current ideas are right, it may be the ultimate arbiter of the fate of the universe.

The search for simplicity

The idea of an "elementary particle" is an old one in science. At any point in history someone trying to understand the nature of the physical world is confronted with a bewildering complexity. Whether this be a complexity of ordinary materials (as it was for the Greeks), of atoms corresponding to different chemical elements (as it was in the 19th century), or of particles that constitute those atoms (as it is today), the natural tendency of the human mind is to try to reduce the complexity by postulating some sort of underlying simplicity. For example, in the 5th century BC the Greek philosopher Empedocles taught that, although there are many substances in the world, they are all different mixtures of four basic elements—earth, fire, air, and water. In a similar vein, 19th-century chemists recognized that the large numbers of chemical compounds that they were analyzing were nothing more than different combinations of about a hundred different chemical elements. By the early 20th century, then, this sort of scheme, which philosophers call reductionism, was firmly entrenched in the minds of most scientists.

The period around the turn of the century was a particularly important one for elementary particles. In 1897 British physicist J. J. Thomson discovered the electron, a particle of small mass and a negative electric charge whose motions are perceived as electric current. In 1919, New Zealander Ernest Rutherford, working at the University of Cambridge in England, identified the proton, the heavy, positively charged particle that counterbalances the electron in the atom. The picture of the atom that emerged from this work is quite familiar in modern folklore. The atom consists of a heavy, positively charged nucleus around which the lighter, negatively charged electrons circle in orbits, much as the planets circle the Sun in the solar system. For all practical purposes, all of the mass of the atom is concentrated in the nucleus.

The one problem with this picture was that for chemical elements heavier than hydrogen, the mass of the atom was roughly twice as much as the combined masses of the protons in the nucleus. This led Rutherford to postulate that there must be a third, as yet undiscovered particle in nature, a particle roughly as heavy as the proton but without the proton's electric charge. This particle he called the neutron, a name suggested by its electrical neutrality. With the inclusion of the neutron, the reductionist strategy once more had succeeded brilliantly. Instead of a hundred different "elementary" atoms, one for each chemical element, only three particles were truly worthy

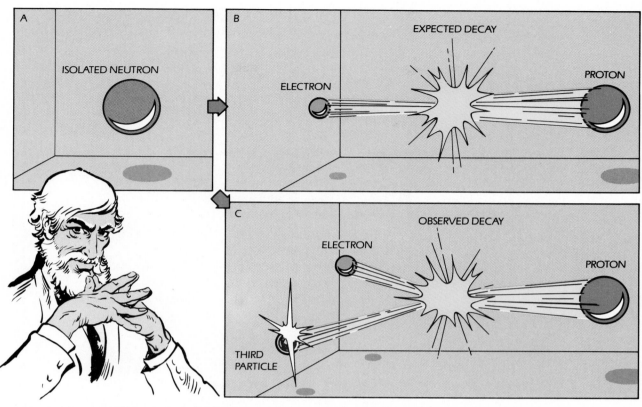

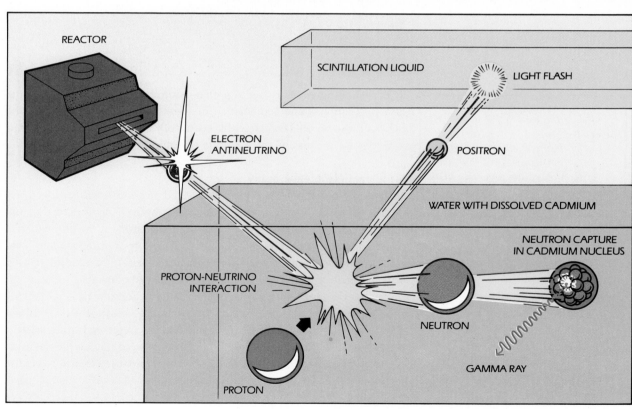

First, tentative observations of the neutrino were made in 1953 by Reines (left) and Cowan (right) at the Hanford nuclear reactor in Washington state. Their later experiment at the Savannah River reactor proved to be the definitive one.

of the name "elementary"—the proton, neutron, and electron. Everything else was simply some combination of these three. The discovery of the neutron, which would complete this beautifully simple picture, was awaited with great eagerness by the scientific community.

New particle please apply

In 1932 the neutron, with all of the expected properties, was seen in a laboratory study by British physicist James Chadwick. This discovery should have been the icing on the reductionist cake; the quest for the ultimate simplicity in nature should have been over. Fortunately or unfortunately —depending on one's point of view—this was not the case. Further study showed that the neutron had a spectacular property: it was unstable.

This fact meant that when experimentalists tracked a neutron moving through space by itself, they found that the particle disintegrated inside of a few minutes. In its place they were able to detect a proton and an electron. In the language of particle physics, the neutron decayed into a proton and an electron. In point of fact, all of the particles that have been discovered in the last several decades are unstable in this sense; they all decay into other particles if left to themselves. (*See* top diagram on page 213.)

214

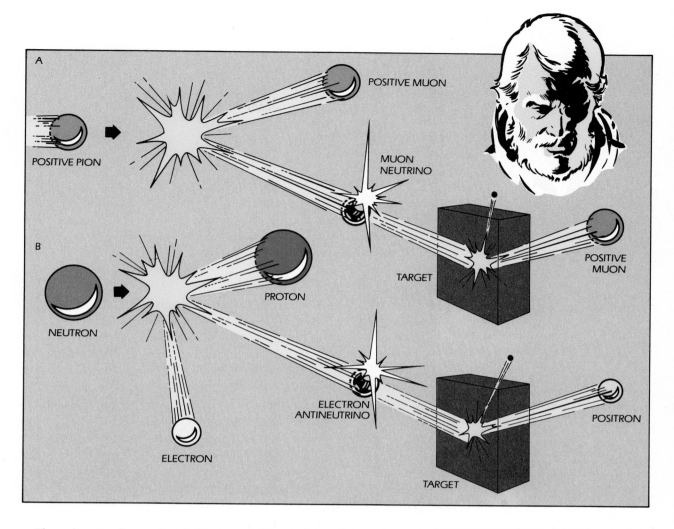

A

POSITIVE PION

POSITIVE MUON

MUON
NEUTRINO

TARGET

POSITIVE
MUON

B

NEUTRON

PROTON

ELECTRON

ELECTRON
ANTINEUTRINO

TARGET

POSITRON

The radioactive decay of nuclei in atoms had been observed since the time of Marie Curie, so in a sense the decay of the neutron was nothing new. Nevertheless, the fact that an "elementary" particle was unstable tended to focus scientific attention on the decay process. For some time scientists had been having problems understanding the decay of both nuclei and particles, problems that can be outlined most easily in terms of the neutron.

Think of a neutron sitting stationary for a few minutes in empty space. Suppose that when it decays, the proton comes away moving directly to the right. Intuition prompts one to expect the electron to be found moving directly to the left, just to keep things balanced. This intuition is actually a special case of the law of conservation of momentum. The law states that in isolated systems the total momentum has to remain constant. Because momentum is defined to be the mass of an object times its velocity, and because the original neutron in the example is stationary (*i.e.*, has no velocity), the total momentum of the system is zero. According to the law, the system must then remain zero for all time, so that if the proton moves to the right with some momentum, then the electron had better move to the left just fast enough to cancel the momentum of the proton and keep the total momentum at zero.

Diagrams illustrate the way in which experimental distinctions can be made between neutrinos that have been formed in conjunction with different kinds of particles. For example, when neutrinos and muons are produced together, such as happens in the decay of pions (A), the neutrinos are capable of creating muons when they are directed against a matter target. By contrast, when neutrinos are produced together with electrons in neutron decay (B) and then are directed against a target, they can create electrons (specifically positrons). Such observations led to the realization that there exist more than one kind of neutrino.

FERMILAB MAIN RING

Production of a neutrino beam at the Fermi National Accelerator Laboratory begins with the extraction of a beam of protons from the main ring of the laboratory's proton synchrotron. Extracted protons interact with a metal target to produce pions and kaons, which decay primarily into muons and neutrinos (including antineutrinos). A long earthen bank filters out the muons, leaving only pure neutrinos. Various targets and detectors can be located in the path of the beam for the conduct of experiments.

The momentum law is one of the great cornerstones of classical physics and is used in explaining all manner of phenomena from planetary orbits to the trajectories of artillery shells. It would certainly be surprising if the law did not hold in the decay of the neutron. Yet when a neutron decays in the laboratory, scientists find that when the proton moves to the right the electron does not move exactly toward the left, but in a slightly different direction. If the proton and electron are the only particles involved in neutron decay, the law of momentum conservation is clearly violated.

This possibility was so repugnant to the scientific mind that no one was willing to accept it. A great deal of high-powered thought went into finding a way out of the dilemma, and in 1931 Austrian physicist Wolfgang Pauli found a way. Suppose, he suggested, that there was a third, as yet undetected particle involved in the decay process. If this were the case, then this particle would make up the momentum deficit and everything would work out

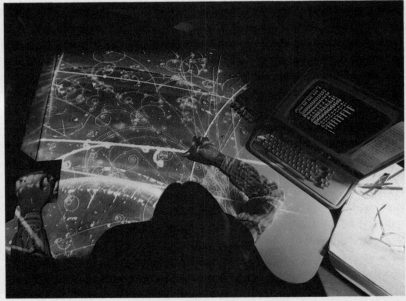

Fermilab worker examines particle tracks photographically recorded from a bubble chamber located in the path of a neutrino beam. Although neutrinos do not produce tracks, their rare interactions with matter in the chamber create showers of particles that leave distinctive calling cards in the chamber liquid.

Dan McCoy—Rainbow

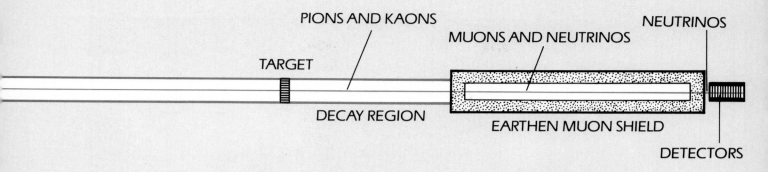

PIONS AND KAONS

NEUTRINOS

MUONS AND NEUTRINOS

TARGET

DECAY REGION

EARTHEN MUON SHIELD

DETECTORS

properly. If there were such a particle, an unstable neutron and the momentum law could coexist.

If this hypothetical particle carried an electric charge, it would be seen in the experimental apparatus in pretty much the same way that the proton and electron are seen. Consequently, the particle must have zero electric charge. In view of this fact, physicists in the early 1930s labeled this particle the neutrino ("little neutral one"). Further work indicated that the mass of the neutrino was probably zero (or close to it) and that the particle traveled through space at the speed of light.

The neutrino, then, came into physics in a rather different way than other particles. The proton and electron were seen in the laboratory before they became important in theory. The neutrino, on the other hand, was a vital element in understanding elementary particles from the moment it was first conceived, and yet it was a full quarter century before anyone was able to detect one in an experiment. During this period physicists simply had to take the existence of the particle on faith.

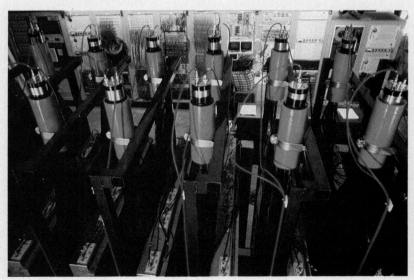

Dan McCoy—Black Star

Portion of a long array of light-detecting photomultiplier tubes stands ready at Fermilab for studying the interaction of a beam of high-energy neutrinos with atomic electrons.

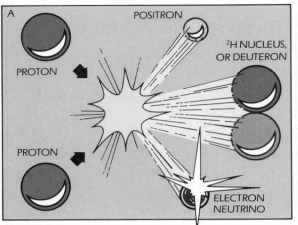

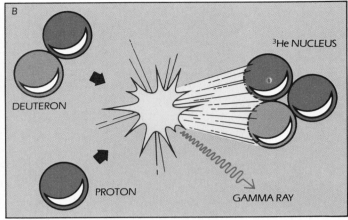

A

POSITRON

PROTON

²H NUCLEUS, OR DEUTERON

PROTON

ELECTRON NEUTRINO

B

³He NUCLEUS

DEUTERON

PROTON

GAMMA RAY

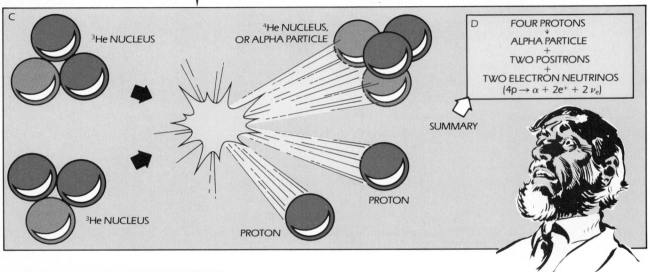

C

³He NUCLEUS

⁴He NUCLEUS, OR ALPHA PARTICLE

³He NUCLEUS

PROTON

PROTON

D

FOUR PROTONS
↓
ALPHA PARTICLE
+
TWO POSITRONS
+
TWO ELECTRON NEUTRINOS
$(4p \rightarrow \alpha + 2e^+ + 2\nu_e)$

SUMMARY

number	reaction
1	$p + p \rightarrow {}^2H + e^+ + \nu$
	or
2	$p + e^- + p \rightarrow {}^2H + \nu$
3	${}^2H + p \rightarrow {}^3He + \gamma$
4	${}^3He + {}^3He \rightarrow {}^4He + 2p$
	or
5	${}^3He + {}^4He \rightarrow {}^7Be + \gamma$
6	${}^7Be + e^- \rightarrow {}^7Li + \nu$
7	${}^7Li + p \rightarrow 2\,{}^4He$
	or
8	${}^7Be + p \rightarrow {}^8B + \gamma$
9	${}^8B \rightarrow {}^8Be^* + e^+ + \nu$
10	${}^8Be^* \rightarrow 2\,{}^4He$

Ghost hunting

The reason that it took so long to confirm the existence of the neutrino is intimately connected to the reason that it was not seen in the decay of the neutron. The neutrino happens to be a particle that does not interact readily with matter. When scientists detect a particle like the proton or electron, what they actually do is detect the effect that it has on matter through which it passes. For example, if a proton moves through some material it will exert a force on atomic electrons because it has an electric charge. Occasionally these atomic electrons will be torn from their atoms. What is actually observed, then, is a trail of disrupted atoms in the wake of the proton, and not the proton itself. Similarly, neutrons can be detected by observing their collisions with atoms in a material.

For the neutrino, however, such collisions are exceedingly rare. If one imagined a typical neutrino traveling through a dense substance like lead, about 3,500 years would pass before it interacted with a single atom. Obviously, detecting the presence of a neutrino is not a simple job.

If a single neutrino in a detector has a very small chance of interacting with anything, one way to proceed is to flood the detector with neutrinos.

218

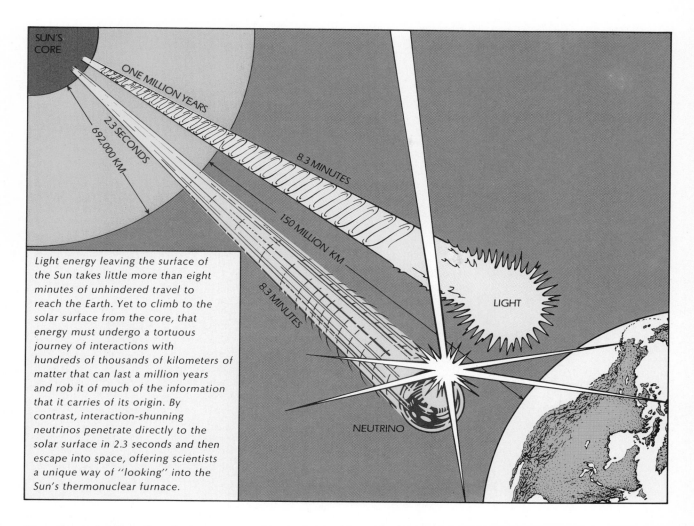

SUN'S CORE

ONE MILLION YEARS

2.3 SECONDS

692,000 KM

8.3 MINUTES

150 MILLION KM

8.3 MINUTES

LIGHT

NEUTRINO

Light energy leaving the surface of the Sun takes little more than eight minutes of unhindered travel to reach the Earth. Yet to climb to the solar surface from the core, that energy must undergo a tortuous journey of interactions with hundreds of thousands of kilometers of matter that can last a million years and rob it of much of the information that it carries of its origin. By contrast, interaction-shunning neutrinos penetrate directly to the solar surface in 2.3 seconds and then escape into space, offering scientists a unique way of "looking" into the Sun's thermonuclear furnace.

Since the probability of producing an interaction is obtained by multiplying the very small chance that any given neutrino will interact with an atom by the total number of neutrinos passing through, it is clear that boosting the number of neutrinos high enough will give a rate of interaction that is measured in minutes or hours rather than in millennia. This was the basis of the strategy used by U.S. physicists Clyde Cowan, Jr., and Frederick Reines in 1956, when they finally detected the neutrino experimentally. (*See* bottom diagram on page 213.)

Their flood of neutrinos was produced by radioactive decay within the Savannah River nuclear reactor in South Carolina. Something like a billion neutrinos per second passed through the detector, but even with this many particles the experimenters saw the results of a neutrino-initiated interaction only about once every 20 minutes. It took five years of work before, for the first time, the faith of the previous generation of physicists in the existence of the neutrino could be justified with laboratory results.

The neutrino discussed thus far is always produced in nuclear reactions in conjunction with an electron. In the decay of the neutron, for example, a neutrino and electron are produced together, not just a neutrino by itself.

Basic thermonuclear process that is thought to power the Sun—the fusion of four protons to form a helium-4 nucleus, two positrons, and two electron neutrinos—is diagramed in several steps (A–C) on the facing page and summarized as an equation (D). The accompanying table lists these and other principal reactions believed to be taking place in the solar core.

Tank at the Homestake Gold Mine in South Dakota is 14.6 meters (48 feet) long and 6.1 meters (20 feet) in diameter and is filled with 380,000 liters (100,000 gallons) of tetrachloroethylene (C_2Cl_4). Its deep underground location shields it from cosmic rays and other particles except for the neutrinos that it was designed to detect.

For the reactions that took place in the Savannah River reactor, the same statement is true. Within a decade of the verification of the existence of this neutrino, however, another rather startling fact emerged from the laboratory. Even though the neutrino has no mass and no charge and is almost undetectable, there appear to be more than one type of neutrino in nature.

This discovery resulted from the fact that many of the elementary particles discovered between 1930 and 1960 have properties similar to those of the neutron in that they decay in such a way that the conservation of momentum would be violated if there were no neutrino. Many of these particles ultimately produce electrons and neutrinos as decay products, as the neutron does, but others produce another particle called the mu (μ) meson, or muon. This particle was discovered in 1936 and has a mass about 200 times that of the electron. The term meson ("intermediate one") was coined to describe particles whose mass was between that of the electron and the proton. The muon has the same electrical properties as the electron and, indeed, is identical to the electron in almost every way except for its mass.

220

Adapted from information supplied by Brookhaven National Laboratory

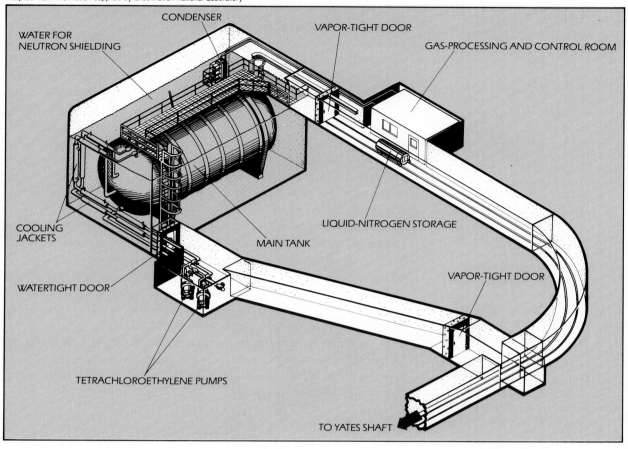

WATER FOR
NEUTRON SHIELDING

CONDENSER

VAPOR-TIGHT DOOR

GAS-PROCESSING AND CONTROL ROOM

COOLING
JACKETS

MAIN TANK

LIQUID-NITROGEN STORAGE

VAPOR-TIGHT DOOR

WATERTIGHT DOOR

TETRACHLOROETHYLENE PUMPS

TO YATES SHAFT

When particles decay such that the muon is included among the decay products, reasoning similar to that outlined for neutron decay told scientists that an unseen neutrino must be there as well. It was reasonable to ask whether the neutrino produced in these reactions is the same as the one produced in conjunction with the electron.

In 1962 Leon Lederman and co-workers performed an experiment at Brookhaven (New York) National Laboratory to answer this question. They directed neutrinos that had been produced in conjunction with muons against a target and looked at what was produced. They found that these neutrinos were capable of creating muons when they hit the target, but that no electrons were made. An exactly analogous result would have been seen had they used neutrinos made in conjunction with electrons. From this result they concluded that there are, in fact, two different kinds of neutrinos in nature. One is associated with the electron and the other with the muon. The electron neutrino cannot produce muons, and the muon neutrino cannot produce electrons. (Diagram is on page 215.)

This situation suggests strongly that if there exists another particle like the electron or muon, there also exists another kind of neutrino as well. This idea is now accepted by most particle physicists. In 1975 experimenters at Stanford University led by Martin Perl uncovered a third electronlike parti-

Schematic of Homestake neutrino detector locates the main tank, two pumps to purge the tetrachloroethylene of argon atoms with helium gas (see illustration and caption on page 222), a tank of liquid nitrogen for trapping the argon, and a gas-processing and control room. The Yates shaft leads to the surface 1,480 meters (4,850 feet) above.

221

cle, dubbed the tau (τ) meson, with a mass more than 3,000 times that of the electron. By 1981 the neutrino associated with this particle had not yet been seen, but everyone was confident that it would be some day. So, a quarter century after the first fleeting glimpse of the neutrino in the laboratory, knowledge of this ghostly particle has grown such that scientists can speak with some confidence of at least three different kinds of neutrinos in nature.

During the 1970s an entire new branch of physics was born. Called neutrino physics, this discipline uses the neutrino to probe the basic nature of matter. It may seem strange that, after spending 25 years trying to find a particle, physicists can now create and control this particle well enough to use it as a tool. The key to this new development is something already discussed above, the fact that many particles exist that decay into neutrinos. The general scheme, used at such particle laboratories as the Fermi National Accelerator near Chicago, is to create an intense, fast-moving beam of these particles. This beam is then directed down a long tube. During their flight the particles decay, leaving a beam of, for example, neutrinos and muons. In the next step, this decayed beam passes through a long pile of dirt. The muons interact with the matter in the pile and drop out of the beam. The neutrinos, however, pass through and emerge as a pure beam that can be used in experiments. (*See* diagram on pages 216–217.)

Currently neutrinos figure importantly in two major problems of science. One of these has to do with the nature of the reactions that keep the Sun burning, and the other relates to the amount of matter in the universe and, consequently, to its ultimate fate.

Too few for solar physics

Since the 1930s it has been known that the energy which keeps the Sun bright and, incidentally, supports all of the life on the Earth is generated by

Neutrino detection technique used in Raymond Davis's experiment depends on the capture of an energetic solar neutrino by a chlorine-37 nucleus in tetrachloroethylene, followed by emission of an electron and transformation of the chlorine nucleus to radioactive argon-37. In the capture process the ^{37}Ar receives enough energy to break free of its parent molecule and moves into the surrounding liquid. Periodically the accumulated argon is removed from the tank by purging with helium gas and then is trapped out of the helium gas stream with a liquid-nitrogen-cooled charcoal filter. The collected argon gas is removed from the trap, purified, and placed in a proportional counter, which tallies the radioactive decay of the gas. ^{37}Ar has a half-life of 35 days.

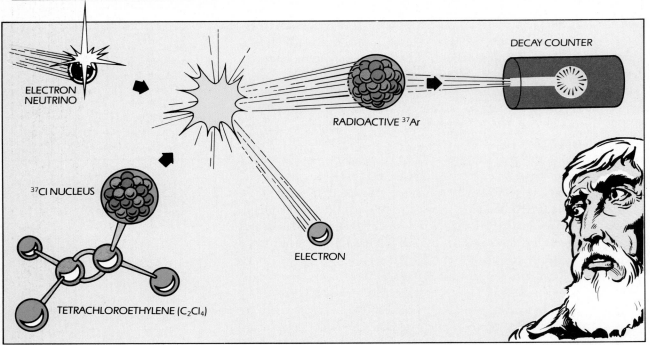

ELECTRON NEUTRINO

DECAY COUNTER

RADIOACTIVE ^{37}Ar

^{37}Cl NUCLEUS

ELECTRON

TETRACHLOROETHYLENE (C_2Cl_4)

nuclear reactions in the core of the Sun. "Known" has a rather special sense here, because no one has ever seen the core of the Sun. When astronomers look at the solar surface with a telescope, it is rather like looking into a murky pool of water. They can see into the Sun only 160 kilometers or so (about 100 miles), while the nuclear reactions are going on at the center, some 700,000 kilometers (400,000 miles) from the surface.

These nuclear reactions generate energy, of course, and this energy percolates its way to the surface of the Sun. Unfortunately, it takes about a million years to do so, so that the light which reaches the Earth now was generated well before the dawn of human civilization. Needless to say, this light retains very little information about the core. The reason is that, in the matter that makes up the Sun, light will travel an average of only a meter or two before it interacts with an atom. Energy coming from the core, then, resembles a running back in a football game trying to come through a swarm of tacklers rather than a sprinter moving straight to his destination.

In the early 1960s Raymond Davis, Jr., of Brookhaven National Laboratory began to wonder if it was possible to "see" directly into the nuclear reaction region. He knew that the theory which describes the activity in this region predicted that neutrinos—specifically electron neutrinos—are being emitted. Unlike the Sun's visible light, these neutrinos would not interact much with the matter in the Sun but would come right out. A solar neutrino arriving at the Earth would be less than ten minutes old. Davis reasoned that if he could detect these neutrinos, he would have a "telescope" capable of studying the heart of the Sun. (*See* illustrations on pages 218–219.)

The problem, of course, is to detect those electron neutrinos once they get to the Earth. For example, every moment billions of solar neutrinos pass through the body of each person on the Earth, yet so reluctant are they to interact with matter that only one atom in a person's body will be disturbed in ten years. To get around this problem, Davis used as an electron-neutrino detector a 380,000-liter (100,000-gallon) tank of the cleaning fluid tetrachloroethylene a mile underground at the Homestake Gold Mine near Lead, South Dakota. By going this deep he could be sure that practically nothing except neutrinos would get to his detector. On the average, less than one atom per day in a tank the size of ten railroad cars will be affected by neutrinos. The task of finding this atom is a prodigious one, but still possible. (Diagrams of the detector and experiment are on pages 221–222.)

When Davis first began running his experiment in the late 1960s, the results were startling. Solar neutrino abundance is customarily measured in terms of the solar neutrino unit, or SNU (pronounced "snew"). One SNU corresponds to about one atom every five days in the Davis apparatus. Conventional theories predicted about 20–30 SNU when Davis began his work, but he found almost none. More than a decade of work has since gone into this experiment, and it has been checked by almost every scientist with an interest in this field. The result still stands. There are only between one and two solar neutrino units coming from the Sun, and the best that theorists can do is bring their prediction down to about five. There is, in other words, a long-standing discrepancy of about a factor of three between the theory that is believed to describe the Sun's core and what is measured.

223

Many exotic ideas have been proposed to explain this result. One even suggests that a black hole at the center of the Sun is slowly gobbling up the interior. More solar neutrinos do not reach the Earth because the core is already gone, although the surface will remain bright for a million years while the last of the energy percolates out.

From the point of view of the neutrino, however, there is another proposal. Suppose that for some reason the electron neutrinos that leave the Sun do not remain electron neutrinos during the entire transit to the Earth but change spontaneously into other kinds of neutrinos. Suppose, in other words, that a beam of pure electron neutrinos oscillates, eventually converting itself into a beam that contains equal numbers of all types of neutrinos. This sort of oscillation is seen in other kinds of elementary particles—albeit only those with a mass that is not zero—so it is not an outrageous suggestion. In fact, it was proposed quite seriously by a group of Japanese physicists just a year after the discovery of the muon neutrino.

Such an oscillation indeed would explain the Davis experiment. Since three types of neutrinos are known, a beam of pure electron neutrinos starting from the Sun would wind up on Earth with only one-third of the original number of this type of neutrino. And because only electron neutrinos trigger Davis's detector, the discrepancy of a factor of three is readily explained. Lest this way out of the dilemma seem too encouraging, however, it should be pointed out that there are many other ways of explaining the discrepancy. These include such rather mundane possibilities as incorrect measurements of some of the nuclear reaction rates that go into the theoretical prediction. Nevertheless, the possibility of neutrino oscillations is a very real one at this time.

A small mass of evidence

As implied above, technical arguments can be used to show that such oscillations can occur only if the neutrino has some sort of mass. Heretofore, this discussion has been following the conventional wisdom and simply calling the neutrino "massless." But how well is it known that the mass of this particle is actually zero? How good are the experiments that provide this information?

From measurements of the decay of the neutron, the neutrino mass can be deduced by straightforward arguments. At present, it is a certainty that its mass is less than one ten-thousandth that of the electron, but there is lively scientific debate as to whether it is truly zero or just very small. Some important consequences would follow if the mass turned out to be something other than zero.

In 1980 two results bearing on this question were announced. Reines and co-workers at the University of California at Irvine, again working with neutrinos from the Savannah River reactor, reported that the number of electron neutrinos from the reactor was less than would be expected if there were no oscillations and hence concluded that the neutrino must have a mass less than the limit stated above. At the same time, Soviet physicist E. F. Tretyakov and colleagues, who were studying the nuclear decay of hydrogen-3 (tritium), announced an improved measurement of the neutrino mass,

Process studied by Reines and co-workers in investigations of neutrino oscillations involves the interaction of reactor-produced electron antineutrinos with hydrogen-2 (deuterium) nuclei in a container of heavy water. Theoretically this interaction has a fixed probability of proceeding along either of two routes: a charged-current reaction, in which the neutrino converts the nuclear proton to a neutron accompanied by the emission of a positron, and a neutral-current reaction, in which the neutrino simply splits the nucleus into its components. Reines's measurements of the comparative frequency of these two reactions indicated that fewer charged-current reactions were taking place than theory predicted. As an explanation he suggested that, over the travel distance from the reactor to the detector, some of the electron neutrinos transformed into muon neutrinos. Although the muon types could interact with deuterium nuclei by way of the neutral-current route, their energy was not high enough to let them take part in the charged-current reaction, which would have required them to produce muons, as opposed to much lighter positrons, in their interactions with protons in the deuterium.

which also turned out to be nonzero. These results, far from settling the issue, only served to stimulate further inquiry.

For a new fact to be widely accepted, it has to be checked by many different experimenters. In 1981 a collaboration of French, West German, and U.S. scientists, working with a reactor at Grenoble, France, but using a different approach, announced that their results were not consistent with those from Irvine. Other decay measurements also tend to cloud the acceptance of the Soviet result. Currently the experimental picture of the neutrino mass is uncertain. In fact, it has turned into one of the more interesting areas of physics, and there are at least a dozen experiments planned or in the works to find an answer. Debates, arguments, and contradictory results are a sure sign that a scientific field is alive and interesting.

Cosmological consequences

But supppose that the neutrino does turn out to be massive. Are there any reasons, other than a purely academic one, for anyone to be interested in the outcome of the debate?

It is generally well accepted that the universe had its origins in a "big bang" that occurred about 15 billion years ago. At that time all of the matter in the universe was contained in an unimaginably dense point, and the expansion of the universe that can be seen today is nothing more than the result of that first initial explosion. It is reasonable to ask whether this expansion will ever reverse itself (a "closed" universe) or whether the universe of today will simply thin out into oblivion (an "open" universe). The question has to do with the amount of matter in the universe. If there is enough matter, then the force of gravity eventually will overcome the outward

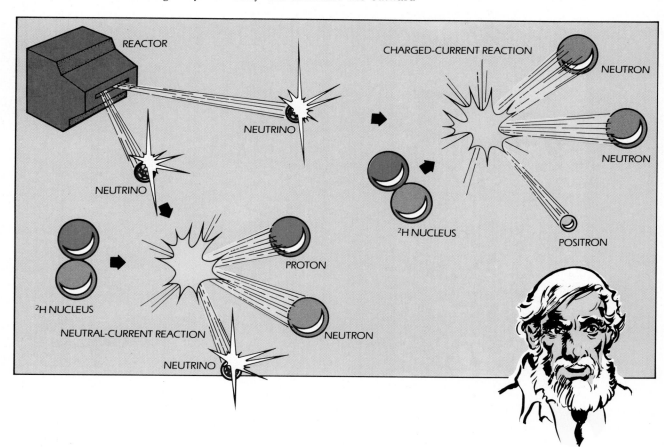

motion of the galaxies and pull them back toward the center, much as the Earth's gravity reverses the direction of a ball thrown into the air. If this were the case, the universe would be closed, and it is possible that the future contraction of the universe, the "big crunch," would lead to another concentration of matter and another big bang. In this picture, there would be no beginning and no end to the universe, just a series of cycles. (See *1980 Yearbook of Science and the Future* Feature Article: THE STRUCTURE OF THE UNIVERSE.)

If all of the visible matter in the universe—the stars, gas, and dust that astronomers can detect—is added up, the total is only about 10% of the critical amount needed to cause a reversal of the expansion. The search for the remainder has taken on an almost religious fervor among some members of the astronomical community who favor a closed universe, and the suggestion that the neutrino might have a mass was seized upon as a perfect solution to the problem. After all, there is no way one could detect a sea of massive neutrinos in the universe, since they would be spread around much more thinly than those coming from the Sun. By estimating the numbers of these neutrinos from calculations of the number of nuclear reactions that have taken place during and since the big bang—a figure believed to be several hundred per cubic centimeter—and then multiplying by the neutrino mass reported by the Irvine group, some astronomers have claimed that the mass needed to close the universe has been accounted for: 90% of the total mass of the universe is in neutrinos, and this mass will ultimately bring the universe back to its starting point.

Astronomers who opt for a closed universe find their idea of a cosmos filled with enormous quantities of unseen matter supported in work that is

Soviet physicists who presented evidence in 1980 for a tiny rest mass for the neutrino studied a traditional subject of neutrino research, the radioactive beta decay of the hydrogen-3 (tritium) nucleus. In this decay process a nuclear neutron spontaneously transforms into a proton, emitting an electron and an electron antineutrino. From records of the spectrum of energy and momentum of these electrons obtained from their capture in matter, a probable rest mass—or at least some limits to the mass—can be calculated.

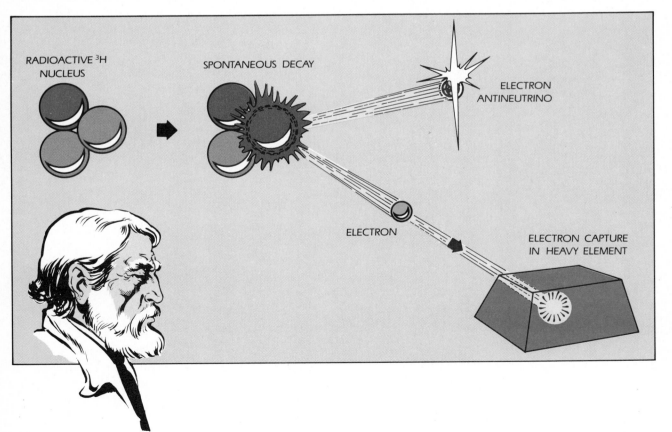

RADIOACTIVE ^{3}H NUCLEUS

SPONTANEOUS DECAY

ELECTRON ANTINEUTRINO

ELECTRON

ELECTRON CAPTURE IN HEAVY ELEMENT

trying to solve another astronomical puzzle—the "missing mass" problem. By observing such phenomena as the orbits of stars in individual galaxies and the motions of galaxies in clusters of galaxies, scientists can estimate the total mass that should be present in the universe to account for the gravitational dynamics they see. The problem is that this estimate far exceeds the amount of matter that actually can be detected. In fact, it is difficult to understand why clusters of galaxies simply do not fly apart given the amount of matter that can be found in them. Consequently some form of undetected matter—gas, dust, rock, dark stars, and even black holes—has been invoked to supply the missing mass, although it is not clear that the amount of extra mass postulated in these ways is really enough to close the universe. Neutrinos now offer yet another possible answer. Neutrinos with mass would not travel at the speed of light but would be slowed down by gravitational forces. Over billions of years neutrinos that have been produced since the big bang, which probably outnumber protons, neutrons, and electrons by billions to one, could have become bound in orbits around galaxies and clusters in the form of massive neutrino halos. Cumulatively their mass would contribute a powerful gravitational effect to the systems that captured them.

So, even though the neutrino is elusive, the ultimate fate of the universe seems to hinge on the question of whether or not it has a small mass. Even a mass of a few millionths of that of the electron would make the neutrino the dominant form of matter. The next few years should be interesting ones for the neutrino enthusiast.

Abell 1060 (above) and the cluster in the constellation Hercules (left) number among clusters of galaxies whose total observable mass falls far short—for example, by 80% for the Hercules cluster—of the amount needed to keep their component galaxies gravitationally bound. Some cosmologists have employed the concept of neutrinos with mass to postulate the existence of huge clouds of neutrinos held by gravity to these clusters, thus accounting for the "missing mass."

227

WHEN ADVERTISING TURNS TO SCIENCE

by Stanley De Nisco

Beneath the polished veneer of many a TV commercial and magazine ad lies a solid core of scientific ideas, scrupulous tests, and exhaustive compilations of fact.

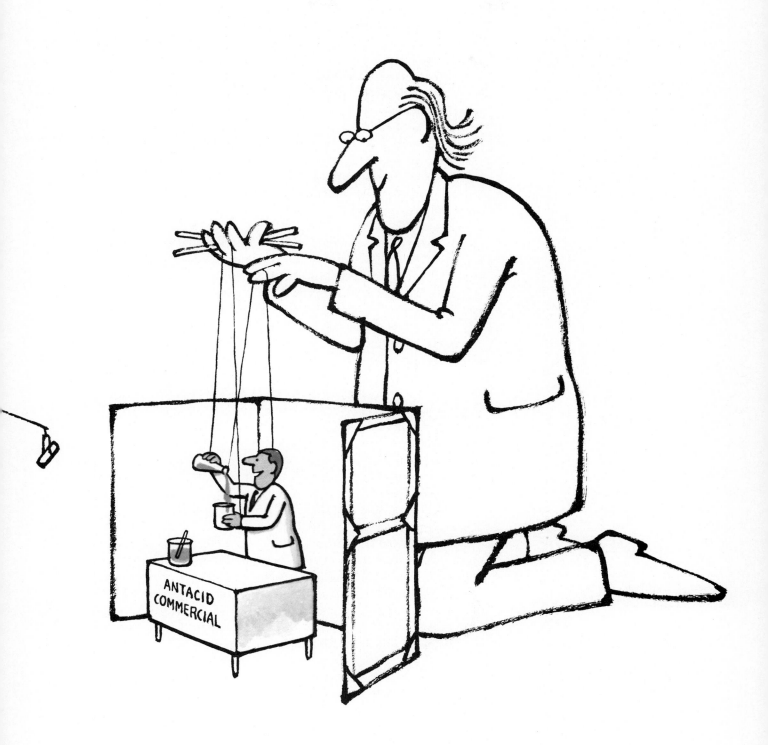

Years ago advertising was simple. The barber pole told where one could get a shave and haircut and even have minor surgery performed. If a person were thirsty, the signpost outside a tavern said it all even if the person could not read. Three balls hanging above a door identified the place as a pawn shop. Today advertising is a much more complex business, but it still performs the same function that it did then—selling a product or a service.

With the inception of mass production, the growth of cities, and the spread of population over vast stretches of land, direct contact between a manufacturer and his customers has all but vanished. Now, to reach consumers down the block, across the nation, or halfway around the world, manufacturers rely on printed matter and electronic communications. Newspapers and magazines owe their continued survival to pages and pages of advertisements. Radio and television programs are constantly interrupted to carry sales messages. Although many people profess annoyance with such "intrusions," without advertising they would be hard put to know what products exist, what their merits are, or what brand offers the most for their money. Advertising plays an undeniably vital role in today's consumer-oriented society.

It may seem surprising at first glance that science should have anything to do with advertising. Science deals in basic knowledge about the physical world and its application to human concerns. Advertising, on the other hand, deals in persuasion. Yet both are linked in a fundamental way. According to one of the great advertising men, Theodore L. Bates, a sales message must offer a unique and memorable benefit to the consumer—a unique selling proposition (USP). And the development of a USP starts with facts, the stock-in-trade of science. What is the function of each of the ingredients in a product? How does the product compare with competing products? How will it benefit the consumer? How does it work? Finding answers to these questions is a task for science, which consequently enters into practically every aspect of developing a sales message, from assisting copywriters and devising television demonstrations to interpreting government regulations and helping to anticipate legal problems.

Scientists become involved in the advertising business by a variety of routes. Advertising agencies may engage scientists as consultants to solve problems and give advice, or they may hire outside laboratories to gather facts and conduct tests. Agencies also rely on their clients' research and development (R and D) departments for scientific information about their products. One agency, Ted Bates Worldwide, Inc., of New York City, has the unique distinction of operating its own science department and product-testing laboratory. It is from this vantage point, where science and advertising are probably at their most intimate, that this article is written.

STANLEY DE NISCO, a biochemist by training, is Vice President and Director of Science at Ted Bates Worldwide, Inc., New York City.

Illustrations by John Everds

Translating technical information

The copywriters, account executives, and lawyers in an ad agency are not trained scientists. Their understanding of the technical information about a product depends on its assembly and accurate translation into nontechnical language. At Ted Bates the science department handles this job, which can best be illustrated by a case history.

The agency has been assigned a new antacid product. It is the first time it has handled such a product. Before the agency's staff can even start contemplating how to advertise it, they must know what an antacid is and why people take them. How effective is it in relieving symptoms, and how do various brands of antacids compare? The science department prepares a fact booklet. Because antacids are taken to relieve certain stomach symptoms, the introductory chapter reviews the anatomy and physiology of the stomach with simple illustrations. It describes the shape of the stomach—a J-shaped organ about ten inches long—and the approximately 35,000,000 gastric glands that it contains.

Of particular interest is the type of digestive juices secreted by these glands. Because antacids counteract or neutralize acids, the digestive juice of most concern is hydrochloric acid. Excess hydrochloric acid in the stomach results in heartburn or upset or sour stomach. What causes the stomach to secrete such an excess? Hydrochloric acid secretion is normally not continuous but intermittent. Under certain conditions, however—for example, during such emotional states as anger, resentment, or hostility—secretion increases. The thought, sight, or odor of food also stimulates secretion. Presence in the stomach of such foods as meat, particularly liver and fish and their extracts, results in excess acid. This type of information helps the agency's writers develop selling ideas and ways of dramatizing them.

The fact booklet also discusses the physical and chemical properties of an antacid. Definitions are given for acid, base, pH, neutralization, and other technical terms relating to this category of drugs. If the product underwent

human clinical studies, the reports are summarized, highlighting results that could be developed into USP's. The writers are also given facts on how the product compares to competitive brands. Such claims as "takes care of twice as much stomach acid" and "neutralizes 47 times its weight in acid" resulted from basic information provided by science.

The science department prepares fact sheets on foods, analgesics, cold remedies, cosmetics, and many other products. The people on its staff consider themselves general scientists rather than specialists. They appreciate marketing problems and in their research are always looking for potential USP's. They subscribe to technical journals in all fields to keep abreast of the latest developments. Informative articles relating to a product handled by the agency are sent to account people and writers. An accompanying commentary highlights points of interest that may suggest new selling points, product improvements, line extensions, or even a new product.

The science department also acts as a conduit between agency personnel and the client's R and D departments. Meetings are held with the client's scientists to discuss the composition of a product, to review test procedures and data, to determine if the product is unique in any respect. Everything possible is learned about a product. Because members of the science department are technically trained, it is easier for them to communicate with their opposites than it is for marketing people or writers.

Another source of information—and inspiration—for agency scientists is the scientific gathering. To illustrate, a client asked an agency scientist to attend its medical conference exhibit promoting low-cholesterol, high-polyunsaturated foods. In discussing these foods with physicians, particularly their value in lowering cholesterol levels in the blood, the scientist learned that doctors were finding it difficult to convince their patients to eat fewer eggs. Egg yolk, part of a very nutritious food, is also the highest single source of cholesterol. The agency brought this problem to the attention of its client, who in turn developed a new product, a yolk-free egg substitute fortified with vitamins, which provides egg nutrition without the cholesterol.

Performance testing

A trained scientist without a laboratory is like a doctor without a stethoscope. Searching the literature for information is no more important than actually putting a product through its paces to determine how it will perform for the consumer. The laboratory operated by the Ted Bates agency is used to evaluate products and develop demonstrations. In it are the expected trappings—analytical balances, beakers, flasks, test tubes, pH meters, a photographing microscope, and an instrument that shines ultraviolet light and daylight on an object and measures the return. But it is also equipped with washers and dryers to evaluate laundry and dish detergents and fabric softeners, a stove to prepare foods, and a vinyl tile floor to test floor waxes.

A product undergoing testing is always pitted against its major competitors. They first are compared side by side for any physical differences. If the product is a liquid, is it more viscous or less viscous than competitors? If it is a powder, how do the particles compare under the microscope? If the product is a tablet, like aspirin, how fast does it break up? For this last case lab-

oratory workers place various brands of tablets in a disintegration apparatus that simulates the action in the stomach. This device consists of several clear plastic tubes with wire mesh bottoms. The tubes are suspended from an arm that automatically raises and lowers them simultaneously into a beaker containing simulated stomach acid. The beaker is kept at a constant 37° C (98.6° F), representing body temperature. A tablet is placed in the bottom of each tube, and the time the tablet completely disappears from the tube is recorded. Not all brands of a drug break up in the same period of time, indicating that some may take longer to disintegrate in the stomach.

With liquids like shampoos, in addition to determining physical characteristics, the laboratory staff makes pH determinations. These readings indicate the degree of acidity or alkalinity of a product. A highly alkaline shampoo, for example, can strip the hair of its natural oils leaving it lusterless and brittle. Volunteers are recruited to shampoo their hair in the laboratory; luster, feel, and combing ability are evaluated. Strands of hair washed with different brands of shampoo are also compared under the microscope.

Writers, account people, and art directors are invited to participate in these tests. It is particularly important for writers to see firsthand how the product performs and compares to its competitors. Many selling points have evolved from such sessions, for writers often suggest ways to evaluate a product that may have been overlooked by the scientists.

Substantiating advertising claims

An advertising agency and its client must be able to support every claim they make about a product and its benefits. Their success again depends heavily on the technical information that science can provide about the product. For example, the scientific basis for a claim that a fluoride toothpaste, used regularly, significantly reduces the incidence of tooth decay comes from the client's R and D departments. Support for a caries reduction claim requires that hundreds of children of various ages be tested for a minimum of two years. Independent dentists examine these children before the study commences to determine the number of missing, filled, and decayed teeth. The children are given toothpastes marked only with a code number and told how and when to brush. To eliminate biases on the part of the examiners and subjects, neither the children nor the dentists know what brand of toothpaste they are testing. Only at the end of the two-year period is the code broken. Periodically the children return to the dentists, who note any new cavities that appear during the test period. These studies are conducted in different sections of the country to determine if differences in numbers of cavities may be the result of diet, water, or other factors indigenous to a certain section of the nation. The results are statistically evaluated and usually published in dental journals. Agency scientists review these technical papers both to substantiate claims being made for the product and to determine if new claims can be discovered.

Broadcasting networks require documentation of claims made for a product before commercials can be aired. Storyboards are presented to the network review boards with a written statement detailing the scientific evidence supporting the claim. References are given and copies of published

reports are attached. These review boards often raise pertinent questions, which must be answered in writing. For example, a question was raised as to the actual amount and concentration of the acid that is shown neutralized by one antacid tablet. For a toothpaste commercial the networks questioned the claim that most dental caries occur in the back teeth. The networks also may request to see clinical support for claims of product superiority.

Sometimes agency writers come up with a claim for which there is insufficient evidence. The agency's scientists then must decide if the claim is feasible. If there is reason to believe so, preliminary tests are performed, and if these look promising, the results are discussed with the client's R and D. The client's scientists will either confirm the findings themselves or assign the project to an independent laboratory. Whether or not the claim stands depends on the results of these tests.

Reviewing claims with the writers helps save time and money. To put a great deal of effort into developing an idea that cannot be substantiated is a waste of talent. Rejecting ideas at an early stage, however, can have a positive effect. It is the philosophy of the science department at Ted Bates that when an idea is rejected on scientific grounds, two alternates are offered. Even if these are not acceptable to the writers, they very often stimulate new ideas.

Visual demonstrations

In television advertising an integral part of the unique selling proposition is the demonstration that reinforces the selling message. The demonstration has to be simple, and it must honestly and accurately show how the product

235

works. To assist in developing TV commercials the science department at Ted Bates tests various ways of demonstrating a product. Time is an important factor, for most television commercials run 30 seconds from beginning to end. The demonstration cannot take more than about ten seconds of this time. Fortunately, certain video techniques are permissible such as "time wipe" and "cut," which indicate passage of time. Where time is a key ingredient of the commercial message itself, the actual time elapsed must be superimposed on the screen. In devising a demonstration, scientists carefully record the time it takes to work.

On some occasions an actual demonstration is not feasible. It is up to science to find a suitable analogy. For example, it has been scientifically established that fluoride ions in a fluoride toothpaste migrate into tooth enamel and change its chemical structure. This change makes the tooth impervious to acid attack and thereby cuts down on caries. To show how fluoride ions actually get into the enamel surface, however, requires radioactive techniques. This kind of demonstration would frighten consumers. It would be difficult, if not impossible, to explain in 30 seconds that the fluoride was made radioactive for this case alone, to show that it actually gets into tooth enamel. The consumer might get the impression that this brand of toothpaste was radioactive.

Hence, when the science department actually set out to devise a TV demonstration for the product, it needed an accurate alternative to show fluoride uptake. Both laboratory tests and studies in humans showed that

236

the fluoride ion from a dentifrice is absorbed to a depth of one micrometer (about four hundred-thousandths of an inch) in tooth enamel. Various analogous means were investigated to represent this action including, at the suggestion of one writer, the absorption of liquid by a stick of chalk. In this concept—the one that eventually was used—a vegetable dye solution, representing fluoride, is painted on a piece of chalk, representing the tooth. Chalk is highly absorbent, although the degree varies with the brand. Some brands are coated, entirely preventing absorption; others absorb too rapidly. The rate and depth of dye penetration were critical factors in this demonstration because it was necessary that the dye not penetrate completely. From the client's R and D specialists, it was learned that the dye could not color more than 10% of the cross section of the chalk to represent accurately what occurs in the tooth. A second limitation was that, when the dye solution was brushed on the chalk, no more than three-fourths of the circumference could be coated. This restriction represented the results of clinical studies which indicated that people brush differently, often missing parts of the tooth. After undergoing many trials in the laboratory, the demonstration was perfected to meet the above criteria.

An advertising scientist, however, always strives to develop demonstrations using the actual product. For instance, a demonstration was needed for a dishwashing liquid used for washing dishes by hand. Independent clinical studies already had proved that this product did not result in rough, red hands. But did it clean dishes? The agency's science laboratory conducted tests in which water temperature, size of dishes, kinds and amount of soiling, quantities of liquid detergent added to the water, and other conditions were strictly controlled. The only variable was the brand of detergent. According to the client's R and D, a dishwashing liquid stops cleaning effectively when all the suds in the dishwater disappear. In the laboratory hundreds of plates were soiled with such common foods as gravies, catsup, and spaghetti sauce. Their quantities were accurately weighed so that each dish carried the same kind and amount of food debris. Then the dishes were washed, with each cleaned dish evaluated separately and the suds observed. Repeated tests definitely established that the client's brand cleaned more dishes than some other brands—in fact, 50% more than one competitor. Results of this kind are not surprising. Products differ in composition, and quality control in manufacturing can make a big difference in the way a product performs. A consumer purchasing the client's brand of dish liquid would not be disappointed if package directions were followed.

Another example of developing a demonstration actually involved using the product according to package directions. The item, a denture cleaning tablet, is dissolved in a cup of water, and the dentures are soaked in the solution. Like natural teeth, dentures become stained. This solution cleans by virtue of both foaming and bleaching actions. Although clinical tests had proved its effectiveness, the problem was how to adapt these tests into an acceptable TV message. At the time the commercial was being put together, U.S. television networks felt it to be in bad taste for commercials to show natural teeth or dentures in a demonstration. At one creative meeting someone used the phrase "pearly teeth," which led to the idea of a demonstration involving a string of pearls. However, the surface characteristics of pearl and denture acrylic differ so much that such a demonstation would not portray accurately how the product performs on dentures. Consequently it was asked: Why not create a string of "pearls" from denture acrylic?

The science department went to work contacting dental-supply manufacturers for acrylic blocks, which were then machined into pearls. Next, its scientists discussed the problem of staining with dentists and denture manufacturers, who pointed out that certain foods and beverages including blueberry and cherry pies, coffee, tea, and tobacco stained dentures. From the client's R and D it was learned that staining takes place in the plaque enveloping the denture. Plaque is the film of bacteria that adheres to both natural teeth and dentures. Although plaque could not be built up on the acrylic pearls the way it is in the mouth, a satisfactory laboratory method exists in which teeth are soaked in a synthetic plaque solution. Once the acrylic pearls were so treated to coat them with plaque, they were actually placed in a blueberry pie and baked in the oven. After the pie cooled, the pearls were removed and placed in the denture cleanser solution according to package directions. They emerged sparkling clean, offering proof that the cleanser worked. Tests were conducted with coffee, tea, and tobacco stains, with similar results. Finally a television commercial was made incorporating this demonstration.

The science department devised another demonstration showing how the denture cleanser removes stains from between teeth. This time the acrylic material was machined into small blocks, attached with tiny hinges, and separated to represent the spaces between teeth in dentures. They were treated in the same manner as the acrylic pearls; that is, covered with plaque, then stained, and finally cleansed in the denture solution. Stains disappeared not only from the surface of the blocks but also from between the blocks.

Filming the commercial

Science department members work closely with the producers, directors, and others involved in the actual filming or taping of demonstrations for TV commercials. At preproduction meetings, during which the demonstration is discussed in detail, the science department specifies exactly how the demonstration is to be performed before the camera so that it reproduces the laboratory test in every respect. In showing the acid-neutralizing power of an antacid, for example, a beaker containing hydrochloric acid and a pH indicator is used. The hydrochloric acid is of a predetermined concentration (0.1 normal). The indicator is a standardized solution that changes color in a specified pH range—to signal when the acid in the beaker has been neutralized to the degree specified in the claim. The antacid product that is added to the acid is purchased at a retail store. When the demonstration finally is performed before the camera, it is exactly as it was in the laboratory.

A writer once suggested a dramatic way to demonstrate the hardness of a brand of nail polish: play table tennis with polish-coated balls. In testing the idea the agency's science department painted table tennis balls with two coats of nail polish, because most women apply two coats. After the balls had dried and had received a sound paddling from the laboratory staff, they were

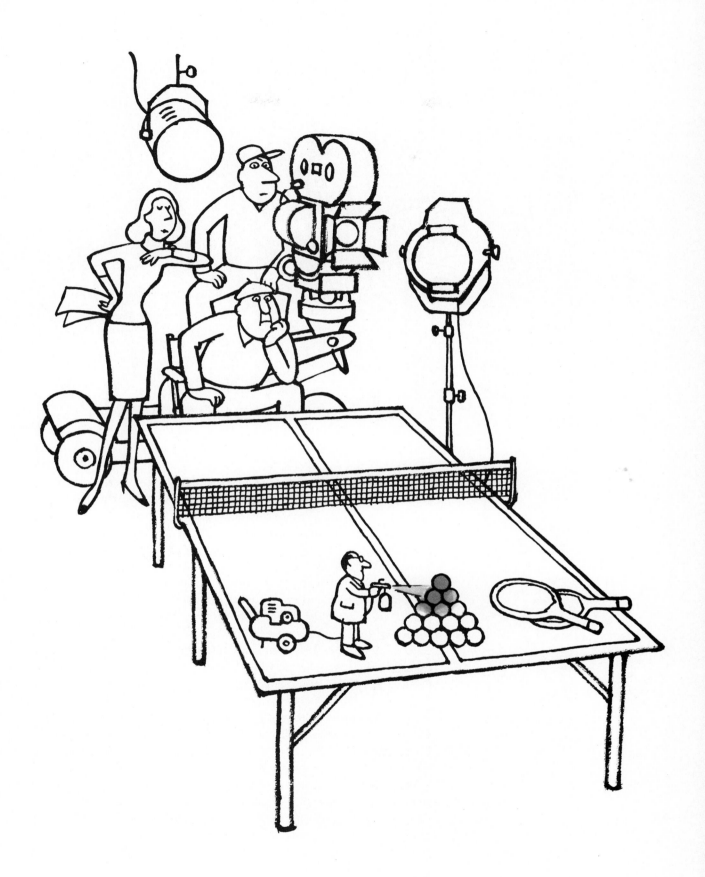

inspected under magnification for chips and cracks. This test was repeated a number of times with new balls, various shades of polish, and even different players—all with outstanding results. In filming the demonstration, the same procedure was followed. The young women who appeared in the commercial were professional players.

Dealing with humans to demonstrate a product benefit offers a more difficult challenge. For instance, how could it be demonstrated "live" that a brand of eyedrops removes redness from the eye? The product contained a medically approved decongestant. It was on the market and was being used by millions of people. Clinical studies had confirmed its effectiveness. To test the feasibility of producing a "live" commercial, models were asked to participate in a test. They were informed about the test and asked to sign a consent order. They then visited an ophthalmologist for a thorough eye examination to make sure that they did not have an eye affliction. Those that passed came to the laboratory, at which the ophthalmologist was present. Redness was induced by either blowing smoke into their eyes or having the models stare. The eye drops were then applied according to package directions, and the disappearance of redness timed with a stopwatch. Within seconds redness vanished. The results of trials with ten subjects indicated that it was feasible to film the demonstration "live" for a commercial.

To assure governmental regulatory agencies as well as the networks that such demonstrations are valid and not shams, a member of the science department witnesses the filming of the demonstration and is responsible for its accuracy. He is the technical director for the commercial.

240

The science department files a written report with the agency for each demonstration. The report names the product, client, title of the commercial, its running time, where and when it was produced, and the object of the demonstration. It also briefly discusses prior documentation, lists materials used in the demonstration, and gives results and conclusions. Anyone wishing to check the demonstration can refer to this report.

Legal and science

One of the many functions of an ad agency's legal department is to guard against the possibility of illegalities creeping into their sales messages. Consequently once again the advertising scientist is in demand for the technical facts supporting a claim or demonstration. At Ted Bates scientists and lawyers review the scientific rationale for a commercial in the form of a friendly adversary encounter. The lawyers act as devil's advocates, listening to the technical details supplied by science and eliciting answers to questions that might be raised by regulatory agencies, networks, and consumer groups. With this information in hand, the legal department then decides whether a commercial is relaying the message supported by the facts or is implying an unsubstantiated meaning.

Although each claim in a given commercial may be rooted in granite and the demonstration documented, the overall impression that the commercial conveys is the deciding factor on its legality. This final verdict rests with the legal department.

The science department also helps agency lawyers understand the U.S. Food and Drug Administration's (FDA's) monographs on over-the-counter (OTC), or nonprescription, drugs. In 1972 the FDA instituted an OTC drug review to determine the safety and effectiveness of these products. In preparing its monographs the FDA recruits panels of outside experts to review published and unpublished information on various classes of drugs. The panels also include two nonvoting members, one representing industry, the other consumer groups. Each panel submits a report covering its conclusions and recommendations to the commissioner of food and drugs with respect to the safety and effectiveness of various active ingredients used in a class of drugs and to the labeling of the products. Ingredients are classified one of three ways: Category I—generally recognized as safe and effective and not misbranded; Category II—not generally recognized as safe and effective, or misbranded; or Category III—available data insufficient to permit final classification at this time. From the reports a proposed monograph is drafted and published in the Federal Register, after which interested parties may comment and submit additional data. After reviewing the comments, the FDA publishes a tentative final order, proposing a monograph in the form of a regulation. Public objections can be voiced, and if the commissioner feels the objections to be well taken, hearings are scheduled. A final monograph is then published and becomes law. Thereafter, a nonprescription drug must conform to these regulations.

Forty-four product categories of OTC drugs were being evaluated as of late 1981. To date only one final monograph has been published, the antacid monograph.

Because of the scientific language used in the monographs, it is difficult for a nonscientist to fully comprehend the rules and regulations set forth. The science department prepares summaries of the monograph in nontechnical terms, highlighting sections that apply to a product that the agency is handling. It also includes label claims that are allowed and not allowed—important information for the writers. Although advertising claims do not come under the jurisdiction of the FDA, but rather the Federal Trade Commission (FTC), the FTC regards advertising claims as extensions of label claims. Label claims often use terms that are technical and unfamiliar to the consumer, whereas of necessity the advertising message must be written in words that the consumer can understand. These words, nevertheless, must still convey the same meaning as the label claim.

Teamwork

In helping to develop unique and memorable selling messages, the scientists in advertising work as members of a creative team. They provide the writers with basic facts about a product and its competitors. They serve important roles in developing, testing, and filming demonstrations. They assist the legal department by substantiating claims and documenting demonstrations and work closely with clients' R and D in obtaining technical information about a product. In so doing they have made science an integral part of the advertising world.

Science
Year in Review

Science
Year in Review
Contents

Anthropology

Evolution was much in the news in 1981. Creationists moved to introduce "creation science" in public school classrooms, while, based on recent fossil findings, paleoanthropologists proposed remarkable hypotheses on hominid evolution. Also during the year anthropologists studied the cultural implications of the use of infant formula and increasingly turned their attention to the scientific study of tourism.

Human evolution. Anthropologists found themselves defending the principles of evolution in courts in Arkansas and other states. The Balanced Treatment of Creation-science and Evolution-science in Public Schools Act was signed into Arkansas law in March 1981, but was later struck down by a federal judge in January 1982. Similar legislation was also proposed in Louisiana and California. In Louisiana and Arkansas advocates of this legislation hailed creationism as a science, while in California evolutionism was described as a religion. In each case an attempt was made to place evolutionism and creationism on the same level. (For additional information, *see* Year in Review: U.S. Science Policy.)

The Arkansas legislation made much of the fact that differences of opinion existed among scientists on the specifics of evolution. This observation was true for anthropology, as anthropologists sharpened debate on important theoretical problems apart from the legal issues raised in Arkansas and elsewhere. In this connection important fossil discoveries in 1973 were examined by Donald Johanson and other paleoanthropologists for clues to the evolutionary sequence of hominids. Anthropologist C. Owen Lovejoy argued in *Science* in 1981 against the prevailing view of human evolution as a direct consequence of brain expansion and concomitant advances in material culture. "Lucy," the name given the three-to-four million-year-old *Australopithecus afarensis* specimen found by Johanson, was described as being bipedal or fully erect. Lucy's brain, however, was not enlarged, and her pelvis showed no modification for the birthing of large-brained infants. Furthermore, she lived some two million years before the first known use of tools.

In the face of this evidence Lovejoy proposed that monogamous pair-bonding was the primary difference between early hominids such as Lucy and apes. Pair-bonding insured that males would be directly involved in the struggle for survival of their progeny. Accordingly, intensified parenting and monogamous pair-bonding were believed to precede advances in material culture and cranial capacity. Lucy's evolutionary success, therefore, had to be accounted for in the social and reproductive behavior of her group.

Objections to assumptions of bipedal Australopithecines were raised by physical anthropologist Jack Prost in the *American Journal of Physical Anthropology* (1980). Prost argued that the Australopithecines had life habits profoundly different from any human group. Therefore, some of the skeletal comparisons on which the assumption of bipedal locomotion was made might have been invalid.

In reaching his conclusion Prost reviewed collections of behaviors, including running and climbing, in humans, chimpanzees, and baboons. He concluded that the Australopithecines, Lucy included, were quadrupedal (four-footed) vertical climbing animals, an assertion at variance with researchers who concluded that they were wholly bipedal. Prost determined that although the social life of these animals took place primarily in trees, they would have been competent terrestrial walkers as well. In his view bipedalism

Babies are fed by bottle and breast at a health center in Togo. Bottle feeding became a controversial issue, especially in less developed countries, because it was found that infant formula was often overdiluted or used in insufficient quantity and thus did not provide adequate nutrition.

Bernard Wolff—UNICEF

245

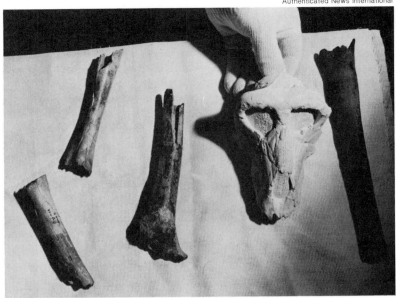

Fragments of bones belonging to an Australopithecine hominid who lived two million years ago were discovered in Romania. They were the first fossils of their kind to be found in Europe.

evolved as an adjunct to quadrupedal vertical climbing.

Support for Prost's position came from electromyographic studies by Jack Stern and Randall Susman. Comparative studies of gibbon, chimpanzee, and orangutan gluteal musculature while walking and climbing showed that the Australopithecines could have been part biped and part climber.

Additional hypotheses about human evolution were contributed by Peter Wilson and Nancy Makepeace Tanner. In *Man, the Promising Primate* Wilson emphasized the importance of learning, or culture, in the solving of "evolutionary problematics." In *On Becoming Human* Tanner initiated another theoretical corrective, this one designed to explore the often neglected role of females in human evolution. She argued that females probably pioneered the exploitation of plant food with tools.

Debate continued in 1981 also at the level of broad evolutionary theory. During the year there was a challenge to the assumptions of the modern synthesis, the theory that has dominated evolutionary biology for the past 40 years. Modern synthesis views evolution as moving at a regular, steady pace. This model of steady advance, however, is not confirmed by the paleontological record, which reveals a history of stasis (stable equilibrium) rather than change within individual species.

The paleoanthropological record, for example, showed the brain size of *Homo erectus* persisting virtually unchanged from roughly 1.5 million to 200,000 years ago. If brain size is so adaptively important, some theoreticians were asking, then why did it remain relatively constant for 1.3 million years? Proponents of the "punctuated equilibrium" model argued that this stability is, in fact, a reflection of oscillation around a mean. In their view evolution is not smoothly progressive but episodic.

Infant health and medical anthropology. Medical anthropologists during the year were carefully monitoring the impact of the worldwide marketing and use of infant formula. It had been discovered that insufficient, overdiluted amounts of formula, coupled with unsanitary administration, provided a severe threat to infant health. Anthropologists pointed out that the problem of poor infant nutrition was not entirely a result of a reliance on formula but sometimes resulted from culturally determined infant feeding patterns.

Formula manufacturers and health scientists agreed on the advantages of mother's milk over formula. The hundreds of nutrients in breast milk cannot be chemically replicated in formula. Infants require the antibodies available in mother's milk to fight infection before their own immunity defenses are completely in place. "For us to think that in 40 years we can duplicate what has happened in four million years of human development is very arrogant," commented pediatrician Gerald Gaull. Diseases easily combated in a well-nourished child, such as chicken pox and measles, were found to overwhelm one who was poorly nourished. As breast feeding declined, infants died from malnutrition at earlier ages.

The aggressive promotion of formula traded on the image of the upwardly mobile woman offering her infant a bottle filled with the latest scientific advance. Even in a culture with a strong commitment to breast-feeding, such as Taiwan, there were signs of change. In that nation in the late 1950s weaning typically occurred at about 24 months; in the mid-1960s it had been reduced to 16-18 months, and by 1972 the mean duration of lactation had dropped to 12-13 months,

246

with a concomitant increase in formula use. Physician Barbara Harrell reported that the Taiwanese associate bottle-feeding with progress and wealth.

In the United States, according to the National Fertility Study, the percentage of mothers who breast-fed their babies declined by nearly half in a comparison of mothers born in the 1940s with those born in the generation before them. Formula misuse was found to be prevalent in low-income families in the U.S. in conformance with the worldwide pattern. In the 1970s breast-feeding underwent a resurgence among middle-class women as they sought to return to "natural" child rearing. Breast-feeding in the U.S. remained minimal by world standards, however, and among lower-income women the movement toward total reliance on formula continued to build.

A number of social and demographic factors worked together to account for the rapid increase of dependency on infant formula in the less developed countries. As women relocate from rural settings to urban centers, they may fail to lactate in response to the unaccustomed stress. One recent study in Guatemala, for example, found more frequent and more extended breast-feeding among rural Indians than among their urban counterparts.

The option of breast-feeding is also diminished as women enter the work force outside the home. Harrell found that women living with their mothers-in-law were more likely to resort to bottles and to wean their children at an early age than were women managing households on their own. She speculated that the op-

tion of bottle-feeding might enable the grandmother to interact with the grandchild.

Studies in agricultural societies, such as India, found infant mortality rates significantly higher for girls than for boys during the second year of life. Anthropologists linked these statistics to the relative importance of sons over daughters in agricultural societies, where parents may feed their boys preferentially.

In a related development anthropologists also reported the improper use of medicines among tribal and ethnic peoples. Problems result from a lack of instruction on use and shelf life. One drug recommended for motion sickness in the U.S., for example, was sold in Malaysia in 1979 as a cure for morning sickness. Patients were found taking drugs without any foreknowledge of potential risks or without an understanding of the complexities of side effects.

Research indicated an overuse of antibiotics in less developed countries, where they were sold as cure-alls, available generally without prescription. In Tanzania, for example, a 45-year supply was found of an antibiotic that has a shelf life of two years at best. Anthropologists joined with health and medical organizations in seeking international controls to halt the indiscriminate use of antibiotics and other drugs.

Anthropologists in 1981 brought to the attention of pharmaceutical manufacturers the needs of health providers in less developed countries. Research conducted or sponsored by those companies had focused on the needs of the industrialized countries, but the problems facing people elsewhere were enormously

Tourists gather on the Greek island of Rhodes in the Aegean Sea. Anthropologists were increasingly studying tourism as a significant aspect of the culture of a nation or a religion.

© Brian Seed—CLICK/Chicago

different. Cultural Survival, Incorporated, a group of anthropologists monitoring such situations, reported that virtually no money was expended in search of cures for Chagas' disease, schistosomiasis, trypanosomiasis, and onchocerciasis, though millions of people in the less developed nations were suffering from those diseases.

Anthropology of tourism. Anthropologists in 1981 continued their efforts to keep current with events in the changing world, as well as to refine the conceptual frameworks applied to traditional topics. As self-contained, "primitive" cultures began disappearing during the first half of the 20th century, anthropologists turned to studies of peasant societies. Then, perforce, anthropologists gamely explored "modern" cultures. The burgeoning interest in tourism in 1981 was an extension of this process of the reformulation of anthropology.

Anthropologists increasingly agreed with Dennison Nash's assertion that tourism is not a frivolous topic, nor is it inconsequential to the tourist-generating or host societies. Disagreement was registered, however, on the question as to whether tourism ought to be studied as a theoretical subject on its own or whether it must be incorporated as a variety of some broader phenomenon, such as the study of play, the process of acculturation, or the transformation of the preindustrial world.

Among topics explored by anthropologists were the "prototypes" of tourism in preindustrial societies, the ethnographic context of tourism in several intercultural settings, the separation of tourism from the impact of "development" more generally, and the nonuniform internal response to tourism in host societies. Several anthropologists viewed tourism as a uniquely modern phenomenon. Oriol Pi-Sunyer, for one, included the "commercialization of leisure" in his model, while Erik Cohen focused on the concept of "commercialized hospitality." The case presented by Pi-Sunyer for tourism argued that it was a phenomenon characteristic of industrial culture, where people are searching for "the natural and the simple." Other researchers, noting the artificiality associated with interactions in tourist settings, hoped to provide cultural or historical accounts for this pattern.

The cultural significance of modern tourism must be regarded in the contrast between "work" and "play," argued Nelson Graburn. Other anthropologists focused on the cultural context of receptivity in the host setting. The paradoxical mix of intimacy and distance characteristic of tourist interactions caught the attention of numerous anthropologists, who began exploring the significance of such findings. The leading researchers in this field were hoping that by making their colleagues in anthropology mindful of the issues, more fruitful contributions would be forthcoming.

—Lawrence E. Fisher

Archaeology

Major developments in archaeology during the last year included the application of a new technique of radiocarbon dating, the discovery of a decline in human body size at the end of the Upper Paleolithic period in Europe, and a new method of determining the date of the earliest humans in the Americas. Research also shed new light on the agricultural basis of the Mayan civilization, explaining how that rich and populous culture could have been supported on the available land.

Radiocarbon dating. Newly completed atomic accelerator laboratories at Oxford in the United Kingdom and at Tucson, Ariz., were dedicated to the application of a revolutionary new technique for the dating of extremely small samples of archaeological importance. Conventional methods of carbon-14 (^{14}C) dating rely upon measurement of the radioactive decay of carbon-14 into carbon-12. This method has been of overwhelming importance and will continue to be used for the great bulk of radiocarbon dating, but it is limited by its requirement for quite large samples of datable material. Samples of the required size have not been available in many instances, with the result that many scientifically important discoveries have gone undated. Particularly in the older age ranges, samples of very large size are required, and the practical dating limit of the ^{14}C method is about 40,000 years except under the most ideal circumstances.

The new technique now being made operational by the new laboratories is capable of measuring single atoms of ^{14}C, distinguishing them from the nonradioactive ^{12}C by their greater atomic mass. The method relies on the measurement of velocity and energy of particles in an ion beam produced by an accelerator. Samples only a few milligrams in size can be used, and the method is much more rapid than that which required counting the spontaneous decay of radioactive isotopes over long periods of time. Direct measurement also makes possible an increase in the age range of radiocarbon dating. It is expected that determinations as early as 60,000 to 70,000 years should be routinely obtainable, and under ideal conditions ages of over 100,000 years should be measurable.

Potential new areas of application include the dating of human remains during the crucial period of evolution between Neanderthal man and fully modern forms of *Homo sapiens,* and the dating of minute amounts of carbon contained in pottery, iron, animal and plant remains, and geological sediments. It should also be possible to test and evaluate the accuracy of the controversial amino-acid racemization dating method that has been applied to human bones, often with quite problematical results. (The method is temperature-dependent, and relies on the tenuous assumption that the paleo-temperatures to which a dating sample was subjected can be accurately reconstructed.) The direct

The ruins of a synagogue that survived the seventh-century Islamic conquest of Palestine were recently unearthed in Israel. They indicate that some Jews were allowed to practice their religion openly after the conquest. The synagogue was built over an older Jewish temple.

carbon-14 dating of the actual extracted chemical materials used in racemization dating could lead to a reliable calibration of this method, allowing its extension to much earlier ranges of time and providing increased confidence in the results.

Human body size. Cultural and environmental changes at the end of the Upper Paleolithic period in Europe brought about a reduction in human body size, according to a recent study by David Frayer of the University of Kansas. Frayer hypothesized that the invention of the bow and arrow, known to have occurred in late Upper Paleolithic or early Mesolithic times about 10,000 years ago, would have made hunting a much safer and less rigorous pursuit than it had been earlier, when the spear was in use as the main weapon of the hunt. Hunters could kill large game animals without battling them at close quarters as had been necessary in earlier times. Under these conditions, large size and strength, crucial to the survival of Paleolithic hunters, would have become less crucial during Mesolithic times.

A related factor, also of obviously great importance, was a change in the kinds of game animals available to human hunters after the end of Paleolithic times. With the end of the glacial age the elephant, rhinoceros, reindeer, and other large animals became extinct over most of Europe. They were replaced by smaller red deer, roe deer, elk, aurochs, and boar, which inhabited the forests that replaced the open tundras of the glacial period. Thus, both cultural and environmental factors led to a situation in which the size and strength of the human hunter became less important to his survival, and under these conditions, according to Frayer's hypothesis, the influence of natural selection in maintaining large body size in human populations would have been relaxed. With positive selection for large size no longer a factor, the generally lower nutritional demands of smaller organisms would have made a reduction in human size advantageous.

The test of this hypothesis was simple and straightforward: Frayer gathered and compared data on the length of limb bones from a large sample of human skeletons of both Upper Paleolithic and Mesolithic age and determined that there was indeed a size reduction from the former to the latter of 7–10% in various skeletal measurements, amounting to a calculated reduction in overall stature of about 5%. A similar explanation has been advanced to explain the greater robustness of ancient Australian aborigines as compared to those of recent times, and future studies may determine this theory to be of general application in world prehistory.

Early man in the Americas. The dating of the earliest Americans has been, and continues to be, a controversial topic. Previously obtained dates on human skeletons from California of 48,000 years and 70,000 years, based on the controversial amino-acid racemization dating technique, were recently challenged by a redating of the specimens using uranium series analyses. The amino-acid racemization dates imply that fully modern forms of *Homo sapiens* were present in the Americas far earlier than previously believed possible. The Sunnyvale (Calif.) skeleton, earlier given an age of 70,000 years by amino-acid racemization dating, was found by uranium series analysis to have an age of approximately 8,300 years; the Del Mar (Calif.) skeleton, attributed an age of 48,000 years based on amino-acid racemization, was placed at about 11,000 years by the uranium series analysis.

The uranium series dates agree much better than did those based on amino-acid racemization with several radiocarbon determinations that were obtained on geological contexts of the skeletal remains. Radiocarbon dates of about 10,000 years ago were obtained from freshwater snail shells found in a geological stratum beneath that in which the Sunnyvale skeleton was found, while radiocarbon dates ranging between 4,500 and 12,000 years ago were obtained on mollusk shells in the seaside midden from which the Del Mar skeleton is believed to have come. Although the uranium series dating method is itself subject to serious error under some conditions, the congruence of its results with those of the radiocarbon method reinforces the validity of both. The new dates are important because they suggest that the radical revamping of concepts about human migration into the New World that would be necessitated by acceptance of the amino-acid racemization dates is probably unnecessary.

New discoveries reported during 1981 expanded archaeologists' understanding of Paleo-Indians in the New World. The Vail site, near the Canadian border in western Maine, was identified as an ancient killing ground and associated campsite, apparently occupied about 11,000 years ago. A series of well-made fluted spear points of the Clovis type were recovered there along with other artifacts. Though no carbon-14 dates were obtained for the site, an age range between about 11,500 and 11,000 years ago has been established for Clovis sites elsewhere in the U.S., and it is presumed that the same dates may be applied to the Vail area. The place of discovery was near Aziscohos Lake, an artificial body of water occupying a broad valley. Low lake levels exposed the site, which was located near the valley edge about 200 m (660 ft) from a crossing point on the meandering river that occupied the valley prior to its flooding.

The activities of early hunters at the site were clearly indicated by the discovery of two distinct clusters of artifacts. Excavations near the river crossing turned up ten fluted spear points. Four were complete, the others broken. Nothing else was found; the bones of the animals no doubt ambushed at the crossing were not preserved, though this is not surprising considering the exposed nature of the spot and the antiquity of the event. The absence of any butchering tools, however, implied that follow-up activities took place elsewhere. That place was located along the valley edge some 200 m distant, where among a rather dense scattering of stone flakes, chisels, scrapers, and knives were found the bases of two of the broken fluted points excavated at the killing ground. Eight different clusters of tools and flakes were found, indicating the positions of individual camps or dwellings.

Based on the number of stone tools present, the re-

Fluted spear points, estimated to be 11,000–11,500 years old, were found at the Vail Site in western Maine. There, ancient Indians killed animals at stream crossings and also maintained a campsite. The absence of other tools implies that butchering of the animals was carried on elsewhere.

searchers estimated that Paleo-Indian hunters returned to the Vail site perhaps as many as 30–50 times. If caribou were the quarry of these hunters, their annual migrations are predictable enough that people could have lain in wait for them at the Vail site season after season with dependable results. After the kill had been made and processed, the hunters moved on. As comparable finds continue to be made in the New England region, it should prove possible to work out the annual cycle of Paleo-Indian activities in more detail.

Mayan discoveries. The rich and highly elaborated Mayan civilization of the Yucatan Peninsula and adjacent regions has long posed for archaeologists the problem of how such an advanced and flourishing culture could have been economically supported. It was long believed that the primitive slash-and-burn system of cultivation, practiced historically by natives of the region, must have provided the major portion of Maya subsistence. It became increasingly clear, however, that such a system, whereby small plots were cleared, farmed for several years, then abandoned to lie fallow for a decade or more while other fields were cleared, farmed, and fallowed in turn, could not possibly have provided an adequate economic base for the dense populations of the Mayan civilization. The recent culmination of years of archaeological work involving aerial photography, radar mapping, ground survey, and excavation devoted to this problem now makes it clear that the Mayan agricultural system was far more sophisticated and highly organized than previously supposed.

A study of extensive areas in the Mayan lowlands, using highly advanced radar equipment originally developed by the U.S. National Aeronautics and Space Administration (NASA) for use in space probes examining the surface of the planet Venus, had indicated the existence of very large areas over which lattice works of small and large aboriginal canals occur. Especially around the great site of Tikal, largest in the Maya area, such canalized terrain is extensive, but it has been recognized around other major centers as well.

Ground checks performed by a number of investigators, guided both by the new radar imagery and by older aerial surveys, revealed many of these patterned areas to be ancient fields. In particular, excavations at Pulltrouser Swamp conclusively established the existence of an organized system of small and large canals draining a large swampy region. Also demonstrated was the presence of raised fields created by digging canals and then piling up the excavated materials between the canals high enough to provide adequate drainage for crop growth. Stone hoes and pottery found in these fields attest to farming activity.

It is conservatively estimated that the 300 ha (740 ac) of such fields identified at Pulltrouser Swamp would have required some 6,000 worker-years to construct, but once constructed could have supported about 4,000 people the year around. Clusters of small settlements immediately surrounding the swamp probably housed the agricultural workers in villages of several hundred. The complex is dated between 200 BC and AD 850, placing it in the Late Preclassic and Classic periods of Maya civilization.

The planning and organization implied by the extensive earthworks make it clear that the Pulltrouser Swamp fields must have been created by a powerful governmental authority. The occurrence of apparently similar complexes throughout the Mayan lowlands demonstrates the strength of this central authority and in terms of archaeological science establishes at last a plausible interpretation of the economic base that underlay the development of Mayan civilization.

—C. Melvin Aikens

Architecture and civil engineering

Architecture. Modernism has been and still is the predominant architectural movement of the technological age. During recent years the so-called post-modern movement has received much attention in the media. After announcing the death of the modern movement, the post-modernists have focused upon styles rooted in the architectural past.

By 1981 this attempt to ignore the modern movement, and instead to consult the history books as the first step toward creating a new movement, was viewed by many as a largely unsuccessful effort. For, while some designs can refer to historic precedent for the solutions to their programs, there are programs for which no precedents exist. Critics are calling attention to the fact that those who turn to history for precedents unwarranted by the problems at hand are finding no real solutions.

One post-modern architect, the 1981 Pritzker Architecture Prize recipient, James Stirling, provided a good example of what is described above in his renovation and expansion of Rice University's School of Architecture in Houston, Texas. In this project the exterior and the interior were treated as two separate designs; while the facade is faithful to the historic contexts of the surrounding buildings, the interior is distinctly modern. This plan is controversial among architectural critics for having broken the unity of design.

Also an academic building, though having as its context the crest of a hill on a landscaped estate, the newly completed American Academy of Arts and Sciences in Cambridge, Mass., serves as a whole and successful example of the use of the architectural past as a source of new creation. In this case architects Gerhard Kallmann and Noel McKinnell of Kallmann, McKinnell & Wood looked no farther than to the immediate precursor of modernism, the Arts and Crafts movement. The influence of that movement dominates the entire

251

Thorncrown Chapel in the Ozark Mountains of Arkansas was designed by Fay Jones, a former apprentice to Frank Lloyd Wright.

building, not just the facade. By choosing a style shaped by many architects, including Charles Rennie Mackintosh and Frank Lloyd Wright, Kallmann and McKinnell created an atmosphere for scholars that may be compared to that of a 19th-century country house.

A former apprentice to Frank Lloyd Wright, architect Fay Jones revealed his craftsmanship during the year in the Thorncrown Chapel, a wayfarer's chapel situated in the Ozark Mountains of northwestern Arkansas. With an ability to turn oak and fieldstone into forms of elegant beauty, Jones confined his design to materials that could be carried by two men down a narrow hillside path. In addition, these materials are indigenous to the Ozarks. Placed upon a beautiful wooded knoll, the chapel was designed to be visited by nature-loving hikers.

Such compatibility with surroundings is not so easily discerned in the case of the Hartford (Conn.) Seminary Foundation. Architect Richard Meier claims, however, that his white porcelain-clad steel building, rather than bearing no relationship to the New England vernacular austerity of design, may be seen as its descendant. While the merits of the exterior of this building have been debated, the achievements of the interior are applauded, particularly Meier's use of daylighting. He based his plan on the belief that "a coming together under light" is the common element in all houses of worship. Like building spires that reach for

the heavens, creating a space in which to congregate both man and light is a religious gesture. "Light seems to come from everywhere in this building, to the extent that you're not always sure of its source," said seminary president John Dillenberger. Throughout the building there is multidirectional light: combinations of artificial light, daylight from windows, and diffused sidelight from glass blocks. All windows have built-in sunshades, and illumination can be controlled by these and supplemented by cove lights.

In recent years the idea of daylighting—the use of natural light as a source of interior illumination—has attracted increased attention. There are many cases in recent history of the successful use of daylighting in design. Three outstanding examples from the last two decades include the Kimbell Art Museum in Fort Worth, Texas, designed by Louis Kahn; the Massachusetts Institute of Technology chapel in Cambridge, Mass., designed by Eero Saarinen; and the Yale Center for British Art in New Haven, Conn., also designed by Kahn. The potential benefits of this design approach are a reduction in the operating costs of a building due to energy conservation, and an improved interior visual environment. Current studies are focusing on the use of various Sun-control devices and their cost efficiency in relation to reducing lighting demands. Models are becoming increasingly important as tools in the analysis of daylit spaces. Proponents of daylighting have cited long-term savings and connection with the outdoors as advantages not to be denied by the initial costs of installation. However, the major setback for daylighting research in 1981 was the high cost of money, a problem that affected construction in the U.S. in general.

In parts of the world where the cost of money is not so great a consideration patronage of innovative design is more apparent. The Aga Khan School of Nursing in Karachi, Pak., is a good example of uninhibited innovation. In their design architects Payette Associates and Mozhan Khadem sought climate control as the main goal, and in this the building succeeds. Maximum window exposure is to the west and southwest to reap the greatest benefit of the prevailing breezes, and for cross ventilation in the dormitories bedrooms open onto single-loaded corridors. The building forms are horizontal, oriented inward toward courtyards, and they have flat roofs shaded and cooled by ancient thermal devices known as wind scoops, which pick up the prevailing breezes and channel them across the rooftops. To combat a climate that is usually hot and dry, walls are of double masonry block with insulation between layers to reduce the absorption of heat. The textured-cement plaster finish used upon all exterior wall surfaces, known as "weeping" plaster, is dribbled onto the wall surface by an ancient handcraft method to produce tiny vertical shadows that reduce glare. The light color of the plaster matches the surrounding desert and lessens heat absorption. And, one more detail in a totally coordinated design, each bedroom opens upon a gallery covered by a trellis of bougainvillea that provides both shade and privacy.

Elsewhere in the Middle East is a structure that undertakes not only the problem of the climate but also the predicament of directing and circulating up to two million people within a 70-day period. This period, known as the Haj, is the time of the Muslim pilgrimage when pilgrims from Africa, Indonesia, Pakistan, and other parts of the world swarm into Jidda, the port of Mecca. The structure is the Haj Terminal of the new Jidda International Airport (largest in the world) in Saudi Arabia. To solve the problem of sheltering the pilgrims from the desert heat, the architectural firm of Skidmore, Owings & Merrill and engineering consultant Horst Berger of Geiger-Berger Associates designed a fabric tension (tent) structure consisting of two major units. The designers started the bottoms of the tents 20 m (65 ft) above the ground on columns from which the fabric then stretches up to 35 m (115 ft), where it is attached to support rings held by cables that rise to the top of the columns at 45 m (148 ft). The steel rings are open for continuous ventilation, making the area covered by the roof cool and breezy. Besides the advantage of cooling, the fabric roof provides natural light.

Far from being a first, the Haj Terminal is the beneficiary of technology developed in over a decade of

The National Aquarium on Baltimore's Inner Harbor emphasizes geometric form and outline (below). Designed by Cambridge Seven Associates, it houses some 5,000 fish, mammals, birds, and amphibians in innovatively designed exhibit areas (above).

fabric tension and air-supported structures. Whether used as a historic reference to the nomads' tents in the Middle East or simply to attract attention as in the case of the Florida Festival structure at Sea World in Orlando, Fla., fabric roof structures are a new element in the relationship of function and form. The Haj Terminal and the Florida Festival structure are examples of fabric tension-supported structures. Examples of fabric air-supported structures are the United States pavilion, built in 1970 in Osaka, Japan, and the Pontiac Silverdome, built in 1975 in Pontiac, Mich. Both of these, as well as a host of tension structures, were engineered by Geiger-Berger Associates of New York. Using computer technology to extend the principles of four-sided tension structures to larger polygonal structures, the firm manipulated the geometrical configurations by modifying the support systems. Other recently completed examples of fabric tension structures are Bullock's department store in San Mateo, Calif., and the pavilion of the Franklin Park Zoo in Boston.

While Jidda International is the largest airport in the world, the new Central Passenger Terminal Complex at Hartsfield Atlanta International Airport in Georgia is the largest terminal complex. As the 1981 Outstanding Civil Engineering Achievement Award of Merit recipient, this complex's unique characteristic is that more than 70% of its arriving passengers transfer to other planes. To accommodate these transfers the architectural team of Stevens & Wilkinson, Smith Hinchman & Grylls, and Minority Airport Architects & Planners designed a plan that consists of four parallel buildings housing a total of 138 airplane gates, more than in any other airport in the world. In this layout transferring passengers never enter the central terminal. In addition to two terminal buildings there are an international concourse, a transit station, and a central mechanical house, all linked by an underground people-moving system. This plan defines a new category in typical airport layouts. Prior to this design the Transportation and Research Board of the National Academy of Sciences had divided airport terminals into three categories according to function. This new fourth category is one of a centralized terminal with a linear satellite gate complex. As in the case of the Haj Terminal, an unprecedented problem was solved by an unprecedented design.

—Lindsay Li; Arlen Li

Civil engineering. During 1981 there were some historic firsts in civil engineering and construction. For the first time in history China's Yangtze River was dammed. On Jan. 4, 1981, during the tenth year of construction on the Gezhouba Hydroelectric Project,

Haj Terminal at Saudi Arabia's new Jidda International Airport allows air circulation in the desert heat by having no exterior walls and shelters travelers from the Sun with a tentlike fabric roof.

the main channel of the river was diverted through a 27-gate spillway. The main channel's upstream cofferdam, designed with double concrete core walls keyed into bedrock, withstood July 1981 flood flows that were the worst in 80 years. Cost estimates for the dam, started in 1971 and scheduled for completion in 1986, were expected to exceed $2.2 billion. The project was to include two powerhouses with locks, a spillway, and two silt sluices. These structures were to be part of the 40-m-high main dam, which would be flanked by earthen wing dams that cross a shallow 2,000-m-wide section of the river at the mouth of the Yangtze gorges.

Another engineering milestone nearing completion was the $1 billion rotating dam on the River Thames in the U.K. Scheduled to begin operating in the fall of 1982, the dam was reputed to be the world's largest movable flood defense. The barrier was designed to protect London without obstructing the view from the city or restricting river traffic. The nine concrete piers that stretch 500 m (1,700 ft) across the river contain hydraulic machinery that can raise 20-m-high gates in 30 minutes to block the flood tide. The gates rest in concrete sills flush with the river bottom when not in use, thus allowing ships to pass. Britain's Rendel, Palmer, and Tritton designed the barrier.

About 30 m (100 ft) below the surface of Manhattan in New York City a laser-guided tunnel boring machine (TBM) successfully cut four tunnel tubes through hard rock. Two of the new tunnels, each 6 m (20 ft 2 in) in diameter and 440 m (1,455 ft) long, were to be part of New York City Transit Authority's (NYCTA) rail system. The other two tunnels, 6.6 m (22 ft) in diameter and 400 m (1,320 ft) long, were for use by the Long Island Railroad. According to the NYCTA project manager progress for the first tube averaged 6.2 m (20.5 ft) per day and 8 m (26.4 ft) per day in the second tube. NYCTA designed the rock tunnel section and also served as construction manager for the entire project.

In San Francisco another tunneling system averaged 9 m (30 ft) per day on a 926-m- (3,057-ft-) long sewage transport tunnel. The contractor, Ohbayashi-OAC, used an earth-pressure balance machine to bore a 3.6-m- (12-ft-) diameter tunnel under San Francisco's Fisherman's Wharf in 4½ months. The 52-m- (170-ft-) long machine, its alignment governed by a laser beam, was custom-built for the $12.7 million job by Mitsubishi Heavy Industries in Tokyo.

In the largest highway recycling project ever undertaken the Illinois Division of Highways reconstructed a 29-year-old, 24-km (15-mi) segment of Interstate 94 outside Chicago. The segment was rebuilt from the

A 243-hectare (600-acre) refuse disposal in the City of Industry, Calif., was transformed into a recreation-conservation area containing 2 golf courses, 17 tennis courts, riding trails, and a conference center.

National Engineering Company

subgrade to the final pavement. The contractor chose the cost-effective and energy-efficient options of crushing the old pavement and reusing it as porous granular embankment. The old asphalt overlay was milled and recycled. It was mixed with 70% virgin material and used as bituminous subbase for the reconstructed expressway.

Perhaps the most widely acclaimed civil engineering project completed in 1981 was the transformation of a 240-ha (600-ac) refuse disposal in the City of Industry, Calif., into a valuable and beautiful civic recreation area. The American Society of Civil Engineers named the Industry Hills Civic Recreation-Conservation Area the outstanding civil engineering achievement of 1981. The site served as a refuse disposal between 1951 and 1969 and, although all disposal operations had ceased, health and safety hazards continued to damage surrounding areas. Subterranean fires, pollution, exposed debris, unsightly cut slopes, and barren earth characterized the area. In its place today stand two 18-hole championship golf courses, 17 tennis courts, an Olympic-size pool, riding stables and riding trails, hiking and nature trails, picnic and recreation areas, and a conference center that overlooks the San Gabriel Valley. The project includes a resource reclamation system that captures methane gas from the former landfill operation and uses it as an energy source for the conference center and the pool. Overall design coordinator and designer for many of the project's civil engineering elements was the National Engineering Company of Industry.

—John Davis

Astronomy

The last visit to Saturn for the near future, this time by Voyager 2, dominated solar system astronomy during the last year. Stellar astronomy again advanced by virtue of ultraviolet and X-ray data obtained from satellites. Sensitive detectors and persistent observers extended the distances to which the universe has been probed.

Instrumentation. A novel instrument designed to improve the efficiency of obtaining the spectra of faint galaxies was constructed by John M. Hill, J. R. P. Angel, John S. Scott, and Delvin Lindley of the Steward Observatory at the University of Arizona and by Paul Hintzen of the U.S. National Aeronautics and Space Administration's (NASA's) Goddard Space Flight Center. Usually, in obtaining high-resolution spectra of faint objects only one object may be observed at a time, and the procedure always requires scarce observing time at a large telescope.

Hill and his collaborators were interested in measuring the spectra of the many members of distant clusters of galaxies in order to obtain the individual radial velocities needed to study the dynamics of the clusters. To circumvent the necessity of observing member galaxies one by one, they designed a multiple-object spectrograph. They used quartz fibers to bring the light of more than 20 objects simultaneously to a spectrograph, thereby obtaining spectra for all the sources at the same time.

In the prototype instrument Hill and his co-workers accurately drilled an aluminum plate with a set of holes, each located where a galaxy of interest would fall at the focus of their telescope. A second plate with a linear array of holes was placed where the slit of the spectrograph would normally be found. The holes in the two plates were paired, and each pair was connected with a single quartz fiber. Thus the light of all the galaxies that was imaged on the entrance holes passed to the spectrograph at the same time but gave rise to individual spectra. In one case the research group obtained the spectra of 26 galaxies with the 2.3-m reflector of Steward Observatory in a single three-hour exposure. This represented nearly a sixfold increase in observing efficiency.

The original instrument requires that a new entrance plate be made for each field of galaxies to be studied. In 1982, however, the group was building a modified instrument that would have 32 remotely positioned quartz fibers. Proper care in polishing the quartz fiber ends and the use of antireflective coatings were expected to make the new instrument equal in light-transmitting efficiency to a slit spectrograph. The instrument was expected to provide up to a thirtyfold increase in data acquisition at the telescope without requiring the considerable time needed to prepare an entrance aperture plate.

Solar System. The voluminous data returned by Voyager 1 were still being studied when Voyager 2 made its rendezvous with Saturn in August. Voyager 2's course had been corrected in order to obtain pictures of Saturn's satellites that had not been seen well by Voyager 1. The vidicon tubes aboard Voyager 2, used to image the planet and its satellites, had better resolution than those of its predecessor, and, in addition, the photopolarimeter on Voyager 2 functioned, unlike the one that had failed on Voyager 1.

The rings of Saturn again revealed thousands of separate ringlets to the vidicon, but the photopolarimeter, observing the star Delta Scorpii through the rings, demonstrated that down to a resolution of tens of meters the ringlets numbered in the hundreds of thousands. The thin F-ring, for example, consisted of at least ten separate components. The boundaries of the various divisions were also shown to be extremely sharp; for example, the transition between the A-ring and the Encke division is less than 1 km (0.62 mi) wide. The strange braids and kinks in the F-ring were not seen by Voyager 2, but a narrow ringlet was observed in the Encke division that was replete with kinks more

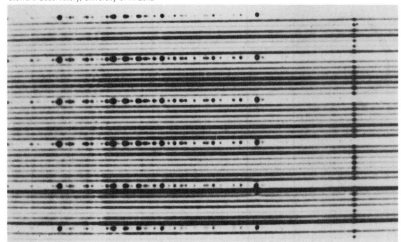

Spectra of 37 galaxies in the distant cluster Abell 576 were obtained at the same time by using a multiple-object spectrograph, known as Medusa. The spectra are then measured for their radial velocities in order to gain an understanding of the dynamics of the cluster.

closely spaced than the ones viewed by Voyager 1 in the F-ring.

Radio signals from Voyager 2, beamed through the rings at wavelengths of 3.6 and 13 cm, yielded information on particle sizes in the rings. No particles larger than 11 m in diameter were detected. The number of particles of smaller size increases rapidly. For example, there are 120–200 particles per sq km of projected ring surface in the 9–11-m range and 1,700–6,000 in the 3–5-m range.

The spokes seen on the rings by Voyager 1 appeared again. Time-lapse photographs showed that new spokes form rapidly as old ones die out, extending radially outward across some 20,000 km (12,500 mi) of ring surface in as little as 12 minutes. The rapidity of the formation was surprising. The spokes are still believed to be caused by ionized dust lifted from the rings by magnetic activity within Saturn. There is also the possibility that the spokes are associated with the electrical discharges that were detected by both Voyagers.

The cloud and wind structure in Saturn's atmosphere was more clearly seen by Voyager 2 because of the better resolution of its vidicons. Banded winds and jet streams were observed at higher latitudes than on Jupiter. Saturn, like Jupiter, has convection eddies that carry heat from the planet's hot interior and supply the energy to drive the winds.

The satellites viewed by Voyager 2 were Iapetus, Hyperion, Enceladus, Tethys, and Phoebe. Iapetus, an outer moon, was first seen by Giovanni Cassini in 1671, when he noted that it must be dark over half of its surface because it was only visible on one side of Saturn. The Voyager measurements confirmed that it reflects only 4–5% on the face held in the direction of orbital motion by tidal locking with Saturn. The other side reflects 50% of the light that strikes it. Some of the craters in the bright hemisphere of Iapetus have dark floors. Three competing ideas have been presented to explain the satellite's strange appearance. One is that it has an intrinsically dark surface covered by a bright frost layer but that as it orbits Saturn the frost on the forward surface is eroded by collisions with particles. A second is that the dark region results from material given off by the more distant Phoebe and swept up by Iapetus. Last, the dark regions are caused by the upwelling of material from inside the body of Iapetus itself.

Voyager 2's images of Tethys, one of the inner, major moons of Saturn, revealed a huge rift or fissure extending three-quarters of the way around its surface and numerous craters, one a gigantic 400 km (250 mi) in diameter. The huge crater has collapsed walls and a floor that has rebounded to the curvature of the surrounding terrain, suggesting that the satellite was warm enough after the impact for material to flow into the crater and fill it up again.

Enceladus appears to be the most geologically evolved satellite of Saturn. The Voyager 2 pictures reveal it to have at least five distinct regions based upon crater density. The regions with virtually no craters underwent a resurfacing process no longer than one billion years ago, about one-quarter of the satellite's age. The energy required to cause this is believed to have been supplied by tidal friction.

Hyperion has the most bizarre shape of the larger satellites, looking like a pock-marked hamburger patty. It is the only markedly nonspherical Saturnian satellite that has a dimension in excess of 400 km.

Phoebe, the outermost satellite, has a low reflectivity, only 5%, and orbits Saturn opposite to all the other satellites. This moon is thought to have been formed elsewhere in the solar system and then captured later by Saturn.

By 1982 Voyager 2 was en route to Uranus. If its equipment continues to function reasonably well, it may in 1985 provide data of value about that planet. In

Saturn was photographed by the Voyager 1 space probe on Oct. 18, 1980 (left), and by Voyager 2 on July 12, 1981 (right). The pictures reveal that considerable changes took place in the planet's northern hemisphere between encounters by the spacecraft.

the meantime the information both Voyagers have returned from Jupiter and Saturn will continue to occupy many scientists.

Sun. Evidence that the solar 11-year cycle of activity is long-lived and connected with changes in the Earth's weather was found in the mountains of South Australia. G. E. Williams, an Australian geologist, discovered fossilized, stratified, annual lake-bed deposits in late-Precambrian rocks formed about 600 million years ago. The deposit layers reveal cyclical fluctuations with 11-, 22-, and 90-year periods, the same periods seen in solar activity. The layers reflect greater or lesser sediment deposits in ancient lakes due to glacial melt-off during late-Precambrian time. Williams proposed that the rocks record the influence of solar activity on the rate of melt-off.

Stars. Two extremely red stars were discovered during the year by Gerard Gilmore and I. Neill Reid of the Royal Observatory in Edinburgh, Scotland. In studying the spatial distribution of low-mass, hence, cool, faint stars, they photographed the south galactic polar region with the 1.2-m United Kingdom Schmidt telescope and made photometric observations from the blue to the near-infrared regions of the spectrum with the 3.9-m Anglo-Australian telescope.

Two stars stood out among the many that were mea-

sured because they were about 100 times brighter in the infrared region than in the visible. The energy distribution of the first one was similar to that of many bright red supergiants. Such stars are extremely luminous, generating nearly 40,000 times as much energy as the Sun. This star lay in the direction of the Sculptor group of galaxies and had the apparent brightness expected of a red giant at the distance of the Sculptor group. No detectable galaxy is associated with the star, however, and so the researchers concluded that it is a bright star located in a dwarf elliptical galaxy in the Sculptor group, roughly eight million light-years from the Sun.

The other star is actually so faint that it could be detected only in the infrared. Its radiation at wavelengths of 0.9 and 2.2 micrometers corresponds to a body with a temperature of only 2,250 K. The Sun radiates nearly 400,000 times more energy in visible light than does this star. Based on its observed brightness, the star can only be about 80 light-years away. It is the first intrinsically faint star discovered without first recognizing its nearness from studies of its proper motion. It ranks among the least luminous stars known.

Bernard Bopp of the University of Toledo and Robert Stencel of the University of Colorado reported on several stars, similar to the variable star FK Comae,

258

which they observed via satellite in the ultraviolet region of the spectrum. These stars show characteristic spectra of G or K type giant stars (large, moderately cool stars) and vary in brightness by 10 or 30% with periods of a few days. They are peculiar because they have broad, variable emission lines in hydrogen and ionized calcium, characteristic of a rapidly rotating star. But cool giant stars normally do not have high rotation rates except for some stars such as RS Canum Venaticorum. The latter is a binary star in which the giant component has been caused to rotate with the same period as the orbital motion because of tidal interaction with its companion. In its spectrum FK Comae does not show evidence of being binary. The variation in its brightness is not due to eclipses by a companion but instead to large starspots or flares on its photosphere, its luminous surface layer. The ultraviolet spectrum of FK Comae has bright, high-temperature lines that indicate strong activity in the chromosphere similar to that in the RS Canum Venaticorum stars. (The chromosphere is the lower part of the atmosphere of a star.) Strong chromospheric lines appear in rapidly rotating stars.

Bopp and Stencel calculated that if FK Comae-like stars were reduced to their former main-sequence sizes without a change in angular momentum they would spin so fast that they would be unstable. The stars, therefore, could not have had the necessary angular momentum as single stars earlier in their evolution to account for their current rotation. Furthermore, since no companion star is present to supply the angular momentum to account for the high spin rate, the two scientists concluded that the stars are coalesced binaries; that is, they developed from close, rapidly orbiting binaries in which the more massive primary evolved into a giant, expanding to envelop its companion and capturing the orbital angular momentum of the system. The result is a G-type giant spinning with equatorial speeds of about 100 km per second with a rotation period of only a few days.

A group of 16 astronomers headed by G. S. Vaiana and associated with the Harvard Smithsonian Center for Astrophysics studied X-ray data on 143 stars obtained by the Einstein Observatory in space. Before this satellite was launched, few ordinary stars beyond the Sun were known to emit X-rays. The improved measuring ability of the X-ray telescope aboard the satellite allowed many ordinary stars to be detected as X-ray sources rather than just the more exotic and stronger ones, such as supernova remnants and clusters of galaxies. Only very cool giants and supergiants were not found to be X-ray sources.

The X-rays from a star originate in a hot corona surrounding the star. These results, therefore, show that the phenomenon of stellar coronas is common and not restricted to any particular spectral class of star as had been previously thought.

Our Galaxy. It has been known since the 1950s, both from visual and 21-cm observations, that our Galaxy is spiral in shape. Visual observations, mainly depending upon the recognition of bright blue stars and the nebulosities associated with them, have resulted in the identification of three spiral arms. The arm in which the Sun resides is known as the Orion arm and is roughly 30,000 light-years from the center of the Galaxy. The other two arms, the Perseus and the Sagittarius-Carina, are, respectively, about 6,000 light-years more distant and more close than our arm. The arms are named for the constellations in which they predominantly appear to lie. Additional spiral arms were not identified because astronomers lose the ability to recognize the objects that mark the arms due to distance and interstellar matter.

In recent months, however, Marc Kutner and Kathryn Mead of Rensselaer Polytechnic Institute at Troy, N.Y., identified a fourth arm half again as far from the galactic center as the Orion. The arm extends over an arc of about 45° on the sky, through the constellations of Cygnus and Vulpecula. Kutner and Mead discovered the arm by observing 2.6-mm radio waves rather than visual wavelengths; at 2.6 mm carbon monoxide emits radio waves. They found a chain of clouds roughly 180–240 light-years in length stretched along the arm over a total distance of nearly 45,000 light-years. Carbon monoxide has been detected before in interstellar space and is usually associated with much more abundant molecular hydrogen. Apparently what Kutner and Mead found was the edge of a spiral arm where interstellar gas has been accumulated and piled up by a den-

High-resolution image of Enceladus was made by combining several photographs obtained by Voyager 2 on Aug. 25, 1981, when it passed within 119,000 kilometers (74,000 miles) of the satellite of Saturn.

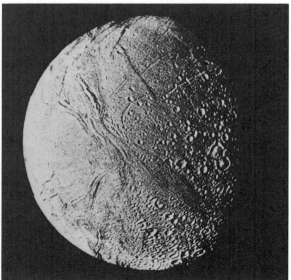

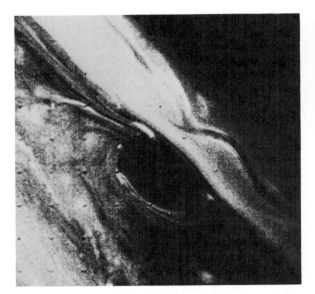 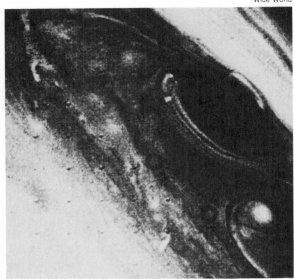

Circulation around a large brown spot in the atmosphere of Saturn is revealed by Voyager 2 from distances of 2.7 million kilometers (left) and 2.3 million kilometers (right). The spot may represent an opening in the planet's upper cloud deck through which darker underlying clouds can be seen.

sity wave traveling through the disk of the Galaxy. These are the regions where interstellar matter densities are believed to increase to the point that star formation may take place.

The findings of Kutner and Mead indicate that star formation may occur over much larger stretches of the Galaxy than previously thought. The clouds that they discovered radiate at a rate corresponding to a temperature of 6 K, half the temperature of interstellar clouds in the vicinity of the Sun. Because these clouds are more distant from the galactic center than the Sun, this finding is consistent with the idea that the clouds are heated by cosmic rays from more central regions of the Galaxy.

A startling revelation about our Galaxy's past may result from a study conducted by Alex W. Rodgers and colleagues at Mount Stromlo and Siding Spring Observatories in Australia. Using new, sensitive equipment mounted on the Mount Stromlo 1.9-m reflector, they examined the south galactic pole region for faint A-type stars. Stars of the faintness they were trying to observe are very distant, approximately 10,000 light-years from the galactic plane. They lie well outside the disk of the Galaxy and are referred to as galactic halo objects. (The galactic disk is the flat distribution of stars and interstellar matter in the spiral arms and plane of the Galaxy.)

Halo objects, unlike stars in the disk of the Galaxy such as the Sun, normally reveal a deficiency in metals. They are believed to have formed early in the life of the Galaxy, before the original galactic material was polluted by heavy elements synthesized in the interiors of massive stars and subsequently thrown into interstel-

lar space by supernovas. But despite the expectations, the A stars measured by the Australian group for the most part had compositions like that of the Sun rather than like that of normal halo objects.

Because A stars have lifetimes as main-sequence stars no longer than about two billion years, considerably short of the approximately ten billion-year age of most halo objects, they must have formed well after the earliest star formation in the Galaxy. Also, because these A stars all have nearly the same composition, they must have formed at the same time from material significantly different from the primordial material of the Galaxy.

Rodgers and his colleagues proposed that the A stars formed after a collision of a gas-rich satellite galaxy with our Galaxy. According to their view the stars of the two galaxies would pass essentially unimpeded through each other, but the gas between the stars would be swept out and remain behind, trapped in our Galaxy. The compression of the gas caused by the collision would provide ideal conditions for the formation of stars. The mass of the satellite galaxy would have been about 100 million solar masses in order to account for the A stars detected. Thus, it appears that in the dim past our Galaxy participated in a form of intergalactic cannibalism.

Extragalactic Astronomy. A number of X-ray sources have been identified with clusters of galaxies. Mark D. Johnston along with co-workers at the Massachusetts Institute of Technology and the Smithsonian Astrophysical Observatory searched the Palomar Observatory Sky Atlas and the European Southern Observatory survey photographs for clusters of galaxies near

Three views of the crater-marked Saturn satellite Hyperion were revealed by Voyager 2 from distances of (left to right) 1,200,000 kilometers, 700,000 kilometers, and 500,000 kilometers.

otherwise unidentified X-ray sources. The source 4U 1708-23 coincided with a previously unrecognized cluster in Ophiuchus. The cluster is only 10° from the direction of the center of our Galaxy, and fortunately lies behind one of the less dense regions of interstellar matter in the plane of the Milky Way or it might be totally obscured.

The cluster has a central density about 100 times that of nearby regions of space. A D-type elliptical galaxy is located at the cluster's center. The D-type galaxies are thought to be oversized, overmassive, and extremely luminous as a result of capturing and literally consuming some of their former neighbors. The X-rays from the cluster originate in a hot diffuse intergalactic gas at a temperature of ten million K. This gas was swept out in collisions between member galaxies of the cluster.

The largest galactic distance ever measured was reported by Hyron Spinrad and John Stauffer (University of California, Berkeley) and Harvey Butcher (Kitt Peak Observatory). They measured the red shifts of giant elliptical galaxies associated with two radio sources (3C 427.1 and 3C 13). The red shifts of the systems were 1.175 and 1.050, respectively, placing them at a distance from the Earth of roughly ten billion light-years. The galaxies are extremely luminous, but at their great distances they are very faint in the sky. Spinrad estimated that the age of the galaxies is about 16 billion years, 6 billion years from their evolutionary appearance plus the 10 billion years the light from them has taken to reach us.

One of the most surprising and puzzling results during 1981 was announced by Robert P. Kirshner (University of Michigan), Augustus Oemler, Jr. (Yale Ob-

servatory), Paul L. Schechter (Kitt Peak), and Stephen A. Schectman (Mount Wilson). They had made a deep-sky survey of extragalactic objects in six selected regions, each subtending about a degree on the sky. Three regions were observed in the southern sky and three in the northern. The southern measurements did not reveal any surprises, but the northern samples, each at the apex of a triangle roughly 35° on a side and centered on the constellation of Bootes, revealed a discontinuity in galactic red shifts. Only one galaxy was found with a red shift corresponding to a distance between 700 million and 1 billion light-years. Furthermore, there was an enhancement in the number of galaxies on either side of this gap. It is as if there is a huge hole in the universe.

Similar voids, much smaller in extent, have been noted before. In 1982 the observers continued their work, measuring more closely spaced samples in Bootes to make sure that the counts in the three already observed samples are not simply statistical accidents.

While irregularities in the distribution of matter in the universe exist, one of the primary assumptions of modern cosmology is that, overall, matter is uniform in distribution throughout the cosmos. This premise is part of what astronomers have called the "cosmological principle." The apparent void discovered by Kershner and his colleagues does not by itself destroy this principle, but it does pose a problem for cosmologists. They must attempt to answer the question of how such a large spatial variation could form from the homogeneous distribution of matter at the time of the Big Bang.

—W. M. Protheroe

261

Chemistry

For many chemists the past year was again one of dedication to the pursuit of alternate sources of energy and chemical raw materials for industry. Light-driven water-splitting processes; the elucidation and application of "C_1 chemistry," in which carbon monoxide is used as a basic starting material for hydrocarbons and other organic compounds traditionally derived from petroleum; and lightweight, high-power storage batteries, including one based on electrically conducting organic polymers, highlighted work in this field. Investigators also improved their theoretical understanding of transition-metal organometallic compounds and achieved several important syntheses of natural products, notably the antibiotic erythromycin and a large portion of a compound with anticancer activity. Independent results from several groups of researchers suggested that the effects of chlorofluorocarbons on the Earth's stratospheric ozone layer may be less than previously estimated. In 1981 two products of the chemist's bench, aspartame and polydextrose, won approval in the U.S. as sugar substitutes.

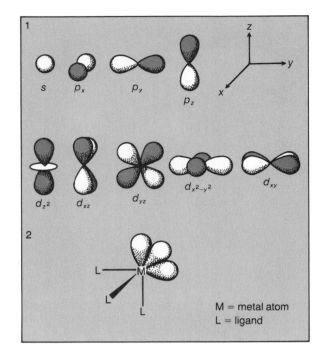

M = metal atom
L = ligand

Inorganic chemistry

Inorganic chemistry had a good and a bad year in 1981 in terms of several of its leading research scientists. It was a good year because Roald Hoffmann of Cornell University, Ithaca, N.Y., shared a Nobel Prize with Kenichi Fukui of Kyoto University in Japan for their work in theoretical chemistry (*see* SCIENTISTS OF THE YEAR). An example of the way in which Hoffmann's research into the theory of bonding in metal complexes contributed to the efforts of experimental inorganic chemists is described below. The bad news was the untimely deaths of Paolo Chini, 53, of the University of Milan in Italy and Rowland Pettit, 54, of the University of Texas. Chini is often called the father of metal-cluster compounds, and Pettit was one of the most creative investigators in the field of transition-metal organometallic chemistry. Pettit's recent contribution to the important coal-liquefaction Fischer-Tropsch reaction is discussed below.

Theoretical inorganic chemistry. Quantum chemistry affords the exact mathematical solution to the na-

ture of bonding in chemical compounds. Unfortunately most molecules are too large and complicated to allow for explicit calculations, even with the use of sophisticated computers. For molecules of fewer than ten atoms, computers do permit calculation of most of the observable properties of the molecule, plus some that are unobservable. For molecules of fewer than five atoms, the calculations are so good that they can be used to predict the spectra of molecules not found on Earth but detectable in interstellar space.

Although exact calculations cannot be made for the bonding in most molecules, the principles of quantum mechanics, which work for small molecules, can be applied qualitatively to more complicated molecules. Chemistry is an experimental science, and in the past 30 years chemists have prepared and investigated the reactions of many new compounds known as transition-metal organometallic compounds, which are made from organic groups bonded to atoms of the transition elements of the periodic table. Chemical theory does not predict the existence of these compounds or their

sandwich

inverse sandwich

6

L_nM (with C≡O and H) → (formyl with O=C, L_nM, H)

CO + H₂

H_2

$L_nM + CH_3OH$

7

acetyl group | most metals | M = zirconium, titanium, niobium, tantalum, and others

8

Th ⋯ H + CO ⇌ (Th—C(=O)—H with OR)

reactions. Fortunately, chemical theory elegantly applied by Hoffmann has accounted qualitatively for the existence of such compounds as well as their bonding, structures, and reactions.

Such tasks have been accomplished by considering the available frontier (valency) electron orbitals and their symmetry. Molecular orbitals on the ligands (groups attached to the metal) with the best geometry for maximum contact with the orbitals on the metal give rise to the strongest chemical bond, which in turn controls the structure and the reaction of the compound. Transition metals readily form complexes with many different ligands because they have nine different frontier orbitals (*see* 1). There is one *s* orbital, which is spherical; three dumbbell-shaped *p* orbitals oriented along each of the three spatial (x, y, z) axes; and five *d* orbitals, four with cloverleaf shapes and one (d_{z^2}) along the *z* axis with a sausage belt in the *xy* plane. The geometries of these nine orbitals make transition metals very versatile in their ability to interact with molecular orbitals of many different types of ligands.

The fragment approach is one theoretical tool that several investigators have used successfully to make sense of the tremendous variety of structures of compounds provided them by synthetic organometallic chemists. For example, the generalized fragment ML₃ has a molecular orbital structure (2) that requires the metal to attach itself to additional ligands. Many compounds are known that have the ML₃ fragment attached to other ligands (*see* 3 for examples).

Transition-metal organometallic chemistry had its beginning in the early 1950s with the discovery of ferrocene. Metals other than iron were then used to form analogous compounds, which came to be called sandwich compounds because the metals seemed to be between two pieces of "bread," flat cyclopentadienyl rings (4) The 1973 Nobel Prize for Chemistry was

awarded jointly to Ernst O. Fischer and Geoffrey Wilkinson for their work on sandwich compounds. Recently Hoffmann and co-workers used an ML₃ fragment to predict compounds of the inverse sandwich type (5). These compounds subsequently were prepared, a testament to the utility of good qualitative theory for the experimental chemist.

Insertion of CO into metal-hydrogen bonds. Carbon monoxide (CO) activation to produce hydrocarbons and organic compounds containing oxygen is an extremely active area of research. One of the promising approaches to this goal involves attaching CO and hydrogen (H) to the same metal atom and allowing the two to react (6). The reaction in which hydrogen migrates from the metal to the carbon atom seems logical, for it is well known that methyl groups migrate in this fashion. In spite of this, all of the many able attempts to encourage this reaction failed until the past year. The initial indication of what types of metals might work best was provided by the observation of Carlo Floriani of the University of Pisa in Italy. He found that unlike most metals, which are attached to the acetyl group only at carbon, early transition metals (those in the first columns of transition metals in the periodic table) are attached to both carbon and oxygen (7).

Attachment of oxygen to the early transition metals is in accord with the well-known affinity of early transition metals for oxygen. Much the same is true of the inner transition metals, the lanthanides and the actinides. With this background information Tobin Marks of Northwestern University, Evanston, Ill., very cleverly designed an actinide (thorium) organometallic compound that undergoes the desired hydrogen migration to produce the formyl compound (8). He reasoned correctly that a metal which also bonds to the oxygen of the formyl group would enhance its stability and provide the driving force for hydrogen migration to the neighboring CO. Now that this reaction has been dem-

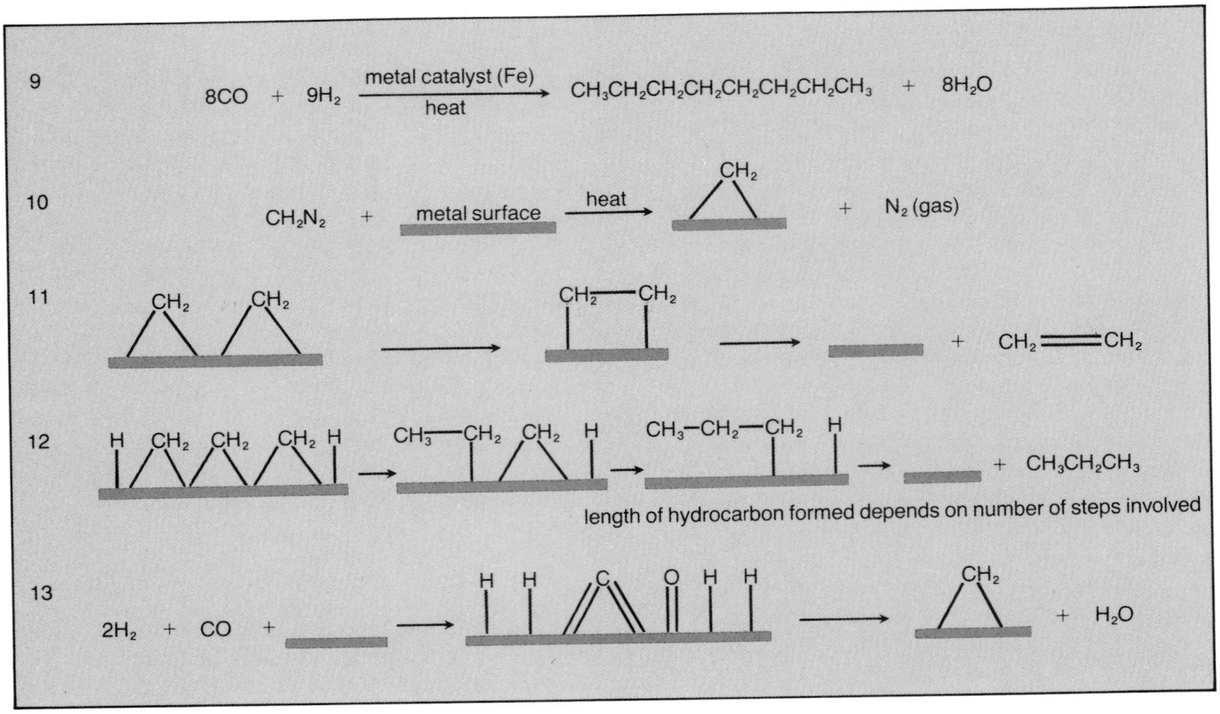

$$9 \quad 8CO + 9H_2 \xrightarrow[\text{heat}]{\text{metal catalyst (Fe)}} CH_3CH_2CH_2CH_2CH_2CH_2CH_2CH_3 + 8H_2O$$

$$10 \quad CH_2N_2 + \text{metal surface} \xrightarrow{\text{heat}} CH_2 + N_2 \text{ (gas)}$$

11

$$CH_2 \quad CH_2 \longrightarrow CH_2{-}CH_2 \longrightarrow \quad + \quad CH_2{=\!=}CH_2$$

12

$$H\ CH_2\ CH_2\ CH_2\ H \longrightarrow CH_3{-}CH_2\ CH_2\ H \longrightarrow CH_3{-}CH_2{-}CH_2\ H \longrightarrow \quad + \quad CH_3CH_2CH_3$$

length of hydrocarbon formed depends on number of steps involved

13

$$2H_2 + CO + \quad \longrightarrow \quad H\ H\ C\ O\ H\ H \longrightarrow CH_2 + H_2O$$

onstrated, there remains much research to do to find the ideal metal compound for the most efficient production of hydrocarbons or organic compounds containing oxygen.

Coal liquefaction. The technology of coal gasification and liquefaction is well developed, and in the early 1980s it was being used commercially to provide gasoline for South Africa. This technology is based on the work of two German chemists who in 1926 discovered a reaction that is now named after them, the Fischer-Tropsch reaction (see *1978* and *1981 Yearbook of Science and the Future* Year in Review: CHEMISTRY: *Inorganic chemistry*). The reaction gives a mixture of hydrocarbons, but it is illustrated here for the production of octane (9).

Although this reaction had been known for more than half a century, there remained uncertainties and differences of opinion as to the details of how the reaction takes place (the reaction mechanism). Recent experiments elegantly designed and executed by Pettit at the University of Texas largely answer the age-old question of the mechanism of this reaction. He decided to check experimentally the original suggestion of Fischer and Tropsch that the reaction proceeds by polymerization of methylene groups (CH₂) on the metal surface. This check was done with diazomethane (CH₂N₂), which is known to decompose thermally to give methylene and nitrogen gas (10). In the absence of hydrogen, adjacent methylene groups on the surface combine and come off as ethylene (11). In the presence of hydrogen, polymerization does take place to give a mixture of hydrocarbons, including octane (12). With the knowledge that CO and H₂ fragment on metal surfaces, it follows that these molecules can generate methylene groups, which then go on to form hydrocarbons (13).

These experiments provide very strong evidence that the Fischer-Tropsch reaction proceeds by a methylene polymerization mechanism. With this additional knowledge chemists may be able to improve the efficiency of the process and to make coal liquefaction more cost-effective.

—Fred Basolo

Organic chemistry

Structure determinations and syntheses of natural products, syntheses of nonnatural products, and studies of reaction mechanisms continued to occupy organic chemists during the past year, and all of these fields experienced substantial advances. Adding to this panoply of accomplishments were noteworthy events in biomimetic chemistry, industrial chemistry, and the chemical literature.

Natural product synthesis. A number of complex compounds made by living cells were totally synthesized in the laboratory during the year. Two that involved particularly intense efforts are aklavinone (1) and erythromycin (2). Aklavinone is the nonsugar portion of a compound called aclacinomycin A, which was isolated several years earlier by a group of Japanese chemists and which shows promise as an anticancer

aklavinone

drug. The synthetic challenge combined with the commercial possibilities attracted no fewer than four separate research groups headed, respectively, by Patrick N. Confalone of Hoffman-LaRoche, Andrew Kende of the University of Rochester (N.Y.), Yoshito Kishi of Harvard University, and Tsung-tee Li of the Syntex Research Center. In mid-1981 three of these groups simultaneously reported the synthesis of aklavinone. Just as a game of chess can be played in an almost limitless number of ways, a complex organic synthesis can be carried out in many different sequences. Not surprisingly, each of these syntheses had its own distinctive pattern.

A more formidable synthetic challenge was provided by erythromycin, a mold metabolite produced by *Streptomyces erythreus*, and one of the best known antibiotics. The presence of a large ring, ten chiral centers (carbon atoms carrying four different substituents, making possible the existence of mirror-image isomers), and two unusual sugars in its structure posed problems that were surmounted only through the efforts of an army of 50 chemists working for almost ten years under the direction of the incomparable Robert B. Woodward of Harvard University. But in the sum-

mer of 1979 Woodward died, and the final direction of this expansive project was left to his colleague Kishi.

Natural product structure. Before a natural product can be synthesized, its structure must be known, and structure determination has been a major part of organic chemistry from the earliest days of the science. Over the years nature and the synthetic chemist have engaged each other in a contest, nature producing complex structures that seem to defy total synthesis and the chemist attempting to meet this challenge. This past year's syntheses of aklavinone and erythromycin, combined with the previous syntheses of such complex molecules as strychnine, chlorophyll, and vitamin B$_{12}$, all attest to the fact that the chemist has been waging a good, perhaps even a winning, battle.

Recently, however, nature came forth with a new challenger, brevetoxin B (3), which possesses devilish structural and stereochemical complexity. This compound is produced by the alga *Ptychodiscus (Gymnodinium) brevis,* which is more familiarly known as red tide. Inhabitants of southern coastal areas in the U.S. are acquainted with the periodic bloom of red tide that kills fish and other sea life and fills the air with an almost invisible but highly irritating material. Extracts from this alga yielded mixtures of toxins from which brevetoxin B was separated by Koji Nakanishi of Columbia University, New York City, using a technique called flash chromatography developed by his colleague W. Clark Still. A crystal of brevetoxin B was subjected to X-ray crystallographic analysis by Jon Clardy of Cornell University, Ithaca, N.Y., and the information that he obtained was sufficient to establish a spectacular structure that contains 11 rings and 23 chiral centers. This means that over eight million stereoisomeric forms of brevetoxin B are possible, of which the naturally occurring material is just one.

erythromycin

brevetoxin B

Whether nature has checkmated the synthetic chemist with this latest ploy remains to be seen.

Nonnatural product synthesis. Although natural products are many and varied, the chemist actually has outdone nature in the number, if not the complexity, of compounds synthesized. The majority of the more than five million compounds listed in *Chemical Abstracts* are products of the chemist's laboratory. Of particular note among the many new ones made during the year is a large, three-dimensional, topologically spherical compound called dodecahedrane (4), which represents the chemical expression of one of the Greek "cosmic figures" (the others are the tetrahedron, cube, octahedron, and icosahedron). Leo Paquette and colleagues of Ohio State University came tantalizingly close to achieving a synthesis of a "perfect" version of this compound, failing only because of a pair of "extra" methyl groups attached to the dodecahedrane cage. Although there seemed to be no way to directly excise these methyl groups, modification of the 19-step synthesis worked out by Paquette might produce dodecahedrane itself.

If the appeal of dodecahedrane is more aesthetic than practical, many other nonnatural compounds were made in the past year for very practical reasons. Levonantradol (5), for example, is the outcome of a six-year program under the direction of M. Ross Johnson of Pfizer Inc. to design a molecule based on the active ingredients of *Cannabis sativa* (the marijuana plant) that incorporates the structural features necessary for analgesic activity. Levonantradol accomplishes this goal; it is stated to be considerably more potent than the natural opiate morphine, and it is hoped that it will be less addicting.

Biomimetic chemistry concerns processes in the laboratory that are designed to mimic those in nature. Because virtually all biological reactions are catalyzed by large protein molecules called enzymes, one area of biomimetic chemistry involves attempts to build en-

zyme mimics. A striking advance in this endeavor was reported early in the year by Ronald Breslow of Columbia University, who showed that by careful adjustment of the size and shape of a guest molecule to make it conform to the spatial requirements of the cavity of a host molecule, an increase of ten million in the rate at which the guest molecule reacts can be achieved. The host molecule that he used was a doughnut-shaped compound called cyclodextrin (6). The carefully chosen guest molecule was cylindrical in shape and fit snugly in the middle of the cyclodextrin doughnut. It is this kind of complementarity between an enzyme (the host) and its substrate (the guest) that accounts for the remarkable effectiveness of nature's catalysts.

Reaction mechanisms relate to the chemist's desire to learn exactly how a reactant is transformed into a product—how the atoms and electrons move, what are the structures of the entities between reactant and product, and whether or not intermediates are formed. In an attempt to deal with this problem in a fundamental way, Japanese physicist Kenichi Fukui of Kyoto University published in 1954 what he called the "frontier orbital" theory. His ideas were couched in a mathematical form that was inaccessible to the majority of experimental organic chemists, however, and it remained for Woodward at Harvard and Roald Hoffmann (now at Cornell University, Ithaca, N.Y.) to extend Fukui's ideas and present them in a pictorial form that was immediately appealing and understandable. The influence of these ideas on the way in which chemists think about reactions has been enormous, in recognition for which Fukui and Hoffmann were jointly awarded the 1981 Nobel Prize for Chemistry (*see* SCIENTISTS OF THE YEAR).

Their theory has particular relevance for reactions that are said to be "concerted," which means that old bonds break and new bonds form simultaneously without the intervention of intermediates. To obtain experimental evidence, however, as to whether a reaction

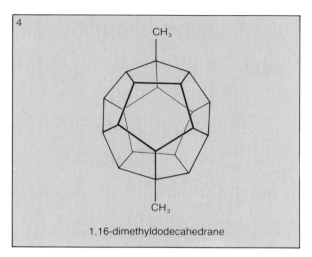

CH₃

CH₃

1,16-dimethyldodecahedrane

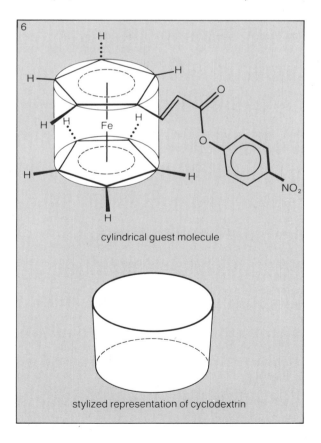

levonantradol

cylindrical guest molecule

stylized representation of cyclodextrin

falls in this category is often difficult. For example, the concertedness of the conversion of hydrazobenzene to benzidine (7), known as the benzidine rearrangement, has intrigued chemists for many decades and has been the subject of considerable debate. The controversy was settled only in the past year by the collaborative effort of Henry Shine of Texas Tech University and Harold Kwart of the University of Delaware. These scientists pooled their talents, and using hydrazobenzene isotopically labeled with nitrogen-15 in one case, carbon-13 in another case, and deuterium in a third case, they analyzed the benzidine by a sophisticated mass spectrometric technique and showed that the effects of the isotopic substitution were completely commensurate with a reaction pathway involving no intermediates. Happily, this is in accord with the Fukui-Woodward-Hoffmann theory, which predicts that the benzidine rearrangement should indeed be concerted and, in the parlance of the theory, should be a [5,5]suprafacial sigmatropic process that is "allowed."

Industrial chemistry. The discoveries that occur in academic laboratories are usually revealed to the scientific world more quickly than those from industrial laboratories. Nevertheless, very sophisticated research is conducted today in many industries, and when it is successful it appears as a new plant process. A great deal of effort has been devoted over the past several years to what is called "C_1 chemistry," in which carbon monoxide, rather than hydrocarbons from fossil fuels, is used as a starting material (see *Inorganic chemistry*, above). This year Texaco Inc. unveiled a process whereby carbon monoxide can efficiently convert acetic acid to longer chain fatty acids, using hydrogen gas as the source of hydrogen and ruthenium compounds as the catalysts for inducing the formation of the new carbon-carbon and carbon-hydrogen bonds.

Sophisticated though such processes are, they rely completely on nonnatural materials for their success.

But a new trend is taking place in some industries: natural products—in particular, recombinant DNA molecules—are being pressed into service. Currently, products being manufactured by recombinant DNA technology include such glamorous molecules as interferon and insulin, but it is anticipated that less exotic, but highly profitable, industrial commodities such as aldehydes, ketones, and fatty acids will eventually yield to this technology. To provide the appropriate recombinant DNA molecules large programs are under way to accumulate a "library" of these compounds. For this purpose, methods for the synthesis of small polynucleotides (*i.e.*, chains of 10–25 nucleotide units) have been

hydrazobenzene → benzidine

so perfected that commercial DNA-synthesizing machines appeared during the year.

Chemical literature. Scientific anniversaries usually celebrate a famous man or woman, a significant experimental discovery, or an important theoretical development. One anniversary of 1981 was different, for it celebrated one of the world's greatest compendia of information, *Beilstein's Handbook of Organic Chemistry*. One hundred years earlier Friedrich Beilstein, born of German parents but living most of his life in Russia, published a volume that he called a *Handbuch*, in which he had collected physical and chemical data for all of the 15,000 organic compounds known at that time. The idea proved so popular that a second edition of three volumes and then a third edition of eight volumes followed only a few years later, forecasting the escalation in size that was to occur during the ensuing century. By 1981 the fourth edition and supplements to *Beilstein*, as the collection is familiarly known, is housed in 230 volumes that contain 200,000 pages, consume about 8 m (26 ft) of shelf space, and cost about $91,000. The forthcoming publication of a fifth edition has been announced, and in recognition that English has become the universal language of science, it will be written for the first time in English rather than in German. How many volumes, pages, meters of shelf space, and thousands of dollars it will entail can only be left to the imagination.

—C. David Gutsche

Physical chemistry

Physical chemists spent 1981 doggedly pursuing the elusive goal of their science: understanding chemical reactions and processes in terms of fundamental interactions at the molecular, atomic, and subatomic levels. Using lasers (a favorite tool), molecular beams, computer-based models, elaborate detection systems, and other complex equipment, they improved their theories of chemical reactions at surfaces and in the atmosphere, of combustion processes, and of the quantum nature of molecules. They also made advances in applying their techniques to the much more complicated problem of biological systems. Investigators suffered some setbacks as well in 1981: the once promising ability of laser energy to produce specific chemical reactions continued to fade, and, in the U.S., the Na-

tional Resource for Computation in Chemistry (NRCC) closed. The NRCC had been established in late 1977 to give chemists access to powerful computers not available in their own laboratories and to run workshops where chemists could work on computational problems of broad relevance to their community.

Surface chemistry. A large number of chemical reactions, including many of industrial importance, occur at solid surfaces. Understanding the chemistry of such diverse processes as catalysis, adhesion, corrosion, and radiation damage ultimately requires understanding the ways in which the molecules of a gas or a liquid interact with molecules at the surface of a solid. Unfortunately, surface structure is much more complicated than the structure of the bulk material, and surface interactions are correspondingly difficult to examine experimentally. In 1981, work continued on such techniques as electron scattering, ion scattering, surface diffraction of X-rays, and extended X-ray-absorption fine-structure spectroscopy that allow physical chemists to look at the structure of and processes occurring in the first layer or first few layers of molecules or atoms at a surface.

Some noteworthy findings came out of that work in 1981. J. Peter Toennies and co-workers at the Max-Planck-Institut für Strömungsforschung in Göttingen, West Germany, demonstrated a phenomenon they call selective desorption. A phenomenon known as selective adsorption has been known since 1933. That process is observed when a beam of atoms is directed at the surface of a single crystal, and the intensity of the scattered beam is measured. It turns out that the intensity of the scattered beam depends on the orientation of the crystal in relation to the incident beam. The

hydrogen-family radicals cycle from one form to another

$$O_3 + \text{ultraviolet light} \rightarrow O_2 + O$$

$$O + H_2O \rightarrow 2OH$$

$$OH + CO \rightarrow CO_2 + H$$

$$H + O_2 \rightarrow HO_2$$

$$HO_2 + NO \rightarrow OH + NO_2$$

1

phenomenon is explained by a diffraction process that leads to the capture of atoms by the surface.

Using very precise time-of-flight measurements of helium atoms scattered from a lithium fluoride crystal surface, Toennies showed that a selectively adsorbed helium atom travels across the crystal surface as much as 500 angstroms before undergoing an inelastic interaction with a surface phonon, which results in its desorption. (One angstrom is a hundred-millionth of a centimeter.) A surface phonon, essentially, is a vibration. In other words, Toennies found that the helium atoms are selectively adsorbed on the crystal surface, travel along the surface until they encounter a single surface vibration, and then leave the surface as a result of that interaction.

Another advance was that of Richard Zare and co-workers at Stanford University, who used a technique called laser-induced fluorescence (LIF) spectroscopy, a technique developed by Zare, to probe the internal-state distribution of molecules scattered from a surface. Zare used a beam of nitrogen oxide molecules that had been put through a process of supersonic expansion cooling, which lowered their temperature to about 16 K ($-431°$ F). The beam was scattered from the surface of a single crystal of silver with a temperature of about 700 K (800° F). LIF spectroscopy was used to measure the rotational excitation of the molecules after they leave the surface. If the molecules remained at 16 K after leaving, then the interaction could be explained by simple elastic scattering; if they came off at 700 K, then the interaction with the surface would be entirely responsible for the rotational

Argonne chemist Michael K. Bowman works with optical-magnetic spectroscopy apparatus he adapted to study crucial first event in bacterial photosynthesis.

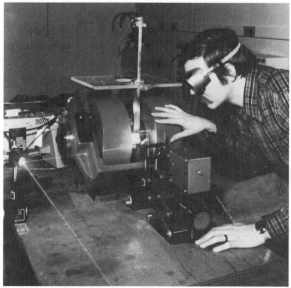

Argonne National Laboratory

2

state of the scattered molecules. What Zare found was that the molecules left with a temperature of about 400 K (260° F) and that this temperature is relatively independent of the temperature of the silver crystal. What investigators still need to do is to distinguish the processes that lead to this incomplete rotational accommodation.

Another type of advance in surface chemistry was made by Gabor A. Somorjai and co-workers at the University of California in Berkeley. Somorjai developed a technology he called a high-pressure/low-pressure cell. The purpose of the cell is to allow researchers to use experimental techniques that require very high vacuums to study a surface before, after, and during a surface catalytic reaction that occurs under very high pressures. The goal again is to understand the chemistry that takes place at the surface. Until very recently the design of catalysts had been largely an art requiring a great deal of trial-and-error experimentation. Somorjai is using his technology to study catalytic reactions on platinum surfaces of various configurations to understand which surface configuration leads to the greatest catalytic activity. The goal is to transform the art of catalyst design into a technology based on science.

Atmospheric chemistry. Physical chemists continued to contribute to the understanding of chemical processes occurring in the atmosphere that have important environmental consequences. One such area is the effect of chlorofluorocarbons and nitrogen oxides on stratospheric ozone (O_3). The ozone layer is constantly being formed and destroyed by natural processes, but chlorine atoms, produced by ultraviolet radiation in sunlight breaking down chlorofluorocarbons in the atmosphere, greatly enhance ozone destruction. Computer models that have been designed to predict overall atmospheric chemistry incorporate kinetic information and concentrations of reactants for 100 or more reactions. Many of those reactions involve radicals, which are very reactive species that have a single, unpaired electron.

Recent results from a number of independent researchers working on the kinetics of four different radical reactions all indicated that the effect of chlorofluorocarbons is less than had been thought. A key group of radicals in atmospheric chemistry is the hydrogen family of radicals: atomic hydrogen (H), the hydroxyl radical (OH), and the hydroperoxyl radical (HO_2). In a number of reactions with each other and with water, oxygen, and other molecules, these radicals cycle from one form to another (*see* 1). Their relevance to chlorine involves the fact that the primary deactivation reaction of chlorine is with naturally occurring methane in the atmosphere to form hydrogen chloride and a methyl radical (CH_3). Hydrogen chloride does not destroy ozone. The hydroxyl radical, however, reacts with hydrogen chloride to produce water and regenerate chlorine (*see* 2); essentially it short-circuits the deactivation of chlorine. Therefore, reactions that destroy hydrogen-family radicals tend to reduce the effect of chlorine on ozone.

Researchers including A. R. Ravishankara and co-workers at the Georgia Institute of Technology in Atlanta, Frederick Kaufman and co-workers at the University of Pittsburgh, Leon Keyser at the Jet Propulsion Laboratory in Pasadena, Calif., Ian Barnes and co-workers in West Germany, and others found that four reactions which act to destroy hydrogen-family radicals are significantly faster than had been thought (*see* 3). The researchers used a number of sensitive techniques to determine the kinetics of the radical reactions. These findings along with other research have reduced the projected effect of chlorofluorocarbon use at 1977 levels to about a 6% reduction in stratospheric ozone. The projection had been as high as a 17% reduction.

Combustion chemistry. The mechanism of the combustion of even the simplest molecules is not well understood. For example, in the combustion of methane (the simplest hydrocarbon) and oxygen about 100 distinct steps have been identified. With more complicated molecules the first step is often pyrolysis, the process of breaking the molecules into smaller fragments with heat, after which each fragment undergoes a series of reactions similar to those for methane, resulting in an even more complex mechanism. As in atmospheric chemistry many researchers are turning to computer models to understand combustion, and in 1981 some definite progress was made in perfecting those models.

Work also progressed in studying the elementary reactions of combustion. For example, Yuan T. Lee and co-workers at the Lawrence Berkeley Laboratory in Berkeley, Calif., used crossed molecular beams to determine the mechanism of oxygen reacting with unsaturated hydrocarbon molecules. Lee overcame two problems associated with such reactions: the primary polyatomic radical products are often highly energetic and do not allow the parent ions to be identified by mass spectrometry, and fast chain reactions initiated by those primary products make it difficult to deduce them from final products. The low density of molecular beams permits only one collision (if any), thus preventing secondary reactions. Measuring the angular and velocity distributions of products at all mass numbers that can be detected allows positive identification of primary products. Lee showed that in the reaction of oxygen and ethylene ($O + C_2H_4$), the primary product was CH_2CHO rather than CH_3 and HCO as had been previously believed.

Quantum mechanical effects. In 1981 J. Douglas McDonald and co-workers at the University of Illinois in Urbana became the first researchers to unambiguously observe quantum-beat phenomena in polyatomic molecules. Quantum beats are essentially a periodic fluctuation in fluorescence intensity caused by the mixing of closely spaced singlet and triplet excited electronic states. (The spins of two electrons are either paired, giving rise to a spectroscopic singlet in a magnetic field, or unpaired, giving rise to a triplet.) Quantum beats had been predicted since early in the history of quantum mechanics and had been observed for some time by physicists working with single atoms and such diatomic molecules as iodine. McDonald was able to observe the beat patterns in biacetyl and methylglyoxal by taking advantage of pulsed molecular nozzle beam sources that cool the molecular beam to about 1 K ($-458°$ F) or less, thereby isolating a single rotational level. At higher temperatures rotational and vibrational levels mix, a phenomenon that smears out the beat pattern. The group is using the spectra to learn about the vibrational structure of the triplets of the molecules and about coupling between the singlet and triplet states.

Trevor J. Sears, P. R. Bunker, and A. R. W. McKellar of the National Research Council in Ottawa made the first assignments of three rotational-vibrational lines in the carbon-dioxide-laser magnetic resonance spectrum of gas-phase methylene (CH_2). Methylene is interesting because its ground, or unexcited, state is a triplet, whereas most molecules in the ground state are singlets. The group's work will provide information about the structure of methylene.

Biological systems. Because biological molecules are often much larger than simple organic molecules and because biological systems are complex, understanding them in terms of physical chemistry is difficult. Yet, progress was made in comprehending one of the most basic biological systems—photosynthesis.

James R. Norris and co-workers at Argonne National Laboratory near Chicago studied the initial charge-separation events in bacterial photosynthetic reaction centers with an adaptation of a technique called reaction-yield-detected magnetic resonance spectroscopy, an optical magnetic technique. In the work a pulsed laser initiates the reaction, which involves the transfer of an electron from chlorophyll to a molecule called pheophytin, forming a radical pair. Using the technique the researchers were able to determine both the electron exchange interaction and the electron-electron dipolar interaction, neither of which had been determined before because the lifetime of the radical pair is only about ten billionths of a second. The technique provides a probe to test model synthetic photosynthetic systems, which many researchers are trying to build, for true charge separation.

—Rudy M. Baum

Applied chemistry

Once again and quite understandably, a substantial proportion of recent research in applied chemistry was directed toward solving the world's energy problems,

with major developments in photochemical cleavage, solar energy, ethanol production, and batteries. Other important discoveries involved artificial sweeteners and a silver-free film.

Photochemical cleavage. A method of splitting an oil-refinery waste (hydrogen sulfide, H_2S) into a potential fuel (hydrogen) and a valuable chemical element (sulfur) attracted the attention of several major California oil companies. Michael Grätzel, director of the Physical Chemical Institute at the Swiss Federal Polytechnic Institute in Lausanne, and his associates, together with Ezio Pelizzetti of the Institute of Analytical Chemistry at the University of Turin in Italy, devised a novel catalyst system—colloidal cadmium sulfide (a semiconductor) with 0.1% by weight of ruthenium dioxide on the particle surfaces—for splitting hydrogen sulfide with visible light. The amount of hydrogen sulfide presently extracted from refinery gases and other industrial wastes is enormous, about 2.3 million tons annually in the U.S. alone. When hydrogen sulfide is passed into a dispersion of the catalyst in aqueous sulfide solutions and exposed to visible light, hydrogen gas is generated and sulfur is precipitated in almost quantitative yield and at an astonishingly high rate. The splitting of hydrogen sulfide in this system actually is mediated by the splitting of water. In fact, Grätzel inadvertently discovered the process when he failed to remove all of the hydrogen sulfide involved in the preparation of cadmium sulfide used in his earlier water-splitting system. The new process promises a simple alternative to conventional methods for removing hydrogen sulfide from industrial effluents.

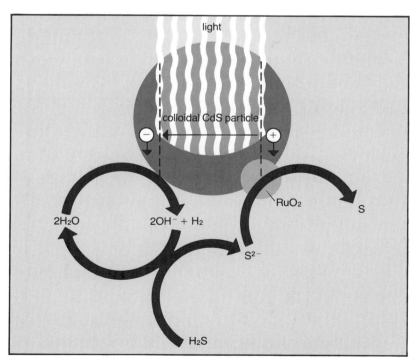

Schematic diagram outlines light-powered catalytic process for splitting hydrogen sulfide (H_2S) using an aqueous, transparent suspension of cadmium sulfide (CdS) particles loaded with ruthenium dioxide (RuO_2). Light striking a particle liberates electrons and creates positively charged "holes." The electrons go on to reduce water molecules to hydrogen (H_2) and hydroxide ions (OH^-); the latter strip hydrogen from H_2S and reform water, leaving sulfide ions (S^{2-}). Concurrently the RuO_2 removes the positive holes from the CdS, thereby preventing unwanted electron-hole recombination, and oxidizes the sulfide ions to elemental sulfur.

In a related development a research study for the continuous generation of hydrogen from water on a commercial scale using a light-responsive catalytic system is under way at Sibit, the titanium dioxide-producing subsidiary of Italy's Montedison SpA. The catalyst system is an outgrowth of Grätzel's previous research (see *1982 Yearbook of Science and the Future:* CHEMISTRY: *Inorganic chemistry* and *Applied chemistry*) and consists of colloidal titanium dioxide doped (selectively adulterated) with niobium pentoxide and loaded with platinum and ruthenium pentoxide.

A thermochemical cyclic process for producing hydrogen and oxygen gases from water was patented by chemists Paul R. Robinson and Carlos E. Bamberger of the Oak Ridge (Tenn.) National Laboratory. Reaction of manganese titanate and sodium hydroxide with steam at 400°–500° C (750°–930° F) forms sodium manganite, sodium titanate, and hydrogen. Hydrolysis of the spent mixture at 80° C (176° F) yields an intimate mixture of sodium manganite and hydrated titanium dioxide, which can be treated with steam at 600° C (1,110° F) to regenerate manganese titanate and sodium hydroxide and to liberate oxygen.

Solar energy. Although the U.S. Department of Energy (DOE) scheduled sharp cuts in spending for solar and conservation programs while increasing the budget for research in nuclear power, development of solar energy technology for generating industrial process steam passed a milestone in July 1981 with the dedication of a demonstration system installed at an Ore-Ida Foods, Inc., potato-frying operation in Ontario, Ore., near Boise, Idaho. Designed and developed by TRW, Inc., Redondo Beach, Calif., in conjunction with DOE and Ore-Ida, the system augments an existing gas-fired boiler used to supply heat to potato fryers. About 75% of energy-intensive businesses, which use 65% of all energy consumed by U.S. industry and which include industries dealing in textiles, paper and pulp, chemi-

cals and allied products, petroleum and coal, and glass, stone, and clay products, are potential users of the new technology. The system uses 930 sq m (10,000 sq ft) of collectors mounted in a north-south orientation, which focus the solar energy onto narrow receivers. Pressurized water circulating through the receivers is heated to 250° C (480° F).

A photoelectrochemical cell using chloroplasts (the photosynthetic cell organelles of green plants) to convert and store solar energy with a power conversion efficiency of close to 1% has been developed by biochemist Elizabeth L. Gross and co-workers at Ohio State University, Columbus. Efficiencies of previous biomimetic systems ranged only around 0.002%. Broken chloroplasts are placed on a filter between compartments containing an electron donor, iron(II), and an electron acceptor, flavin mononucleotide. Platinum electrodes are placed in each compartment, and the voltage so generated when the cell is exposed to light is measured across a load resistance.

Garbage into fuel. Although the U.S. federal gasohol (90% gasoline, 10% ethanol) program is intended to reduce gasoline consumption and lower that country's dependence upon foreign crude oil, the quantity of petroleum saved will be considerably less than initially expected. Furthermore, diversion of large amounts of corn to the production of ethanol could raise the price of corn and other agricultural products in the U.S. Therefore, the news that a $160-million plant to make ethanol from municipal garbage and agricultural, industrial, and forest wastes will be built at Petersburg, Va., is most welcome. Using a process developed by the Gulf Oil Chemicals Co. and the University of Arkansas Biomass Research Center, the plant is expected to produce 50 million gallons of ethanol annually for use in gasohol at a cost of $0.70–1.15 per gallon. The process will use several enzymes to convert cellulose into fermentable sugars, which will then be converted into

Construction of a working laboratory model of a polymer battery is diagramed. Sandwich of polyacetylene-film electrodes is sealed in an airtight glass ampule filled with an appropriate electrolyte. The separator, which keeps the electrodes from shorting, is porous to the electrolyte. Wire mesh serves to carry current evenly to and from the electrode surfaces.

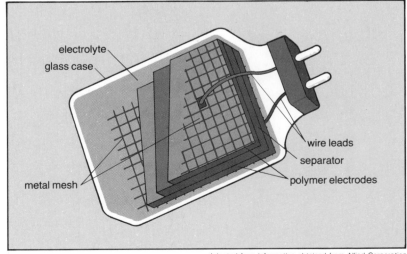

electrolyte
glass case
wire leads
separator
polymer electrodes
metal mesh

Adapted from information obtained from Allied Corporation

Ore-Ida Foods, Inc./TRW, Inc.

Array of Sun-tracking solar collectors augments gas-fired steam system used to fry potatoes at an Ore-Ida Foods plant in Ontario, Oregon. The parabolic-trough collectors heat pressurized water, which transfers the energy to a steam flash tank for steam production. Steam is ultimately delivered to the heat exchanger of one of several potato fryers.

ethanol by addition of yeast. The ethanol will be extracted by a patented process permitting reuse of some of the enzymes and yeast for fermenting another batch of cellulose.

Batteries. A lightweight rechargeable organic storage battery that uses neither metal ions nor free metal was developed by chemist Alan G. MacDiarmid and colleagues together with physicist Alan J. Heeger at the University of Pennsylvania in Philadelphia. The battery uses polyacetylene, the simplest possible organic polymer, which is normally a semiconductor but which upon oxidative or reductive doping undergoes a conductivity increase of one trillion and becomes, in effect, a metallic conductor.

The electrochemical cell is prepared by immersing two small pieces of polyacetylene film in an electrolyte—*e.g.,* a solution of tetrabutylammonium perchlorate in propylene carbonate—and connecting each film to one terminal of a DC power source. The cell is charged by passing current through it, whereupon the polyacetylene strip serving as the anode is oxidized and becomes doped with perchlorate ion, while the strip serving as the cathode is reduced and becomes doped with tetrabutylammonium cation. The extent of doping depends on how much current is passed through the cell during charging. Doping to the extent of 6% is easily produced, and levels of 18–20% are envisioned. As in conventional cells the ions do not undergo any electrochemical reactions, but they maintain electrical neutrality in the system. However, they impregnate the films, which are permeable to the electrolyte. The charging process produces two conducting polyacetylene electrodes that have equal but opposite oxidation

states. During discharge of the cell, electrons flow from the less oxidized anode to the more oxidized cathode until both electrodes attain the same oxidation state; *i.e.,* the electrodes become "undoped" and revert to their original neutral state. The cell is then ready for recharging.

The polyacetylene electrodes are electrochemically reversible and show no visible degradation after a number of charge-discharge cycles. A cell with polyacetylene electrodes of one square centimeter (about 0.155 sq in), weighing only 4 mg (0.000141 oz) and doped at 2.4%, provided 2.5 volts in an open circuit and 22.2 milliamperes of current in a circuit of minimal resistance. By increasing the level of dopant and the size of the electrodes, investigators believe that the energy density (energy per unit weight) of the plastic battery can be made to exceed that of conventional lead-acid batteries. Because they produce so much power for so little weight, organic batteries should be ideal for powering electric cars and may well be used for this purpose within a decade.

The C & D Batteries Division of Allied Corp. obtained an exclusive license to use the polyacetylene battery technology in the U.S., Canada, and Japan, while the German firm of Badische Anilin- und Soda-Fabrik (BASF) acquired the European rights. Furthermore, Ronald R. Chance, leader of the Conducting Polymers Group at Allied's Corporate Research and Development center in Morristown, N.J., together with his colleagues discovered that polyphenylene could serve as the basis for a rechargeable organic battery. Each polymer has its advantages and disadvantages. Since polyacetylene comes in flexible sheets, its batteries might be fabricated in various shapes. Polyphenylene usually comes as a powder that must be compressed or extruded under high pressure. Undoped polyacetylene deteriorates in air, whereas undoped polyphenylene is stable in air to 400° C (752° F). When doped, both polymers are unstable. Both types of batteries can store three times as much energy as a lead-acid battery, and their energy can be drawn off ten times faster than from a lead-acid battery.

Another contender for supplanting the lead-acid battery is the ceramic sodium-sulfur system known as the "beta battery," under development by the General Electric Co. and Chloride Silent Power Ltd. in the U.K. According to General Electric the battery, which could outperform lead-acid batteries by a wide margin in utility energy storage and vehicle propulsion applica-

Selenium-based film, intended for microfilm and graphic-arts use, consists of an aluminized Mylar sheet coated with a thermoplastic that contains a layer of selenium particles (a). Before use the film is sensitized by charging (b). Light from the image being copied transfers negative charges to the selenium particles (c). Thermal development softens the thermoplastic layer, allowing the negatively charged selenium to migrate toward the positive aluminum layer (d).

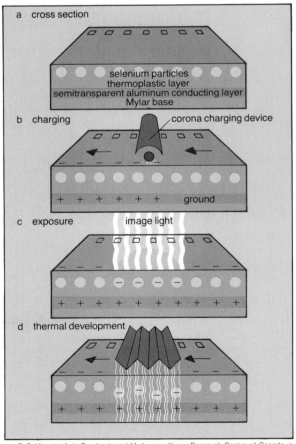

P. S. Vincett, A. L. Pundsack and M. Jurman, Xerox Research Centre of Canada, a Division of Xerox Canada Inc.

tions, should be ready for large-scale demonstration by the mid-1980s.

The beta battery uses a solid ceramic electrolyte of beta alumina—a mixture of oxides of sodium, aluminum, lithium, and magnesium—which separates the reactants: liquid sodium and sulfur. Whereas lead-acid batteries operate at ambient temperatures, the beta battery must be maintained at 300°–350° C (570°–660° F) to achieve maximum efficiency and to keep the reactants and products molten. It can store about four times more energy than a lead-acid battery of equal weight and has the capability of undergoing three times as many charge-discharge cycles.

Artificial sweeteners. In such countries as the U.S., where an estimated 40% of the population is overweight and the average American consumes 38.6 kg (85 lb) of sugar annually, low-calorie sweeteners are important products. In 1981 the U.S. Food and Drug Administration (FDA) approved two sugar substitutes, and a third one was developed by a NASA bioengineer from an idea that he had while he was designing life-detecting experiments employed by the Viking landers on Mars.

Aspartame was synthesized by scientists at G. D. Searle & Co. of Skokie, Ill., from two common amino acids: aspartic acid and the methyl ester of phenylalanine. Twenty-two amino acids are the building blocks of the protein in foods and in the human body; since the body normally metabolizes aspartame into its constituent amino acids, the new sweetener is safe (except for persons suffering from phenylketonuria, a rare hereditary disease). Aspartame, which is 200 times sweeter than sugar, will be marketed as a table sweetener under the trade name Equal and as an additive called NutraSweet in such dry foods as cereals and powdered soft drinks; it is already on the market as a soft drink sweetener in Canada. Its only drawbacks are that it is not indefinitely stable in liquids (it has a shelf life of about six months) and it does not brown well when baked.

The second sugar substitute, polydextrose, produced by Pfizer, Inc., of New York City, is a polymer consisting of different size molecules ranging in molecular weight from 162 to 100,000. Containing only one calorie per gram, compared with four calories per gram for sugar, it is made by mixing and melting 89% glucose, 10% sorbitol, and 1% citric acid. It is similar to sugar in that it is bulky, water soluble, and, unlike aspartame, brownable. Although it is not sweet, saccharin or aspartame could be added for this purpose. The strength of polydextrose lies in its ability to provide bulk in commercial products in which sugar, fat, or carbohydrates previously provided that quality.

The third sweetener, called L-sucrose, or left-handed sugar, was developed by NASA's Gilbert Levin, who wondered if life on Mars could possibly be a mirror image of life on Earth. Because the many right-handed organic compounds involved in the life process also can exist as left-handed molecules and because the body's digestive enzymes can metabolize only the right-handed forms, Levin expected that L-sucrose, unlike D-sucrose (the common, right-handed variety), would taste sweet but would pass unchanged through the human digestive system, making it noncaloric. Also, because bacteria could not metabolize it, it could not contribute to tooth decay.

L-sucrose actually had been known for some time but had been believed to have a bitter taste, which Levin showed was due to an impurity. His sweetening process was patented by Biospherics, Inc., of Rockville, Md., which produced an L-sugar indistinguishable by taste from the right-handed version. It is still expensive to synthesize in large quantities; current options include making it from chemical components, discovering a naturally occurring source, or producing it by genetic engineering.

Silver-free film. For years scientists have sought alternatives to the expensive element silver used in conventional photographic film. In 1981 Paul S. Vincett of the Xerox Research Center in Mississauga, Ont., described for the first time a new film that uses selenium, a relatively cheap by-product of copper refining, instead of silver. The film consists of a thin aluminized Mylar sheet covered by plastic that contains a layer of selenium particles near the top. Just before the film is to be used, it is pulled by machinery through a corotron, a wired apparatus common in office copiers, which uses about five kilovolts to ionize the air, spraying the resulting negatively charged ions onto the film. If a selenium particle receives enough light from the part of the image to which it is exposed, the particle picks up a charge from the ions; otherwise it remains uncharged.

To develop the picture, the film is warmed. As the plastic softens, the charged particles migrate through it toward the grounded aluminized sheet, whereas the uncharged particles remain. Because the particles that migrate and disperse have a different appearance from the stationary ones, a pattern or image is formed. The new film is thus developed almost instantaneously by heat without the tedious steps required in conventional chemical developing.

Although the new method produces very sharp images, the film's speed, or sensitivity to light, is lower than that of most conventional film, and its main applications are in information-recording machines such as microfilm and digital recording as well as in graphic arts, in which photographic films are used to produce printing-plate intermediates. Vincett continued to work on a selenium-based silver film replacement sensitive to infrared light for use at night.

—George B. Kauffman

See also Feature Articles: SURPRISING NEW USES FOR SULFUR; SEA OF SALT, SEA OF LIFE.

Earth sciences

The crust, oceans, and atmosphere of the Earth continued to engage the attention of scientists during the past year. Significant research efforts focused on the increasing amount of carbon dioxide in the atmosphere and its possible effect on climate, the extraction of petroleum from siliceous rock, motions of the crustal plates along California's San Andreas fault, and hydrothermal vents in the deep ocean.

Atmospheric sciences

Atmospheric scientists continued to give a great deal of attention to the chemical constituents of the atmosphere. Of particular interest were the upward trend of carbon dioxide and its effects on global climate, and the possibility that man-made substances such as chlorofluorocarbons may cause reductions in stratospheric ozone.

Also of continuing concern to researchers were the roles of sulfur and nitrogen oxides in the production of acid rain. In addition, there was considerable research on a wide variety of topics dealing with the entire atmosphere.

Solar Mesosphere Explorer was launched by NASA to study the atmospheric concentration of ozone and the elements that contribute to its formation and destruction.

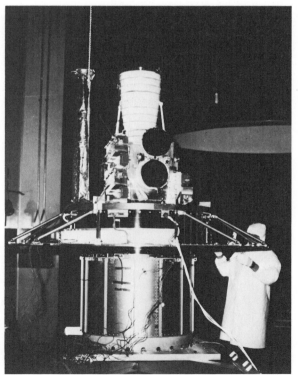

NASA

Global climate and carbon dioxide. Carbon dioxide in the atmosphere, currently about 338 parts per million (ppm), continued to increase at a rate of about 1 ppm per year. Because the level of carbon dioxide affects the radiation budget of the air-earth system, there was much research on how the global atmosphere was responding to the increase. Estimates of future population growth and energy consumption, the factors that underlie the increase, led many experts to conclude that before the middle of the next century atmospheric carbon dioxide will be about double the 288 ppm that existed in the year 1880.

By means of complex mathematical models it has been estimated that, because of the so-called greenhouse effect in which the Sun's radiation is partially prevented by the carbon dioxide from returning to space, a doubling of the CO_2 in the atmosphere will lead to temperature increases at the Earth's surface of about 2–3° C on a global average. Warming would be expected to be greater in polar than in equatorial regions.

James Hansen and his associates at the Institute for Space Studies of the U.S. National Aeronautics and Space Administration (NASA) reported that over the past century average surface air temperatures rose 0.4° C, with a 0.2° C warming over the decade and a half ending in 1980. The temperature trends were characterized by fluctuations that appeared to the authors to be caused by "variability of stratospheric aerosols and solar luminosity." The magnitude of the change in the average temperature is regarded to be consistent with the possible warming effects of carbon dioxide, but the record is not adequate to conclude that such is actually the case.

Evidence for atmospheric warming over the last 50 years was found from studies of the Antarctic ice pack. From an analysis of satellite data George J. Kukla and Joyce Gavin at the Lamont-Doherty Geological Observatory at Columbia University found that from 1973 to 1980 the summer ice pack had decreased from about 8.2 million to 5.7 million sq km. (One sq km = 0.39 sq mi.) Data contained in U.S. and Soviet atlases along with reports from research and whaling vessels indicate that during the 1950s summer ice packs were heavier than those of recent years. These results correspond with warming in the region between lat 55° N and 80° N, but it still cannot be concluded that the temperature increases and ice melt were caused by increases in atmospheric carbon dioxide.

The characteristics of global climate in the historical and geological past continued to receive widespread attention. For example, Fekri Hassan at Washington State University studied flood stages of the Nile River over the period AD 640 to 1921. He found that major episodes of low discharge occurred during the years 930 to 1070 and 1180 to 1350; high floods occurred during the years 1070 to 1180 and 1350 to 1470. The last two episodes corresponded with above-average rainfall in equatorial East Africa. Low discharges were correlated with cold climate in Europe.

John E. Kutzbach at the University of Wisconsin at Madison calculated globally averaged solar radiation for July 9,000 years ago and found it to be 7% greater than at present. He used this result in a low-resolution climate model to simulate the general circulation of the atmosphere at that time. It exhibited intensified monsoons, a result that conforms with paleoclimatic data from India, Africa, and Arabia for a period from 5,000 to 10,000 years ago.

The warm climate believed to be prevalent during the mid-Cretaceous period about 100 million years ago was simulated by Eric J. Barron, Starley L. Thompson, and Stephen H. Schneider at the National Center for Atmospheric Research (NCAR) in Boulder, Colo. Their climate model showed that the distribution of land and sea over the globe, different from that of today, was an important factor in accounting for the warmth of the period.

Ozone. Research continued on the possible effects on the stratospheric ozone layer of nitrogen oxides from high-flying airplanes, chlorofluorocarbons, and other substances. It became increasingly evident that the processes of ozone formation and destruction are manifold and complex.

Although federal legislation in the United States has appreciably reduced the manufacture and release into the atmosphere of fluorocarbons, the restrictions deal with only about half the global releases. The destructive effects of fluorocarbons already in the air, if they occur as postulated by some theorists, are expected to continue for a decade or two. Such a possibility has stimulated research on techniques for measuring atmospheric ozone. On October 6 the National Aeronautics and Space Administration launched a Solar Mesosphere Explorer satellite designed to measure the concentration of ozone and the elements that contribute to ozone formation and destruction. Charles Barth of the University of Colorado reported that observations are planned for a period of three years.

Scientists at the U.S. Environmental Protection Agency developed an instrument that can measure ozone concentration and distribution in a vertical column. The device employs two visible wavelengths, one absorbed by ozone and the other not absorbed. By a comparison of the signal distributions within the two, ozone profiles can be calculated. The instrument has been mounted on an airplane and used to obtain the vertical profile of ozone under the flight altitude. Such a device, if it could be used on a satellite, could yield data on worldwide patterns of ozone and their variations with time.

J. W. Waters and his associates at the Jet Propulsion Laboratory developed a balloon-borne, microwave limb scanner for measuring stratospheric ozone and chlo-

Radome in Montana contains radar equipment for use as part of a large-scale field experiment on summer rain and thunderstorms. Airplanes carrying on-board computers and measuring devices are also included in the study.

rine monoxide, the gaseous constituent produced by industrial sources that is suspected of being an agent in the destruction of ozone. The instrument measures microwave thermal emissions in three spectral bands at wavelengths of about 1.5 mm. Two balloon flights revealed decreases of chlorine monoxide at sunset, in accordance with predictions made from theory.

A one-mm microwave device for measuring chlorine oxide from the ground was constructed by Alan Parrish and his associates at the State University of New York at Stony Brook. Measurements were made on 17 days during January and February 1980 near Amherst, Mass. The researchers found less chlorine oxide below 35 km (22 mi) and a greater increase with height than would be expected from theoretical models. Although the models were for summer conditions, the Stony Brook group suspected that they have shortcomings because they fail to account for certain important reactions.

On the basis of satellite data Donald F. Heath at NASA's Goddard Space Flight Center reached preliminary conclusions that between 1970 and 1979 at an elevation of 40 km (25 mi) ozone concentration decreased at a rate of 0.5% per year. This small change occurred at the altitude where destructive effects of fluorocarbons have been predicted to occur. The data, however, are not adequate to allow a conclusion that the reported decreases in ozone resulted from chlorofluorocarbons or any other man-made substance.

Atmospheric modeling and the tropics. Over the last decade a series of field programs, of increasing size and scope, have been concerned with studies of the general circulation of the global atmosphere. During the summer of 1974 observations of the atmosphere and ocean between lat 10° S and 20° N over the Atlantic Ocean were made by means of balloons, ships, airplanes, radar, and weather satellites. This project was

called the Global Atmospheric Research Program's Tropical Experiment (GATE).

Robert A. Houze, Jr., at the University of Washington and Alan K. Betts of West Pawlet, Vt., recently summarized findings resulting from GATE. Their investigations reaffirmed and elucidated the idea that convective clouds over equatorial oceans play a major role in transporting energy from the lower layers of the atmosphere to the upper troposphere, about 10–13 km (6–8 mi) above the Earth's surface.

They found that deep convection was associated with clusters of cumuliform clouds ranging from small nonprecipitating ones to large cumulonimbus clouds containing active updrafts and downdrafts and yielding precipitation. The clusters, some 100–1,000 km (62–625 mi) in horizontal extent, were covered by high-altitude layers of ice-crystal clouds caused by the outflow from the tops of the cumulonimbi. These upper-level layer clouds, within which updrafts prevailed, yielded fairly steady precipitation that was accompanied in lower altitudes by descending air. The downdrafts in the cumulonimbi and in the surrounding regions of the clusters filled a shallow layer near the Earth's surface with stable air. Houze and Betts concluded that "to simulate the effects of tropical convection in large-scale numerical models of the atmosphere, a variety of phenomena," such as the ones described above, must be taken into account.

Acid rain. Many lakes in the northeastern U.S. and northwestern Europe have experienced increased acidification over the last few decades. In reviewing the sources of the acidity Ruth Patrick, Victoria P. Binett, and Steven G. Halterman at the Academy of Natural Sciences of Philadelphia noted that some lakes are naturally acidic as a result of geologic or biologic factors but concluded that the "apparent" recent increase in acidity of many lakes in the northeastern United

States may be explained in terms of various processes related to energy production.

During this century total coal consumption has undergone pronounced increases and decreases, but at present it is about the same as in the early 1940s and 1920s. However, over the last three decades the average height of power-plant smokestacks has increased, and there has been an appreciable increase in the use of precipitators and scrubbers. In particular, since about 1960 there has been a pronounced growth in the use of petroleum, particularly for transportation.

Patrick, Binett, and Halterman cautiously concluded that human activities have been responsible for the observed increases in the acidity. In addition, a 1981 report by the Committee on the Atmosphere and the Biosphere of the U.S. National Academy of Sciences determined that, although the linking of power-plant emissions to acid rain is inconclusive, "we find the circumstantial evidence for their role overwhelming."

In Washington, D.C., several legislators introduced bills to restrict appreciably the release of sulfur dioxide into the atmosphere. The Environmental Protection Agency opposed this action. Kathleen Bennett, an associate administrator of the EPA, testified that such legislation is premature. She expressed the view that, before requiring expensive measures to reduce sulfur dioxide releases, it must be shown conclusively that those releases are the cause of acid rain.

Weather modification. Although cloud seeding continued to be widely used throughout the world to increase rain and snow and decrease damaging hail, there remained uncertainties about the efficacy of the efforts. The high natural variability of precipitation makes it difficult to detect the relatively small though economically significant precipitation increases or decreases (10–20%) that cloud seeding might produce. The difficulties are compounded seriously by inadequate knowledge of the natural processes of precipitation formation. Much still needs to be learned about the initiation and spread of ice crystals and the interaction of clouds with the surrounding environments. During the past few years there has been a shift in emphasis from the conduct of cloud-seeding experiments to the study of the physics of clouds and precipitation, particularly in the U.S.

Modification of hailstorms by means of cloud seeding continued to be an intriguing subject. Since the early 1960s various scientific groups in the U.S.S.R. have been consistently claiming astonishing success in this endeavor. For example, in 1974 a leader in the Soviet Hydrometeorological Services reported that damage to agriculture by hail in seeded areas was reduced by 70–95%.

These claims were viewed with skepticism by many atmospheric scientists in the U.S.; nevertheless, in view of the potential value of an effective hail-suppression technique, attempts were made to test the Soviet

procedures. Their most unique feature is that the seeding agents are fired into incipient hailstorms by means of artillery or rockets. The goal was to cause the formation of many small hailstones in clouds that, if left unseeded, would produce fewer, but larger, damaging hailstones. An experiment carried out by NCAR in the early 1970s failed to support the Soviet findings.

During the last few years there has been in Switzerland a hailstorm-seeding experiment that closely duplicates one of the Soviet programs, including the use of rockets purchased from the U.S.S.R. As of 1982 results of these tests had not been reported.

Nancy C. Knight at NCAR reported in 1981 that there are significant differences in the microphysical properties of hailstones in various geographical regions. She found that the embryos, the small ice particles around which hailstones grow, can be separated into two categories: graupel, made up of aggregates of ice crystal frozen together; and ice particles that originate from the freezing of water drops. The Soviet seeding procedures are considered to have a greater chance of success in storms where hail originates on the latter type of embryo.

Knight's analysis showed that over Oklahoma, the midwestern United States, South Africa, and Switzerland the percentage of hailstones forming on frozen-drop embryos ranges from 42–83%, with the percentage being consistently higher in hailstones having diameters exceeding 2.5 cm. In eastern Colorado and Wyoming and in western Nebraska, where NCAR's hail-seeding tests were carried out, 27–29% of the stones having diameters exceeding 2.5 cm had frozen-drop embryos.

Knight's investigation also revealed that the higher the cloud base temperature (in general, the lower the elevation), the greater the likelihood of frozen-drop embryos. Her results suggest that a hailstorm-seeding technique that might be effective in one region will not necessarily be effective in a different one.

General circulation of the thermosphere. The thermosphere, at the highest reaches of the Earth's atmosphere, is characterized by air temperatures that increase with height. At 100 km they average about 73° C; they increase steadily with height to about 730° C at 300 km and remain fairly constant up to heights of about 500 km. The temperature and other properties of the thermosphere have been measured, mostly over the last decade, by means of ground-based optical and radar observatories and from Earth-orbiting satellites.

The primary sources of energy for maintaining high temperatures in the thermosphere are solar ultraviolet radiation and heating associated with auroras. The solar energy is steady and predictable; the auroral energy is intermittent and variable.

Raymond G. Roble, E. Cicely Ridley, and Robert E. Dickson at the NCAR adopted a model of the three-dimensional general circulation of the lower atmosphere to simulate the general circulation of the thermosphere. They tested the model for conditions at equinox, when the Sun is over the Equator at noon (about mid-March and mid-September), and at a solstice. The Equator-to-pole meridional circulations depend to a critical extent on the degree of auroral heating. During equinox the meridional circulation is symmetrical around the equatorial plane. At the solstice, when geomagnetic activity is extremely quiet, there is rising air in the summer hemisphere and sinking air in the winter hemisphere in the form of a giant convection cell. Active auroral activity produces a second convection cell with rising air over the winter polar regions and very strong winds. Sinking air is found at middle or lower latitudes, depending on the degree of auroral activity.

—Louis J. Battan

Geological sciences

Exploration for new sources of energy, the devising of means to dispose of hazardous radioactive wastes, and the intensive study of the San Andreas fault in California in an effort to predict future earthquake activity there were among the major developments of the year in the geological sciences.

Geology and geochemistry. The search for energy resources continued to be a dominant theme in the

geological profession in 1981. There was no sign of any slackening in the demand for geologists by the petroleum industry, and enrollment, especially in those universities and colleges that specialized in the training of petroleum geologists, continued to increase. Ironically, universities found themselves in competition with the very industry they were attempting to serve for people qualified to teach the courses required of a petroleum geologist. Some geologists expressed concern about the large number of petroleum geologists who might not be employable after the present resurgence in domestic petroleum exploration comes to an end. The general attitude among educators was optimistic, however, with the expectation that the demand for qualified geologists would last at least into the 1990s.

The intense demand for skilled personnel by the petroleum industry led to discussions, both in universities and in industry, about how geologists should be trained. The oil companies for the most part supported the view that geologists should be provided with a firm foundation in the basic sciences, such as chemistry and physics, as well as with a broad background in the fundamental principles of Earth science. It has, however, been difficult to resist the inevitable tendency toward specialization in geological education at a time when the goals of society appear to be so specific and plainly identified. P. Gerald Cooray reported in an article published in *Episodes* that his extensive experience

Growing dome is visible in the crater of Mt. St. Helens in September 1981. Volcanic activity continued at a high level during the year, but no major eruptions occurred. Mt. Rainier is in the background.

led him to conclude that specialization in geological education in the third world would have particularly unfortunate consequences. He believes that undergraduate education in less developed countries should be as broadly based as possible. Specialization, where needed, could be provided by postgraduate study or by in-service training.

Petroleum exploration and extraction. It is a remarkable fact that with the high level of activity in petroleum exploration in recent years it was only in July 1981 that the level of seismic exploration for oil and gas exceeded that reached nearly 30 years ago. The Society of Exploration Geophysicists reported that in the fourth quarter of 1952 there were 710 seismic crews at work in the United States and surrounding waters. After sharp declines during the late 1950s and 1960s the number of crews in the field had risen to 711 by July 1981.

Not only has exploration activity increased, there has also been a renewed interest in known but undeveloped sources of oil. As the demand for petroleum products continued and their production became more profitable, prospects that had been rejected as economically unattractive were being reexamined. The Getty Oil Co., for example, undertook a program to test the feasibility of extracting oil from diatomite near Bakersfield in southern California. Diatomite is a rock that is composed almost wholly of the siliceous shells of unicellular organisms called diatoms. The oil is trapped in the spaces within and between the shells. The rock, though quite porous, has a permeability too low to permit recovery by conventional pumping methods. The diatomite occurs at depths ranging between 370 m and the surface and can, consequently, be mined. Getty Oil planned to build pilot plants to test two methods of extraction, one employing solvents and the other retorting. Although the deposit has been known since the beginning of the century, only recently has the extraction of the oil from it been considered economically justified.

In the Soviet Union there also appeared to be increasing interest in sources of petroleum that require special techniques for their development. The Swedish consulting firm Petrostudies reported that a major oil field was discovered by Soviet geologists at Bazhenov in western Siberia. There, an oil-rich bituminous shale called bazhenite was estimated to hold a reserve of 619 million tons of petroleum.

Radioactive waste disposal. The development of nuclear fission as a source of energy continued to be plagued with technical and political difficulties. The problem of devising a safe and economically feasible method of disposing of radioactive waste continued to engage the attention of geologists. In an article published in *Science* Isaac J. Winograd, a hydrologist with the United States Geological Survey, suggested that in arid regions where there are thick unsaturated layers containing natural barriers to the migration of waste material, waste might be safely buried at relatively shallow depths. An area where such conditions are met is in the Great Basin of the western United States, according to Winograd. He suggested that radioactive waste might be buried in craters such as Sedan Crater, which was created by an atomic explosion at Yucca Flats, Nev., in 1962. Winograd's research convinced him that large volumes of transuranic radioactive waste might be safely isolated from the biosphere in this vast crater for hundreds or even thousands of years at a cost far below that necessary for deep burial.

John D. Bredehoeft and Tidu Maini, also writing in *Science*, enumerated the distinct advantages of locating repositories of radioactive waste in densely crystalline rocks such as granite. Because groundwater can be an important agent in the transport of waste materials, they suggested that waste repositories in crystalline bodies be located beneath sedimentary layers in which the movement of groundwater is particularly well understood.

Geothermal power. Geothermal sources of energy appear to be safe and noncontroversial but can, at best, meet only a small part of the projected demand for energy. The United Nations Development Program, which has been supporting geothermal development since the 1960s, established, with the government of New Zealand, the Geothermal Institute at the University of Auckland.

It is the goal of the Institute to provide the highly trained personnel needed for an increased rate of discovery and development of geothermal resources. Members of the three classes already graduated from the one-year postgraduate course appeared to be making important contributions to the geothermal research programs in several less developed countries.

Deep Sea Drilling Project. Despite the abundant economic support for energy-related research a number of geologists, like scientists in other fields, expressed concern in recent months about what appeared to be a trend toward decreasing support for research directed at understanding nature rather than controlling it. But in geology, and in other sciences as well, practical and purely scientific concerns often broadly overlap and even coincide. The Deep Sea Drilling Project, for example, has been supported by the petroleum industry, presumably in the expectation that it would yield technical and scientific knowledge that might be used in the discovery and production of oil. The project has, however, generated knowledge that increases fundamental understanding of the Earth and its history but does not have immediate practical application. Cores obtained by drilling into the material that covers the ocean floor have provided a nearly uninterrupted sedimentary sequence that has, among other things, greatly benefited the study of ancient climates. Fay Woodruff, Samuel M. Savin, and Robert G. Douglas reported that an analysis of stable isotopes in the shells of Miocene benthic foraminifera recovered from cores obtained at Deep Sea Drilling Project site 289 document the establishment of a large Antarctic ice cap and the decline of oceanic temperatures to near their present levels during Miocene time (7 million to 26 million years ago). This view differs from one offered earlier by R. K. Matthews and R. Z. Poore that large volumes of continental ice had been present as early as Oligocene time (26 million to 38 million years ago).

Changes in oceanic water circulation appear to be the favored hypothesis in accounting for the growth of continental ice. Cooperative studies among geochemists, oceanographers, and geophysicists may be expected to resolve many of the outstanding issues that have arisen in the attempt to infer climatic conditions in the geologic past.

Geology and environmental pollution. It is clear that the practical application of scientific knowledge has not been fully exploited. There is evidence, for example, that governments and industries have not taken full advantage of the knowledge of geologists in their attempt to control environmental pollution. Patrick McLaren pointed out in an article published in *Episodes*, for example, that geologists have seldom been consulted in the event of catastrophic oil spills. He argued convincingly that a detailed knowledge of coastal geology is fundamental to an assessment of the susceptibility of coastal environments to oil pollution.

The U.S. Geological Survey has achieved a remarkable balance between discharging its responsibility to provide individual citizens and industries with economically significant geological information and, at the same time, to pursue long-range goals of scientific research. Dallas Peck, who had been chief geologist at the Survey since 1977, was appointed to the directorship in 1981. The appointment ended concern among geologists that because of the role of the Survey in preparing petroleum reserve estimates and in other politically sensitive energy-related matters, the new director might be chosen from outside the ranks of the organization.

Basic research. Despite the emphasis on the search for energy and on other immediate goals geological research directed at fundamental understanding continued at a quickening pace. In an issue of *Science* devoted to a review of the "Solid Earth" Orson L. Anderson reviewed the progress of the study of the Earth's internal properties during the past decade and went on to assess prospects for progress in this study in the decade to come. In Anderson's view the decade just past has been largely devoted to an elaboration of knowledge already in hand at the beginning of the decade. He concluded that increasing attention to dynamic features of the Earth's core and mantle foretell increasing emphasis in that area during the 1980s.

In the aftermath of the explosive eruptions of Mt. St.

A 0.63-centimeter aluminum projectile shot through an argon atmosphere having a pressure of 570 millimeters at a velocity of 5.5 kilometers per second creates a crater in pumice about 12 cm in diameter. The photographs were taken 2.5 milliseconds apart. The study attempted to duplicate on a small scale a hypothesized impact of an asteroid with the Earth.

Helens in the state of Washington in 1980, a great number of studies during 1981 were devoted to an attempt to deepen the understanding of this dramatic event. For example, Alan Robock estimated that the May 18, 1980, eruption of Mt. St. Helens had a negligible effect upon climate. His calculations showed that the eruption would result in a maximum temperature depression of 0.1° C in the winter in the polar region. A change of temperature of this magnitude is so small as to be undetectable among much larger natural fluctuations.

William L. Donn and Nambath K. Balachandran of the Lamont-Doherty Geological Observatory of Columbia University estimated on the basis of theoretical analysis and observational data that the explosive yield of the May 18, 1980, eruption was approximately 35 megatons. It is interesting to compare this yield, modest by the standards of some of the great volcanic eruptions of history such as Krakatoa, with the explosive yield of man-made devices. For example, the explosive yield of the first hydrogen bomb exploded by the U.S. was 15 megatons.

Efforts to find correlations between volcanic activity and other geological events continued in the hope of achieving a better understanding of, and even the ability to predict, volcanic eruptions. Of particular interest in this regard was seismic activity that precedes, is coincident with, and follows eruptions. Although hope was expressed that episodes of volcanism may be predicted, volcanologists were not confident that the precise time and magnitude of destructive volcanic events would be predictable in the near future.

Historical research by Roy Bailey of the U.S. Geological Survey led him to conclude that the eruption of Mt. St. Helens along with the steam emitted from Mt. Baker and seismic activity near Mt. Hood and Mt. Shasta have caused the Cascade Mountains to be more active during the past five years than at any time during the past century. This research suggested that volcanic activity in different parts of the range may be connected.

It has often been suggested that volcanic eruptions may cause climatic changes. Michael Rampino, a geologist at the Goddard Institute for Space Studies, reversed the causal order by proposing that climatic changes might result in volcanic eruptions. Rampino believes that atmospheric cooling increases the velocity of the trade winds that blow opposite to the direction of the Earth's rotation and act as a brake to this motion. Such a braking force is, according to Rampino, sufficient to cause magma flow in convection currents and thereby trigger volcanic eruptions. He maintained that his hypothesis is supported by the fact that coincident with an increase in the number of large volcanic eruptions since 1940 has been a 0.9° F decrease in atmospheric temperature.

In 1980 Luis Alvarez, Walter Alvarez, Frank Asaro, and Helen Michel announced the hypothesis that the impact of an asteroid with the Earth and resulting dust cloud might have caused a period of darkness lasting as long as three years. A period of darkness of this length would make photosynthesis impossible and result in the collapse of the food chain, leading to the mass extinction of the dinosaurs and other animals.

This hypothesis was examined by scientists at a conference sponsored by the Lunar and Planetary Insti-

tute and the National Academy of Sciences at Snowbird, Utah, in October. The participants agreed that the geochemical evidence for such an impact was compelling, but most of them believed that a three-year period of darkness was excessive. Brian Toon of the National Aeronautics and Space Administration (NASA) presented evidence that the period of darkness after the event would not be as long as three years but might be closer to three months. Paleontologists at the conference reported that there was no fossil evidence of widespread extinctions of terrestrial animals and plants at the estimated time of the asteroid impact. Some of them did, however, present evidence of widespread and rather sudden extinctions among marine organisms. Hans Thierstein of the Scripps Institute of Oceanography reported, for example, that his analysis of cores from the Deep Sea Drilling Project indicated that at the boundary between the Cretaceous and Tertiary periods (65 million years ago), the time at which the cataclysmic impact is thought to have occurred, 49% of all genera of floating marine organisms disappeared.

International cooperation. International cooperation has always been especially significant in geology because a knowledge of conditions at different places on the Earth's surface plays a crucial role in the development of the science. As the theoretical foundation of geology is broadened and deepened, the exchange of ideas among Earth scientists of different nationality has assumed added significance. The vast number of international conferences and symposia held during 1981 was testimony to that fact.

A group of European geologists established the first continent-wide society of Earth scientists. Scientists of any nationality may become members of the European Union of Geosciences, although its officers must be citizens of 1 of the 21 member countries of the Council of Europe. The union was intended to promote cooperation not only among Earth scientists but also among all scientists interested in the Earth and its inhabitants. The union will publish a journal, *Terra Cognita.* In a notable, but perhaps less dramatic, attempt to lower the barriers to the exchange of geological information, the Academy of Sciences of the U.S.S.R. published several geological maps with legends in both Russian and English.

Future outlook. In the immediate future one can expect that the search for fossil fuels and the search for other sources of energy will continue to occupy the attention of a substantial proportion of professional geologists. Fundamental geological knowledge and the theoretical foundation provided by physics and chemistry will assume an even greater significance in the search for sources of energy than it has during the decade just past. At the same time, and scarcely separable from these practical pursuits, the search for fundamental knowledge of the Earth and its history will continue within the context of the great theoretical advances of the 1960s and 1970s.

—David B. Kitts

Geophysics. The late Perry Byerly, the longtime head of the Seismographic Station at the University of California at Berkeley and a pioneer in earthquake studies during the first half of the 20th century, once observed that high seismic risk was the price one paid for living amid the beauty of a coastline flanked by high mountains. This is true with a vengeance in California, where the entire coastline is lined by major active faults. The sad irony is that the same broad fertile valleys adjacent to good harbors that attracted people to California in the first place, are probably all the by-products of major active faults. And thus almost by design great population and industrial centers have grown up in areas of maximum seismic risk.

The topography and geology of coastal California is dominated by the San Andreas fault system, a long curvilinear transform fault that joins the spreading center in the Gulf of California to the triple-junction at Cape Mendocino, near the California-Oregon border. A transform fault is one of the three major types of faults that form the boundaries of the very large "plates" that make up the crust, or "outer skin," of the Earth. Motion along transform faults is mainly horizontal, as two plates slide by one another along what geologists call strike-slip faults. The long linear valleys adjoining San Francisco Bay, in which most of the people and industrial development of the area are concentrated, were formed by faults of this type, and most appear to be active today. Some vertical motion also takes place along transform boundaries on what are called thrust faults, apparently the consequence of compressive forces that result from irregularities or bends in the plate boundary. It is faults of this type that have produced the large flat basins, flanked by high mountains, within which the people and development of the Los Angeles area are concentrated.

It might seem that in a rational world both of these areas might be avoided for development and reserved for agriculture or some activity less sensitive to seismic hazards. Unfortunately, this is not an entirely rational world, and both the San Francisco and Los Angeles areas are among the fastest growing in the U.S., with concentrations of vital electronic, aerospace, and military-industrial facilities. Since it is not possible to move this development and those people to a less hazardous region, scientists, engineers, and government agencies have long sought to find ways to reduce the danger to people and society.

For about ten years the U.S. has had a program in earthquake prediction and hazard reduction, one aimed at reducing the loss of life and property damage

Geologist Henry Fielding Reid was a pioneer in the study of earthquakes; he analyzed the deformation in the Earth's crust that accompanied the great San Francisco earthquake of 1906.

NOAA

in future large earthquakes and at mitigating, if possible, the enormous social disruption that will accompany a great earthquake in a major metropolitan area. During this same ten-year period similar programs have been underway in Japan, China, and the Soviet Union. Work on a wide variety of fronts is under way, and it is gradually becoming clear which lines of research hold the most future promise and which have proven barren. This discussion will focus on work in California, where much of the seismic risk in the U.S. is concentrated and where work is under way on enough different problems to illustrate most of the important issues.

Plate tectonics and seismic risk. The single greatest advance in the understanding of the Earth in the 20th century was the weaving together in the 1960s of a myriad of theories and observations into what is now called plate tectonics. This is a model of the Earth in which the surface is divided into rigid blocks (seven large ones, many small ones), each about 100 km (60 mi) thick. These blocks are in constant motion relative to one another at rates averaging a few centimeters per year. Deformation is concentrated primarily at, or near, the edges of these blocks. This deformation between adjacent blocks occurs primarily as slip in large earthquakes. The San Andreas fault forms such a boundary between the North American and Pacific plates, and the great 1906 earthquake accommodated 3–4 m of horizontal motion between these two pieces of crust.

Because there is now a (relatively) all-inclusive model that explains how and why these motions occur, questions of seismic risk and earthquake prediction can be more clearly posed. Geologists now know, for instance, that almost all very large earthquakes in California will occur on, or very near, the San Andreas fault. Such earthquakes are less likely by at least a factor of ten on faults more than 100 km from the San Andreas. Similarly, because it is known that the North American and Pacific plates move by one another at a relatively constant rate, there is strong reason to expect that the great earthquakes which accommodate that motion will occur at more or less regular intervals. These two simple observations taken together have a profound implication, for they remove one major uncertainty from the problem; it is now known that along most of the San Andreas fault in California great earthquakes similar to those observed in the last 150 years will occur again, and they will do so on a time scale of hundreds of years or less.

A second major contribution of plate tectonic theory to the understanding of seismic hazards is that it now permits scientists to combine with some confidence many different measurements, covering different time periods, of how fast the plates are moving and thereby refine their estimates of how frequently great earthquakes might occur. Extremely precise measurements

Carl Byoir & Associates, Inc.

Quality control measurements are made on a seismic support ring made by Borg-Warner Corp. Such a ring will be used to collar a power plant pump to keep it from moving in an earthquake.

of the Earth's magnetic field were developed in World War II to detect submerged submarines; subsequent developments led to a detailed picture of the variations in the magnetic field throughout most of the ocean basins. The recognition of a characteristic pattern of long linear variations in this field played a crucial part in the development of the theory of plate tectonics. Calculations based on the pattern of magnetic anomalies in the Gulf of California indicate that the Pacific plate, the large block of the Earth's crust that underlies the Pacific Ocean, is moving to the northwest, past the North American plate, at a rate of about 5 cm per year. This estimate represents an average rate over the last 4 million years and is in fairly good agreement with measurements covering the last 2,000, the last 100, and even the last 10 years. This agreement implies rather strongly that the motion of the plates at depth is smooth on time scales as short as 100 years. This is an important finding because it is these plate motions that drive the earthquake machine, and if the motions had proven to be highly irregular, it would have presented an almost insurmountable obstacle to predicting long-term earthquake recurrences.

A third area in which plate tectonic theory is contributing to current progress in earthquake research is in providing a conceptual framework within which workers from many different disciplines can reconcile their otherwise unrelated theories and observations. While this development does not hold any prospects for short-term earthquake predictions, it may in the long run be the most crucial.

The fundamental difficulty of all earthquake research is that the subject is absolutely inaccessible. Large earthquakes nucleate at a depth of 10 km (6 mi) or greater in the Earth's crust; the practical difficulties of drilling to that depth in a major fault zone are so great that it will probably never be accomplished. Thus it is unlikely that geologists will ever have samples of the material within which earthquakes are generated nor will they ever be able to directly measure conditions, such as temperature or stress, at that depth. Therefore, progress in understanding earthquakes will have to be made by inference and indirect arguments. This is by no means a hopeless situation, but it does place a high premium on building a fundamentally sound theoretical basis on which to proceed. It is in this regard that the U.S. program in earthquake research is soundest. In one sense the San Andreas fault can be viewed as an enormous outdoor laboratory in which it is possible to study all aspects of the problems of plate interaction and earthquake generation.

Much of coastal California was created within the last ten million years by the northward progression of the Mendocino Triple-Junction, the region near Eureka, Calif., where the San Andreas fault bifurcates into a transform fault that trends east-west and a subduction zone that trends north-south. (A subduction zone is a region where the edge of one crustal plate descends below the edge of another.) A great deal of geologic interpretation has been focused on working out the details of this process during the last decade. But almost nothing is known of the corresponding processes at depth. Recent progress in a number of geophysical disciplines is beginning to shed some light on this problem.

The ultimate force that drives the plates that make up the Earth's outer layer is the flow of heat from the Earth's interior, where it is generated by the decay of radioactive elements, to the surface, where it is radiated away as infrared radiation. Geophysicists estimate this thermal flux by measuring the temperature gradient in a hole drilled into the Earth. A large number of such holes have been measured by Art Lachenbruch and his colleagues at the U.S. Geological Survey as part of the earthquake program, and a detailed picture of the pattern of heat flow is beginning to emerge. One prominent feature of this pattern is a broad region of high heat flow centered on the San Andreas fault. This feature is now believed to be the result of hot material from the upper mantle flowing into the "hole" left by the descending slab as the triple-junction migrated north.

This conclusion is strengthened by work just com-

pleted by Survey scientists on the gravity field of northern California. They found that the slab of oceanic crust which dips beneath Washington and Oregon and is responsible for the long line of active volcanoes that cap the Cascade Range terminates to the south near Cape Mendocino. They believe the hot mantle material flows in along the southern boundary of this slab.

A third approach to this question utilizes the dense network of seismograph stations operated by the Geological Survey in California. Survey scientists have studied seismic waves that have been recorded on this network from large earthquakes throughout the world. They found an unusual zone of low-velocity material dipping to the east beneath California and concluded that it represents the "fossil record," so to speak, of the flow of hot mantle material during the last 5–10 million years.

One implication of these results is that the North American plate may be only about 25 km (15½ mi) thick in this region, less than half the thickness expected. This implies that the forces which drive the plates, and are the direct cause of motion on the San Andreas fault, may also be applied at this shallow depth. This is an important result, if true, for the depth at which this force is applied controls many of the details of the pattern of strain along the San Andreas, and it is the understanding of this pattern that provides one of the major hopes of predicting future great earthquakes.

Strain studies and geodetic instrumentation. Since an earthquake is an abrupt deformation of the Earth's crust, one approach to understanding how it occurs is to study the deformation between large events. Using geodetic monuments established on mountain tops in the 19th century, Harry Fielding Reid of Johns Hopkins University studied the deformation accompanying the great 1906 San Francisco earthquake. He noted that the large abrupt motions that took place near the fault during the earthquake were matched by a long slow strain accumulation, the motion during which was opposite to that observed during the earthquake. Reid suggested in 1910 that by studying these motions one might be able to predict the time of the next earthquake. Nothing learned since that time has changed this picture, and much of the work in earthquake prediction today is devoted to doing precisely what Reid suggested: understanding the long slow process of strain accumulation that occurs between earthquakes.

In pursuing this research, however, a fundamental difficulty exists; the motions that occur between earthquakes are very small, of the order of a few parts per million (ppm) per decade. To appreciate the difficulty this presents, a person's thumb and forefinger held an inch apart represents approximately a one ppm change in a line 15 mi long. This is the amount of change that is observed in three years in such a line across the San Andreas fault in central California. Thus it became clear in the 1970s that if geologists wanted to predict

An earthquake in Iran in June 1981 killed more than 1,500 people and left thousands homeless.

when earthquakes will occur on a time scale shorter than decades, they would have to be able to make reliable deformation measurements at the 0.1 ppm level; some scientists, in fact, believe that measurements at the 0.01 ppm level will be required. In the past ten years several fundamentally important steps have been made in this direction, and experiments now under way suggest that reliable long-term measurements at the 0.1 ppm level are possible.

In the 19th century the science of geodesy, the study of the shape and deformation of the Earth, was founded by men using the conventional surveying techniques of the time: the measurement of distances by the use of a chain of constant length, and the measurement of angles, both horizontal and vertical, with a precise transit. These techniques have an inherent precision of at best several ppm. While this is sufficient to measure the gross deformations accompanying earthquakes and was used by Reid in his observations of the 1906 San Francisco quake, it is of no value in studying those motions in sufficient detail to be of use for earthquake prediction. The great advance in this field came about when it became possible to measure very precisely the time of flight of a light beam between two points and thus directly determine the distance between them. Making only first-order corrections for the speed of light in the atmosphere allows the possibility of observations at the 1 ppm level.

However, further improvement in these measurements required that the correction for the speed of light in the atmosphere be improved, for the estimate of the refractive index of light along the ray path became the limiting factor. During the past decade Jim Savage, Will Prescott, and their colleagues at the U.S. Geological Survey developed techniques for directly measuring the temperature and humidity along the ray path, by use of instruments mounted on aircraft that fly along the ray path as the measurements are made. They showed that this improves the precision of the measurements to about 0.5 ppm or better.

Hundreds of lines up to 30 km (18.5 mi) long were measured repeatedly in this way in the past decade; as a result a number of features of the deformation became clear. One is that high strain rates, of the order of 0.5 ppm per year, are confined to the San Andreas fault, where the largest earthquakes are expected. Conversely, low strain rates, of the order of 0.1 ppm per year or less, are found in regions where very large earthquakes are extremely rare and may not occur at all. Intermediate values are confined for the most part to those regions where magnitude 6–7 earthquakes are expected, primarily adjacent to the San Andreas.

Another use of their results has been to estimate how frequently large earthquakes might be expected along given portions of the San Andreas. If one can estimate the strain change that will occur in the next earthquake, then the time between events is that strain change divided by the strain accumulation rate. This calculation was used to estimate that a repeat of the great 1906 San Francisco earthquake might occur in 150–200 years, suggesting that it is likely still some decades away. A similar calculation for southern California, however, suggests that a great earthquake there on the San Andreas might be expected at any time. The difficulty with those techniques is that they are expensive and difficult to use; costs of aircraft time in particular are rising rapidly. Fortunately, a new instrumental development shows promise of bypassing this difficulty and improving the precision of the measurements as well.

286

Within the last few years a group at the University of Washington in Seattle developed a technique for estimating the refractive index along the ray path by using two different color lasers simultaneously. Since different colors of light have different velocities for a given refractive index, it is possible to use the flight times of different colors to estimate the refractive index indirectly. Larry Slater, now of the University of Colorado in Boulder, used one of those instruments to measure lines up to 8 km (5 mi) long on a daily basis at two different sites along the San Andreas and showed that precisions approaching 0.1 ppm are possible with this technique. He also found changes in line lengths as large as 0.3–0.5 ppm occurring over periods of weeks to months that appeared to be correlated with slip events on nearby faults.

Another approach to the refractive index problem was taken by Jon Berger and Frank Wyatt of the University of California at San Diego. At their Pinyon Flat Observatory along the San Jacinto fault, east of Los Angeles, they built three 1-km-long steel tubes within which to make measurements in a vacuum. Since the speed of light is a constant in a vacuum, they eliminated (so to speak) the refractive index problem. Because of the continuous operation of their instrument and the power of interference techniques to resolve very small changes in path length, their instrument has an intrinsic precision that approaches one part per billion. In practice, however, the yearly variations in the line lengths exceed 1 ppm, with the largest changes occurring during and after heavy rains. By a painstaking process of elimination Berger and Wyatt established that these large apparent changes were entirely due to movement of the near-surface soil layer within which the end points of their instrument were anchored. These near-surface movements are controlled almost entirely by the weather. The two scientists were attempting to overcome this difficulty by establishing "optical anchors" between the end points of their instrument and points located 10–20 m below the surface; in this way they hoped to reduce their yearly levels to 0.1 ppm or better.

Another approach to the problem of near-surface movement caused by weather was taken by Selwyn Sachs and Alan Linde of the Carnegie Institute in Washington, D.C.. Working with colleagues around the world, they developed and tested a strain meter that can be placed in a borehole at depths up to 800 m. Because the instruments are extremely simple and reliable, they can be cemented into the holes, essentially becoming part of the Earth. While long-term drift problems remained to be solved, overall performance was exceptional, and the best installations suggested that levels as low as 0.01 ppm may be possible. Many of these instruments were operating in the area south of Tokyo, where Japanese scientists fear that a very large earthquake could occur in the near future.

Attempts are under way at two locations in southern California to test further many of these instruments and techniques. Clusters of instruments were established at those locations, permitting the direct comparison of the results obtained by each in an attempt to identify remaining problems and further reduce ppm levels. Scientists from throughout the world were watching the results of these tests closely, and decisions may soon be possible as to which of these instruments and techniques are sensitive and reliable enough to justify deployment in heavily populated regions of high seismic risk.

—Allan Lindh

Hydrological sciences

During the last year research in the hydrological sciences dealt with such topics as the relationship of hydrological processes to the geomorphological structure of drainage basins, the origin and structure of hydrothermal vents in the deep ocean, and the circulation of the ocean in the tropics.

Hydrology. One of the major events of 1981 in hydrology was the International Symposium on Rainfall-Runoff Modeling, which convened at Mississippi State University. This symposium was a truly international occasion, attracting experts from throughout the world to participate in 32 technical sessions. It was clear from this meeting that the concepts used by hydrologists in modeling the transformation of rainfall into streamflow have advanced considerably in the last few years, but it was also apparent that much remains to be done. Two particular themes stood out as both attracting current attention and being crucial to the future development of the subject.

The first of these topics is the study of the spatial variability of hydrologic parameters and variables, in particular those associated with movement of water through the soil. Recent papers involving large numbers of detailed field measurements from studies in Australia, Canada, Israel, Nigeria, and the U.S. demonstrated that parameters governing water flow in soil may be much more highly variable in space than hydrologists have previously liked to believe. This spatial variability is not without some structure. Soil scientists have long recognized that even within a relatively homogeneous area there may be trends in soil properties, for example, with distance down a hillslope. The recent field experiments demonstrated that on flat sites in an apparently uniform soil there is a tendency for hydrological properties to be correlated in space. However, superimposed on this spatial structure is a large local variance so that adjacent measurements may yield very different values.

There are a number of important implications of this work. The first is that a large number of field measurements may be necessary to characterize the distribution of values of any particular parameter or variable within a given area. Second, because of the non-linearity and three-dimensional nature of the flow processes concerned, it may be difficult to represent the hydrological response of any area by using some "average" parameter value as has been the usual practice in the past.

An American Geophysical Union Chapman Conference held near Fort Collins, Colo., in July 1981 was devoted to the subject of spatial variability in hydrology. The papers and discussion at the conference showed that there are both practical and theoretical difficulties to be overcome before the problems posed by spatial variability are properly understood. There was, however, some consensus that the major limitation is going to be one of obtaining sufficient field data on which to base theoretical developments. At present, the measurement of hydrological parameters at a large number of sites is extremely time-consuming and expensive. Consequently, the number of available data sets is, as yet, very small.

This may change to some extent in the future, at least for some characteristics of interest. At the Mississippi symposium recent developments in the remote

Soil moisture patterns (light areas are dry and dark areas wet) are revealed in a photograph taken high over bare fields in Oklahoma. This remote sensing technique will be useful in forecasting floods and scheduling irrigation.

Edwin T. Engman, Hydrology Laboratory, USDA, Beltsville, Maryland

sensing of hydrological variables were summarized by E. T. Engman of the U.S. Department of Agriculture's Hydrology Laboratory in Maryland. Remote sensing of surface soil moisture levels and snow water content by using microwave frequencies appears to be a promising technique for the future, one that will have important repercussions in such diverse hydrological applications as forecasting floods and scheduling irrigation to obtain maximum benefit for crop yield. It will also allow a direct assessment of the spatial pattern of variables of crucial importance to the processes of streamflow generation, with the advantage that areas may be sampled sequentially through time.

Another issue of importance to hydrologists concerned the integrative nature of hydrological processes at large time and space scales, and their relationship to the geomorphological structure of drainage basins (hillslope form, drainage density, stream lengths, etc.). Geomorphological development of hillslopes is generally a long-term process, governed by the availability of water for chemical and mechanical weathering and erosion. A close link should therefore be expected between hydrology and geomorphology. In addition, differences in geomorphological structure between drainage basins within a climatic region may have an important effect on the hydrological response of those basins to rainstorms.

The link between hydrology and geomorphology is a fundamental, but as yet poorly understood, problem that is both of purely scientific and great practical interest. Understanding of the way in which climate, vegetation, and geology affect the geomorphological structure of drainage basins seems certain to have considerable pragmatic value for engineering and management purposes, both in assessing the potential for erosion under different land management strategies or because of extreme natural events, and also in the design of measures to prevent or reduce damage. The structure of drainage networks in river basins often exhibits underlying symmetry that was first expressed in the form of empirical "laws" by Robert Horton in a paper published in 1945. In that paper, the first that attempted a quantitative synthesis of hydrology and geomorphology, Horton also provided an analysis of hillslope form based on assumptions of homogeneity of surface runoff production over the catchment area.

Since Horton's time there has been a succession of attempts to explain the structure of hillslopes and drainage basins. There is much that remains to be done in this area, but advances in the last year concentrated on the simpler problem of understanding the effect of geomorphological structure on short-term hydrological responses.

The recent developments were given impetus by Ignacio Rodriquez-Iturbe and co-workers at the Universidad Simon Bolivar in Venezuela. Their approach was to relate drainage basin morphology and hydrological response in a probabilistic manner. Thus, they attempted to equate the response of the basin to the distribution of residence times for a large number of hypothetical water particles input randomly over the basin. Any particular particle would follow a flow path over the hillslopes and through the channel network in a manner dependent on its point of input. The probability that the particle would follow a particular path, and consequently the distribution of residence times, is therefore dependent on the structure of the basin. Under identical conditions basins of different structure will have different responses to rainfall input. A relationship between structure and hydrological response can be represented mathematically so that such differences can be predicted.

This formulation was recently generalized by Prof. V. K. Gupta and others at the University of Mississippi so as to relax the assumption of a linear hydrological response that was implicit in earlier work. These researchers showed that a functional dependence between the mean residence time and rainfall intensity arises naturally from the geomorphology-based theory. Their results remained to be verified on a larger sample of drainage basins but appeared to represent an important theoretical advance.

Common to both these recent studies and to Horton's pioneering work is the assumption that rates of runoff are homogeneous over a basin area. Hydrologists now know, however, that this assumption is of only limited validity, certainly in humid temperature regions. The volume of water that makes up the peak streamflow resulting from a given rainstorm may come from only a small proportion of the basin. Because of the general downslope flow of water this proportion will also depend on hillslope form and may be expected to vary with the previous moisture status of the soils in the area. This process will also be complicated by the spatial variability of soil hydrological properties cited earlier.

There is a certain paradox in the two themes discussed. The detailed studies of the effects of spatial variability stress that it may be very difficult to make predictions of the overall response of a hydrological system in terms of simple mathematical functions. On the other hand the studies of the interdependence of hydrology and basin geomorphology stress the integrative nature of the system as a whole and show that good predictions may be made with relatively simple theory. Understanding and resolving this conflict will be a fruitful research topic for the future.

—Keith Beven

Oceanography. *Hydrothermal vents.* The subject of hydrothermal vents continued to be of major importance during 1981. A major region of undersea hot springs on the Juan de Fuca Ridge off the Oregon-Washington coast was discovered. Others had been found on the East Pacific Rise near the Galapagos

Islands and at lat 20° S, and off the mouth of the Gulf of California.

All of these hot springs are in areas of seafloor spreading along the East Pacific Rise, an underwater ridge near the west coasts of North and South America. In these regions the rising hot water dissolves minerals from the rocks through which it passes. These dissolved minerals become a food source for an extensive chemosynthetic bacterial community, of considerable interest to biological oceanographers. The heavy minerals, including silver, lead, zinc, and copper, rapidly precipitate out of solution and are deposited in the vicinity of the vent. The mineral concentration of zinc and silver is ore-grade, and the samples appear to have economic potential.

An increased understanding of deep-ocean mineral deposits may help scientists involved in land-based geologic exploration, since some segments of continental material seem to have originated in the oceans. A potential long-term benefit may be the actual extraction of mineral slurries from deep-ocean vent systems. Because the process of venting and mineral deposition appears to be nearly continuous on a global scale, the minerals may represent a renewable resource. Two current obstacles to deep-ocean mining, however, are the absence of proven technology for the project and the relatively rapid rate at which the deposited minerals are degraded and released into surrounding waters.

A continuous series of active hydrothermal vent fields was discovered at lat 20° S on the East Pacific Rise. They were found to be of both the animal community type found near the Galapagos Islands and of the mixed animal community and active high-temperature metal sulfide deposition type found near lat 20° N and on the Juan de Fuca Ridge. In the lat 20° S fields the presence of hydrothermal activity was demonstrated by temperature anomalies that were correlated with methane plumes. The technique of using methane measurements together with cameras and dredging appeared to be the most powerful exploration method for the discovery and mapping of active hydrothermal sites.

Ocean circulation. A special focus developed on tropical ocean circulation and air-sea interaction as new results began to show a physical basis for coupling between anomalous conditions in the tropical regions and mid-latitude winter climates. The results from the North Pacific Experiment "shuttle," an 18-month set of ship and aircraft expeditions between Hawaii and Tahiti during 1979 and 1980, provided a remarkable set of data on the seasonal and longer variability of the temperatures, currents, and wind in this climatically important region.

Direct current measurements from moored buoys were made simultaneously in the central and eastern Pacific at the Equator; these data together with the tide gauges at the Galapagos revealed the passage of

Photos, Fred N. Spiess, Scripps Institution of Oceanography, University of
California, San Diego

Hot water spews forth from an undersea vent (right) at
a rate similar to that of a fire hose. The black
particulates in the water are sulfides, and in the
foreground is part of the submersible "Alvin." Such
vents support a rich variety of plant and animal
life (above).

long waves trapped near the Equator due to the dy-
namical effects of the curvature and rotation of the
Earth. Strong meandering and complex internal structure of the equatorial currents were observed by drifting buoys, tide gauges, and deep current meter observations. This information will be used to develop a
monitoring program for large-scale ocean-atmosphere
interaction processes in the tropical Pacific.

Experiments continued in the North Atlantic on
eddy motion and small-scale features, and expeditions
across the Atlantic to define the temperature and salinity for heat transport calculations were carried out.
West Germany undertook a major study of currents,
temperatures, and density structure in the eastern
North Atlantic as part of its contribution to the World
Climate Research Program.

An interdisciplinary study of ocean "rings," large circular eddies in the Atlantic, showed clear evidence of
phytoplankton patchiness as revealed by satellite measurements and demonstrated the usefulness of this
technique for revealing large-scale patterns of biological variability in the ocean.

Coastal circulation was also a major focus of research. An experiment was carried out from April to
August 1981 on currents, temperature, salinity, and
winds off the northern coast of California. A wide variety of instruments was used, including moored buoys,
aircraft wind gauges, surface drifting buoys, (ocean)
bottom pressure gauges, and bottom-mounted tripods
with current meters. This study is the initial phase of a
long-term, large-scale west-coast shelf experiment

that is designed to yield improved understanding of the
currents.

Polar regions. Active work in oceanography took
place near both poles during the past year. In Antarctica scientists from the United States and the Soviet
Union joined in an expedition in October and November 1981 to the ice-covered Weddell Sea aboard the Soviet research vessel "Mikhail Somov." The team had
hoped to find an open area or "polynya" in the central
area of the sea, which is located directly to the south of
the Atlantic Ocean, adjacent to the Antarctic continent.
Heavy ice conditions precluded the formation of the
polynya, however, and so the team focused on collecting an interdisciplinary data set from the water under
the ice. This comprehensive set represents the first
investigations during the winter of the Weddell Sea, an
important area for the formation of Antarctic bottom
water. Information was collected on physical, chemical, and biological properties of the seawater and sea
ice and also on atmospheric conditions. Preliminary
investigation of the data revealed some information
concerning the possible initiation of the formation of a
polynya.

In the Arctic attention focused on the studies of the
interaction of the ocean and the atmosphere in the
vicinity of the edge of the ice. This region, called the
marginal ice zone, is the crucial area where polar air,
ice, and water masses interact with more temperate
ocean and climate systems. The exchanges that take
place there influence hemispheric climate and have a
significant effect on petroleum exploration and pro-

duction, naval operations, and commercial fisheries. Preliminary satellite and shipboard measurements were made in 1980 and 1981 in the eastern Arctic, the Greenland Sea, and the Bering Sea. This information, on ice extent, temperature, and salinity, was to be used in planning for a major study scheduled to take place in 1983.

The Swedish Arctic Expedition collected a variety of data on physics and chemistry in the Arctic basin between Svalbard and northern Sweden; and a number of measurements of wind and ice motion on drifting ice floes and the pack ice were made with automatic data buoys by U.S. agencies.

Near-bottom and biological studies. A major program of studies in the deep ocean was begun in the North Atlantic on the Nova Scotia continental rise at a depth of about 5,000 m. Detailed measurements of topography, currents, and light transmission were used to characterize the physical and geological aspects of the environment, and biological studies were undertaken to characterize the living environment and its interaction with sediment transport. The structure of the fauna at the Nova Scotia site appeared to be molded by the high near-bottom current velocities. Initial results revealed that the deposit feeders produce fecal pellets composed of individual sediment particles often bound together with mucus. These pellets can be important agents in sediment transport processes; laboratory studies were being carried out to determine their properties.

Other biological studies in the laboratory and in the ocean showed clear evidence of a potentially strong effect of the time period over which nutrients are made available to phytoplankton. This leads to the conclusion that steady-state models of phytoplankton growth are not valid; the changes in time in the nutrient environment have significant effects on the growth rates.

Seafloor studies. In the general area of the geology and geophysics of the seafloor the International Program of Ocean Drilling continued its successful project of deep sampling with the drilling ship "Glomar Challenger." The schedule for the year took the ship from Fort Lauderdale, Fla., to Puerto Rico, West Africa, the Bay of Biscay, the Rockall Bank, and then through the Panama Canal to the Costa Rica Rift near the Galapagos.

The combined results of the Atlantic legs provided a major advance in understanding the early evolution of passive margins (boundaries around bodies of water) by providing data that allow the dating of geological sequences and analysis of the paleontological and sedimentological changes that are associated with different events. The drilling near the Costa Rica Rift provided major excitement late in the year. The drill string penetrated more than 1 km (0.62 mi) into oceanic crust, a record depth of penetration. The drilling

penetrated past the expected pillow basalts, and data to date confirmed the current models of crust structure.

During 1982 the "Glomar Challenger" is scheduled to move to the North Pacific. There, it will undertake studies on the paleoenvironment and drilling in the Japan trench.

—D. James Baker, Jr.

See also Feature Articles: Sea of Salt, Sea of Life; Scarcity Amidst Plenty: The Problem of Water.

Electronics and information sciences

The further development of powerful supercomputers, the introduction of a filmless camera, continued expansion of the microcomputer industry, and the settlement of two major antitrust suits were among the highlights of the last year in electronics and the information sciences.

Communications systems

During the last year the telecommunications industry experienced continued technological innovation and

Submarine cable telephone repeaters are manufactured at a British subsidiary of International Telephone and Telegraph Corp. The cable will link Australia, New Zealand, and Canada.

ITT Corporation

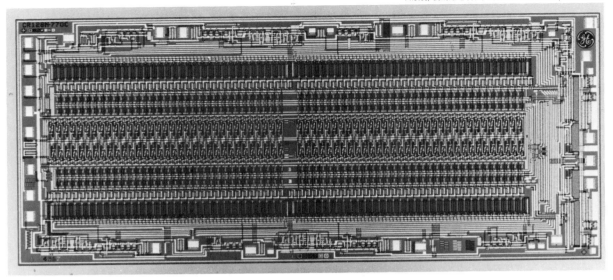

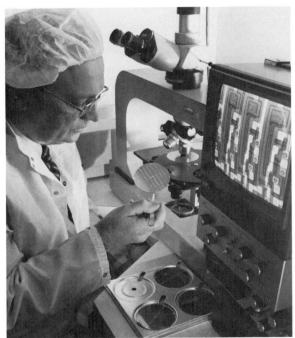

Top, an integrated circuit was developed by General Electric Co. for improving radio communications under conditions of extreme electromagnetic interference. Above, a GE scientist examines a wafer that contains nearly 200 of the circuits.

regulatory controversy. Of the innovations, advances in semiconductor chips and fiber optics were the most important because of their direct influence on the worldwide telephone network. As usual, events throughout the year demonstrated that government regulation is as important as technological advance and often tempers its effect.

The most innovative semiconductor chip was a switching device, known as a crosspoint array, produced by Mitel Corp. of Kanata, Ont. It switches any of 256 voice or data communications channels (inputs) to any of 256 output channels while replacing 100 medium-scale and small-scale integration-based parts. As a large-scale integration-based part the switching chip is highly reliable. It promised to revolutionize the techniques used for switching in private branch exchanges and telephone switching offices because it uses so little space and power.

The cross-point array is concerned with electrical logic signals. But optical logic design is equally important when telephone signals are carried on fiber-optic cables and must be switched. This technology received a boost during the year at Bell Telephone Laboratories in Murray Hill, N.J., with the construction of a two-input switch (known as an AND gate) on a semiconductor chip. An electrical output signal from the gate depends on the simultaneous presence of a pair of input light signals at different wavelengths.

While many industrial firms investigated semiconductor chips suitable for switching, others looked into chips suitable for generating and receiving the light signals on fiber-optic telephone lines that carry data as well as voice signals. For example, IBM Corp. designed a chip that acts as an optical receiver. It converts light to electrical pulses at megabit-per-second data rates. In fact, IBM's Thomas J. Watson Research Center in Yorktown Heights, N.Y., claimed that the new design can take full advantage of the 200-megabit-per-second (or more) information-carrying capacity of the latest fiber-optic cables.

While the abovementioned developments were taking place in the U.S. and Canada, telecommunications chip and fiber-optics technology did not stand still in Japan. For example, Nippon Telegraph and Telephone

Public Corp. built what it claimed was the world's first fiber-optic laser-driven superheterodyne receiver. It tested the receiver both as a 300-MHz analogue device and as a 100-megabit-per-second digital device. With the superheterodyne design a receiver can pick out signals on the optical fiber even if they are only a few megahertz apart in frequency. Thus, more telephone conversations can be put on the fiber.

American Telephone and Telegraph Co. (AT&T), the giant of the U.S. telecommunications industry, engaged in additional rounds with U.S. government agencies. In Congress it failed to win dismissal of the government's antitrust suit. In January 1982 AT&T agreed to divest itself of the 22 Bell System companies that provided most of the local telephone service in the U.S. However, it would retain ownership of its long-distance lines; of Bell Laboratories, its research and development division; and of Western Electric, its manufacturing arm. The settlement also would allow AT&T to enter previously prohibited areas such as data processing and communications between computers (see *Computers and computer science*, below).

Ever anxious to find more uses for the telephone, AT&T extended its influence into the home information market. To the dismay of Canada's Telidon organization, England's Prestel, and France's Antiope, which were already in the business, AT&T announced its own plans for home and business services. It also announced tests to try out its ideas.

—Harvey J. Hindin

Computers and computer science

Supercomputers. During 1981 Control Data Corp. delivered its first Cyber 205 supercomputer, which it claimed was the world's most powerful. With this model the firm hoped to capture a significant share of a market previously dominated by a relative newcomer to the computer field, Cray Research, Inc. Cyber 205 and Cray 1 supercomputer systems typically cost between $8 million and $18 million. Though relatively new, these supercomputers both have their roots in developments that started many years ago.

Seymour Cray was the chief designer of the Control Data 6600 computer, which was considered to be a supercomputer when the first one was delivered to the Lawrence Livermore National Laboratory in 1964. He was also chief designer of the next generation supercomputer, the Control Data 7600, first delivered in 1969 and still one of the most powerful scientific computers in general use. Cray left Control Data in 1972 to establish Cray Research, Inc., where he designed the first of a new generation of supercomputer, the Cray 1. The first Cray 1 was delivered to the Los Alamos (N.M.) Scientific Laboratory in 1976, and more than 30 others had been delivered by the end of 1981.

At a press conference late in 1981 Cray revealed some of the design details of a new Cray 2 computer, which was expected to be an order of magnitude more powerful than the Cray 1 and to usher in a new generation of supercomputers in the mid-1980s. Cray also announced that he was resigning as chief executive officer of Cray Research, Inc., and would continue the development of the Cray 2 as an independent contractor under contract to the corporation.

The Cyber 205 had its origins in the STAR-100 development project at Control Data Corp. that began in 1965. The project was ambitious for its time and encountered difficulties. The first STAR-100 system was delivered to the Lawrence Livermore National Laboratory late in 1974. Several more were manufactured, but their performance was only marginally satisfactory. The two STAR-100 computers at Livermore were eventually replaced by Cray 1 systems.

There were persistent rumors that Control Data was going to drop out of the very large-scale computer mar-

Control Data Corporation

Miniaturization of computer components can be seen by comparing the large-scale integrated circuitry (left) used in Control Data's new Cyber 205 with a logic circuit of equivalent power (right) used in the firm's older STAR-100.

F. Fallside et al., Cambridge University Engineering Department

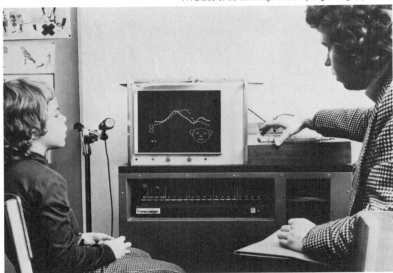

The Computer Vowel Trainer helps deaf children learn to talk. On the screen appears a pattern that corresponds to a vowel sound made by a person with full hearing; the deaf subjects then try to match that pattern. When they are successful, the teddy bear smiles.

ket, but the corporation's engineers decided that a new computer based on the STAR-100 but using modern technology would be a successful and powerful supercomputer. The redesign was done in two phases, first the Cyber 203, an interim machine announced in 1976, of which only three were actually installed, and then the Cyber 205, the first of which was delivered to the United Kingdom Meteorological Office in 1981.

In order to discuss the computational speed of these supercomputers a few definitions are needed. Numbers are stored in scientific computers in a floating-point format that is equivalent to standard scientific notation. (In scientific notation a quantity is denoted by one number multiplied by a power of the number base; for example, the fixed point value 975.9 could be expressed as $.9759 \times 10^3$. In floating point format the number .9759 and the power 3 would be stored together as two parts of a single computer word, for example, 0039759000. This example uses the number base 10, and it thus illustrates decimal floating point format. The same process using the number base 2 produces the binary floating point format used in these computers.) Typical instructions on such computers add or multiply two floating-point numbers and produce a floating-point result. The effective computing speed of a scientific computer is best stated in terms of the number of floating-point operations it can perform per second while executing computational programs. For fast computers the speed is usually stated in millions of floating point operations per second, abbreviated to megaflops.

Megaflops should not be confused with MIPS, or millions of instructions per second, frequently used as a measure of speed of the popular large computer systems. In most cases the MIPS rate must be divided by 4 or 5 to obtain the equivalent speed in megaflops. As of

1982 the Cray 1 and the Cyber 205 were the only computers being manufactured that could operate at over 20 megaflops, and both could reach peak computing speeds in excess of 100 megaflops. They achieved these tremendous speeds through the use of vector processing in addition to the more conventional scalar arithmetic processing used on ordinary computers.

A vector is simply a list of numbers of the same kind, such as a list of floating point numbers. Thus a particular vector of length 25 might consist of the numbers stored in 25 consecutive memory locations. A programmer might specify that another vector of length 25 be the numbers stored in every fifth memory location starting at location 100 and ending at location 220. This vector is said to have constant stride equal to 5.

When one has to deal with ordinary numbers and with vectors in the same discussion, it is usual and convenient to refer to the single numbers as scalars. Vector-processing units provide vector arithmetic operations that correspond to the conventional arithmetic operations provided in a scalar arithmetic unit. Consider two vectors A and B, each of length 100. A vector add operation is a single instruction that creates a new vector C of length 100, where each element of C is the sum of the corresponding elements of A and B.

These vector operations can be carried out very rapidly through the use of pipelined segmented arithmetic units. Consider, for example, the Cyber 205, which has a basic 20-nanosecond clock cycle. (A nanosecond, ns, is one-billionth of a second.) The actual addition of two numbers takes five of these clock cycles: it consists of five steps, each of which takes one cycle. The add pipeline is set up so that two operands, one from each vector, enter the add unit each cycle and move through each of the five steps in sequence, one cycle behind the preceding pair of operands. The first result comes out

294

after five clock cycles, but the following results come out at single clock cycle intervals. Results thus come out of the add unit (or the multiply unit) at the rate of one every clock cycle, that is, one every 20 ns. On the Cray 1 the clock cycle is even faster, and so there are results every 12.5 ns. The Cyber 205 can have multiple vector pipelines, and a two-pipeline machine produces a result every 10 ns. It should be noted that a result every 10 ns corresponds to 100 million results per second, *i.e.*, 100 megaflops.

Even though they are both vector computers, the Cyber 205 and the Cray 1 differ considerably in their logical organization. One of the most important differences is in the way in which they handle vectors. In the Cray 1 there are eight special vector registers, each of which can store up to 64 elements of a vector of 64-bit floating point numbers. Vectors in memory must be moved into vector registers for processing because the vector arithmetic processor receives its operands from and stores its results in the vector registers. In the Cyber 205 vector operands up to 65,535 words in length stream from memory into the vector pipelines, and the results stream directly back into memory. The Cray 1 performs best on short vectors and on vectors with constant stride. The Cyber 205 shows up best when working with long vectors stored in sequential locations in memory.

The effective computing speed of both computers when doing real scientific computation is, of course, very much lower than the peak speed of more than 100 megaflops mentioned above. It is important for potential purchasers and users of these machines to be able to evaluate effective speeds. This is usually done by assembling a set of jobs that are thought to be representative of the workload that is to be run on the machine. Such a set of jobs is called a benchmark, and several interesting benchmark studies of supercomputers were done in 1981. Their results were of great interest to specialists in large-scale scientific computing. As expected, they showed a great variation in effective computing speed depending on the nature of the computation. The Cyber 205 runs faster on some types of programs, the Cray 1 on others.

Research in cryptography. Cryptography deals with enciphering or transforming messages and data so that they cannot be read or understood by anyone who has not been provided with special devices and/or appropriate keys. Data can then be deciphered and read only by the intended users. The National Security Agency (NSA) is the U.S. government agency that is concerned with guarding the security of military and diplomatic communications. NSA employs cryptographers who try to devise ciphers that cannot be broken, and cryptanalysts who try to break ciphers devised by similar agencies in other countries. Scientists working for NSA in those areas have always been required to have the highest levels of government security clearance. They

Robert J. Marchbanks, Brunel University, U.K.

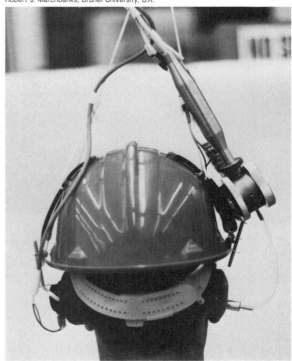

Computer measures the movement of a subject's eardrum in response to a repeated musical note and thus diagnoses diseases of the inner and middle ear.

rarely publish anything about their activities.

With the tremendous increase in the use of computers to store data that may be confidential or sensitive, and the increased use of shared communication lines to transmit such data, cryptography has become an area of computer science research. The publication of the results of this research in scientific journals with unrestricted worldwide circulation has become a source of concern to NSA.

The National Bureau of Standards published a Data Encryption Standard (DES) in 1977. It is important to have a standard encryption method so that encryption and decryption can be mechanized. As in most military cryptography the encryption method is not secret. Security is achieved through the use of secret keys. A private 56-bit key is used to encipher a message, and that key must be known in order to decipher the message.

Critics of the standard have published papers suggesting that a longer key should have been specified in the DES. They discuss ways in which potential security violators might be able to break the cipher. Spokesmen for NSA have recommended that articles of this type, and other articles in the area of cryptography, may contain information that should be cleared by a government security agency before publication.

There has also been considerable interest among computer scientists in the development of secure

295

methods of setting up and distributing keys. There have been several suggested systems based on studies of the time required to compute solutions to certain mathematical problems, such as that of finding the prime factors of very large numbers. Some computer scientists fear that such pure research areas might be affected by proposed restrictions on the publication of results in cryptography.

Thus, there exists a confrontation between those who argue that the right to publish should be limited in the interests of national security, and others who argue that restraints on the publication of the results of non-governmental research are never appropriate in a free society and that the effects of such publication on national security would be negligible. In 1980, in response to a request by the NSA, the American Council on Education formed a Public Cryptography Study Group consisting of representatives of societies in the areas of education, mathematics, and computing and also one representative from the NSA. The report of the group was presented on Feb. 7, 1981. It recommended the establishment of a voluntary procedure whereby authors and publishers would be urged to submit manuscripts on cryptography to the NSA for screening prior to publication. They recommended that this voluntary system be set up on a trial basis and evaluated at some future time as to its value and effectiveness.

Antitrust suits. On Jan. 8, 1982, the U.S. Department of Justice announced the end of two major antitrust suits of great significance to the computer field. A suit against IBM Corp. was dropped after 12 years of litigation, and a negotiated agreement was reached after 7 years in a suit against American Telephone and Telegraph Co. (AT&T).

Antitrust suits against IBM by the U.S. Department of Justice have played an important role in the development of the computer industry. They began in the 1930s, when, after a case that went to the U.S. Supreme Court, IBM was no longer permitted to require that customers who rented IBM punch-card machines use only IBM-manufactured punch cards.

IBM continued to dominate the punch-card field, and after the introduction of electronic computers in the early 1950s, the firm captured a very large share of that market as well. This led to new allegations of antitrust violations against IBM, which resulted in the famous consent decree of 1956. This decree addressed many issues, but probably the most important was the agreement that henceforth IBM would offer computers for sale as well as for rent. Also, IBM's service bureau business would have to be carried out by a separate company, which was established and called the Service Bureau Corp.

Many of the terms of the consent decree expired in 1966. A study instituted by the Department of Justice in 1967 came to the conclusion that IBM was again in violation of antitrust laws, and the suit just terminated grew out of that study. In the years since 1967 a number of computer companies brought private antitrust suits against IBM. A settlement in a suit by Control Data Corp. resulted in the transfer of Service Bureau Corp. to Control Data. However, the private suits that actually went to trial were decided in favor of IBM, and those decisions probably had some influence on the decision of the Department of Justice to drop its own action.

Although the suit was withdrawn, it can be argued that directly and indirectly the various antitrust actions did achieve their objectives. The computer industry was very different and much more competitive when the antitrust suit was dropped in 1982 than it had been in the late 1960s when it was begun.

The Ideographic Word Processing System developed by Wang Laboratories can create, edit, and print documents in Mandarin Chinese, simplified Chinese, and Japanese. By employing a coding system, it requires only a relatively small number of keys to generate 10,000 characters.

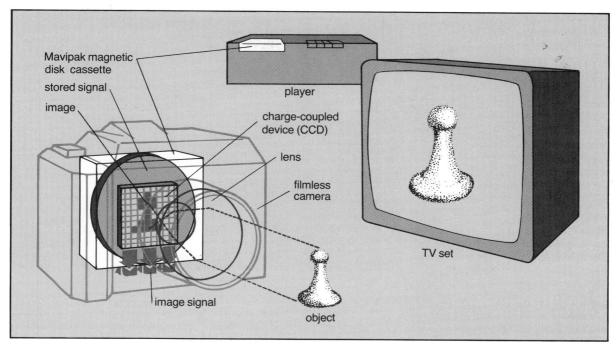

Mavipak magnetic
disk cassette

stored signal

image

player

charge-coupled
device (CCD)

lens

filmless
camera

TV set

image signal

object

The Mavica, filmless camera for still pictures developed by Sony Corp., focuses the subject image onto a light-sensitive charge-coupled device, which converts it into electrical impulses for storage on a magnetic disk. The disk is then inserted into a special player that reproduces the image on a TV set.

Computing and communications have become intimately interrelated, and the antitrust suit against AT&T was watched with great interest by the computer industry. As a result of the settlement of that suit AT&T divested itself of its local operating companies. This was expected to increase competition in the data communications area, but other indirect results might be even more important. Regulatory agencies have ruled in the past that AT&T and its subsidiaries had to limit their activities to the area of communications and could not sell computing equipment or computer services. These rules have become increasingly difficult to interpret or to enforce as the distinctions between computing and communications have become blurred.

As a result of the restructuring of AT&T in the current settlement, it was expected that regulations against AT&T entering the computer field would be relaxed or perhaps completely eliminated. With its position in the communications industry; its very powerful research arm, Bell Laboratories; and its manufacturing subsidiary, Western Electric; AT&T could thus become an important factor in the computer industry.

—Saul Rosen

Electronics

The unprecedented progress in electronics has its roots in the transistor, invented more than 30 years ago by Bell Laboratories. Like the vacuum tube the transistor can amplify weak signals, process data in a computer, and perform numerous other functions in electronic and power circuits. Unlike the tube, however, the transistor is tiny, more reliable, less costly, and does not require the power needed to boil off electrons from the filament in order for a tube to function.

Over a dozen years ago the integrated circuit (IC) evolved from the processing techniques employed in the manufacture of transistors. This led to complete circuits that may contain dozens of transistors and other components that were fabricated in a single thin chip of silicon having an area of approximately 100 sq mm. Following this there appeared the large-scale-integrated (LSI) and the very large-scale-integrated (VLSI) circuits, containing tens of thousands of transistors. The microprocessor, sometimes referred to as "a computer on a chip," which performs arithmetic, logic, and control operations, and the microcomputer are examples of VLSI circuits.

The dimensions of components in a silicon chip are typically a few micrometers in width (a micrometer is equal to one-millionth of a meter). To achieve higher packing densities, that is, more transistors per a chip of a given size, devices with sub-micrometer dimensions are required. Considerable progress was made in recent months in achieving dimensions of less than one micrometer by using X-rays and electron beams for laying out a circuit on a silicon chip. This led to the integration of some 600,000 transistors in a chip occu-

Sony Walkman cassette player provides high-quality sound from a miniaturized unit.

pying an area equal to a fraction of a postage stamp.

Various processing innovations over the past year resulted in devices with high current and voltage ratings. For example, National Semiconductor Corp. developed a voltage regulator (a circuit that maintains the voltage across a connected piece of equipment constant, regardless of changes, for instance, in the line voltage) that can deliver up to 10 amperes in current. Transistors are available that can withstand voltage levels as high as 1,000 volts without deleterious effects. Another area of development is the use of gallium arsenide (GaAs) in place of silicon for integrated circuits. Integrated circuits made from GaAs chips exhibit faster switching speeds than those with silicon. This is an important characteristic for circuits used in high-speed computers.

Speech recognition. Being able to dictate a telephone number instead of dialing it or to dictate a program to a computer instead of entering it on a keyboard are indeed exciting prospects. During the past year considerable advances in speech recognition by several firms resulted in equipment that responds to a limited vocabulary. Efforts were being pursued to extend the recognition of single words to fluent speech, and early results appeared promising.

The basic notion behind speech recognition in a widely used system is the matching of a spoken word with an electrical pattern of the word stored in a computer. The stored pattern is called a template. It contains the sound energy and frequency information for the word. To compensate for different speaking rates, a technique called dynamic time warping is employed. For example, the voice input to a microphone or telephone is converted to analogous electrical signals. The computer then evaluates the signals, a process called feature measurement. The time scale is adjusted by a warping circuit, and a comparison is made with the stored set of templates. If a match is realized, the computer recites the word for confirmation. With the use of this procedure accuracies greater than 95% have been realized.

Interstate Electronics Corp. of Anaheim, Calif., introduced a 100-word speech recognition system for less than $500. Targeting the application for games and toys, it also marketed a chip that can recognize a maximum of eight words and sells for $10. Auricle Inc. of Cupertino, Calif., offered a system that recognizes 40 words and can be expanded to 128 words with an accuracy greater than 99%. The unit sells for $2,500.

Car electronics. In the early 1970s the only electronic equipment found in most cars was the radio. With the emergence of the microprocessor and microcomputer and the declining costs for each, these devices have found such applications in automobiles as monitoring the exhaust and adjusting the timing for greater fuel economy, calculating the distance one can drive on the remaining fuel in a tank, and informing the driver if a malfunction exists in the engine. A car with computer-controlled springs to ensure a smooth ride, regardless of road conditions, is a possibility in the next few years.

Because of the trend toward smaller cars using efficient four-cylinder engines, some experts contended that precise control of fuel efficiency by means of microcomputers is not practical. The Solid State Division of RCA Corp. introduced a two-chip system that is much less costly than a microcomputer. Called the Rombic, it consists of two chips: a read-only memory (ROM) and a controller. Following the instructions stored in the ROM, the controller adjusts the spark advance at different car speeds for maximum fuel economy.

Two disappointments. In 1979 Exxon Corp. announced the invention of an electronic control system

298

for motors that would improve their efficiency and reduce energy consumption upward of 50%. To produce the equipment, Exxon declared that it needed an experienced manufacturer of motors and controls. Amid strong criticism from many other oil companies and consumer groups, Exxon purchased Reliance Electric Co., a leader in the field of motors and controls. But in 1981, because of inherent technical problems and rising costs, Exxon decided to scrap the project.

Three leading companies in the field, Rockwell International Corp., Texas Instruments Inc., and National Semiconductor Corp., decided in 1981 to abandon the manufacture of bubble memories. The reasons given were declining profits in what were, at best, marginal operations. Intel Corp. consequently remained as the leading manufacturer of bubble memories in the U.S., and Hitachi, Ltd., and Fujitsu, Ltd., in Japan.

The bubble memory, once heralded as a major innovation in computer technology, provides storage capacities for one million or more bits (0's and 1's that a computer processes) of information. It was to compete with mass storage units such as the floppy disk, which is popular with personal computer enthusiasts. Like the disk, it is a nonvolatile memory; that is, information is not lost in case of a power failure. This is an important feature for a mass storage memory in computers. The bubble memory is rugged and has no moving parts, like the mechanical drive needed for a disk, but in other respects the disk systems are less complex.

Future uses of bubble memories will most likely be confined to military equipment and specialized applications. One example of such an application is the "all circuits are busy, please place your call later" message stored in a bubble memory that is being used by American Telephone and Telegraph Co.

Filmless 35-mm camera. Sony Corp. demonstrated a video 35-mm still camera, which, instead of film, employs a charge-coupled device (CCD) for recording a photographed scene that is then stored in a magnetic erasable disk. This novel camera is aptly labeled the Mavica (magnetic video camera).

A charge-coupled device is a semiconductor component that may be thought of as a sandwich consisting of a top layer of metal electrodes, a middle insulating layer, and a bottom layer of silicon. Packets of a finite electrical charge are created in specific locations in the silicon layer. Each location is called a storage element; in the Mavica the CCD is an array of 570 by 490 such elements. When the camera is focused on a scene, the light striking the elements is converted to corresponding electrical signals and transferred onto an erasable disk similar to those used in computers. Up to 50 color pictures can be stored on the disk at a rate of 10 pictures per second.

The recorded pictures may be transmitted over telephone lines or viewed on a television screen with the use of a playback unit. Work was under way to develop a hard-copy picture, improve the quality of the picture (its resolution is inferior to the conventional color print), and to record 60 pictures per second. The disk was expected to sell for $3; the camera plus a playback unit will cost about $900.

Portable stereo. As if from another planet, a new sight emerged on the landscape in 1981: people walking around with attached earphones. This phenomenon stems from the introduction by Sony of the Walkman cassette player, an instrument that offers high-quality sound from a miniaturized unit. Some units also provide FM reception and can record off the

Hewlett-Packard interface loop (HP-IL) allows the HP-41 calculator to take readings from various instruments, such as voltage, and instruct a printer to record a particular value when required.

Courtesy, Hewlett-Packard Company

Automated carousel consists of 70 canisters, each of which contains 100 computer chips. By using a central arm under computer control, the operator can fill an order for the chips needed to make a logic component.

air. For low noise and good dynamic range, metal-particle tapes are used.

Personal computers. In the field of personal computers a large number of basic units were available, ranging in price from $100 (Sinclair ZX81) to more than $1,000 (Apple, IBM, and others). Invariably, expansion of memory and the addition of other desirable accessories, such as a printer, can swell the price to over $2,000; for business applications, it can be close to $10,000.

Considerable progress was made in programmable calculators. In addition to the availability of small printers for hard copy, an interface loop developed by Hewlett-Packard allows its HP-41 calculator to take readings from various instruments, such as voltage, and instruct a printer to record a particular value when required.

—Arthur H. Seidman

Information systems and services

Computer-based information systems, which until a few years ago were used exclusively by very large corporations, are now found in small businesses, professional offices, and in the home. Home computers are the fastest growing segment of the industry, and while their numbers are few, their influence is spreading and new services for the home computer hobbyist are developing. User groups, organized according to computer brand, such as the Applecore clubs or Atari groups, provide an effective means of exchanging information. A particularly interesting development is the "home computer bulletin board," used to send personal messages from one home computer user to another or to list notices and advertisements, almost always without charge. One such bulletin board was operated by a housewife hobbyist out of her Los Angeles home. The service became so popular that in 1981 it received 70 to 100 calls a day from throughout the world.

With so many people of all ages and abilities using computer systems, there is a need for more computer education and for the development of a higher level of computer literacy. Handicapped people, especially the visually and hearing impaired, can use computers to improve their communication skills and to find productive employment in the data processing industry. For example, the Arkansas Enterprises for the Blind has helped almost all of its programming graduates find jobs. At the school students with low vision may use terminals equipped with video magnification systems, while totally blind students use an optacon, an optical scanning device that can read a cathode-ray tube (CRT) screen while providing the user with raised, vibrating print characters that can be "read" with the index finger. The American School for the Deaf in West Hartford, Conn., introduced its 10th–12th grade students to computer-assisted instruction by providing drill exercises in mathematics and other subjects. In addition, self-study computer tapes helped train students for computer operator and programmer jobs in data centers.

U.S. information systems. The number, importance, and especially the value of information data bases continued to expand rapidly. A report issued by International Resource Development, Inc., stated that the revenues from online data base services, which exceeded $1,250,000,000 in 1981, were predicted to quadruple to more than $5.5 billion in 1991. The expansion was expected to result from increased corporate use of financial and credit information data bases. Consistent with the above was a report, released by LINK Resources, that predicted a $3.4 billion market for 1985. This report stated that news data bases are expected to be the fastest growing group, while business and credit information, financial statements, and full-text legal data bases will be important contenders.

As evidence in support of the above predictions, a service called "The Wall Street Journal Highlights Online" offered subscribers access to the headlines and summaries of the *Wall Street Journal*'s front-page stories, a synopsis of the World-Wide column, the full text of the Business and Finance column, and edited versions of major editorials and commentaries. The service was designed to provide a quick overview of the paper to be read by active business people at either the home or office terminal. Another service, called "Harfax (Harper & Row Facts) Industry Information Database," provided access to sources of industry-intensive data such as those issued by investment banking firms, trade and product directories, and statistical and economic reports. The data base contained about 20,000 bibliographic records, each of which included an abstract indicating the kinds of statistical information reported rather than summarizing the source document itself.

Lawyers and other professional and business researchers have access to expanded legal data bases and to the contents of the *Encyclopaedia Britannica* through computer terminals leased from Mead Data Central. The legal research system, "Lexis," is a full-text collection of general federal law, including decisions of all federal courts, plus specialized libraries of taxation, securities regulations, labor, and case law of all 50 states. The "Nexis," or news service, provides access to the full text of stories from major newspapers, magazines, wire services, and newsletters covering general and business news. Subscribers were also able to use their computer terminals to search and display the full text of articles in the 15th edition of the *Encyclopaedia Britannica*, plus the *Britannica Book of the Year*, the *Medical and Health Annual*, and the *Yearbook of Science and the Future*. However, this service was not available to home computers or to schools and libraries.

Specialized Centers for Industrial Technology were established through the assistance of the U.S. Department of Commerce and the National Science Foundation to encourage technical innovation and the utilization of federally owned or originated technologies. In addition, three regional Inventor Information Resource Centers, in Massachusetts, Georgia, and California, were established by grants from the National Bureau of Standards. These centers provided inventors with access to computerized data bases and to published sources about inventions and innovations, especially those related to energy and the environment. They also helped independent inventors obtain information on methods of marketing and producing inventions and made them aware of government programs and agencies offering assistance.

As a general service to all, Federal Information Centers, with toll-free telephone access, were established in metropolitan areas, usually in federal buildings, throughout the U.S. The staff of specialists, many of whom speak more than one language, answer questions concerning federal assistance, consumer services, energy conservation, and a wide variety of other topics such as canning and preserving foods, special di-

The 1981 summer catalog of Sears, Roebuck and Co. was put on a videodisc that included sound and motion for in-store use and home viewing by 1,000 families.

ets, home maintenance, and recreational facilities. Government publications were provided free or for a nominal price.

International information systems. Barriers to international information flow were being investigated by the U.S. House of Representatives Subcommittee on Government Information and Individual Rights. The subcommittee found that while most governments recognized the importance of information and information technology and were developing comprehensive plans and programs with respect to international communications and information transfer, the U.S. government had no coordinated information policy. This lack of policy resulted in inadequate representation of U.S. interests in debates over the structure of international communications and the free flow of information. In view of these findings the subcommittee recommended that a Cabinet-level Council on International Communications and Information should be established for a period of five years to coordinate development and implementation of a uniform, consistent, and comprehensive policy.

The International Atomic Energy Agency (IAEA) was chartered to assist member states in advancing peaceful uses of atomic energy. The Nuclear Data Section of IAEA compiles, exchanges, and disseminates accurate nuclear data and assists in the transfer of such data, mainly from developed to less developed

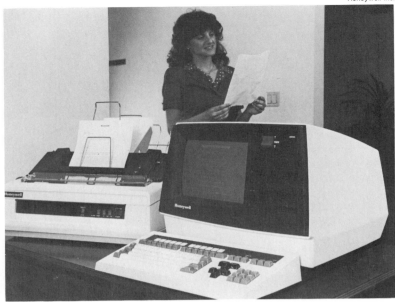

Infowriter system developed by Honeywell Inc. can perform such functions as document preparation, records processing, printing, and sorting. As part of an office network it can share data-processing files with a remote host computer.

countries and in the exchange of nuclear data between eastern and western member states. Through these services IAEA developed an awareness of the needs for nuclear data in science and technology in all parts of the world and identified specific knowledge gaps that proved useful in stimulating and coordinating nuclear data measurements.

The United Kingdom's Scientific Documentation Center operates an information service on Sewage and Municipal Waste Disposal and was seeking to meet user requirements for new services in the recycling of waste materials and the elimination of pollution caused by ordinary and nuclear wastes. Both current-awareness and retrospective-type information services are available.

The Northern Research Information and Documentation Services located in Ottawa collects and stores information on the current Canadian northern research activities and catalogs it according to subject, geographic area, and the organization engaged in the research. The information is disseminated through publications and may also be accessed on-line through CAN/OLE, an automated information retrieval service of the Canadian Institute for Scientific and Technical Information.

As part of its national telecommunications program, called Télématique, France introduced "smart card," an updated version of the credit card in which a tiny electronic integrated-circuit chip containing a coded personal data file is embedded. At the time purchases are made or bills paid, the card, together with an identification code, is entered and processed. The information stored in the chip's memory identifies the bearer, checks the money value of the transaction against the credit balance of the card, and, if the balance is positive, completes the transaction, transfers funds from the holder's bank account, and updates both the bank balance and the card's credit limit. It is anticipated that this method of electronic transfer of funds will replace current payment systems such as cash, checks, and credit cards because it offers security against theft and fraud, avoids the high clerical costs of processing, and provides greater flexibility in use. Furthermore, the French claim that when appropriate personal information is stored on the chip the card could also function as a passport and security identification. They planned to market the smart card in the U.S.

Information science research. The Lister Hill National Center for Biomedical Communications undertook a Document Capture Project to design, develop, and evaluate an experimental system that will electronically store, retrieve, and display documents acquired by the U.S. National Library of Medicine. The long-term goal of the program was to introduce advanced telecommunications and data-processing technology in order to help the library fulfill its mission as a national archive for biomedical literature and an interlibrary loan service center. The experimental system was to be developed and evaluated by pursuing three concurrent research projects: document capture, data storage and transfer, and document display.

One especially interesting new technology that was being actively investigated by organizations in the U.S., Europe, and Japan was the optical disk. Optical disk systems make use of laser scanners to read a document and transmit the image in digital form to a storage device or to display the image on a high-resolution cathode-ray tube. Unlike the video disks that are available on the consumer market and that are unalterable once they are stamped with the image of a movie at the factory, optical disks make use of a direct-read-after-write (DRAW) system; this makes the information stored on them alterable. Other advantages of the optical disk include the high storage capacity of from 10,000 to 100,000 pages per side and the rapid access time. Unfortunately, as of 1982 a number of technical problems remained to be solved and the price was still too high for the mass market. However, industry observers predicted that those problems would be solved in about five years.

—Harold Borko

Satellite systems

Earth-orbiting satellites that utilize their vantage points in space for economic benefit and military purposes are termed applications satellites. There are three basic classes of such satellite systems: communications, Earth observation, and navigation. They are developed and operated by individual and groups of nations and by private industrial concerns.

The U.S. and the Soviet Union continued to dominate such activities because of their large booster rockets. Both nations launched satellites for other countries. However, France, Japan, and China, as well as the European Space Agency (ESA), continued to develop their own space launch capabilities. Eleven ESA member nations planned future use of the French-developed booster (Ariane) in competition with the U.S. Delta launch vehicle or the piloted (reusable) space shuttle.

After many technical delays the space shuttle "Columbia" made its first, eminently successful, manned orbital flight in April 1981, followed by a second flight in November (*see* SPACE EXPLORATION: *Manned Flight*.) Japan launched two satellites successfully with its newly operational N-II boosters. Likewise, ESA had two successful launches of the Ariane, in June and December, completing the test phase of that booster. Four Ariane launches were scheduled for 1982.

Communications satellites. Of all types of applications satellites the communications satellite has exhibited the greatest activity in growth and economic value. The rapid growth of national and international communications during the 1970s resulted partly from the use of these satellites. The International Telecommunications Satellite organization (Intelsat), a consortium of 106 nations, of which the Communications Satellite Corp. (Comsat) is the U.S. member, continued to grow in size and capability. Global transmissions of telephone, television, facsimile, and digital data are provided by large spacecraft in geostationary orbit. (A geostationary, or geosynchronous, orbit is at an altitude of 35,900 km (22,300 mi) above the Equator. At that height a satellite travels at the same angular velocity as

Antenna of the Intelsat 5 is made of graphite fiber composites. Each Intelsat 5 can relay more than 12,000 telephone calls and two TV channels simultaneously.

the surface of the rotating Earth and thus remains at a constant point above the Earth. Three such satellites can provide global coverage, except at the highest latitudes.) At the beginning of 1982 Intelsat had seven satellites in operation, stationed over the Atlantic, Pacific, and Indian oceans, plus one or more standbys at each location.

The use of Intelsat for global transmission of television news increased markedly in 1981. The coverage of the attempted assassination of U.S. Pres. Ronald Reagan in March totaled 107 hours of transmission time. The 118 hours of satellite transmission covering the British royal wedding were seen by an estimated 700 million viewers throughout the world.

For the past five years high-quality voice and telegraph communications to ships has been provided by three Marisat geostationary satellites, owned and operated by Comsat. Commencing in February 1982, the International Maritime Satellite Organization (Inmarsat) was scheduled to begin operations. Comprised of 35 maritime nations, Inmarsat will at first lease the Marisat system from Comsat. Supplementing this system will be the Marecs A satellite launched by Ariane in December 1981, placed over the Atlantic Ocean. Marecs B was scheduled to be launched in April 1982 for Pacific Ocean coverage. Intelsat planned to supplement global maritime communications further with a special subsystem that would be carried on three future Intelsat 5 satellites, to be launched in 1982–83.

Two Intelsat 5 satellites were launched in May and

November by the U.S. National Aeronautics and Space Administration (NASA) on a cost-reimbursable basis. Each of the satellites weighed 1,950 kg (4,300 lb) and had the capacity of handling 12,000 simultaneous telephone calls plus two television channels. An improved version, Intelsat 5A, capable of 15,000 telephone calls, was on order. Three new Earth stations became operational in 1981, in Yemen, West Germany, and Ghana. This brought the total in the Intelsat network to 287.

Four communications satellite systems were functioning in the United States in 1981. They were operated by Western Union, AT&T, RCA, and Satellite Business Systems. Others were awaiting approval.

In August two 24-hour radio programs were initiated by Satellite Music Network, using RCA's Satcom 1. At least four other radio network programs by satellite were anticipated, providing a variety of music, talk, and religious fare. Such programs are transmitted to radio stations for broadcast in their geographic area.

Direct transmissions from satellite to user Earth stations were being offered in a wide variety of educational and recreational services. Teleconferencing, for example, is a system of conference via television. The concept is simple; a program is produced, transmitted "up-link" to a communications satellite, "down-link" to a small receiving antenna, and finally to television screens at one or dozens of locations. Prominent in this form of communications was the Holiday Inn chain of hotels. In 1981 some 200 Earth stations had been installed in Holiday Inns, in 40 states and 126 cities throughout the U.S. More than a dozen national conferences used this video network. Meetings ranged from several hundred attendees at 15 locations to nearly 5,000 viewers at 100 locations.

The types of organizations interested in teleconferencing are many: large corporations; government agencies; political parties and labor groups; medical, scientific, trade, and professional organizations; and religious groups. Reduction in cost of travel and of lost working time can make such a system cost-effective.

In the medical field the U.S. Army Health Service Command was linking its major centers for graduate medical education and residency training with live demonstrations of intricate surgery. In the private sector the American Hospital Video Network offered more than 100 hours per week to a national market of 7,000 hospitals. Programming was aimed at physicians, nurses, and management. A competitor, Hospital Satellite Network, planned broadcasts in 1982 with programming for both medical staff and patients.

The Public Service Satellite Corporation (PSSC) operated a satellite-access facility and network control center at Denver, Colo. PSSC offered video conferences and continuing education to 110 member organiza-

Communications satellites provided 118 hours of television coverage of the British royal wedding. Approximately 700 million people throughout the world viewed the proceedings.

tions, which included libraries and state organizations. The U.S. Public Broadcasting Service (PBS) also offered national teleconferencing to its member stations.

The oldest geostationary communications satellite as of 1982 was NASA's Applications Technology Satellite 1 (ATS 1). Launched in 1966, the ATS 1 pioneered the use of communications satellites for health care, education, public safety, emergency communications, and mobile Earth station applications. During 1981 experiments included voice transmission among 11 Pacific island nations, the Trust Territory of the Pacific, Australia, New Zealand, Hawaii, and California. Other experiments provided medical care communications for Alaska, technology transmissions between Japan and Australia, and coordination of oceanic research vessels in the Pacific and Gulf of Mexico regions.

Fourteen applications for direct television broadcast satellite systems were awaiting approval by the U.S. Federal Communications Commission in 1982. Of those it was expected that four or five would be approved during the year. Japan and ESA were also developing direct broadcast systems.

Earth observation satellites. This category of applications satellites consists of three major types: meteorological (weather), Earth resources, and military reconnaissance.

Weather satellites. The National Oceanic and Atmospheric Administration (NOAA) has primary responsibility for U.S. operational environmental satellite systems. NOAA operates and provides satellite data on a global basis, observing and forecasting weather conditions and assessing data obtainable from land and marine images. In June the NOAA 7 satellite was launched, joining NOAA 6 as the polar-orbiting weather satellite system.

In addition, NOAA operates the Geostationary Operational Environmental Satellite (GOES) system. At the year's end GOES 4 was operational as the western and GOES 5 (launched in May) as the eastern U.S. geostationary satellite. Visible light and infrared radiation images from those satellites, obtained every one-half hour, provided the photographs for daily televised weather forecasts throughout the U.S. Additional sensors on NOAA satellites provided atmospheric temperatures and water-vapor content at various altitudes. In January the aged synchronous meteorological satellite (SMS 1) was deactivated. It was then boosted up and out of orbit to alleviate cluttering of the geostationary-altitude orbit. This operation was the first time that a U.S. satellite had been so maneuvered.

An ESA Meteosat 2 weather satellite was launched into geostationary orbit by Ariane in June. Meteosat 2 provides weather images for its coverage range of Europe, Africa, the Middle East, and parts of South America. In August Japan launched its geostationary meteorological satellite, GMS 2. The two GOES, Meteosat, and GMS 2 thus provided a continuous global weather

GMS 2, Japan's newest weather satellite, is tested by its builder, Hughes Aircraft Co. The satellite was designed to relay weather pictures and other data covering approximately 170 million square kilometers (68 million square miles) in the western Pacific.

watch except for the polar regions; those areas were covered by the polar-orbiting NOAA 6 and NOAA 7 satellites.

Earth resources satellites. The two polar-orbiting Earth-observation satellites developed by the United States, Landsats 2 and 3, continued to provide useful information in 1981 despite some operational problems. Monitoring and mapping the Earth's surface with multispectral imagery, the Landsats continued to provide information to all nations. In 1981 Indonesia signed an agreement with NASA for the establishment of a Landsat ground station.

An improved spacecraft, Landsat D, was scheduled to be launched in 1982. It was to carry a multispectral scanner as well as a sophisticated "thermatic mapper." After the checkout of the craft (which would become Landsat 4 when in orbit) NOAA was charged with the operational management and supporting services until the private sector could take over the land remote-sensing program. This move would permit NASA to concentrate its efforts upon new scientific and developmental activities.

During the second flight of the space shuttle orbiter

"Columbia" remote sensing experiments were carried out in the cargo bay. During its three-day flight the orbiter obtained radar "photographs" across four continents, a distance of 80,000 km (48,000 mi) and encompassing 26 million sq km (10 million sq mi). This area, approximately the size of the U.S., covered portions of Africa, the Middle East, Asia, Europe, Mexico, and the U.S. Remarkably clear images were obtained of fish schools in the Yellow Sea, the South China Sea, and the Mediterranean; the tops of thunderclouds; wind patterns on the sea surface; and distinct types of soil and rocks of geological interest.

Plans for the Search and Rescue Satellite-Aided Tracking System (Sarsat) satellite proceeded, and the craft was scheduled to be launched by NASA in late 1982. This multinational effort (U.S., Canada, France, Norway, and U.S.S.R.) was designed to make possible the location of an automatic emergency distress beacon within a ten-mile radius. Such a beacon is carried on all U.S. vessels and could be used by aircraft. The first Sarsat will cover the western North Atlantic and eastern North Pacific oceans.

Military reconnaissance satellites. The U.S. and Soviet Union continued launching reconnaissance satellites to observe and remotely sense the other nation's military movements, electronic transmissions, nuclear explosions, and ballistic missile launchings. The Soviet Union relied primarily upon small film-recoverable satellites with an operational lifetime of 12–14 days. The U.S. proceeded with emphasis upon larger satellites with "search and find" cameras and a lifetime of six months or more. Of the 98 satellites launched by the U.S.S.R. in 1981 it was estimated that perhaps half were military reconnaissance in purpose.

Navigation satellites. NASA launched the Navy 20 (Nova 1) satellite in May, an improved version of spacecraft used in the Transit satellite navigation system. The Transit system is utilized by the U.S. Navy surface and submarine fleet. However, receivers and miniature signal processor units are available to commercial ships as well. Less accurate than the Navy equipment but able nonetheless to achieve all-weather positioning within a one-mile radius, the commercial units cost approximately $10,000. The military version was reported to be able to locate position within a radius of 0.1 mi.

—F. C. Durant III

Energy

After several years of steady turmoil, energy developments in 1981 appeared modest but reassuring. Producers, consumers, and politicians concentrated on adjusting to the numerous past events. After the barrage of major energy legislation in the United States from 1974 to 1980, legislative initiatives were lacking. The administration of U.S. Pres. Ronald Reagan preferred to rely on existing discretionary powers and the appropriations process to initiate its proposed reduction in government regulation of energy.

The critical market development during the last year was the substantial further evolution of consumer response to the massive oil price rises since the early 1970s and particularly to the most recent round in 1978 and 1979. Evidence suggested that worldwide oil use declined sharply in 1981 and was at the lowest levels since the early 1970s. This decline could best be ex-

Representatives of the Organization of Petroleum Exporting Countries (OPEC) meet in Geneva in May 1981. They were unable to agree on a new pricing policy in the face of the worldwide oversupply of oil that developed during 1980.

Brucelle—Sygma

plained as reflecting the normal consumer response to higher prices.

Role of OPEC. A major effect of the decline in the use of oil was growing concern about a "weakening" of the control of world oil prices by the members of the Organization of Petroleum Exporting Countries (OPEC). While these observations superficially resembled those made about OPEC in the early 1970s, their meaning probably was quite different. Previously, weakness often was expected to produce the collapse of OPEC and the return of oil prices to their 1970 level. Weakness in 1981, however, concerned doubts about the ability to raise prices further and the possibility of increased friction among OPEC members that could modestly reduce prices.

A more profound change occurred in the perception of the nature of oil supply problems. Previously, analysts had been divided between those concerned only with OPEC control of supplies and those worried about the physical availability of oil. The second group believed that no matter which OPEC policies were in force, continued depletion of world oil resources would put steady pressures on costs and push prices up further. In this connection numerous studies appeared stressing the need for some sort of energy transition by which replacements for oil would be found.

Those concerned only with OPEC countries argued that, given present prices and their impacts in reducing consumption and stimulating both OPEC oil production and the use of alternative fuels, OPEC supplies would last much longer than those who were concerned about physical supply believed. To them the critical problems centered on how the OPEC countries managed supply and how the consuming countries prepared for the crises that would inevitably disrupt, at least temporarily, world oil flows. The 1981–82 developments demonstrated the critical importance of OPEC

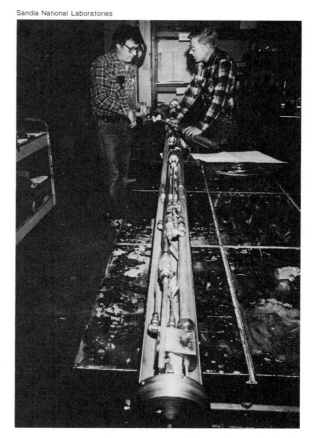

Workers assemble instrumentation package of Project DEEP STEAM, an effort to recover heavy oil from deep reservoirs by the injection of steam.

policies. In formulating their policies for this period the OPEC members behaved like the owners of substantial resources that are unlikely to be exhausted within the next several decades. Their critical problem for the future thus was one of stemming the desire to produce, and they began seeking ways to better control output.

After the first massive oil price increases of 1973 world oil output tended to rise through 1979, but OPEC production only exceeded 1973 levels in 1977. In 1980 and 1981 world and OPEC output both dropped. The 1979 drop in Iranian production had been offset largely by rises in Saudi Arabia. Subsequently, Iranian output continued to drop, and war with Iran also reduced Iraqi production; Saudi output levels rose slightly in 1980 but by December 1981 were 16% below the December 1980 level. Declines in output occurred in both 1980 and 1981 for other OPEC members. Mexican output continued the sharp rise of the 1970s, causing it to produce more than any OPEC country except Saudi Arabia.

Despite the disruption of Iranian and Iraqi oil production during the past year supplies were abundant,

Table I. World Crude Oil Production
(000 bbl per day)

Country	1973	1979	1980	1981 (3rd qtr.)
U.S.	9,208	8,552	8,597	8,539
Canada	1,800	1,496	1,424	1,267
Mexico	465	1,461	1,937	2,278
United Kingdom	2	1,568	1,622	1,780
U.S.S.R.	8,465	11,460	11,770	11,800
Algeria	1,097	1,154	1,012	625
Iran	5,861	3,186	1,662	1,200
Iraq	2,018	3,477	2,514	1,100
Kuwait	3,020	2,500	1,656	962
Libya	2,175	2,092	1,787	717
Saudi Arabia	7,596	9,532	9,900	9,885
Indonesia	1,339	1,591	1,577	1,600
Nigeria	2,054	2,302	2,055	848
Venezuela	3,366	2,356	2,167	1,933
OPEC	30,989	30,928	26,890	21,018
World	55,748	60,165	59,452	53,917

Source: U.S. Department of Energy

and prices weakened. This experience illustrated that, as has often happened before, political instability in supplying countries can occur without disrupting supplies. The danger existed, however, that policymakers might once again overreact. Having often overstated the danger to supplies of political instability, they might go to the other extreme of ignoring political problems. Fears existed that such optimism would leave oil-consuming nations inadequately prepared for what was considered to be the inevitability of a crisis that would disrupt supplies.

An important issue as of 1982 was the long-term relationship between Saudi Arabia and other OPEC nations. During recent years Saudi Arabia had become an increasingly dominant member of OPEC. Observers of the organization noted that Saudi restraint of production had been a critical aspect of the supply and had had the effect of forcing up prices. Less attention was given to the nature of the Saudi limitation. Rather than actually reducing outputs, the Saudis needed only to expand output less than was possible. Production declines elsewhere—notably in Iran—enabled the Saudis to maintain higher output than would have otherwise been possible without depressing prices. Thus, controlling output was less onerous to the Saudis than it would have been had other OPEC countries been trying to produce more.

The situation was complicated by the continued inability of OPEC members to develop a coordinated production plan. Instead, a price structure was maintained that involved efforts to reflect accurately the value of oil quality and transportation cost advantages (or disadvantages) of the different OPEC countries. Persistent difficulties arose in properly setting such prices.

A particular problem was the setting of appropriate prices for Libyan and Nigerian crude oils. Both countries had been able to benefit from two basic sources of economic advantage, higher quality oil and proximity to market. Better quality in terms both of ease of refining into expensive products such as gasoline and of low sulfur content allows a crude oil to obtain higher prices. Proximity to markets in terms of lower transportation costs allows the owner to charge a higher wellhead price. Both, Libya and Nigeria raised the prices of their crude oil considerably and as a result suffered substantial sales reductions.

Overall, pressures on the Saudis were developing in several directions. Countries with limited ability to expand output wanted the Saudis to reduce their production and thereby force up prices. Countries with expansion potential wanted the Saudis to cede markets. The Saudis themselves professed to be divided on the proper strategy. As of 1982 they sought to limit their share in output reduction and resist pressures from others for greater decreases.

The OPEC countries were trying to reach a consensus on the best policy in the face of considerable uncer-

tainty about the effect of higher prices on sales and in the face of the divergent interests of the member countries. However, the recognition that output restraint is highly profitable remained the controlling force. The discord was over details rather than basic principles. Thus, the prevailing view was that discord would at most lead to modest drops in prices and not to substantial declines. This view implied that the 1979–80 OPEC price increases were larger than desirable to promote long-range profitability.

U.S. policy. The Reagan administration effected a radical change in the tactics of energy policy. Prior administrations had requested (and obtained) major new energy legislation every year since 1973. President Reagan refrained from seeking major new laws but concentrated on budgetary changes and the exercise of administrative discretion to alter energy policy. This restraint from seeking new legislation involved sacrificing immediate implementation of Reagan's energy goals for full concentration on spending and tax objectives considered more critical. However, the administrative and budgetary initiatives were sufficiently extensive to produce a significant change in the policy climate.

The first major initiative was the speedup of deregulation of crude oil prices. Immediately after his inauguration Reagan abolished the system of controls initially imposed by Pres. Richard Nixon in 1971 and extended by subsequent legislation. Decontrol was absorbed with modest impact. For example, unleaded regular gasoline prices rose from an average of $1.30 per gallon in January 1981 to $1.42 in March 1981 and then drifted downward to $1.33 in February 1982. In contrast, prior to the OPEC price rises of 1979 and 1980, unleaded gasoline prices averaged $0.67 per gallon in 1977.

Moreover, none of the political repercussions that decontrol was predicted to produce actually occurred. No noticeable public outcries emerged. Even the small refiners, who had been given a cost advantage under

Table II. Consumption of Major Fuels in the United States (000,000,000 BTUS)

Year	Coal	Natural gas	Petro- leum	Water	Nuclear	Total
1947	15,824	4,518	11,367	1,326	0	33,035
1960	10,120	12,390	19,920	1,650	1	44,080
1970	12,660	21,790	29,520	2,650	24	66,830
1973	13,300	22,512	34,840	3,010	910	74,609
1974	12,876	21,732	33,455	3,309	1,272	72,759
1975	12,823	19,948	32,721	3,219	1,900	70,707
1976	13,733	20,345	35,175	3,066	2,111	74,510
1977	13,965	19,931	37,122	2,515	2,702	76,332
1978	13,846	20,000	37,965	3,164	2,977	78,150
1979	15,109	20,666	37,123	3,166	2,748	78,968
1980	15,603	20,495	34,196	3,125	2,704	76,201
1981*	16,100	19,600	31,900	3,000	2,900	73,600

*Ten-month totals

Source: U.S. Department of Energy

Wide World

A 60-meter- (200-foot-) high, 2.5-megawatt wind turbine generator near Goldendale, Washington, began producing power in 1981.

the price control system, were unable to mount support for prevention of the loss of aid intrinsic to the deregulation process.

Other major initiatives were taken by all three agencies with major energy responsibilities: the Department of Energy, the Department of the Interior, and the Environmental Protection Agency. The thrust of change in the Department of Energy was toward curtailment of activities. Generally, programs to support research and development—particularly on conservation, solar energy, and other "renewable" energy sources—were subjected to substantial budget cuts. Proposals were made to reduce activities further in future years. Simultaneously, the Reagan administration chose to reorient the independent Synthetic Fuels Corporation that Pres. Jimmy Carter had established in 1980. The corporation board was filled with Reagan appointees and moved cautiously through consideration of far fewer projects than Carter had advocated.

The Department of the Interior made its major changes in the administration of mineral leasing and of reclamation of surfaces disturbed by coal mining. Leasing programs emphasized increased activity, and

efforts were made to transfer responsibility for implementation of surface mine regulations to the states. The Environmental Protection Agency refrained from issuing major new rules and reduced its staff.

These actions obviously were distressing to those advocating more vigorous control of energy and its environmental impacts. The results also were inadequate to attain Reagan's own goal of removing all of what he perceived to be the undesirable barriers to domestic energy development. At least one avowed goal, more rapid deregulation of natural gas, required changes in legislation.

One modest legislative change was the reduction of some of the "windfall" profits taxes. However, the basic tax system with all its complexities remained in force. Some critics feared that this tax system would significantly deter domestic oil production.

Reagan's criticisms of alleged extremism in environmental policies could be interpreted as implying that radical revisions of the Clean Air Act were needed. The legal difficulties arising from Secretary of the Interior James Watt's efforts to speed leasing suggested that existing laws might prevent attainment of the leasing goals. Another legislative requirement that acquired great symbolic significance was that of abolishing the Department of Energy.

Legislative proposals were limited to outlining in late 1981 a plan to transfer the major functions of the Department of Energy to the Department of Commerce. Legislation to accomplish this was to be considered in 1982. As of early 1982 a decision about natural gas had not been made. Similarly, the administration chose to back away from proposing radical changes in the Clean Air Act and not to press the requirement (in the 1977 amendments to the act) for an extensive 1981 review of the laws.

Another problem arose with appropriate response to any state policies that could excessively harm energy industries. For the federal government the goal of removing such barriers had to be balanced against that of lessening its interference with the states. The Reagan administration explicitly refused to override state authority over pipelines to transport coal. Supporters of such pipelines argued that they should have the same status in federal law that allowed oil and gas pipelines and railroads to use the government's right of eminent domain to secure needed land. Similarly, the administration was silent about state regulation of electric utilities despite concerns that such regulation was reducing profits to an extent that imperiled industry health.

Another possible area of concern was that the ability to effect reform was being hindered by the reluctance to issue regulations. Regulatory legislation increasingly delegated responsibility for specific implementation to the relevant federal agency. This could be quite time-consuming and often prevented action. For example, the Carter administration fell far short of implement-

Solar collector effective in cloudy weather consists of clear vacuum tubes that absorb more heat than flat plates. At the rear is a "Sun simulator" that is used for testing.

ing all the requirements of the extensive 1977 amendments to the Clean Air Act. Rules were established to cover sulfur dioxide emissions from new electric power plants but not for other new sources covered by the amendments. As of 1982 the Reagan administration had perpetuated the uncertainty about regulations. Neither new legislation nor regulations under the old law were available.

Production and consumption. Market developments continued in the directions established since the extensive rise in world oil prices in 1973. U.S. energy consumption in 1981 was about 1% below the 1973 level and was 7% below the peak reached in 1979. Major changes occurred in the role of individual fuels in total consumption. Overall, oil and gas use both declined, while coal use steadily rose. Through 1978 nuclear power use also increased.

The coal and nuclear increases were associated with a shift of final users from oil and gas to electricity. Coal use by the residential and industrial sectors actually declined, but coal use in electric power rose. The de-

cline in the coal share in electric generation that had taken place in recent years sharply reversed itself. Coal use accounted for 52% of heat input to electric utilities in 1981 compared to 43% in 1973. Also, during the first nine months of 1981 industrial use of coal for heat rose sharply above the 1980 levels.

The burden of reduced availability of natural gas was felt most severely by the industrial sector. Industrial gas use in 1981 was about 23% below that of 1973, while residential use was down only 3% and electric power use had returned to 1973 levels. Industrial, household, and electric power oil use in 1981 were well below 1978 levels.

It seemed premature to try to determine the further developments that will occur in total fuel use. It is not yet certain how much limitation will be placed on overall consumption growth and to what extent the decline in U.S. oil and gas production can be stemmed. What was clear was that a remarkable transformation had occurred in the coal industry. By 1982 it had finally completed recovery from the steep consumption decline that prevailed from 1947 to 1960. And, of greater importance, the recovery involved a radical transformation of the industry.

Before 1947, coal was the principal source of unspecialized energy in the United States. Industry wanting pure heat tended to burn coal. The prime specialized use was for coke in making steel, and the variability of demand in the steel industry produced substantial cyclical volatility in the coal markets. By 1982 the predominant use of coal was to generate electricity because coal plants were substantially cheaper to operate than oil-fired facilities. Therefore, demand for coal became far less cyclical because the high-cost oil-fired units absorbed a large proportion of the cyclical declines.

Another important change took place in the regional patterns of coal production and consumption in the U.S. In particular, production growth during the last decade occurred mainly west of the Mississippi River, in Montana, Wyoming, and Texas. Some of this expansion was due to shifts by Middle Western utilities to the use of western coal that was low in sulfur content, but most was due to the rise of coal use in western states that had previously been reliant on other fuels, particularly natural gas.

In 1981 U.S. output of electricity by nuclear power recovered to near its 1978 level. Expansion of nuclear power continued elsewhere in the world; in 1981 the non-Communist countries outside the U.S. showed an increase of nuclear generation of 24% above 1980 and more than four times the 1973 level. Expansion prospects in the U.S. remained dim. As anticipated, several nuclear units in the early stages of development were canceled in 1981. However, cancellations and delays were also affecting planned coal-fired plants, and so it was unclear as to whether these cutbacks were caused by the special problems of nuclear power or by the general problems of slow growth in the electric power industry.

Future prospects. Market developments appear likely to dominate energy behavior in the next several years. Energy consumption and production have proved considerably more responsive to price increases than might have been deduced from the prognoses of the mid-1970s. Instead of strain by consumers to deal with a steady increase of OPEC price pressures, the problem in early 1982 was for OPEC to respond to difficulties in maintaining prices.

Events such as strong economic recovery or a major political crisis could solve OPEC's problems. However, it now seems appropriate to view the future as a series of oscillations between tightness and surplus rather than continual upward pressures on prices.

—Richard L. Gordon

Environment

One of the most intriguing features of the last year was the paradoxical contrast between the rapid advances being made in ecology and environmental sciences, and the lack of influence this work had on management of resources in much of the world. One nation that was a significant exception was China.

Basic research in ecology. Basic ecology has evolved rapidly in the last few years. Using a methodology borrowed from the physical sciences, Robert May of Princeton University demonstrated how it could be used to understand a variety of phenomena that have interested ecologists for several decades. The method involves writing a set of differential equations that describe the essential features in the dynamic behavior of some phenomenon, such as insect population fluctuations. The trick in writing these equations is to make them realistic, yet simple. Then the implications of the equations are exposed through a combination of algebraic manipulation and graphing of sample solutions. These findings are then used to interpret graphs of actual data that have been obtained in field studies or laboratory experiments. In the hands of May and others this method came to fruition in the last year, allowing researchers to obtain answers to a number of questions that have in the past generated controversy among ecologists.

Four new studies completed during recent months indicate the power of the method. For example, it has been known for at least 35 years that forest insect species can exhibit very regular cycles of population abundance in nature. Furthermore, it has gradually been discovered that different species have periods of different lengths. The European pine looper has a period of only 5–8 years, whereas the black-headed budworm has a cycle of 10–15 years in eastern Canada. Also some scientists noticed that epidemic outbreaks of viral or protozoan parasites are observed in the pests in years of peak pest abundance.

Putting these observations together suggests the hypothesis that insect pathogens are somehow determining both the existence of cycles in their hosts and also their periodicity. May and R. M. Anderson proposed a mathematical theory that accounts for these observations. They found that stable cycles can be produced in the insect populations when certain parameters of the insect-pathogen system fall within certain ranges of values. Furthermore, they found that the cycle length increases with decreasing values of the death rate of the pathogens and of the rate of population increase of the insect host. These findings are plausible. The lower the rate of increase of the host, the longer it will take for the insect population to become large enough for

The Mediterranean fruit fly, which originated in West Africa, appeared in California in 1980 and became the center of a controversy involving the safety to humans of aerial spraying of pesticides. Larvae of the fly attack 200 varieties of fruits and vegetables grown in California.

the pathogens to generate an epidemic in their hosts; this would tend to increase the cycle length.

Two other recent studies of this type are timely, given the potentially serious situation involving the Mediterranean fruit fly (medfly). Michael Hassell and May made a useful contribution to a highly controversial issue. Often an insect pest could be controlled by release of several different species of natural enemies (parasites or predators). There have been two schools of thought on the optimum strategy for this situation. Scientists from the first school assert that all potentially effective control agents should be released simultaneously. They argue that it would take a prohibitive amount of research to discover by prior experimentation which of the control agents was the best. Therefore, the optimal strategy is to release all available control agents on the assumption that the best ones would gradually assume numerical dominance over others and achieve effective control of the pest.

The other school has held that if one releases several different species of control agents, a species that would be effective on its own would be less potent because of interference from other species that on their own would be incapable of controlling the pest. It has been argued from theory and also demonstrated in field and laboratory studies that there are cases in which the combined pest-control effectiveness of several parasite species has been less than one would expect to achieve from using just the one most effective species of the group. By experimenting with mathematical models May and Hassell resolved this controversy. They identified two characteristics of parasites that will allow two or more species of such parasites to coexist, depress the host (pest) density, and also remain stable. These characteristics are high parasite searching efficiency and a marked ability to seek out patches of high host density.

Stephen Carpenter also used this method of exploring the implications of equations to consider another problem of insect pest control. Within the last few years a method of pest control was developed called integrated pest management; it consists of using several methods of control in combination. Carpenter found that control methods that increase the pest death rate (such as pesticides) increase the threshold pest population required for spread of the death-causing pathogen and therefore lengthen the time required for the pathogen to control the pest population. On the other hand, control measures that decrease the pest birth rate (such as introduction of sterile males into the pest population) do not inhibit the success of pathogens. Thus, this new development of ecological theoretical work provides a rational basis for determining which types of pest control strategy will work best in combination with one another.

A fourth example of mathematical theorizing in ecology appeared during the year in the work of Lauri Oksanen, Steven Fretwell, Joseph Arruda, and Pekka Niemelä on the dynamic behavior of ecosystems. As with the study by May this research is primarily interesting because of the way theory is deeply rooted in biological data and is then used to interpret data. The issue taken up by these authors concerned the nature of the determining forces operating on the behavior of each trophic (feeding) level in an ecosystem. Suppose, for example, that sea otters eat sea urchins and that the latter eat kelp. This raises the questions of whether the abundance of sea urchins is determined solely by the abundance of kelp, and whether the abundance of sea otters is in turn determined solely by the abundance of sea urchins. In other words, are all natural populations limited only by the availability of the resources they eat? The alternative hypothesis is that each population is limited not only by what it eats but also by what eats it.

The theory presented by the authors argues for the latter hypothesis. On balance, the available data tend to support their theory. For example, when sea otters are absent, populations of sea urchins are dense and kelp beds are almost eliminated. When the sea otter is returned to such situations, there is a decrease in the density of sea urchins and a great increase in the density of kelp. The interpretation is that sea-urchin densities are regulated by the sea otters as well as by the availability of kelp. Furthermore, the influence of sea-otter density is passed on, via the sea urchins, to the kelp. More generally, predators may be thought of as the protectors of the vegetation eaten by herbivores.

The medfly. The medfly problem in California in 1981 was a remarkably revealing example of the nature of environmental problems in the modern world. The approach to dealing with the problem was apparently quite uninfluenced by the type of research in ecology discussed above. On the other hand, politics, government, and the media were important components of the situation as it unfolded.

The Mediterranean fruit fly originated in West Africa but has spread to Europe, the Middle East, South and Central America, Mexico, and Hawaii. The insect had previously appeared three times in Florida, once in Texas, and twice in Los Angeles, and was apparently exterminated in all these cases. The recent infestation, which began in San Jose, Calif., about May 1980, is economically important because the larvae of this species can attack 200 varieties of fruits and vegetables grown in California. A significant portion of the state's $14 billion agriculture industry was thus at risk, as would be the agriculture of Texas, Florida, and other states if the pest should spread.

Two major complications arose in regard to the medfly control campaign. First, the fly was found in a heavily populated area, and many of the residents feared that the spray pesticide used against it might have toxic effects on humans and pets. As a result

From "Prehistoric Raised-Field Agriculture in the Mayan Lowlands," B. L. Turner II and Peter D. Harrison, SCIENCE, vol. 213, no. 4506, pp. 399–405, July 24, 1981

Well-defined ground pattern in Belize is caused by the remains of raised fields above canals and drained swamps, revealing how the Mayan Indians were able to support a large population in that area.

California Gov. Edmund G. Brown, Jr., hesitated to permit aerial spraying. However, the infestation seemed out of control, and there was the risk that the medfly might spread to other states. Consequently, on July 10, 1981, U.S. Secretary of Agriculture John Block announced that if California did not spray the medfly, all produce from California suspected of being infected would be quarantined and could not be shipped to other states. Accordingly, Governor Brown ordered aerial spraying to begin on July 14.

The lesson to be drawn from this incident is that culture and politics are becoming increasingly major elements in large-scale environmental problems. From a purely biological point of view the medfly constituted an emergency, and control action had to be taken immediately to be as effective as possible. However, because the people living in the spray area had come to believe that all pesticides were dangerous to some extent, even in very low dosages, it required political daring to take the biologically necessary action.

A second complication in the medfly situation came about because of an error in one component of the control program. One method of insect pest control is to irradiate vast numbers of male flies so as to induce sterility. These flies are then released into the infested area. The sterile males then mate with wild females, which lay infertile eggs. Two conditions have to be met for this method of pest control to work. The number of sterilized males released must be large relative to the number of wild males, and females of the pest species must mate only once before laying eggs. In the medfly case irradiated flies were identified with yellow dye. Flytraps were routinely used to catch samples of the pests and trace their movement patterns. One of the traps caught a fly that was fertile yet marked with dye. The fly was traced to a commercial laboratory in Peru, where it had supposedly been sterilized. Scientists calculated that as many as 100,000 Peruvian medflies might have been improperly treated and then released at Mountain View, Calif. Subsequent checking revealed that an infestation at Mountain View might have been entirely due to the release of flies from Peru that were not, in fact, sterile.

Many scientists were distressed by the medfly situation. Their first criticism was that the theory of insect pest population dynamics and control had evolved to a high level of sophistication (as discussed above), yet the budget for research on medfly control was minuscule relative to the budget for operations. Second, the operational approach to the medfly control program

313

Cover, April 3, 1981, "Chemical Impurity Produces Extra Compound Eyes and Heads in Crickets," Barbara T. Walton, SCIENCE, vol. 212, photo by E. G. O'Neill, Oak Ridge National Laboratory, © 1981 AAAS

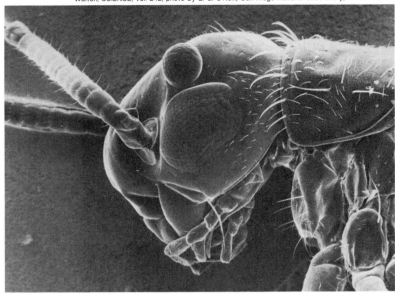

Extra compound eye in a cricket was caused by contamination during the egg stage with acridine, a chemical generated during the production of synthetic fuel.

became a political football, relatively uninfluenced by scientific opinion.

Mayan civilization. Many kinds of scholars have been interested in discovering the reasons for the collapse of powerful ancient civilizations. It is assumed that sufficiently profound understanding of this phenomenon would help scientists and policymakers take the steps necessary to prevent the collapse of modern civilization.

One ancient culture that has been subjected to intensive research in recent years is that of the Mayas, who once flourished in the Yucatán Peninsula of Mexico, Guatemala, and Belize. An elaborate theory for the collapse of this civilization was proposed, basically hypothesizing that the elite class responded to overpopulation and resource depletion by devoting an excessive proportion of the effort of the labor force to work on monuments to enhance the prestige of the elite rather than dealing with the basic resource-population problem. The theory postulates that the Mayan civilization at its peak was highly complex and that once it disintegrated the complexity never returned.

However, this theory raises a question that has not been resolved: Where is the resource base that could have supported the postulated complex civilization? The type of agriculture practiced in the region today, slash-and-burn, cannot support the population densities of up to 600 people per square kilometer characteristic of the Mayas between AD 100–600. (One sq km = 0.39 sq mi.) Ground surveys in the past did not give clear evidence of any different pattern of resource exploitation that would account for these high human population densities. Accordingly, Richard E. W. Adams, W. E. Brown, Jr., and T. Patrick Culbert used imaging radar mounted on an aircraft to explore the terrain of the jungle by penetrating foliage, silt, and root cover. The object was to search for evidence of ancient roads, causeways, or other man-made structures. This technique revealed irregular grids of gray lines in areas of wet swamp located near known archaeological sites. It developed that these lines were produced by slight differences in elevation of vegetation, and ground surveys revealed that they indicate the presence of ancient canals.

From the overflights and a variety of other research, it became apparent that between 1,285 and 2,475 sq km of swamp had been drained by the Mayas for agricultural use. Modern experimental plots in Veracruz, Mexico, indicate that an agricultural system based on drained swamps can support about one person per one-tenth of a hectare. (One hectare equals 2.47 acres.) Thus, this swamp cultivation could account for the very large populations of the Mayan period. It is noteworthy that the largest Mayan cities of the Late Classic period are located only on the edges of swamps. The great numbers of people were evidently made possible by a highly organized society that maintained a complex and large area system of canals and irrigation. These canals also could have been used for bulk goods transportation, which would have been required to support the large numbers of people in the area (50,000 at Tikal alone).

This new work provides a clearer picture of the way in which disintegration of social organization could have sharply decreased the carrying capacity of the environment for people and resulted in the collapse of the civilization. The key step would have been a refusal by the peasantry to support the elite in maintaining the degree of social organization required to keep the canal and irrigation system operational.

314

Economics of organic farming. During the year a team of researchers reported on a comparative five-year study of organic and conventional farmers in the Middle West of the U.S. In this study organic farming indicates no use of modern pesticides or fertilizers. The comparison was between 14 organic and 14 conventional farms in each of the first three years. During the last two years 23 and 19 organic farms were studied, respectively; these were compared with county-level statistical reports of conventional farms. The data were reported in many forms, but perhaps the most interesting set of statistics for each farm type was on the value of production, the operating expense, and the net return, each expressed as dollars per hectare. (All figures are averages for the five years.) As would be expected the operating expenses were lower for the organic than for the conventional farms: $89 as opposed to $134 per ha. The surprise, however, was that the value of production for the organic farms, compared with that of the conventional farms, was not as much lower as might have been expected: $412 as against $464 per ha. The result is that the net returns for the two types of farming are surprisingly similar: $323 (organic) and $331 (conventional).

An important implication of these findings is that organic farmers—because they do not use chemical fertilizers and therefore use less fossil energy per unit of crop output—will be less severely affected than conventional farmers by deteriorating fossil fuel supplies. Also, soil erosion is significantly reduced by the crop rotation and tillage methods used on the organic farms. These results suggest that the present U.S. agricultural system could be shifted toward increased organic farming without deleterious consequences for either farmers or consumers.

Culture, politics, economics, and the environment. Late in 1981 the U.S. Census Bureau reported that of the world's 56 most populous countries, representing 92% of the world's population, the overall population growth rate had declined from 2.1% in 1965-70 to 1.8% in 1975-79. However, this significant decline was largely due to the efforts to limit births in China. When China is excluded from the statistics, there was no decline.

China is noteworthy not only for its attitudes on population and resource conservation but also for its influence as an opinion leader in third world countries. During the year China was host to a meeting of third world countries on population. The communiqué issued at the close of the conference suggested that other countries there had been impressed by China's example in dealing with population growth and intended to follow it.

During 1981 a new organization that may be of great importance for the future came into being. Named the Global Tomorrow Coalition, it is an umbrella organization that included more than 50 other groups, all of which in various ways were concerned with the future. The coalition was formed because: "Groups in many different fields—natural resources, population, protection of wildlife, agriculture, preservation of species, international development and others—are realizing that they share a concern for an agenda of national and global problems that cannot be dealt with successfully on a piecemeal basis."

A new book by Lester R. Brown, *Building a Sustainable Society*, probably represents a well-worked-out statement as to what most members of the coalition believe. They accept the law of diminishing returns of David Ricardo, an early-19th-century British economist, as an important explanation for much of what is happening in global and national economies. (By contrast, the conventional wisdom tends not to take the notion of limits seriously.) To support this belief Brown used standard data sources to show that there is now a worldwide decline in the amount of additional grain being produced per additional unit of fertilizer applied and that recently there has also been a decline in worldwide per capita production of wood, wool, mutton, and fish. Oil production per person peaked in 1973 and is expected to drop significantly in the future. In his book Brown points out a connection between these phenomena and inflation. Thus, although the conventional wisdom does not yet acknowledge this, Brown concludes that environmental phenomena are now an intimate part of the system forces operating on the world economy. He maintains that once this connection becomes more widely understood, it is reasonable to expect that pressures for population limitation and conservation will spread.

—Kenneth E. F. Watt

Food and agriculture

World food and agricultural commodity production generally increased over the past two years, while prices fell. Wheat and rice were two examples. In the U.S. prices of many agricultural imports also fell, notably coffee and rubber. This was at least partly due to the strengthening of the U.S. dollar relative to other major world currencies. The growth rate of productivity in U.S. agriculture dropped to 1% per year in the 1970s, down from the 2% annual increase during the '50s and '60s. At least part of the decline might be attributable to a relative decrease in federal funding for agricultural research.

Agriculture

World meat production in 1981 was almost unchanged from the preceding year, with poultry production increasing, pork decreasing, and beef remaining constant. Increases in milk production in the U.S. and

Combines unload harvested wheat in Oregon in August 1981. The season's record U.S. grain crop led world production of grain to an all-time high.

Western Europe overshadowed declines in the Soviet Union, Poland, Australia, and New Zealand. Sugar production rose to a record 95.8 million metric tons, principally because of increases on the European continent. A record U.S. grain crop in 1981–82 pushed world production to an all-time high. Since the use of grains increased only 1%, stored reserves were reestablished on a worldwide basis.

The dollar value of U.S. agricultural exports rose 10% to a record $44 billion in 1981, but the volume of U.S. export commodities was slightly below the 1980 record. A substantial increase in volume was predicted for 1982, and the value was likely to reach to $48 billion. The agricultural trade surplus (exports less imports) was $27 billion in 1981 and was expected to be about $29 billion in 1982. Although U.S. farm cash receipts had hit record highs each year since 1979, farmers' cash costs had risen even faster, resulting in lower net cash income. After climbing 17% in 1979, cash receipts rose only 3% in 1980 and 4% in 1981. Total cash expenses rose about 9% in both 1980 and 1981, and net income was expected to be about $29 billion in 1981—a 20% decline in two years.

Food prices in U.S. grocery stores in 1982 were expected to rise approximately 6% over 1981; food marketing costs were forecast to climb by 10%, while farm prices would remain nearly unchanged. Prices at restaurants, cafeterias, and fast-food chains would be up about 8%.

Productivity. During the 1970s the growth rate in U.S. agricultural productivity stabilized at about 1% per year, compared with the 2% annual increase during the 1950s and 1960s. This drop in productivity gain was associated by some with a reduction in the number of research discoveries and new technologies relative to food and fiber production. In part, it may reflect a decreased federal share of agricultural research funding. Federal funds support agricultural research at land-grant universities and within the U.S. Department of Agriculture (USDA). Some research is also carried out by agriculturally related industries.

During 1981 and 1982 the executive and legislative branches of the federal government examined the agricultural research, extension, and teaching system. The reviews showed that between 1966 and 1979 the proportion of the USDA budget going to those areas did not grow in real terms, although state contributions to these programs had increased steadily. A 1982 report issued by the Congressional Office of Technology Assessment indicated specifically that the federal government's "expenditures for agricultural research are proportionately the smallest of any major federal research agency," that is, in comparison with other Cabinet-level departments having significant research programs. The report pointed out that "the bulk of the state financed research is being conducted in the farm belt." Since the majority of food consumers are outside the major agricultural producing states, the shift in the

Farmers and fishermen gather to protect agricultural policies of the European Community during a meeting of the European Council at Maastricht, The Netherlands, in March 1981.

financial burden for research meant that "taxpayers in the food surplus states are subsidizing consumers in the food deficit states."

The Agriculture and Food Act of 1981, which places heavy emphasis on research to yield new technologies related to food production, processing, storage, and use, could help rectify this situation. In addition, an assistant secretary for science and education became a part of top-level management within the USDA, reflecting an emphasis on agricultural research.

Crop subsidies. One of the major changes associated with the Agriculture and Food Act of 1981, often referred to as the 1981 farm bill, was a deemphasis on crop subsidies. The history of crop subsidies in the U.S. can be traced to the Agricultural Adjustment Act of 1933. In order to dampen wide fluctuations in food costs to consumers and also protect farmers, this act provided that when production cost exceeded sale price the government would cover at least a portion of the difference, if farmers would agree to sell products at a government-set price. The implicit goal of crop subsidies has been the same for nearly 50 years. Farmers as a group have been economically disadvantaged by new technology that led to continued production increases—often far exceeding needs—lower farm product prices, and depressed farm income. That technology, financed in part by large public outlays, greatly benefited the U.S. public by lowering food prices. Crop subsidies that transferred income from the taxpaying public to farmers helped compensate farmers for their income loss.

The lower rate of productivity gains in the 1970s and the continued expansion of export markets for U.S.

farm products gradually improved farm prices and incomes and lessened the need for crop subsidy payments. Reflecting these trends, the 1981 farm bill provides lower subsidy payments and puts increased emphasis on research, conservation, export markets, and grain reserves to help buffer U.S. grain prices from the variability of world markets.

The farm bill passed the House of Representatives by a vote of 205 to 203 and the Senate by 68 to 31. The reason for the close House vote was the issue of crop subsidies. Major agricultural groups took differing positions on the issue. The American Farm Bureau Federation supported the bill, including the reduction in price-support programs, on the grounds that government should not control food and fiber supply and demand. The National Farmers Union opposed it, pointing out that crop subsidies are aimed more at providing U.S. consumers with inexpensive food than at supporting farmers. The Farmers Union emphasized that in the U.S. only 14% of the average citizen's income goes for food.

Other farm bill provisions. Loss of production capacity through soil erosion is recognized as a problem throughout the world. The 1981 farm bill has a separate title addressing soil erosion and establishes a program to redirect USDA resources to those areas of the U.S. with the most critical soil erosion problems. Key factors of the program include: (1) an analysis of a critical problem area, which may cover several counties or even several states; (2) a request for the secretary of agriculture to designate the area as a "special area"; (3) provision of technical and financial assistance for specific special areas, which are ranked so

Dehydrating plant in Colorado can process up to 30 tons of alfalfa per hour. Alfalfa is considered one of the best feeds for cattle.

that problems will be addressed fully. The mechanism for program implementation involves a contract between the federal government and the individual landowner. Examples of potential special areas include: the Red River valley in the northern Great Plains, which is frequently subject to substantial flood-caused soil erosion; the Arkansas River valley, where saline problems exist; and the Ogallala aquifer, where the groundwater is being depleted rapidly.

One of the most significant provisions in the 1981 farm bill discourages any future embargo that singles out agricultural products. This provision is based on the feeling that the key to success for U.S. agriculture in the 1980s lies in its ability to expand export markets and maintain credibility as a reliable worldwide supplier. Many believe that the U.S. agricultural sector will prosper only if it has free and open access to world markets. After Pres. Jimmy Carter imposed an embargo on shipment of grain to the U.S.S.R. in 1980 in retaliation for the Soviet invasion of Afghanistan, the Soviets purchased wheat elsewhere, resulting in a glut of grain on the U.S. market that drove grain prices down. The bill provides for a government-financed compensation mechanism if agricultural products are singled out for embargo.

Increasing hen productivity. As a result of research and better management, the productivity of the average laying hen in the U.S. increased from 218 eggs per year in 1970 to a record 243 marketable eggs in 1980. This figure could have been even higher, however—perhaps 260 per hen—if the eggs had had sturdier shells. Because the egg represents the end point of the "product investment," egg loss due to damaged shells drives up the cost of all other eggs proportionately.

Through a cooperative project scientists from land-grant universities and the USDA found that feeding layer hens in the evening rather than in the morning would help to produce sturdier eggshells because hens start producing calcium for shells in the evening. Other researchers closely examined the relationship between vitamin D, the female hormone estrogen, and calcium deposition in eggshells. Researchers at Pennsylvania State University selected lines of hens that produce thicker than average eggshells, and these hens showed higher than average estrogen levels.

Medfly infestation. When three Mediterranean fruit flies (medflies) appeared in detection traps in Santa Clara County, California, in June 1980, the California state government hoped that a combination of fruit stripping, release of sterile flies, bait traps, and ground spraying would eradicate the insect. However, the infested area was larger than expected, and quarantines were imposed. Although the infestation was limited to California and Florida, it could have spread to any of the southern states with climates warm enough to harbor the fly or any state where the host crops are grown.

Over 250 varieties of fruits, vegetables, and nuts can serve as hosts to the medfly, although the insect is no threat to other major field crops.

In the past only Florida, Texas, and California have had significant medfly infestations. The first, in central Florida in 1929, was also the worst; 6,000 state and federal workers battled the fly for almost two years with arsenical-molasses bait sprays. The infestation covered 487 sq km (188 sq mi) and cost over $7 million to wipe out. Damage to crops was substantial. The quarantines imposed to contain the 1981 outbreak forced California to institute an aerial spraying program. It was believed that medfly infestation was under control in all areas of the U.S. for 1982.

Leaner meat with less grain. Researchers from the USDA, Louisiana State University, and Colorado State University independently examined systems that might be put into effect if the grain needed to fatten and finish livestock in the feedlot became less available or the price became too high. Current practice is to take animals off range or pasture at an average weight of 295 kg (650 lb) and to fatten them in a feedlot with feed grains for approximately 120 days to a finished weight of about 500 kg (1,100 lb) per animal; after such a regime the carcasses grade out at 75% Choice or better, 21% Good, and about 4% Standard. The research, partly funded by the National Science Foundation, showed that animals fed for as little as 66 days in the feedlot could be graded out at 16% Choice, 53% Good, and 31% Standard. Taste panels found the meat somewhat less tasty but still acceptable, and it contained significantly less fat.

The purpose of these experiments was to investigate whether acceptable beef could be produced with a significant reduction in cultural energy (fossil fuels used to grow grains and produce feeds to fatten livestock), the amount of grain needed to fatten an animal, and the time required in the feedlot. Such savings could reduce production costs and perhaps make beef prices more competitive.

Corn sweeteners versus sugar. In 1981 corn sweeteners—principally glucose, fructose, and dextrose—accounted for about one-third of total domestic sugar/sweetener use in the U.S., up from 17% a decade earlier. The average American consumed almost 58 kg (126 lb) of sugar and sweeteners a year, or 35 teaspoons a day, most of it (75%) in baked goods, soft drinks, and other processed foods. Ten years earlier Americans' average sugar/sweetener consumption was about 56 kg (124 lb) a year, with sugar accounting for almost all of it.

The USDA forecast that corn sweeteners could make up 43% of the sweetener market by 1985. The major reason for the increase was the low cost. Corn sweeteners cost only half as much as sugar made from cane or sugar beets. Furthermore, all the corn needed to produce sweeteners domestically is grown in the U.S.,

Aerial spraying of orchards in California for medflies generated controversy because of its possible adverse effects on humans.

while nearly half of the cane and sugar beets needed for processing into sugar is imported, primarily from Latin America.

—John Patrick Jordan

Nutrition

The shift of the U.S. presidency and Congress in 1981 to a more conservative orientation signaled a different federal nutrition policy and a change of direction for the future. Congressional leaders had assumed that "an inappropriate national dietary life-style" was a major cause of "the rapidly escalating U.S. public health cost." Consequently, early in 1981, the USDA released "Ideas for Better Eating" and "Nutrition and Your Health: Dietary Guidelines for Americans." As of 1982, however, the USDA had no plans to promote these publications. Mark Hegsted, the USDA official instrumental in developing the books, said the program was in limbo because the administration of U.S. Pres. Ronald Reagan had indicated that it did not want "to be in the business of telling people what to eat." Along the same lines Commissioner Arthur Hull Hayes, Jr., of the Food and Drug Administration (FDA) seemed to be introducing a new era in FDA activities when he said, "There was a time when the government would identify a problem, propose a solution and then impose it on you; that is not the way I intend to do business."

Food industry representatives and federal regulatory agencies on food safety redefined safe food as that with an absence of "significant risk" for people, rather than using the term "no risk." G. William Hoagland, administrator of the USDA's Food and Nutrition Service, announced that his agency would not ban the sale of saccharin-containing foods in schools participating in the school lunch program; in June 1981 the Senate extended the exclusion of saccharin from food safety laws prohibiting the use of food additives suspected of causing cancer until 1983. Commissioner Hayes announced that aspartame has been found safe for its intended use, permitting its addition to cold cereals, sugarless gums, drink mixes, instant coffees and teas, gelatins, puddings, and fillings. It could also be sold in tablet form and as a free-flowing sugar substitute.

For years the FDA has struggled with the problem of regulating the retail sale of vitamin and mineral dietary supplements. The new administration's FDA task force withdrew the controversial monograph, written by an advisory panel in 1979, which recommended that these products be labeled as suitable for prevention or treatment of deficiencies only and only when the need for such therapy had been determined by a physician. Such a rule would have classified vitamins and minerals as "over-the-counter" drugs rather than food products, and placed them under the jurisdiction of the Bureau of Drugs. Because they remained classified as foods, excessively high-potency vitamin and mineral items were still being sold without guidance or warning.

Sodium in the diet. Both Congress and the U.S. Department of Health and Human Services showed concern about the relationship between sodium and hypertension. HHS Secretary Richard Schweiker placed prevention high on his list of priorities for the federal health agenda, and the high level of sodium in U.S. diets constituted a major problem in preventive medicine.

In the *Annual Review of Nutrition* (vol. 1, 1981), Melvin J. Fregly of the University of Florida College of Medicine reviewed research data on nondiscretionary sources of sodium. These include sodium that occurs naturally in food or is added in processing, as well as that in water supplies, water softeners, and medications. The discretionary supply is the amount controlled by the consumer when he prepares and eats food. The wide variety of sources complicates study of

Executive of G. D. Searle & Co. samples desserts sweetened with aspartame, the firm's new artificial sweetener. The FDA found the product safe.

the role that this abundant, water-soluble element plays in human physiology.

Salt added at the table and in cooking accounts for about a third of the sodium consumed. Over half comes "hidden" in processed foods such as canned, frozen, and dried ready-to-eat soups, entrees and meats, pickles and relishes, chips and snack items, frozen meals, and baked products. Even such nonsalty foods as puddings, cereals, ice cream, cakes, and baking mixes contain sodium, which is a component of many additives other than salt, or sodium chloride (NaCl).

Commissioner Hayes, a former director of the Hypertension Clinic at the Milton S. Hershey Medical Center in Pennsylvania, is a leading advocate of reduced sodium intake. He told representatives of the food industry that the sodium content of food products should be included on the label so that people could control their intake. He also asked that the food industry market a wider variety of low-sodium products and reduce the sodium content of many popular foods. A voluntary program was being supported by several organizations that agreed to promote sodium labeling, among them the American Meat Institute and the National Food Processors Association.

A bill introduced in the House of Representatives would amend the Food, Drug and Cosmetic Act of 1906 to require the addition of sodium to nutritional labels. It was being supported by Hayes, the House Science and Technology Subcommittee on Oversight and Investigations, and the House Subcommittee on Health.

Nutrition education. Innovative methods are needed to teach young children to taste, explore, and identify foods that are important sources of nutrients. Too often negative approaches are used: this food is bad for you, your health, or your teeth; don't eat "junk food"; this food causes heart disease, cancer, or some other condition. Often amount, frequency, and regularity of eating are ignored, and foods are condemned because they are misused in impulse snacking when it is the manner of eating that is at fault rather than the food itself. At the same time, the omission of certain essential types of food from the diet is overlooked.

People eat food for many reasons—habit, custom, availability, memory of special events—and health and well-being are not necessarily high on the list. An interdisciplinary study of cultural nutrition was underway to examine factors that contribute to changes in dietary habits. Environmental, attitudinal, and behavioral influences are targets of concern to those involved in nutrition education.

Trace elements. Selenium deficiency in some areas of China has been identified as a causal factor in Keshan disease, which is characterized by cardiomyopathy in children and young women. Children in the U.S. whose diets are deficient in cereal, dairy, and meat products also have shown symptoms of Keshan disease. The role of selenium in health maintenance is not well understood, but it has been identified as a component of glutathione peroxidase, an enzyme thought to have a major function in the removal of hydrogen peroxide and other organic hydroperoxides generated in oxidative metabolism in cells and tissues. As a component of a defense system against the buildup of lipid peroxides and free radicals that damage cell mem-

FDA commissioner demonstrates average U.S. adult salt intake for nine months, 5.2 kilograms (11.4 pounds). Too much salt contributes to hypertension for some.

branes and macromolecules, including DNA, selenium is accepted as an essential trace element in human nutrition.

The Food and Nutrition Board of the National Research Council (NRC) proposed a safe intake range of from 50 to 200 micrograms of selenium daily. Actual intakes from 132 daily diets eaten by 22 persons, 14 to

Famine and starvation continue to cause suffering and death in many parts of the world. At left, women and children await emergency feeding at Bume, Ethiopia.

64 years old, ranged from less than 25 to 300 micrograms per day, with a mean intake of 81 micrograms. Of the diets 17% had less than the recommended minimum of 50 micrograms. A positive correlation was found between selenium and other nutrient intakes, including calories. Diets high in selenium (133 micrograms) were also more nearly adequate in most other nutrients. In this study the higher selenium intakes were attributed to the presence of more fish and less processed meat than in diets with less selenium.

A major concern in nutrition is the availability of trace elements to the blood supply of the individual. The bioavailability of trace elements, as well as of iron, phosphorus, and calcium, is greatly influenced by the dietary source; namely, whether the elements are added as inorganic salts, supplied by animal tissues, by plant tissues of varying fiber content, or by water used as a beverage and in food preparation. Differences among individuals of varying ages and states of health are also of concern and are factors in the dietary levels of minerals recommended by the NRC, which are often given as a range rather than a single value. An example is the addition of iron, zinc, copper, and manganese in the formulation of diets for infants who are not fortunate enough to receive mother's milk. Various molecules of these elements were being tested in an effort to determine the bioavailability of each element in a given formulation.

The problem of bioavailability is magnified in asymmetric diets such as vegetarian diets and those that are excessively high in fiber content. For example, research on the phytate content of foods indicates that the formation of insoluble zinc-phytate molecular complexes inhibits the bioavailability of zinc. Furthermore, soluble zinc compounds (or ions) in saliva and pancreatic fluids, which are normally reabsorbed, are excreted when phytate intake is high. Since grains, legumes, fruits, and vegetables supply phytates as well as mineral elements, excessive intakes of nonrefined plant foods can be a problem. Thus the old adage is still true: "Enough of a good thing is enough."

—Mina W. Lamb

Life sciences

Interactions among differing species of plants and animals, both as individuals and as part of larger ecosystems, continued as a dominant theme of biological research during the past year. Investigators studied the mutualistic relationships between nectar-producing flowers and their insect partners, examined the ways in which plants prevent hybridization and grafting between species, offered evidence that the genes for drug resistance now so common in microbial agents of disease may well have originated in the organisms that produce antibiotics, and found that the giant tube

worms recently discovered at oceanic rift sites appear to thrive on dissolved hydrogen sulfide. Molecular biologists made several startling finds, including an alternative helical structure for DNA and an exception to the supposed universality of the genetic code. In a much-publicized trial in Arkansas life scientists and biblical creationists clashed over the teaching of "creation science" in the classroom.

Botany

Ongoing research in botany during the past year included investigations of nectar production in flowers, the physiology of grafts, transpiration measurements in large trees, and dinoflagellate reproduction.

Sweet flowers. The mutualism existing between flowering plants and their animal pollinators is stressed in the most elementary botany studies: flowers produce bright colors to attract insects and other pollinators, which are rewarded by finding nectar in the flowers, while plant pollen gets distributed by the pollinators. This relationship has been investigated al-

Visitors view boxwood and rice at the National Herb Garden in Washington, D.C. The facility enjoyed its first full season in 1981.

most continually to discover aspects of the plant-animal interaction.

One such study, reported during the past year by Edward E. Southwick and Steven E. Sadwick of the State University of New York, Brockport, and Gerald M. Loper of the U.S. Department of Agriculture, focused on the nature and amount of nectar in some common field plants in New York state. Flowers of representatives of nine plant families were sampled by removing nectar with fine glass pipettes for laboratory analysis. It was found that all of the species of plants studied produced nectar containing three principal sugars: sucrose, glucose, and fructose; however, these sugars were found in differing proportions among the species. Differences ranged from nearly 100% sucrose in common milkweed (*Asclepias syriaca*) to nearly equal amounts of the three sugars in species of mock orange (*Philadelphus*) to less than 30% sucrose in the hawthorn (*Crataegus phaenopyrum*). Further observation revealed that flowers with petals formed into a tube have nectar of higher sucrose content and have nectaries (organs in which nectar is produced) that are protected from environmental changes such as humidity. These flowers are characteristic of *Asclepias*. Species with flattened, more open flowers have more exposed nectaries and nectar with lower sucrose concentration. Such flowers are found on *Philadelphus* and *Crataegus*. Analysis of the amount of nectar produced per blossom in 24 hours indicated a range of values from 0.64 milligrams (mg) for viper's bugloss (*Echium vulgare*) to 5.52 mg per blossom for *Philadelphus*. Concentration of the nectar in terms of energy content ranged from 0.72 calories per microliter for the cherry *Prunus mahaleb* to 3.58 for *Philadelphus*.

Observation of honeybee visits to flowers of the plants studied suggested that primary factors of attractiveness are higher energy content, greater volume, and greater accessibility of nectars. Sugar ratios did not seem to affect attractiveness to pollinators in this study, but overall visitation rates were affected by environmental characteristics, such as air temperature, more than by any flower trait.

Another study was done by Robert L. Beckmann, Jr., and Jon M. Stucky of North Carolina State University on the morning glory *Ipomoea pandurata*, a common weed of waste places. It produces nectar of comparatively low sucrose content in nectaries found outside the flowers. These organs are easily reached by a number of hymenopteran insects such as ants and wasps, which agressively defend the flowers from the beetles and caterpillars that are able to feed more unhampered on the remaining parts of the plants. In controlled studies it was shown that some herbivores prefer to feed on leaves and flowers of *I. pandurata*. The defense of the flowers by the hymenopterans protect not only their food source but also the reproductive structures of the plants.

Grafting. Plant grafting is a phenomenon that occurs both naturally and in horticultural practice. In nature grafts happen rather commonly among roots and occasionally among stems of plants of the same species. Growers produce a large number of woody plants for such commercial purposes as fruit production and landscaping by grafting a small branch (scion) of the desired type of plant onto the stem and root system (stock) of another. This method provides a way to propagate desirable plants very quickly while taking advantage of the more robust root systems of otherwise less desirable plants. Grafting is usually limited to plants of the same species; at least it is confined to plants of the same genus. Grafting more distantly related plants results in death of the scion and probably the stock if it is small.

Investigators have explored the reasons for rejection in grafts, and an example was reported during the year by Randy Moore of Baylor University, Waco, Texas, and Dan B. Walker of the University of California at Los Angeles. They carried out two kinds of grafts and then studied sections of the grafted areas under a high-voltage electron microscope. One kind of graft involved the use of scions and stocks of the same species (homograft); in fact, in *Sedum telephoides* stems were cut off and then immediately replaced on the very same plants (autograft). The second kind of graft (heterograft) was done between plants of different species, *S. telephoides* and *Solanum pennellii*. The autografts of *Sedum* were so successful that the grafting region could not be detected at the end of four weeks. Usually *Sedum*/*Solanum* heterografts had failed by that time.

Study of the successful grafts showed that cell death at the cut surfaces produced a necrotic layer to which the stock and scion adhered within 24 hours. Formation of tissue calluses within the necrotic layer occurred in 2–3 days, and continuity between the vascular tissue of stock and scion resulted in 10–14 days. In unsuccessful grafts formation of the necrotic layer and adhesion were noted by 21 hours. Then, instead of callus formation the *Sedum* scions produced a layer of a complex fatty plant substance called suberin along the region of the cut. This layer seemed to prohibit any development of vascular tissue between scion and stock. The scion dried out and fell off 3–5 weeks following grafting. It thus appears that some kind of physiological intolerance on the part of the *Sedum* partner was the basic cause of graft failure.

Potometers. Exploitation of various ecosystems has earned much recent attention because of rapidly accumulating evidence that human activities in nature have far-reaching effects. Indications of these effects range from the well-documented studies done at Hubbard Brook Experimental Forest in New Hampshire that explore the effects of timber harvest on water and nutrient flow to widespread speculation that actual climate changes are resulting from deforestation in

Photos, from "Ultrastructure of the Dinoflagellate Peridinium cinctum f. ovoplanum," D. L. Spector, L. A. Pfiester, and R. E. Triemer, AMERICAN JOURNAL OF BOTANY, vol. 68, pp. 34–43, January 1981

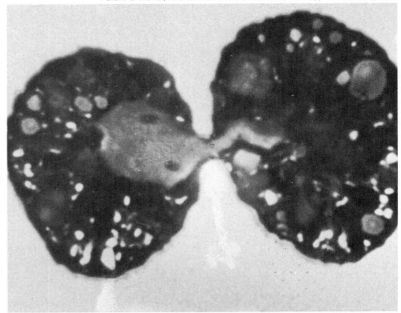

Rarely observed events in the sexual reproduction of the dinoflagellate Peridinium cinctum *were studied and photographed in recent months. Photomicrograph of a section through two fusing gametes (right) reveals fertilization tube bridging the armored cells. A light-colored nucleus in the left-hand member of the pair extends through the tube. Fertilization culminates in the fusion of gametes to form a planozygote (facing page), which progresses to a dormant cyst stage. The large central nucleus of the planozygote is visible as a bounded region of small dark bodies.*

tropical ecosystems like those found in Haiti and Brazil. Definitive studies are frustrated by the complexity of such problems; bit by bit, however, techniques are being developed to help.

Various ecosystem characteristics are influenced by the activity of forest plants in water cycling. In addition to controlling direct evaporation of water from land surfaces, plants influence the loss of water to the ecosystem by evaporating water out of their leaves. The latter process, called transpiration, can be measured in large amounts per tree per day. Various techniques for measuring water loss have been devised, but all are limited in some way. In the search for more satisfactory methods Dennis H. Knight of the University of Montana and his associates reported their success in making whole lodgepole pines into potometers, as such transpiration-measuring devices are called.

These researchers selected various trees from several stands in Wyoming that they thought were good samples of the state's lodgepole forests. Each tree was fitted with a tripod of logs or aluminum poles such that the trees could be cut off at the bottom while remaining in place. Each severed tree was then placed in a reservoir of water and sealed around the reservoir to prevent water loss directly to the air. Any detected water loss was attributed to uptake by the tree and generally equated to transpiration through its needles. The authors believed that these potometers would provide reasonable estimates of hourly and daily transpiration. If a suitable sample of trees is used, this method can estimate transpiration for a whole stand. An important limitation to this method is the size of the tree; a tree larger than 30 cm dbh (diameter breast high) would be difficult to handle.

Dinoflagellate reproduction. Botanists place the microorganisms called dinoflagellates among the Dinophyceae, a class of algae containing mostly unicellular forms with a distinctive structure. Each dinoflagellate typically is flattened and has a transverse constriction, the girdle, around the cell equator. Two flagella are inserted in the girdle; one encircles the cell, and the other trails behind. Many of the forms are armored with thecal plates. Some species produce the well-known red tides along the California and Florida coasts; other species provide the only source of luminescence among the algae.

Dinoflagellates are known for their rarity of confirmed cases of sexual reproduction, an important source of genetic recombination. Some cases have been documented in the past 15 years, but there has been little evidence of the way in which the process takes place, particularly when the reproductive cells have thecal plates. D. L. Spector and R. E. Triemer of Rutgers University, New Brunswick, N.J., and L. A. Pfiester of the University of Oklahoma reported on their microscopic studies of the production and fusion of gametes in *Peridinium cinctum*.

Gametes result from cell division and in *P. cinctum* are armored by thecal plates except where the flagella protrude from the cells. When two gametes establish contact, a fertilization tube forms between the cells, and the nuclei from the two gametes fuse within it. Soon the fertilization tube enlarges and, with the two gametes, becomes one large cell called a planozygote. It is covered with thecal plates and, according to the investigators, may be the stage where meiosis occurs.

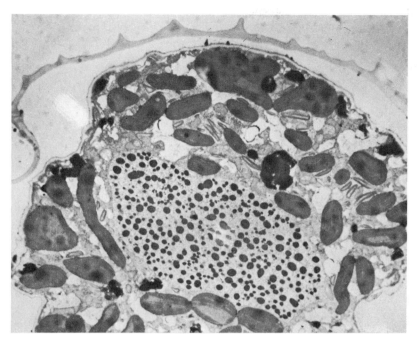

Thus the monoploid genetic condition would be typical of all *Peridinium* cells but the zygote. It was not clear whether meiosis really does occur at this stage.

Species barriers. A fundamental problem in biology is the definition of species. Current practice is to place within the same species those plants that share a common gene pool; that is, those that can or do interbreed on a regular basis. The reproductive barriers that prohibit interbreeding and thus delineate species are of interest to the botanist and are the subject of considerable research.

During the year Dennis Summers and Paul Grun of Pennsylvania State University reported on their experiments with two tuber-forming species of the genus *Solanum.* These naturally occurring potatoes are found growing together in some regions of Argentina, where they commonly do not hybridize. They also grow separately in other regions. Plants of *S. commersonii* were crossed reciprocally with plants of *S. chacoense* by artificial pollination. Barriers to hybridization were observed to be of different kinds in the two different crosses. When *S. chacoense* acted as the female parent, receiving *S. commersonii* pollen, pollen tubes failed to grow down the style of *S. chacoense* pistils, thus effectively blocking the production of seed. When *S. commersonii* acted as the female parent, receiving *S. chacoense* pollen, pollen tubes grew successfully through *S. commersonii* styles to reach ovules in the ovaries and produce seed. Most of the seeds were empty, however, and so could not germinate. Thus interspecific hybridization is blocked in both directions. For several reasons, these investigators believed that the two species originated independently and, when they later came to

grow in the same region, had already developed reproductive barriers of the types observed in these experiments.

Plant questions. Can some plants change their sex? David Policansky of Harvard University observed jack-in-the-pulpit plants (*Arisaema triphyllum*) for three years and found that from one year to another they can change their sex or be neither. He also found that smaller plants tend to be males and larger plants females; for example, a female plant of one year may change to a smaller male plant the next. Policansky suggested that this is an example of environmentally determined sex but did not attempt to explain why larger is better for females.

Why do sensitive plants fold their leaves? Many people are familiar with this common response to touch among some genera of the family Fabaceae (Leguminosae). It is obvious that the reaction reduces leaf surface for whatever reason that function may serve. Thomas Eisner of Cornell University, Ithaca, N.Y., studied a sensitive plant, *Schrankia microphylla,* and determined that its reaction is a defensive one. *Schrankia* is armed with numerous sharp thorns, which are exposed effectively when the leaves are folded. In a photographic study Eisner counted exposed thorns. Before leaf folding he counted a range of 5–145; after folding he found 9–218, respectively. Because these plants also keep their leaves folded at night, it may be that the touch-related mechanism serves to help protect the plant during the day and the normal, non-touch-related folding at night protects the plant constantly when photosynthesis is not required.

What do trees do when their bark is eaten away by

browsing animals? Usually, when bark is removed all around the trunk of a tree, the tree dies. Some trees, however, have the ability to survive this girdling. John P. Bryant of the University of Alaska found that certain Alaskan trees develop adventitious roots when their trunks are girdled by snowshoe hares. Adventitious roots are those grown from parts of the plant above ground, such as high on the stem or even from branches. Such roots enable the girdled trees to live. Moreover, these new roots were found to have high concentrations of terpenes and phenolic resins, which are distasteful and tend to keep the hares from damaging the emergency roots. Bryant carried out controlled experiments that checked the tendency for hares to eat untreated twigs and twigs coated with varying amounts of resin at feeding stations. All treated twigs had decreased palatability in proportion to resin concentration. Although Bryant's experiments were on a willow, *Salix alaxensis*, he believed that other such adventitious-root-forming species as paper birch (*Betula papyrifera*), quaking aspen (*Populus tremuloides*), balsam poplar (*Populus balsamifera*), and green alder (*Alnus crispa*) have similar defenses.

How can plants keep potential insect herbivores away? Although many plants apparently make chemicals that are offensive to their herbivores, visual cues are also used, as was shown by Kathy S. Williams and Lawrence E. Gilbert of the University of Texas. Their work involved two plant species of the genus *Passiflora*, *P. oerstedii* and *P. cyanea*, and a butterfly, *Heliconius cydno*. The butterfly females lay eggs on the leaves of *Passiflora* where resulting caterpillars defoliate the plants and also feed on eggs and larvae of other *Heliconius* butterflies. Experiments in which *Heliconius* eggs were placed on *P. oerstedii* leaves showed that *Heliconius* females tended to avoid laying their eggs on leaves already occupied by eggs. Experiments with *P. cyanea* leaves, which have small structures on their petioles (leaf stems) that resemble eggs, show that *Heliconius* females tend to avoid them also. Thus the production of egg mimics in this species of plant tends to decrease the number of eggs laid on its leaves and hence the amount of damage produced by insect larvae. The butterflies avoid the leaves because they recognize the egg mimics as real eggs, which, if they were eggs, would result in competition among the resulting larvae. Williams and Gilbert presented this evidence as a true example of coevolution of species.

See also Feature Articles: A Giant Flower for the Farmer; Amaranth: Return of the Aztec Mystery Crop.

—Albert J. Smith

Microbiology

In recent months microbiologists continued their research across a broad front of interests, much of it fo-cusing on the search for new sources of energy, the comprehension and control of infectious disease, and the devising of solutions to a variety of environmental problems.

Applied and industrial microbiology. Conversion of biomass by microorganisms to fuels and to feedstock chemicals continued to receive considerable study. Biomass has several advantages over fossil mass such as petroleum: it is renewable, flexible by means of crop switching, and adaptable by means of genetic manipulation. In addition to organisms grown specifically for conversion, biomass includes industrial and urban organic waste products and plant residues remaining after harvest of crops and forestry products.

A major area of emphasis is microbial conversion of biomass to feedstock chemicals, which are chemicals used as starting materials in manufacturing more complex substances. Microorganisms produce a large variety of such fermentation products, the most promising of which contain two to four carbon atoms per molecule. They include ethyl alcohol, acetic acid, acetone, isopropyl alcohol, and butyl alcohol. Some microbial fermentation products in this size range, however, cannot be used by current technology, and the search was on in several institutions throughout the world to find chemical methods for exploiting these substances.

Emphasis also continued to be placed on microbial fermentation of biomass to produce fuels, particularly

Replica of a blood platelet was made by passing X-rays through the specimen and onto a photosensitive resist material. The new IBM technique can show biological materials under the transmission electron microscope in something close to their natural state.

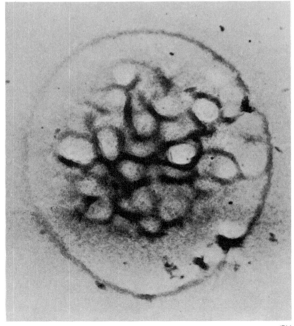

IBM

Israel Siegel, Tian Lin Liu, and Norbert Gleicher—Mount Sinai Hospital Medical Center of Chicago

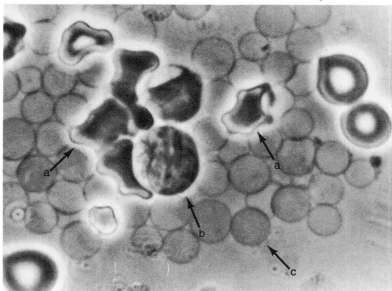

Role for red blood cells in the body's immune defense system, discovered in primates in the 1950s, was recently described in rabbits. Photomicrograph shows rabbit red blood cells (a) adhering to a thymocyte (b), the precursor of white blood cells called T cells, as well as to antigens (c), the foreign substance under immune attack. Red blood cells appear to mediate contact between thymocytes or T cells and antigens.

ethyl alcohol. Although yeast is the traditional ethanol producer, it has serious limitations for large-scale production. For example, large amounts of energy must be used to sterilize the biomass and to distill the ethanol from the fermented product. Moreover, yeast cannot directly ferment much of the readily available biomass material. Such substances as starch or cellulose first must be broken down into sugars by plant or microbial enzymes or by chemical means.

Other microorganisms were being studied as alcohol-producing substitutes for yeast. Among bacteria receiving attention is a species of *Clostridium* that thrives in high-temperature environments. This organism is able to grow directly on and produce alcohol from many plant materials that cannot be used by yeast. It also grows in the absence of air and at temperatures as high as 66° C (150° F). A fermentation system based on *Clostridium* would reduce the amount of energy normally needed for prior breakdown of complex fermentation materials, for sterilization, and for distillation of alcohol.

In the antibiotics industry, a traditional home for applied microbiology, nutritional and genetic manipulation of the source microorganisms and chemical manipulation of the molecular structure of the antibiotics have resulted in many new chemotherapeutic agents. One important family comprises the β-lactam antibiotics, which have in common a characteristic four-membered ring structure composed of three carbon atoms and a nitrogen atom. Penicillin, which is derived from a fungus, is the best known β-lactam antibiotic. In penicillin the β-lactam ring is fused to another, five-membered ring. The cephalosporin antibiotics are also derived from fungi, but the β-lactam ring is fused to a

six-membered ring. The fused ring systems distort the β-lactam ring and increase its reactivity. The β-lactams inhibit bacterial enzymes involved in the synthesis of bacterial cell walls, thereby interfering with bacterial growth.

Penicillin has several shortcomings; two among them are that many infectious bacteria are not susceptible to it and that bacteria readily become resistant to it by producing an enzyme that cleaves the β-lactam ring. In order to overcome these problems chemists have modified the structure of the basic penicillin molecule by adding various chemical side chains to the β-lactam ring to produce semisynthetic versions.

Whereas the penicillins may be considered first-generation β-lactam antibiotics, the cephalosporins are the second generation. Chemists also have prepared numerous semisynthetic cephalosporins that are effective against a broader range of bacterial species and more resistant to enzymatic inactivation.

There also exists a third generation of β-lactams, the monobactams. Although they are structurally related to the penicillins and cephalosporins, their structure is simpler in that another ring is not fused to the β-lactam ring. The first monobactam was discovered recently by U.S. scientists, and several additional monobactams were reported in 1981 by both U.S. and Japanese workers. The monobactams are produced by bacteria, an unusual source since most of the useful antibiotics are produced either by fungi or by species of *Streptomyces*, a genus of microorganisms with both fungal and bacterial characteristics.

Whereas basic monobactams show only modest antibacterial activity, semisynthetic versions with various side chains added to the β-lactam ring are much more

327

active, especially against gram-negative bacteria, which are largely resistant to the penicillins and cephalosporins.

Antibiotic resistance in bacteria continued to be a worldwide problem. This resulted in large part from uncontrolled and excessive use of antibiotics, which serves to select for resistant bacteria from the microbial population.

It is now believed that bacterial antibiotic-resistance mechanisms are derived from the protective mechanisms of antibiotic-producing organisms. Indeed, these organisms generally have been found to contain the same enzymatic-inactivation mechanisms as the antibiotic-resistant bacterial agents of disease. Genes encoding for enzymatic-inactivation mechanisms usually are found in small circular DNA molecules known as plasmids. Plasmids can carry as little as 2 or as many as 250 genes and can exist either autonomously in the cytoplasm of the bacterial cell or integrated into the bacterial chromosome. Recently scientists found DNA similarities between a plasmid gene for antibiotic resistance in a disease-causing bacterial species and the resistance gene in the antibiotic-producing organism. This observation lends credence to the idea that antibiotic-resistance genes from antibiotic-producing organisms end up as resistance plasmids through evolution. Resistance plasmids can be passed from organism to organism by naturally occurring microbial genetic processes.

Research was under way in several institutions in various countries to produce hybrid antibiotics by recombinant DNA techniques. If successful, this effort would result in antibiotics not naturally synthesized. Antibiotic-producing organisms would be given genes that encode for enzymes to change the molecular structure of the antibiotic. Thus, chemical modification would take place within the microbe rather than later in the laboratory. It is also expected that no naturally occurring resistance genes would exist for the new hybrid antibiotics.

Clinical microbiology. Research emphasis in clinical microbiology has concentrated on elucidating biological interactions between the microorganism and the patient, understanding the continuing evolution of microorganisms in their interactions with their hosts, developing effective antiviral and antifungal agents, developing methods for rapidly identifying infectious microorganisms as an aid to treatment of diseases, and applying recombinant DNA technology to the study and control of infectious disease.

One innovative method of rapid identification under study is that of pinpointing a segment of DNA from an infectious microorganism that has a nucleotide base sequence unique to that microorganism. If successful, this technique would permit rapid identifications from very small specimens; for example, the microbes in one drop of pus.

Development of a new vaccine to immunize livestock against foot-and-mouth disease resulted from a collaborative effort between scientists in the U.S. Department of Agriculture and a California "genetic engineering" firm. The bacterium *Escherichia coli* was cloned with DNA from the causative virus of foot-and-mouth disease to produce one of the coat proteins of this virus. Used as a vaccine, the protein stimulates the immune system of vaccinated animals to produce antibodies against the virus. Foot-and-mouth disease is a major affliction of cloven-footed animals such as cattle, sheep, and swine on every continent except Australia and North America exclusive of Mexico. Although the new vaccine is effective against only one of several closely related viruses, it is expected to serve as a prototype for other vaccines. An inexpensive and effective vaccine against foot-and-mouth disease should have great economic benefits, especially for the less developed countries.

Because more is known of the genetics, physiology, and structure of *E. coli* than of any other microorganism, it has become the organism of choice for recombinant DNA experiments. There are problems, however, with its use for expressing cloned genes. *E. coli* belongs to the group of gram-negative bacteria, which produce a toxic substance (an endotoxin) that is difficult to remove from the cloned product. To overcome this problem, investigators were studying other organisms as substitutes for *E. coli*. Scientists in Switzerland recently announced success in cloning *Bacillus subtilis,* a gram-positive organism lacking endotoxin, to produce the core antigen of the hepatitis B virus and another protein antigen of the foot-and-mouth disease virus. *B. subtilis* already is widely used commercially for producing enzymes and antibiotics and in Japan as a food for humans. Moreover, because methods for large-scale growth and for isolating proteins from cultures of *B. subtilis* already exist, this organism may prove useful for producing viral vaccines or such valuable proteins as interferon, insulin, or human growth hormone.

In recent months a unique mechanism of resistance to the antibiotic tetracycline was elucidated. First, scientists from Massachusetts found that bacteria containing a plasmid-resistance mechanism for tetracycline possessed a highly active system for carrying this antibiotic out of the bacterial cell once it had gained entry. Then, scientists from the University of Georgia found that the system that carries tetracycline out of the resistant bacterial cell was more than a thousand times more efficient than the system that transports tetracycline into the susceptible cell. Thus, tetracycline is prevented from accumulating inside the resistant bacterial cell and acting upon its site of attack, the intracellular ribosomes.

Environmental microbiology. Much current environmental microbiology has focused on studies to alleviate environmental problems. For example, a scientist from the University of Illinois who held the patent on a bacterium he developed to clean up oil spills presented evidence for the possibility of producing bacteria to efficiently degrade the persistent synthetic herbicide 2,4,5-T. Texas scientists were experimenting with a mold that shows promise in cleaning up slime waste resulting from phosphate and potash processing. In Colorado microbiologists were studying ways to restore rehabilitated oil shale lands to a normal microbial content. Microorganisms of the correct species must interact with soil and plant roots in order for vegetation to become reestablished on rehabilitated land.

Researchers in California and Minnesota were collaborating on a microbial process for desulfurizing coal with bacteria that feed on iron pyrite (FeS_2), the major source of sulfur in coal. Other researchers, at the University of Georgia, developed an experimental microbial process to remove sulfur compounds from petroleum.

—Robert G. Eagon

Molecular biology

In one sense, recognition of molecular biology as a distinct field of inquiry became possible for the first time in 1953 with the publication by James Watson and Francis Crick of the double helical structure of DNA. The major features of that elegant structure are familiar to anyone who has taken a biology course recently: two antiparallel chains comprising alternating phosphate and sugar (deoxyribose) units on the outside, with the nucleotide bases adenine (A), guanine (G), thymine (T), or cytosine (C), attached to each sugar and oriented toward each other on the inside of the molecule. The sequence of A, G, T, and C along each of the two strands is constrained such that wherever there is an A on one strand there is a T on the other, and wherever there is a G on one strand there is a C on the other. Thus, the two strands of the helix are held together by a systematic set of bonds (hydrogen bonds) between the paired bases A and T or G and C.

The precise sequence of the bases make up the genetic code, which includes all the information needed to specify the thousands of proteins that distinguish one cell from another. But before considering some of what is new and exciting in the code, this article will take up several recent advances in understanding the structure of DNA itself.

ABZ's of DNA. The model of DNA originally proposed by Watson and Crick was based on an analysis of the diffraction of X-rays by fibers of DNA. Two different X-ray diffraction patterns were recognized. One, obtained from relatively moist fibers, was called the B pattern. As the fiber dried, the pattern changed to a more crystalline one, called the A pattern. The molecular models that best fit these patterns differed slightly.

Although both were right-handed helices, the A helix had 11 nucleotides per helical turn, compared with 10 for the B helix. The distance between adjacent base pairs in the A helix was 2.6 Å compared with 3.4 Å for the B helix. (One angstrom, Å, equals a hundred-millionth of a centimeter.) Finally, the base pairs are roughly perpendicular to the helix axis in the B helix but tipped 19° from that axis in the A helix. These differences in the helical parameters have the following consequences for the general appearance of the molecule: the B helix has two grooves, major and minor, roughly 11.7 Å and 5.7 Å wide, respectively, that trace alternating parallel paths along the helix surface. In the A helix, by contrast, these grooves have widths of 2.7 Å and 11.0 Å, respectively. In addition, the depths of the grooves differ radically.

Which of these is the "right" structure for DNA? Does it matter? To answer the second question first, the answer is yes. While the DNA molecule is a repository of genetic information manifest in the sequence of nucleotides, it is also a dynamic participant in the expression of that information. The nucleotide sequences corresponding to individual genes must be transcribed at the correct time and with the correct frequency to produce messenger RNA molecules that will be translated into the amino-acid sequences of proteins, which are the ultimate products of genes. The proteins function both as structural components of cells and as enzymes, biochemical catalysts that carry out all the chemical reactions that occur in cells. Expression of the genetic information in DNA requires interaction between the DNA molecule and numerous proteins: RNA polymerase (the enzyme that catalyzes the transcription of RNA) as well as regulatory proteins that bind to DNA and, in response to chemical signals from the cellular milieu, either repress or promote transcription of particular genes. It should be clear a priori that the association of these proteins with DNA will depend strongly on the detailed structure of the DNA molecule; i.e., whether it is an A helix, a B helix, or something else.

It generally has been assumed that the B helix, which is the fiber form favored at a high degree of hydration, is the correct structure in solution. Direct evidence favoring this assumption has been obtained from measurements of the hydrodynamic or spectroscopic properties of DNA in solution, but such measurements always depend on averaged structural parameters. They do not rule out the possibility that local regions of A helix or of other structures exist at particular sites along a given DNA molecule, for example, where a particular nucleotide sequence is found.

Interest in the detailed structure of DNA was revived in recent years by the introduction of chemical methods for the large-scale synthesis of short pieces of DNA. Some of these synthetic DNA fragments were amenable to crystallization, and during the past year their

Photos, adapted from "The Anatomy of A-, B-, and Z-DNA," R. E. Dickerson, H. R. Drew, B. N. Conner, R. M. Wing, A. V. Fratini, and M. L. Kopka, SCIENCE, vol. 216, pp. 475–485, April 30, 1982

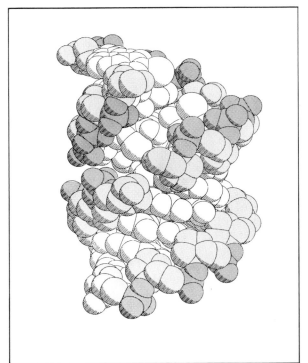
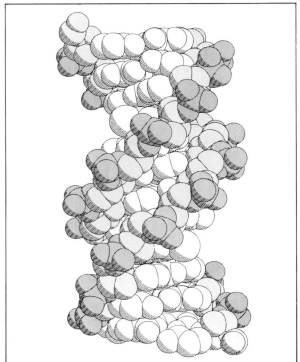

Short sections of the A and B helical structures of DNA (above, left and right) are compared with section of the Z helix (facing page). Dark-shaded spheres represent phosphate units; light-shaded ones, sugar units; and unshaded spheres, nucleotide bases. Zigzag backbone gave Z DNA its name.

structures were determined at very high resolution. One of these fragments, having the sequence CGCGAATTCGCG, was studied in the laboratory of Richard E. Dickerson at the California Institute of Technology. It turned out to have the B helix structure. But a second fragment, CCGG, crystallized as a fragment of A helix. Detailed comparison of the two structures revealed important differences, not only in the sizes of their major and minor grooves but also in hydration; that is, in the association of water molecules with the phosphate ions and the protruding nitrogen and oxygen atoms of the bases in each helical form. From these studies it became possible to propose a mechanism involving differential hydration that would permit a given nucleotide sequence to undergo a transition from the B to the A helix. Such transitions would increase tremendously the variety of possibilities for interaction of regulatory proteins with DNA; their physiological significance, of course, remains to be determined.

Ordinarily biologists with a background in subjects other than physical chemistry would be content to ignore such findings until their functional relevance had been established. But in the past year related observations of the structure of the nucleotide GCGCGC in the laboratory of Alexander Rich at the Massachusetts Institute of Technology produced astonishing results that demanded attention. This structure was a left-handed helix with 12 nucleotides per helical turn. Moreover, the guanine bases were twisted with respect to the deoxyribose in such a way that the phosphates traced a path that was more of a zigzag than a helix, hence the name Z helix.

This unusual structure is not just a curiosity restricted to the crystalline state. Some years earlier it had been noticed that the spectral properties of polymers with the repeating sequence $d(GC)_n$ (in which d represents "deoxyribo") changed dramatically upon addition of large amounts of salt to solutions of the polymer. Those spectral changes are now known to be due to the transition to the Z helix in solution. During the past year workers in the laboratory of Gary Felsenfeld at the National Institutes of Health, Bethesda, Md., discovered that addition of a methyl group to a cytosine base in the DNA fragment dGCGCGC permitted the transition to the Z form to take place at salt concentrations such as occur in living organisms. Rich and his collaborators exploited a related observation (addition of a halogen to a cytosine has the same effect) to prepare antibodies, in rabbits, that bind specifically to Z DNA. These antibodies were then used for an even more dramatic experiment.

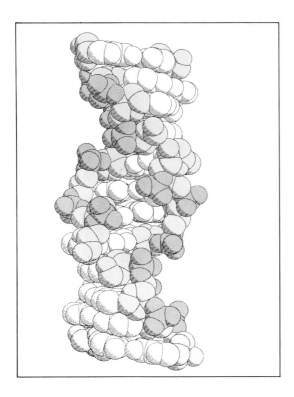

To describe that experiment requires a brief diversion. It is usually impossible to see chromosomes in action by conventional light microscopy. The chromosomes one sees in the light microscope, by examining cells undergoing mitosis, are condensed with numerous extra proteins. At the time that they are visible, they are not actively being transcribed. Nevertheless, there are special situations in nature that do provide a glimpse of chromosomes while they are functioning.

One situation of this kind occurs in the salivary glands of such dipteran larvae as the fruit fly *Drosophila*, where chromosomal DNA is replicated hundreds or thousands of times outside of the process of cell division. For reasons not understood each of the DNA molecules corresponding to a given chromosome is aligned parallel to its isomers. In some regions of these "polytene" chromosomes the DNA is more highly condensed than in other regions. As a consequence the chromosomes appear to have a regular pattern of alternating dark and light bands when viewed in a phase-contrast microscope. The band pattern is exactly reproducible and heritable; it is a manifestation of the order of genes in the chromosome. Rich and his co-workers found that antibody specific for Z DNA bound to the regions of *Drosophila* polytene chromosomes that appear light in phase contrast. This is a remarkable result because it suggests that Z DNA exists in real chromosomes in the living organism. Since Z DNA can be made synthetically, it should now be possible to look for regulatory proteins that bind specifically to Z DNA.

Surprises in the code. Using the sequencing methods introduced by Allan Maxam and Walter Gilbert at Harvard University and by Frederic Sanger and his co-workers at the Medical Research Council Laboratory of Molecular Biology in Cambridge, England, scientists in recent years have determined the complete sequence of progressively longer stretches of DNA. As has come to be expected, following the initial results from Sanger's laboratory on the sequence of nucleotides in the DNA of the bacterial virus ϕX174, which revealed the existence of overlapping genes, nearly every new sequence determination contains another surprise. Two are described below.

The longest sequence determined to date is that of the bacterial virus called T7. This work, by John Dunn and F. William Studier of Brookhaven National Laboratory in Upton, N.Y., required the determination of the sequence of some 39,000 nucleotide pairs. The task of merely recording and printing out the sequence is formidable. Although there are no overlapping genes in this viral chromosome, the sequence does contain an interesting feature. The major protein component of the virus shell is called gp10; the corresponding gene is called gene 10. It turns out that a minor protein component of the shell is a variant of gp10 that is slightly longer. Inspection of the nucleotide sequence of gene 10 shows that the variant is made by translating the messenger RNA to a point near the end of the message and then shifting the reading frame one position. That changes the amino-acid sequence of the protein but also puts the signal for chain termination of gp10 out of phase; consequently the variant protein is longer.

Even more unexpected were the results of the determination, in Sanger's laboratory, of the complete sequence of nucleotides in the circular DNA molecule from human mitochondria. Mitochondria are membrane-bounded organelles found in the cytoplasm of all eucaryotic (nucleated) cells. Roughly the size of bacteria, they are responsible for the production of ATP, the molecule in which the energy derived from the breakdown of such foodstuffs as sugars is stored. Mitochondria are thought to be the evolutionary descendants of bacteria that became associated symbiotically with primitive eucaryotic cells eons ago. Thus, it was of interest to learn in the mid-1960s that mitochondria contain their own DNA . Subsequently it was shown that human and other mammalian mitochondrial DNA contain about 17,000 nucleotide pairs, enough to carry the genetic code for 10–20 proteins. Clearly the nucleus must provide the information for most of the structure of the mitochondrion, including some of its machinery for DNA replication, RNA transcription, and protein synthesis. But what components have been retained by the mitochondrion?

Some of these components had been identified already on the basis of experiments in which RNA molecules isolated from mitochondria were annealed to mi-

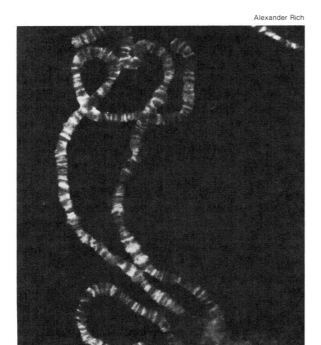

Polytene chromosomes of a Drosophila *larva glow from the presence of fluorescently labeled antibodies that were prepared to bind specifically to Z DNA. The evidence suggests that Z DNA exists in the chromosomes of living organisms.*

tochondrial DNA. In this way it was found that the RNA from mitochondrial ribosomes, the ribonucleoprotein particles that are the workbenches for protein synthesis, is coded by genes located in mitochondrial DNA. The same is true for certain classes of transfer RNA, the small molecular adapters that translate the genetic code. The determination of the nucleotide sequence of mitochondrial DNA locates these genes precisely: there are two genes for ribosomal RNA and 22 for transfer RNA. In addition, there are stretches of DNA that code for 13 proteins. Five of these are known proteins, components of the ATP-synthesis apparatus. The other eight code for proteins whose functions are still unknown.

The surprises concern the extreme economy of organization of the mitochondrial chromosome and the details of the genetic code used by the organelle. In general, eucaryotic nuclear chromosomes have a great deal of "extra" DNA, both between genes and inserted in the interior of genes as intervening sequences. The mitochondrial chromosome, by contrast, has very few nucleotides between genes and possibly no intervening sequences.

Economy has been achieved in another curious way. The nucleotide triplets in messenger RNA that signify termination of protein translation, both in procaryotes such as bacteria and in eucaryotes, are UAG, UGA, and UAA (in RNA molecules uracil, or U, replaces thymine). These are always included in the DNA sequence as TAG, TGA, or TAA, following the triplet for the last amino acid in the protein. In several mitochondrial genes, however, the final coding triplet is followed only by a single T and then by a transfer RNA gene. The terminating triplet UAA is created in the messenger RNA by addition of polyA (a sequence of adenine bases) to the messenger RNA following transcription and processing, which removes the transfer RNA by means of enzymes quite distinct from RNA polymerase.

As a third surprise, the detailed DNA sequence reveals that the genetic code is not as universal as once was thought. It is still true that a single set of code relations (nucleotide triplets corresponding to amino acids) is obeyed by all known procaryotes and eucaryotes, but exceptions are found in mitochondria. In human mitochondrial RNA, UGA codes for tryptophan and not for termination, AUA codes for methionine rather than isoleucine, and AGA and AGG are terminators rather than codewords for arginine.

—Robert Haselkorn

Zoology

Significant achievements in zoology during the past year included the working out of techniques to freeze mammalian embryos and later to transfer them to surrogate mothers. Workers also reported the first successful long-term incorporation of a gene from one species of mammal in a second using genetic engineering techniques. Giant tube worms from thermal vents on the ocean floor were reported to be a new species with an unusual symbiotic relationship with bacteria, and Israeli scientists found that common industrial detergents make effective shark repellents. Evolutionary zoology was the focus of controversy in both the courts and in the scientific community.

Cellular and developmental zoology. James Whitfield of the Canadian National Research Council discovered a basic difference between normal and cancerous cells. He noticed that, whereas calcium is necessary for growth and division of normal cells, it is not required by cancerous cells. The U.S. National Cancer Institute was supporting Whitfield to see if this phenomenon might be used as the basis for a new carcinogenicity test. Normal cells could be treated with chemicals that were suspected carcinogens. If the cells then grew in the absence of calcium, there would be a high probability that the chemical causes cancer in animals. A similar test, the Ames test, which employs bacteria rather than cells from higher animals, has been used for the past several years to screen possible chemicals for carcinogenic effects.

Barbara Durrant, a reproductive physiologist at the San Diego (Calif.) Zoo, was at work on a program of freezing and storing sperm and embryos of endangered species available in captivity. Male sperm cells are stored at −231° C (−384° F) for future use in artificial inseminations and test-tube fertilization. Techniques are available to treat females of a species with hormones that cause them to superovulate; *i.e.,* produce as many as 10–12 eggs at a time rather than one. These eggs are collected by flushing the oviducts with a solution and then are fertilized with previously stored sperm. The resulting embryos may be either artificially implanted in the uteri of surrogate mothers of the same or a different species or frozen for later implantation. Embryo transfer is quite common in the livestock industry, but application to new species requires many details to be worked out about timing of reproductive cycles, responses of animals to hormone treatments, and compatibilities of embryos of one species with surrogate mothers of another. In 1981 Janet Stover and colleagues at the Bronx Zoo in New York City transferred the embryo of a gaur, a large ox native to India, into the uterus of a Holstein cow. The gaur was born in August and seemed to be doing well. Such techniques should allow zoos to obtain several offspring from one donor female per year rather than the usual single calf through natural reproduction.

As a result of these techniques a surplus of embryos may be created, and it would be wasteful to destroy them. Durrant showed that it is possible to freeze and store an eight-cell embryo stage of a rat, then later thaw it and implant it in a surrogate mother rat. A female rat produced by this technique has been raised and gone on to produce her own pups by normal means. As these techniques develop, zoos, in addition to their other duties, may well become banks of gametes and embryos of various species, a sort of frozen ark.

Another research report of 1981 has implications for these artificial fertilization techniques. Thomas E. Wagner and colleagues at Ohio University reported the first long-term successful transfer of a gene from one species of mammal to another using genetic engineering techniques. They isolated and cloned a gene for rabbit beta globin, a part of hemoglobin, and injected the gene into a newly fertilized mouse egg. The eggs were then implanted in a female mouse and developed normally. When the treated mice were born, their hemoglobin contained rabbit beta globin. These mice were allowed to live normally and have produced two generations of offspring with the rabbit beta globin trait. This result indicates that the rabbit gene has been incorporated into the mouse genetic material and can be transmitted to future generations. Similar work was done by Franklin Constantini and Elizabeth Lacy in the Department of Zoology at the University of Oxford, confirming the general nature of the process. In livestock production such techniques could be used to insert genes for weight gain or milk production into eggs during embryo transfer to produce superior animals. Of course, there are also implications for human reproduction and the treatment of genetic diseases.

Neurobiology. The 1981 Nobel Prize for Physiology or Medicine was shared by three neurobiologists. Roger W. Sperry of the California Institute of Technology (CIT) was honored for his discoveries of the functional specialization of the brain showing that in humans the left hemisphere was dominant in language abilities and the right hemisphere superior in nonverbal visual-spatial reasoning. (See *1981 Yearbook of Science and the Future* Feature Article: THE TWO BRAINS OF MAN.) David H. Hubel and Torsten N. Wiesel, both of

Manhar, a guar calf, tags closely behind its surrogate mother Flossie at New York City's Bronx Zoo. The guar was transferred as an embryo from its natural mother to the Holstein cow as part of efforts to increase the ranks of rare animals by obtaining several offspring simultaneously from one donor female. Time from implantation to birth was about ten months.

Brian F. Alpert—Keystone

Zoologist Daniel C. Wilhoft of Rutgers University in New Jersey monitors the temperature of a clutch of snapping turtle eggs. Unlike mammals the sex of snappers and large sea turtles is not determined by sex chromosomes but by the incubation temperature of the eggs. In the wild such factors as air temperature, degree of cloudiness, depth of the nest, amount of vegetation cover, and the amount of shade cast by the surrounding landscape all influence nest temperature.

Harvard University, also shared in the prize for their work on the visual cortex and its functional organization. The awarding of the Nobel Prize in neurobiology emphasizes the growing importance and rapid advancement of this field.

Karl Herup of Yale University and Richard Mullen of the University of Utah have been investigating the development of the brain in mice to determine if heredity directly affects individual cells or simply modifies the environment in which the cells grow. There is a mutant mouse in which the Purkinje cells of the cerebellum are small and few in number and have stunted growth of dendrites. These cells also contain unusually high levels of an enzyme that can be stained, allowing their position to be easily determined. The researchers transferred cells from embryos of mutant mice into embryos of normal mice, thus creating a chimera, an animal whose parts are a mixture of cells from the original embryos. When the chimeric brains were examined, they found that both normal and abnormal types of Purkinje cells were present, showing that the genes rather than the environment influence the development of this cell. Whether this finding holds for other types of nerve cells is yet to be determined.

There is evidence that development of parts of the brain in birds is influenced by hormones. Mark Gurney of CIT has been studying the part of the bird brain responsible for song development, the robustus archistriatalis (RA), which controls the syrinx, the vocal organ of birds. The size of the RA is related to the complexity of the bird's song repertoire, and if the RA is surgically destroyed, the bird is mute. In zebra finches only males normally sing, and the RA in them is more developed than in females. RA growth is stimulated by the male hormone testosterone, and injections of this hormone into castrated males or into females caused RA development and expression of the song vocabulary. Gurney was interested in determining the effect of testosterone at the cellular level, specifically whether it induced the RA cells to make more connections with the rest of the brain or whether it caused the cells to become larger and more numerous. Using castrated males and females, he found that testosterone injections caused the development of more and larger cells in the RA regardless of the sex of the individual.

From this work one might conclude that bird song is both genetically and hormonally controlled. However, Meredith West of the University of North Carolina and Andrew King of Duke University, Durham, N.C., described how song development in cowbirds is socially influenced. A young cowbird is raised by foster parents of a different species, but upon maturation it joins a flock of its own kind where social skills must be used to communicate with other cowbirds regarding hierarchies and mate selection. Song is one form of communication. Although male cowbirds produce a common general song even when raised in isolation, indicating a genetic influence, this basic song can be modified. The investigators described an example in which the females in effect teach the males how to sing. Eastern and southern cowbirds sing different dialects. When a male from one region is exposed to females from another region, he will change his dialect to correspond to the preference of the mute female. Coaching seems related to the way in which the female responds to variations in his song and the social reinforcement received.

Organismal zoology. In 1977 a new ecosystem was

discovered around the hot water vents that occur at rift sites on the ocean floors. One of the exciting finds was the occurrence of giant tube worms associated with the vents. These worms, which reach lengths of 1.5 m (5 ft), were described as a new species, *Riftia pachyptila* (phylum Pogonophora), by Meredith L. Jones of the Smithsonian Institution National Museum of Natural History, Washington, D.C.

Horst Felbeck of the Scripps Institution of Oceanography in California found that the tube worms contain enzymes that can make energy-storing compounds (ATP) from the oxidation of hydrogen sulfide (H_2S) as well as enzymes that synthesize organic compounds from carbon dioxide using ATP as an energy source in much the same way that plants do in photosynthesis. Plants, however, produce ATP by interaction of light with chlorophyll, whereas these worms depend on the H_2S dissolved in the vent water. Colleen Cavanaugh of Harvard University and colleagues found that much of the tissue found in the trunk region of the worms is made up of bacteria—as much as four billion bacteria per gram of tissue—and she suggested that the enzymes to oxidize sulfide and to reduce carbon dioxide are contained in the bacteria rather than in cells derived from the animals. Felbeck also found these enzymes in bivalve mollusks and pointed out the obvious advantage of this symbiotic relationship in the dark rift environment, where the community cannot depend on photosynthetic organisms for energy input.

Of the approximately 250 species of sharks only about 10% have been implicated in attacks on humans. On a worldwide basis only about 50 attacks are reported per year. Despite this low rate there is a psychological aversion to sharks and a high motivation to find an effective shark repellent. In 1972 Eugenie Clark of the University of Maryland discovered that the Moses sole, a fish from the Gulf of Aqaba, secreted a highly toxic milky material that at low concentrations repelled sharks. In 1976 scientists at the Hebrew University of Jerusalem found that the active component was a protein called pardaxin, which alters ion exchange across the gill surface allowing urea and chloride to leak from the blood into the sea and sodium ions to pass from the sea into the blood. Evidently these harmful changes are sensed by the shark, and it will swim away from the pardaxin source. Because collecting the milky secretion from the Moses sole is not an economical way to produce a commercial shark repellent, the compound is not widely available. However, recent discoveries by Eli Zlotkin of the Hebrew University hold promise that a commercial substitute may be found. While studying the chemical structure of pardaxin, he noticed that it was similar to that of common industrial detergents. Zlotkin came to the U.S. and tested the effects of various detergents on sharks with the help of Samuel Gruber at the Rosenstiel School of Marine and Atmospheric Science in Miami, Fla., and found that they mimicked pardaxin's effects. One detergent tested was ten times more potent than pardaxin.

A major zoological mystery has been the "missing-year" phenomenon in the life cycles of various sea turtles. After hatching from nests in warm beach sands, the small turtles head into the surf and are not seen again until they reach pie-plate size, about one year later. It had been widely believed that turtles hatching on beaches in the southeastern U.S. swam to the Sargasso Sea about 160 km (100 mi) off the U.S. coast. University of Georgia scientists, however, found that the energy reserves of hatchlings were not sufficient to allow them to reach this destination, again raising the question of where they go during the first year. Daniel Stoneburner of the University of Georgia's Institute of Ecology approached this problem in a direct manner. He attached a small float containing a ra-

Four-month-old baby panda cavorts for its mother Ying-Ying at the Chapultepec Park Zoo in Mexico City. The zoo-bred rarity was born in the summer of 1981.

UPI

Siberian crane hatchling, the first of this endangered species to be bred in captivity, receives spoon-feeding at the International Crane Foundation in Wisconsin.

dio transmitter to newly emerged loggerhead turtles headed for the surf. Radio tracking showed that all of the young turtles headed not toward the open sea but rather around the barrier island into the salt marshes of the region. Some scientists questioned whether the floats influenced the travel of young turtles, causing them to follow an atypical route. Stoneburner plans to track young in the next breeding season by canoe to determine if unencumbered hatchlings follow the same route.

Knowledge of the life cycles of turtles is essential if

adequate management practices are to be developed to save species from extinction. Development of beach areas of North America and human fondness for turtle soup are rapidly depleting turtle populations. Various projects have been undertaken to attempt to restock breeding beaches. Ridley turtle eggs are now collected in Mexico and taken to Padre Island, Texas, where after the eggs hatch the young are allowed to scurry to the water. It is hoped that the young will imprint on the island and return there to breed. As they enter the surf, the young are scooped up and taken to Galveston, where they are raised in a "head-start" program to a one-pound size and released. George Balays of the Hawaii Institute of Marine Biology found that for green turtles sexual maturity is not achieved until at least ten years of age. There will be a long wait to determine the success of these programs.

It is interesting to note that sex in large sea turtles is not determined by chromosomes as in mammals but rather is the result of the environmental temperature at which the eggs are incubated. At low temperatures males are produced, whereas females result at higher temperatures. In the early 1980s the Endangered Species Office of the U.S. Fish and Wildlife Service was funding research into this phenomenon because, as rearing programs are started, a correct sex balance must be produced. If eggs were incubated at too low a temperature, the hatchlings would be all males, with obvious disastrous results for a breeding program.

Environmental zoology. Decreases in the fish population of the North Sea apparently are having a detrimental effect on puffins that breed on the island of Rost off the coast of Norway. For the past 12 years Gunnar Lid of the Zoological Museum of Oslo studied the Rost colony and noted that chick survival is decreasing. In 1980 all chicks died. According to Lid, the failure to raise the young successfully is due to overfishing of the North Sea. Analyzing commercial fish-

Scarlett, a female peregrine falcon reared and set free in Ithaca, New York, as part of Cornell University's Peregrine Release Program, feeds her adopted young atop the United States Fidelity & Guaranty Company building in Baltimore, Maryland. The falcon had been unable to find a mate, so program workers provided her with a substitute family to mother.

UPI

catch tables from the *Annual Statistical Bulletins* of the International Council for the Exploration of the Sea, British ornithologist Stephen Mills showed that herring catches decreased by 75% during this time. To make up for this, fisheries increased their catches of sand eels and sprats, the main food of puffin chicks, by five- to tenfold, thus depriving the young birds of their accustomed diet. It is trite to indicate that these types of changes are an early-warning system of changes occurring in an ecosystem, but the evidence is there. The disaster of Rost is apparent, but what effect this has for humans is yet to be determined.

Concern for the preservation of marine communities was expressed at the Fourth International Coral Reef Symposium held in May 1981 in Manila, at which 290 papers were presented. A common theme was that coral reefs are in danger from silt, petroleum handling, and thermal pollution as well as from excessive exploitation by those who collect and sell coral for curios. Scientists from the University of Queensland in Australia and the Great Barrier Reef Marine Park Authority described the effects on coral reefs of the crown of thorns starfish, which feed on the polyps producing the coral reefs. Apparently the starfish are increasing in an uncontrolled fashion and destroying the ability of the barrier reef to regenerate itself from the normal wear and tear of ocean waves and currents. Whether the increase in starfish population is a temporary fluctuation or the start of a trend that would have disastrous consequences for Australian coastline ecology and geography is not known.

Evolutionary Zoology. The field of evolution has been the battleground for two controversies that became quite prominent during the last year. In the past few years believers in a literal interpretation of biblical creation have exerted considerable pressure on U.S. state legislatures to pass laws that mandate that whenever evolution is taught in public school classrooms so-called scientific creationism must also be included. During 1981 both Arkansas and Louisiana adopted such laws. Several religious leaders, the American Civil Liberties Union, and the National Association of Biology Teachers brought suit in Arkansas. After hearing the case in U.S. District Court in Little Rock, Judge William Overton struck down the law, ruling that it violated the constitutional separation of church and state. He declared that the Arkansas law "was simply and purely an effort to introduce the Biblical version of creation into the public school curricula" and that creationists do not use the scientific method, in which data are carefully analyzed and weighed, but use instead the literal wording of the book of Genesis as the basis of their belief in creationism and their opposition to evolution.

In the past scientists paid little attention to the creationist movement, but that disregard is now changing to concern. Various state academies of science, the American Association for the Advancement of Science, and the National Academy of Sciences are a few of many professional organizations that have taken a firm stand on the issue, stating that "creation science" is not science and that it should not be considered or taught as such.

Within the field of evolution there is profound debate going on between those who believe evolution of species occurs by gradual accumulation of adaptations through natural selection acting on variations (gradualism) and those who feel that species undergo only minor change for long periods of time and then evolve rapidly and profoundly for short periods (punctuated equilibrium). Gradualism is closely associated with the synthetic theory of evolution, and most biologists believe that this is the way that new species form. The punctuated equilibrium model was proposed by two paleontologists, Stephen Jay Gould of Harvard University and Niles Eldredge of the American Museum of Natural History.

Both viewpoints are compatible with general evolutionary theory, and it should be pointed out that the viewpoints are not mutually exclusive. Both mechanisms may have operated in producing the diversity of modern organisms. The debate essentially concerns the rate of evolution for a species and the time scale involved. To a paleontologist 50,000 years is an instant in geological time, whereas to the biologist working with fruit flies, which produce a new generation every month, the same time period is an eternity. Nonetheless, the debate is healthy and has prompted many scientists to examine in detail the premises and predictions of evolutionary theory.

—Warren D. Dolphin

See also Feature Articles: THE ELECTRICITY OF LIFE AND LIMB; SEA OF SALT, SEA OF LIFE; WHAT MAN HAS DONE TO DOGS.

Materials sciences

Energy conservation, both in materials production and in end-product applications, remained an important concern of materials scientists during the past year. New and existing ceramics found more widespread use in the automotive industry and in the search for lighter, more powerful storage batteries. Metallurgists worked to lower the energy consumption of aluminum extraction processes. One of the most popularized ceramics of recent years, the insulating tile material for the U.S. space shuttle, was finally given the chance to prove its worth.

Ceramics

A major event of the year for ceramists came in April 1981 with the long-awaited testing of the thermal pro-

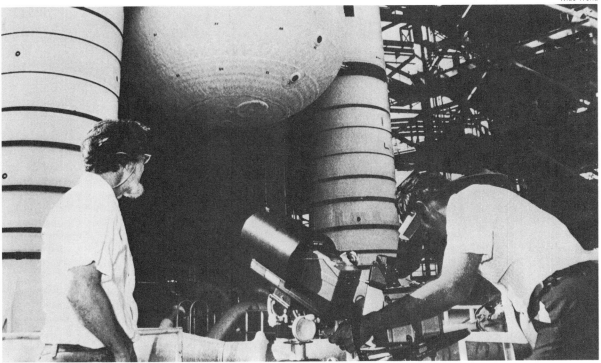

Ceramic-fiber thermal protection tiles on the shuttle orbiter "Columbia" receive an infrared survey from Boeing Services International technicians prior to the craft's second launch in November 1981.

tection tiles on the first space shuttle, the "Columbia." These tiles, which protect the underlying metallic structure from the heat of reentry while saving weight and maximizing payload, were made of very light blocks of almost pure silica-glass fiber. Although about 15 tiles were lost from the "Columbia" during its first flight, they were in noncritical heating areas, primarily on the shuttle's orbital-maneuvering-system engine pods. They were apparently loosened during launch by a combination of engine vibration and the effects of an unexpected aerodynamic shock wave.

Considerably more damage occurred to the tiles during the spacecraft's second flight in November. The surface skin on a number of high-temperature tiles was blistered and even partially or entirely blown away, apparently as a result of rainwater that had seeped through the waterproofing layer on the tiles during the wait for the second launch and then turned to steam during reentry. There was also some gouging of the tiles due to impacts and some charring on the orbital-maneuvering-system pods.

Although these reusable tiles thus proved to be satisfactory for basic shuttle operation, NASA had already developed a stronger, less dense, and more impact-resistant tile material for future shuttle orbiters. The new material, called fibrous refractory composite insulation, is a blend of high-purity silica fibers and aluminum borosilicate fibers. The composite probably will

be used in many critical areas on the second and third shuttle orbiters and may fully replace the all-silica high-temperature tiles on subsequent craft. Another NASA development is a new thermal protection material, a flexible reusable surface-insulation blanket consisting of silica-glass fiber felt sandwiched and stitched in place between face sheets of silica-glass cloth. Installed in a small area of the "Columbia" after its first flight, this blanket material may be used more extensively in troublesome areas on future flights of the "Columbia" and probably will replace many of the rigid low-temperature tiles on the upper wing and fuselage surfaces of the second orbiter vehicle, the "Challenger," and several orbiters to follow.

There was progress in the development of partially stabilized zirconia (ZrO_2) as an important high-temperature structural material. Although dense, single-phase ceramics can be made to be very strong and very resistant to high temperatures and corrosive atmospheres, they are brittle and quite susceptible to fracture by cracks propagating from manufacturing or machining flaws. One very effective means of introducing toughness in ceramics is based on the large change in volume that occurs in zirconia when it transforms from its elevated-temperature tetragonal crystal structure to its room-temperature monoclinic form. Whereas the mechanism responsible for the toughening is still not completely understood, it has been

338

shown that exceptional toughness values can be achieved if fine precipitates of tetragonal zirconia are retained metastably within a ceramic. The effect is thought to be related to the transformation of these particles to the stable monoclinic form in the stress field accompanying a propagating crack.

One of the most interesting of these toughened ceramics is partially stabilized zirconia, in which the metastable tetragonal precipitates are formed in zirconia itself. It has already been shown to be extremely valuable in applications requiring resistance to surface wear; for example, as thread guides in the textile industry and as extrusion dies in the metalworking industry. It may find its most widespread use, however, as cylinder liners and piston caps in adiabatic diesel engines, where its use could permit significant further gains in fuel economy. A particularly important advance was reported by the Commonwealth Scientific Industrial Research Organization in Australia, where a new thermal treatment for partially stabilized zirconia was shown to produce a marked improvement in its thermal shock resistance.

Stabilized zirconia, which had been used for some years as the electrolyte in industrial galvanic-cell oxygen sensors, also achieved more widespread use in automotive engine control. To meet fuel economy and exhaust emission goals and at the same time provide acceptable engine performance, designers have put increasing emphasis on closed-loop engine controls in which an oxygen sensor in the exhaust stream is used to provide continuous adjustment of the air-to-fuel ratio. One such sensor contains a closed-end ceramic tube made of zirconia that has been doped with yttrium oxide. This ceramic is an excellent oxygen-ion con-

ductor, and, when opposite faces of the ceramic are coated with platinum electrodes and exposed to gases with different oxygen contents, a voltage is generated that is directly proportional to the difference in oxygen contents. If one face of the sensor lies in the exhaust-gas stream and the other is maintained at a fixed reference level, then a very large voltage change occurs as the exhaust varies from a fuel-rich, oxygen-deficient condition to a lean, oxygen-abundant state. The output of the sensor therefore can be used with a small electronic computer and control unit to automatically select and maintain optimum carburetor fuel-to-air ratios for any given requirement.

Ceramics were also reported to be an important new filter material for diesel engines. Although diesels have many economic advantages, many of them also emit significant amounts of unburned carbon particles, often in the form of visible soot. In fact, many diesel engines in the U.S. would not meet that nation's 1985 emission standards of 0.125 g/km (0.2 g/mi) without some form of exhaust filter. Corning Glass Works, Corning, N.Y., recently announced development of a ceramic honeycomb filter to reduce such emissions very efficiently. The exhaust gases flow through the porous walls of the filter, and the soot particles, which cannot pass through, are filtered out. With careful control of the average pore size of the ceramic, efficiencies of at least 80% have been obtained in steady-state engine tests with acceptable pressure drops across the filter. To prevent accumulated soot from clogging the filter, the filter is regenerated periodically by adjusting the temperature and oxygen concentration within it in order to ignite and burn the particles. Ultimately, it may be possible to design the filter so that combustion

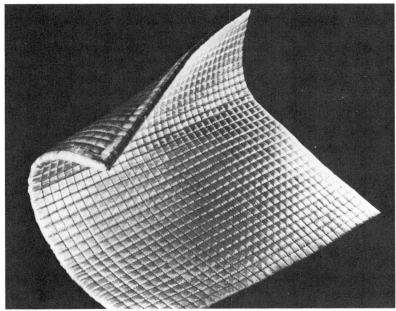

NASA

Thermal protection quilt, formally termed advanced flexible reusable surface insulation, was developed by NASA as a tougher, lighter, and cheaper alternative to silica glass tiles for troublesome areas on its shuttle orbiters. About 1.9 square meters (20 square feet) of the silica-glass fiber and cloth material were installed on the elevon cove area of the "Columbia" after its first flight.

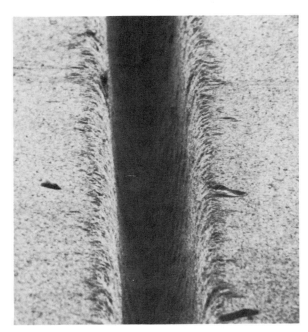 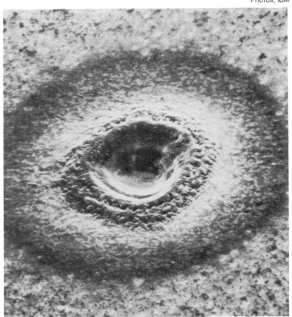

New process developed at IBM combines laser heating and chemical etching to achieve rapid and precise micromachining of ceramics materials. Ceramic immersed in an etchant bath and scanned with a powerful pinpoint laser beam shows a clean cut (left). By contrast, the same material drilled with a laser beam alone exhibits a circular heap of melted and refrozen material remaining around the central hole (right).

of the soot is continuous and equal to the filtration rate.

Significant advances were made in the use of ceramic electrolytes for high-efficiency, long-life rechargeable batteries for applications in the electric power industry and in electric vehicles. Although sodium-sulfur cells with high energy density offer many advantages for these applications, solid electrolyte problems have limited their reliability. The electrolyte, which serves to separate the electrodes, must also provide the ionic transport necessary for proper electrochemical functioning of the cell. Most sodium-sulfur cell research programs to date have concentrated on the use of beta alumina electrolytes. These are ceramic solids with ionic conductivities approaching those of aqueous electrolytes or molten salts. In beta alumina, layers of aluminum and oxygen atoms are separated periodically by planes containing highly mobile sodium ions. An even more conductive composition, beta″ alumina, is known, but its use has been limited by manufacturing difficulties and by its sensitivity to various degradation mechanisms that can cause premature cell failure.

Recently General Electric Co. committed itself to the use of beta″ alumina as its solid electrolyte in order to meet its cost goals for power utility applications and made significant advances in solving some of the problems associated with its practical use. One of the major steps forward has been development of an electrophoretic deposition process in which thin-wall tubes of beta″ alumina are readily formed by attracting fine,

electrically charged particles of a precursor powder to an oppositely charged mandrel. The tubes are then dried, removed from their mandrels, and sintered at high temperatures to form the dense, impermeable tubes needed for successful cell operation. This process yields highly conducting, strong, fine-grained material that is particularly well-suited to the application. A major factor still to be determined is the resistance of beta″ alumina electrolyte to breakdown with time during successive charging and discharging cycles. This information is particularly important for power storage applications in the electric utility industry, because to be cost-effective the cells would need a ten-year, or 2,500-cycle, life. Electric vehicle application would not require as long a service life, but adequate vehicle performance would demand an exceptionally high power-to-weight ratio in the battery system. Despite these difficult requirements, the beta alumina electrolyte battery offers the promise of greater fuel efficiency and compatability with other fuel sources.

—Norman M. Tallan

Metallurgy

In the past year interest again focused on attempts to decrease the energy requirements of metallurgical extraction processes. About 1% of the energy produced in the U.S. is consumed by the aluminum industry, and because the U.S. aluminum industry is committed to

340

the federal government to decrease significantly the energy consumed per unit weight of aluminum produced, particular attention is being paid to the production of this metal.

Aluminum is made by the extraction of pure alumina (Al_2O_3) from the ore bauxite in the Bayer process followed by electrolytic dissociation of the alumina dissolved in molten cryolite ($NaF \cdot AlF_3$) in the Hall-Héroult cell. The former process was introduced in Germany in 1888 by Karl Joseph Bayer, and the latter process was introduced simultaneously in the U.S. by Charles M. Hall and in France by Paul-Louis-Toussaint Héroult in 1886. Prior to 1900 small Hall-Héroult cells consumed 19–20 kw-hr of electricity per pound of aluminum produced (42–44 kw-hr/kg). By 1930 this figure had been decreased to 9–10 kw-hr, and in the early 1980s the rate of consumption in the U.S. was about 8 kw-hr. The most recent figure is still somewhat high because during the years of relatively cheap electricity the primary criteria influencing plant design were low capital costs and high productivity. Currently, improved energy efficiency in aluminum production is being pursued in improvements in the chemistry and technology of the Hall-Héroult cell and in the development of alternative processes.

In the Hall-Héroult cell liquid aluminum is deposited at a horizontal carbon cathode; oxygen, produced at a carbon anode, reacts with the anode to produce carbon dioxide gas. The theoretical minimum energy required to produce aluminum and carbon dioxide at the normal operating temperature of 975° C (1,785° F) from alumina and carbon at 25° C (77° F) is 2.85 kw-hr per pound of aluminum produced. The extra energy requirements in the actual process arise mainly from the electrical resistance of the electrolyte and the polarization of the electrodes, both of which generate the heat necessary to maintain a molten electrolyte and provide a heat balance. As a consequence any attempt to increase the energy efficiency of the process by increasing current efficiency and decreasing cell voltage must make allowance for the effect of such changes on the heat balance of the cell.

The voltage drop across the electrolyte is determined by its conductivity and by the distance between anode and cathode. Liquid aluminum does not wet the carbon anode, and thus in order to ensure complete coverage of the cell bottom a rather thick layer of liquid aluminum must be maintained. The magnetic fields within the cell cause turbulence, in the form of undulations and ripples, on the surface of the aluminum layer, and the minimum distance between anode and cathode, which is typically 4.5 cm (1.75 in), is set by the requirement that such turbulence does not cause electrical shorting of the cell. As it has been calculated that decreasing the anode-cathode separation to less than 2.5 cm (one inch) could save as much as 1.1 kw-hr per pound of aluminum, research is being conducted on

the identification and development of an alternative cathode material that has the necessary physical and electrical properties and is wetted by liquid aluminum. In the past year trials with titanium diboride (TiB_2) showed promise, although the tendency of this material to crack in service has to be overcome. A 5% increase in the electrical conductivity of the electrolyte can be achieved by the addition of lithium fluoride (LiF), which, prior to the escalation in the cost of energy, was considered to be expensive. It is recognized that the full 1.1 kw-hr/lb savings in energy cannot be realized because the decrease in the quantity of heat produced by the electrical resistance of the cell must be offset by operating at higher current density. Thus, unless supplementary heating can be used, the consequent increase in the polarization of the electrodes will decrease the net energy saving to about 0.5 kw-hr/lb.

Of the various alternative processes for aluminum production the possibility of direct chemical reduction of alumina by carbon has been examined closely during the past year. Because of the high chemical stabilities of alumina and aluminum carbide (Al_4C_3) the carbothermic reduction of alumina will require process temperatures in excess of 2,000° C (3,600° F), and the theoretical energy requirement is some 50% greater than that of the Bayer/Hall-Héroult combination. This difference, however, may be more than offset by the fact that the energy efficiency of an industrial submerged-arc electric furnace, in which the carbothermic reduction would be carried out, is considerably higher than that of a Hall-Héroult cell.

Carbothermic reduction involves many practical problems. When a mixture of alumina and carbon is heated, the oxycarbide Al_4O_4C is the first reaction product formed. On further heating the oxycarbide is partially converted to Al_4C_3, and at the final operating temperature of about 2,100° C (3,800° F) a mixed carbide-oxycarbide melt is produced, which upon final reduction produces carbon-saturated liquid aluminum and carbon monoxide gas. At the operating temperature the product gas contains considerable amounts of aluminum and Al_2O vapor, which decreases the metallic yield. Furthermore, the liquid metal product contains about 10% by weight of carbon in solution, which on cooling recombines with aluminum to form Al_4C_3. Thus each pound of melt will produce 0.6 lb of solid aluminum and 0.4 lb Al_4C_3, necessitating phase separation and further purification of the aluminum.

Other alternative processes being considered include the electrolysis of chloride, nitride, and sulfide melts. In the proposed Alcoa smelting process (ASP) alumina produced in the Bayer process is first impregnated with carbon by thermal decomposition of fuel oil in a fluidized bed and then chlorinated in the presence of a catalyst. Aluminum is obtained by electrolysis of the aluminum chloride ($AlCl_3$) in a molten chloride mixture, and the chlorine gas evolved at the anode is

Courtesy, Structural Dynamics Research Corporation, Cincinnati, Ohio

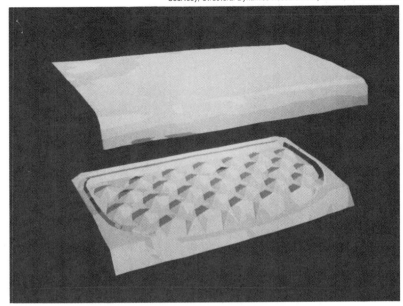

Automobile deck lid, modeled on a computer display, is fabricated from two aluminum-alloy panels and weighs about one-third that of a steel deck lid of the same size. Aluminum made up about 4% by weight of the average automobile in 1981, reflecting a move toward the use of aluminum and aluminum-alloy components to reduce overall weight, increase mileage, and lower fuel consumption.

returned to the chlorinator. Although the decomposition voltage of $AlCl_3$ is 0.65 volts higher than that of alumina, an improved bipolar cell design in the ASP method permits the cell voltage and the electrical energy requirements to be less than in the Hall-Héroult process. The geometric arrangement of the electrodes in the cell facilitates efficient removal of the anode gas, which in turn permits operation with smaller anode-cathode distances. Thus the voltage drop across the electrolyte due to the electrical resistance is decreased, but because of the lowered operating temperature and the larger number of pairs of electrodes per unit volume of cell, the necessary heat balance can still be maintained. Aluminum chloride has a strong tendency to hydrolyze, and hence the ultimate success of the ASP method may depend on the extent to which water vapor can be excluded from the processes that involve handling this compound.

Of the 100 million joules required to produce one pound of primary aluminum, 25% are consumed in the Bayer process for production of alumina. As is the case with the Hall-Héroult process, existing Bayer plants were designed and constructed when energy was not a large part of the cost of extracting alumina from bauxite. In the Bayer process bauxite ore is digested in a hot, pressurized, concentrated caustic soda solution to dissolve the alumina and leave the iron oxide and silicate impurities as undissolved solids. After removal of the solids by filtration, the alumina is reprecipitated by diluting the solution and cooling it to room temperature. The precipitated alumina is then removed by filtration, and the solution is concentrated again by evaporation and reheated for further digestion of bauxite.

Both the efficiency of recovery of alumina from the bauxite and the energy consumption increase with increasing difference between the maximum and minimum temperature attained in the cyclic process. Because the plant is in essence a large system of heat exchangers, energy efficiency can only be improved through more efficient transfer between the various component heat exchangers. In the early 1980s the energy cost of producing alumina in oil-fueled plants was between one-half and one-third of the market price of the alumina produced. With the cost of coal energy at about one-third that of oil, conversion from oil to coal as the energy source in alumina production would decrease production costs significantly. The dilemma facing the alumina producers, however, is caused by uncertainty in the future cost of coal energy and the huge expense of converting from oil-fired to coal-fired boilers. Recently a proposal was made to eliminate the Bayer process by directly chlorinating the bauxite ore, with carbon monoxide as the reductant. Such a process could provide aluminum chloride for the ASP method if the chlorides of such unwanted impurities as iron could be separated from the aluminum chloride.

—David R. Gaskell

See also Feature Article: Surprising New Uses for Sulfur.

Mathematics

The grand theories of mathematics are erected on a foundation of specific problems. Deep problems, ones that resist decades of effort, anchor abstract theories to concrete examples; frivolous problems frequently link parts of one theory with another, thus supporting the entire edifice of mathematical constructs. Students train on problems as a sure way to hone mathematical skills, and researchers solve problems as much for fun as for profit. Strenuous work on a good problem exercises the mind and helps keeps research skills sharp.

Problems and puzzles, some deep, some frivolous, highlighted the world of mathematics in recent months. Public attention was riveted on the mathematican's puzzle par excellence—Rubik's Cube. Featured on the cover of *Scientific American*, described in *Time* and the *Wall Street Journal*, enshrined in *New Yorker* cartoons, this small plastic block—perhaps the most mathematical toy ever invented—became an instant sensation.

The rotations of the faces of Rubik's Cube are actions in a group, one of the most fundamental objects of mathematics. Key combinations of moves used in solving the cube puzzle are just well-known group actions made concrete. For example, the strategy of preparing a position, executing a series of rotations, then reversing the preparation steps is what group theorists call a conjugation: a group element sandwiched between an action and its inverse.

Simple group theory can be used to analyze the enormous complexity of the cube and to provide insight into the various solutions. Conversely, cube actions can illustrate basic concepts of group theory that heretofore were considered acts of mental magic. Although numerous popular books offered step-by-step solutions to the cube, David Singmaster's *Notes on Rubik's Magic Cube* provided a mathematician's analysis, showing that the cube is really a manifestation of what is known as a wreath product of groups. Abstract group theory will never quite be the same again.

Despite the millions of hours invested in solving Rubik's Cube, some serious mathematics did also take place. Indeed, two important long-standing problems were solved, one in algebra, the other in analysis.

The older of these problems is a conjecture made in 1926 by Dutch algebraist B. L. van der Waerden, the author of the first so-called "modern algebra" text for university mathematics. Van der Waerden was studying square matrices, arrays of numbers n rows deep by n columns across. The number reached by adding together all possible products formed by selecting one element from every row and column is called the permanent of such a matrix. (The permanent is similar to the better known determinant, which is formed by alternately adding and subtracting these products.)

As the values in the matrix change, the value of the permanent also changes. Van der Waerden conjectured, based on a combination of empirical evidence and inconclusive theoretical reasons, that the minimum value of the permanent is achieved when every element in the matrix has the same value, namely $1/n$.

This is a very natural conjecture, for usually the maximum or minimum values of a symmetric function like the permanent will occur for symmetric values of the variables. The most symmetric matrix possible is one with equal entries, so in this sense Van der Waerden's conjecture is very plausible. There are exceptions, however, to this heuristic rule that symmetric problems have symmetric optima. One interesting case produces a symmetric solution for 10 or fewer variables, but for more than 14 variables the solution becomes asymmetric. Therefore, conjectures like van der Waerden's really do need proof before being accepted as truth.

It took more than 50 years for that proof to emerge.

In 1981 it was discovered independently by two Soviet mathematicians, D. I. Falikman of the Scientific Research Institute for Automated Systems of Planning and Management in Construction in the Ukrainian S.S.R. and G. T. Egorychev of the L. V. Kirensky Institute of Physics, Siberian branch of the Soviet Academy of Sciences in Krasnoyarsk. Falikman apparently found his proof first, whereas Egorychev's proof was the first to become known in the West as a result of a prepublication report that circulated among a few Western mathematicians. Both proofs rely on a somewhat obscure inequality proved in 1938 by another Soviet mathematician, A. D. Aleksandrov.

Resolution of van der Waerden's conjecture does not alter significantly the direction of mathematics research, because most people believed it to be true and used it as a hypothesis in various theorems. Permanents are useful in combinatorial mathematics, the branch of discrete mathematics concerned with counting the number of ways things can happen. So there is some hope that solution of this important conjecture will lead to improved knowledge of the number of Latin squares and Steiner triple systems, objects used in design of experiments and in analysis of algorithms.

The other major problem resolved in 1981 is a conjecture set forth in 1948 by British mathematician John E. Littlewood concerning the behavior of sums of trigonometric functions, the sine and cosine wave forms that underlie all complex waves. Littlewood observed that superimposed waves of different frequency could never completely cancel; as more and more waves were added there inevitably would be a slow (logarithmic) growth in the overall magnitude of the resulting wave.

The formal statement of Littlewood's conjecture looks impressive (*see* box). It is as hard to prove as it looks. The exponential terms in this conjecture, the powers of *e* in the expression, are wave forms on a circle, corresponding to the trigonometric functions on a line. These exponential terms are known as characters of the circle group, objects of fundamental importance to the mathematical theory of groups as well as to the quantum theory of elementary particles. Littlewood's conjecture limits the kind of cancellation that can occur among characters, by forcing the overall magnitude to grow at least as fast as the logarithm of the number of characters.

After several spectacular near misses by famous mathematicians, the Littlewood conjecture was finally proved by the joint effort of Brent Smith of Illinois State University, Louis Pigno of Kansas State University, and O. Carruth McGehee of Louisiana State University. Their proof did not introduce any special new methods but relied instead on a traditional tool of modern analysis, the Cauchy-Schwarz inequality. This inequality is a generalization to function spaces of the familiar triangle inequality of school mathematics: the

$$\frac{1}{2\pi} \int_{-\pi}^{\pi} \left| \sum_{k=1}^{N} e^{in_k x} \right| dx > \frac{1}{\pi^2} \log N$$

Littlewood's conjecture

sum of the lengths of two sides of a triangle must be greater than that of the third side.

Interestingly, as their paper was going to press in the *Annals of Mathematics,* they found that a somewhat different proof of Littlewood's conjecture was being published at about the same time by S. V. Konjagin in the Soviet journal *Izvestiya Akad. Nauk SSSR.* This rather common occurrence of independent simultaneous solutions of major problems suggests that hard problems must await the right environment for a solution.

Among other problems that were solved, one result shed some light on a major unsolved problem in the theory of computation, to determine which problems have times of solution that grow exponentially with the size of the problem and which do not. The former problems—called NP complete—quickly get out of range of even modern computers, so it is useful to know in advance whether a problem is in this class.

In 1981 Hendric W. Lenstra, Jr., of the University of Amsterdam showed that a certain class of integer programming problems does not exhibit the much-feared pattern of exponential growth. Integer programming problems are widely used in business and industry in assignment and classification problems; they are termed "integer" programs because of the requirement that the solution be in whole numbers, as it must be when the solution represents numbers of people assigned to different jobs.

Although Lenstra's result neither shows nor suggests that all integer programming problems are solvable in polynomial time (the moderate alternative to exponential growth), it does represent a significant and, in some respects, surprising solution to part of the main problem. It is somewhat parallel to Soviet mathematician Leonid G. Khachian's famous 1979 proof that the common problem of linear programming—in which solutions are not restricted to whole numbers—can be solved in polynomial time.

More elementary but nonetheless challenging problems commanded the attention of 185 high-school students from 27 countries who attended the 22nd International Mathematical Olympiad in Washington, D.C., in July 1981. These annual events began in the Eastern bloc countries, where rigorous problem training is a standard part of school mathematics, but later included teams from around the world. In 1981, for the second time in five years, the United States took first place. The U.S. team score of 314 points barely edged second-place West Germany, whose team scored 312.

The two-day exam, prepared by an international committee of mathematics teachers and graded by teams of multilingual mathematicians, consists of six challenging problems from school mathematics, three problems to be done each day in 4½ hours. Each nation's team consists of eight students, selected as a result of stiff preliminary examinations and vigorous pre-Olympiad training sessions. Exam questions are translated into the native language of each participant, with special care so as not to give subtle advantages based on linguistic differences. In 1981 four of the U.S. contestants achieved perfect scores, a record.

—Lynn Arthur Steen

Medical sciences

Advances in the treatment of human fetuses were among the most remarkable achievements in the medical sciences during the last year. Also noteworthy were an outbreak of two rare and serious diseases among homosexual men, the development of a new low-risk technique for viewing blood vessels, the formulation of several effective new medicines for treating skin diseases, the discovery of biofeedback as a useful therapy for habitual clenching and grinding of teeth, and the production of a vaccine for hoof-and-mouth disease of cattle, sheep, and hogs.

General medicine

Fetus as patient. Dramatic progress was reported in 1981 toward extending medical procedures to a previously inaccessible group, human fetuses. The procedures included surgery, selective abortion in cases of multiple fetuses, and dosing the mother with vitamins to correct a fetal insufficiency.

In a striking surgical procedure University of California at San Francisco physicians Mitchell Golbus, Michael Harrison, and Roy Filly tapped a congenitally obstructed urinary tract in one of a pair of unborn twins. The boy and his normal sister were born a month later, and the physicians planned to correct the blockage surgically before the infant was a year old. They expected no long-term adverse effects.

The fetal disorder had been detected in a routine ultrasound scan about the 16th week of gestation, and it was diagnosed about the 26th week as a bladder-outlet obstruction. Had the urine continued to accumulate in the fetus, irreversible renal and pulmonary damage could have resulted. The doctors and parents decided to wait until the 30th week of gestation for surgery, so that the normal sibling fetus would have a chance of surviving if the surgery triggered premature delivery. In the first attempt the catheter would not stay in place in the fetal bladder, but a second attempt, which inserted a newly designed catheter with a flexible "pigtail"

curve at one end, was successful. It drained urine from the fetal abdomen into the amniotic sac.

Another type of fetal surgery also was reported in 1981. A tiny valve was implanted into the skull of a human fetus to drain the fluid accumulated due to hydrocephalus. Without this treatment the pressure buildup could have caused significant brain damage before birth. William Clewell of the University of Colorado Health Sciences Center led the team that installed the valve in a 24-week-old hydrocephalic human fetus. The infant was delivered by cesarean section several weeks prematurely when the shunt clogged and pressure in the brain started to build again. A different type of shunt was inserted after birth.

Studies of prenatally implanted valves in monkeys at the National Institutes of Health also yielded encouraging results. Monkeys with experimentally induced hydrocephaly survived birth and seemed healthy at nine months of age in 80% of the cases where a valve had been inserted during the pregnancy. Only 10% of the hydrocephalic monkeys without valves survived birth, and all died within two weeks. Both in monkeys and in humans that technique still needed to be evaluated for subtle brain damage that might be revealed when developing motor and cognitive skills.

Later in the year Golbus, Harrison, and Filly report-

Twin boy on the left was the subject of the first successful surgical treatment of an unborn child, drainage of his blocked urinary tract.

UPI

ed the first treatment of a human fetus outside the womb. In this case ultrasound revealed that the fetus at 21 weeks of gestation had a blocked urinary tract, and the condition was too advanced to be corrected by simply inserting a catheter. The physicians cut into the womb, withdrew the lower half of the fetus, and surgically bypassed the obstruction. The fetus was returned to the womb and carried to term. Unfortunately the blocked urinary tract had irreversibly damaged the fetus's kidneys, and the infant died soon after birth. Golbus and colleagues remained optimistic that they could perform the same operation on other cases in time to save lives.

The first selective abortion in the United States was reported by Thomas Kerenyi and Usha Chitkara of Mount Sinai School of Medicine in New York City. The procedure was employed in a case in which amniocentesis had shown that one of a pair of fraternal twins was normal but the other had a serious congenital defect. The mother, who was 40 years old and childless and had had infertility problems, said that she desperately wanted to have the normal child but could not face the burden of caring for the abnormal one. The physicians obtained confirmation from a court of law of the parents' right to consent to the operation on behalf of the normal fetus, who was put at some risk. The physicians drew blood from the heart of the fetus with the genetic disease. The normal twin was born healthy four months later. Because the genetic disorder Down's syndrome and fraternal twinning are both common in pregnancies of women nearing the age of 40, Kerenyi and Chitkara predicted that other cases would arise in which only one twin would be detected to have the syndrome.

Inherited diseases sometimes can be treated with large doses of a vitamin or other metabolic chemical. Seymour Packman, Morton Cowan, and Mitchell Golbus of the University of California at San Francisco along with Donald Meyer of Santa Rosa (Calif.) Memorial Hospital announced that they had successfully treated a fetus having an inherited defect in biotin metabolism by giving large doses of biotin to the pregnant woman. The disease was detected by amniocentesis in the woman, who had previously given birth to a son with the biotin metabolism defect. The biotin taken by the pregnant woman passed through the placenta and was absorbed by the fetus. The child was born free of the symptoms of biotin deficiency and at the time of the report was a healthy five-year-old on a regimen of biotin treatments.

Health hazards of homosexuals. A puzzling outbreak of two rare and serious diseases primarily among homosexual men was documented during the year by the U.S. Centers for Disease Control near Atlanta, Ga. The diseases had been associated previously with patients having severe immune system deficiencies, such as those with advanced cancer or those taking immu-

nosuppressive drugs after an organ transplant. The investigators suggested that the new cases among previously healthy men represent an epidemic of immune system breakdown, but as of early 1982 they did not yet know the cause.

The first disease associated with the outbreak was the life-threatening *Pneumocystis carinii* pneumonia. The condition was initially reported in homosexual men in Los Angeles and then in New York City. By the end of 1981 more than 75 previously healthy patients with *Pneumocystis* pneumonia were identified. More than half of those patients died.

An increased incidence was next noted in a type of cancer previously observed occasionally in elderly men and in immunosuppressed patients. Kaposi's sarcoma is a soft-tissue tumor. The cancer was reported in more than 80 patients, some of whom also had *Pneumocystis* pneumonia. Of them 20% who had Kaposi's sarcoma and 30% who had both diseases died. Investigators also tallied a few instances in previously healthy persons of other diseases that normally appear only in immunosuppressed patients.

Among the newly reported cases of *Pneumocystis* pneumonia and Kaposi's sarcoma only one occurred in a woman, and more than 90% occurred in men who were homosexual or bisexual. Cases were reported from 15 states of the U.S. and 2 other countries, but the largest number originated in New York. New York, California, and Georgia together contributed 80% of the cases.

The victims of these diseases did not seem to share a source of infection. Most did not know each other or have sexual partners in common. Immunological examination of a group of patients in New York with *Pneumocystis* pneumonia revealed an immune system defect. Henry Masur and colleagues at New York Hospital-Cornell in New York City demonstrated in the 11 patients that they examined a depressed function of one class of immune system cells, called T cells. The investigators suspected that the patients had somehow acquired a condition in which the immune system became suppressed, causing them to become susceptible to infection by *Pneumocystis carinii* and other disease organisms.

Why homosexual men should suffer from depressed immune system function was the source of much speculation, but no consensus was reached. Some investigators suspected the widespread use of inhalant drugs, especially butyl nitrite, among male homosexual communities. Other researchers focused on the prevalence of an active infection by cytomegalovirus among the affected men. Although cytomegalovirus infection has been linked to transient abnormalities in cellular immunity, it is common among heterosexual men and women as well as among homosexual men. Some researchers believed that it was possible that the cytomegalovirus infections were the result, rather than

Andrew B. Crummy, University of Wisconsin Clinical Science Center, Madison

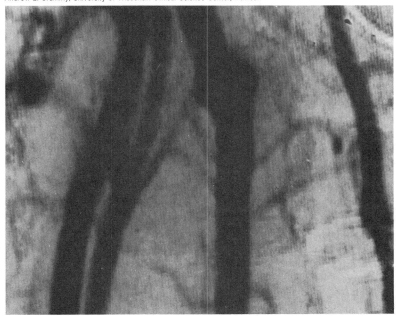

Computerized fluoroscopy reveals a carotid artery that is obstructed on one side and completely blocked on the other. This method of detecting blood flow is less invasive and expensive than standard arteriography and angiocardiography.

the cause, of the depressed immune system activity.

Another explanation suggested was that some homosexual men were suffering from an "immunological overload." The incidence of sexually transmitted diseases is increasing among homosexual men, who are believed on the average to have more sexual partners than heterosexuals. Daniel William, a New York City internist, suggested that rapidly sequential or concurrent infections with many disease-causing microorganisms may paralyze the immune system, allowing the sudden emergence of serious diseases.

While the cause of the outbreak remained a mystery, there was general agreement that the incidence of *Pneumocystis* pneumonia and Kaposi's sarcoma and the number of deaths from those diseases, although still rare, rose dramatically in 1981. The Centers for Disease Control began conducting a national study of cases along with matched controls in order to identify risk factors for the diseases. Meanwhile, physicians were urged to be alert for indications of immune system suppression among homosexual men.

Low-risk look at blood vessels. More than a dozen hospitals began to use a recently developed computer-aided technique to view the pattern of blood flow through a patient's arteries. Such information, displayed on a television screen, can tell where arteries are obstructed in vascular diseases, including heart disease, and can evaluate the condition of grafts that are inserted during artery bypass surgery.

The conventional method of viewing arteries involves inserting a small tube into an artery in the area of interest and injecting a material that is opaque to X-rays. This procedure is costly because it requires hospi-

talization, and the patient risks having a stroke or other vascular injury.

The new computer-aided technique, which has been tested on several thousand patients, can sense far lower amounts of opaque material in the blood than can standard arteriography and angiography. Therefore, the contrast dye can be injected into a peripheral blood vessel, a far simpler and safer procedure than injection into a major artery. Enough material passes throughout the circulatory system to be detected in the arteries under observation. Because the patient does not need to stay overnight in the hospital and because expensive X-ray film is not required, the new procedure is far less costly than the conventional techniques.

Instantaneous subtraction is the key to the computer application of image intensification. In the simplest procedure an X-ray image of the area being examined is taken before the arrival of the contrast material, and this background image, translated into numbers, is then stored in the computer's memory. As the opaque material, injected iodine, passes through the arteries of the area, the monitor displays a pattern that is the difference, point for point, between the new and the background image. This subtraction makes the arteries much more conspicuous on the screen.

The first applications of this technique were directed primarily at examination of the principal arteries that supply blood to the head and neck. The investigators observed constrictions, occlusions, ulcers, and bulgings of these carotid arteries. They also used the technique to study vascular disease in the head, chest, abdomen, and extremities. For example, they used it to determine whether blood vessels beyond an arterial

347

blockage are in good enough condition to justify bypass surgery instead of amputation of a limb.

Although in some cases the new technique allowed physicians to see vessels invisible in more traditional arteriography, in other cases the standard method gave more detail. But because the computerized technique is so simple, safe, and inexpensive, it was expected to make feasible the examination of more patients. Consideration was being given to studies in which subjects who had not yet developed symptoms of vascular disease could be observed for many years.

Gene splicing. In late May the director of the U.S. National Institutes of Health (NIH) reported that a Los Angeles hematologist had been found in violation of federal regulations for protection of human subjects and also of the guidelines for use of recombinant DNA (deoxyribonucleic acid) techniques. In controversial experiments in 1980 Martin Cline of the University of California at Los Angeles (UCLA) attempted "gene-splice" therapy on two women, one in Israel and the other in Italy, having the incurable disease beta-thalassemia major. Cline removed bone marrow cells from each of the women and treated the cells with the genes they were missing in the hope that when returned to the patients the cells would produce normal hemoglobin. There was, however, no report of any beneficial effect. A proposal for similar experiments had been under consideration and eventually was rejected by the UCLA Human Subject Protection Committee.

The punitive measures taken against Cline for attempting this therapy were the most severe ever imposed by the NIH for violations of the recombinant DNA guidelines. An NIH committee announced that for three years Cline must receive prior NIH approval for any research with human subjects and any research using recombinant DNA. The report on Cline's conduct was to be considered during the review of any applications for future research funds from NIH. In addition, each of the NIH institutes funding Cline's research was instructed to consider whether its grant money should be withdrawn.

The various NIH institutes reached quite disparate decisions. The most severe was by the institute that was funding research most closely related to the experiments of Cline's transgression. The National Heart, Lung, and Blood Institute recommended that Cline's three-year grant be discontinued on March 31, 1982, at the end of its first year. The institute had previously authorized $162,000 for the remaining two years. By contrast, the National Institute of Arthritis, Diabetes, and Digestive and Kidney Diseases recommended that funding ($118,000) be continued for the last three years of its ten-year grant to Cline. Finally, the National Cancer Institute (NCI), which had administered two grants to Cline, recommended continued funding of an eight-year project scheduled to finish in May. However, the NCI requested that Cline lose

$30,000 of funds he was to receive through a grant awarded to a collection of projects by several researchers. Cline had previously been removed as the principal investigator of that joint grant. He had also resigned as chief of the division of hematology and oncology at UCLA, but he remained on the faculty there.

Venereal disease. Genital infections with the intracellular parasite *Chlamydia trachomatis* were discovered during the year to be more common in Seattle's venereal-disease clinic than were gonorrheal infections. This finding led investigators to speculate that chlamydia may have become the nation's leading venereal disease. The chlamydia organism infects a man's urethra or a woman's cervix or urethra, often causing only minor symptoms or no symptoms at all. However, the infection can escalate to a variety of diseases in adults, including pelvic inflammatory disease and inflammations of the uterine tube or of the epididymis. In addition, eye infections and pneumonia are common in infants born to infected women.

At the Seattle venereal disease clinic, 18% of 545 women screened had chlamydia infections, while only 12% had gonorrhea, reported Robert Brunham and Walter Stamm of the University of Washington. Chlamydia was cultured also from 14% of 398 male heterosexuals and gonococcus from 12%.

A high incidence of chlamydia infections was also reported among healthy, middle-class women attending an eastern college and among women at an inner-city obstetrical clinic. At the college 5.2% of 458 female students were infected. The incidence was higher in those with many sexual partners and lower in those who used a diaphragm or condoms for birth control. Among economically disadvantaged pregnant women receiving care at the Charity Hospital of New Orleans, 22.6% of those screened were infected with chlamydia. David Martin of the U.S. Public Health Service Hospital in New Orleans said that this was the highest rate of chlamydial infections ever reported outside a venereal disease clinic. Martin reported that more than half of the regular sexual partners of infected women were also infected, although few showed any relevant symptoms. This observation suggested that asymptomatic infections in males are common and play an important role in the continued dissemination of the disease.

Paul Wiesner, the venereal disease control director of the Centers for Disease Control, estimated that there were as many as 3,000,000 chlamydia cases in the U.S. and that about half of the approximately 200,000 babies born each year to infected women develop chlamydia pneumonia or eye infections. Few venereal disease clinics routinely performed cultures to detect chlamydia infections.

Transplant drug. Transplantation of natural organs was made easier by the use of a drug derived from fungus, surgeons reported in 1981. Cyclosporin A effectively suppresses the immune system to avoid graft

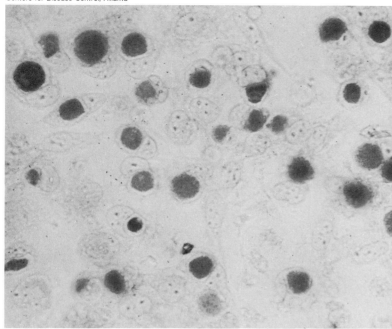

Chlamydia trachomatis organisms are responsible for what may have become the leading venereal disease in the United States.

rejection without harming bone marrow, the source of immune system cells.

The first successful heart-lung transplant using the drug was performed at Stanford University Medical Center in March. In addition, Thomas Starzl of the University of Pittsburgh School of Medicine reported that when he and his colleagues used the drug they had 100% six-month survival of transplanted kidneys and an 80% one-year survival of patients receiving liver transplants. With conventional therapy the success rate was only 60% for kidney transplants and about 30% for livers. The incidence of viral, fungal, and bacterial infections in the organ recipients was much less with the new drug than with conventional immunosuppression therapy, Starzl reported.

Surgeon General. The post of United States Surgeon General was vacant for most of 1981 as Congress changed the requirements of the position to accommodate the choice of U.S. Pres. Ronald Reagan. C. Everett Koop, a former pediatric surgery professor at the University of Pennsylvania and chief surgeon at Children's Memorial Hospital in Philadelphia, needed a legislative exception to assume command of the Public Health Service Commissioned Corps. He was, at 64, just over the age limit for the job, and he had never worked in the Public Health Service or had other significant public health experience.

Koop, a fundamentalist Christian, was an outspoken opponent of amniocentesis, abortion, and homosexual rights. Because of these views and his lack of public health experience his appointment was opposed by several medical groups, labor unions, and feminist or-

ganizations. Koop's medical achievements included heading the team that in 1974 separated Siamese twins at the pelvis and in 1975 and 1977 performed dramatic operations to correct displacements of the heart outside the thoracic cavity.

During the summer of 1981 a series of legislative maneuvers attempted to qualify Koop for the surgeon general post. The age and public health requirements were eventually removed as a provision of the 1982 budget bill. On September 16 President Reagan officially nominated Koop to be surgeon general, and on October 1 at his confirmation hearing Koop promised not to use the job as "a pulpit for ideology." The Labor and Human Resources Committee of the U.S. Senate by an 11 to 5 vote recommended Senate confirmation of the nomination. The full Senate approved Koop as surgeon general on November 16, and he was sworn into office in January 1982.

New vaccines and drugs. A vaccine against hepatitis B became the first new viral vaccine in a decade to be approved by the U.S. Food and Drug Administration. The vaccine was made from the blood plasma of persons who had contracted hepatitis B. It was given in a three-shot regimen, and the protection was expected to last for at least five years. The FDA recommended the vaccine only for people who are at high risk of contracting the disease, such as surgeons, dentists, hemodialysis patients, relatives of hepatitis B virus carriers, male homosexuals, and prostitutes.

The FDA also approved a drug for prevention of second heart attacks and deaths in patients who had already suffered a heart attack. In a study in Norway the

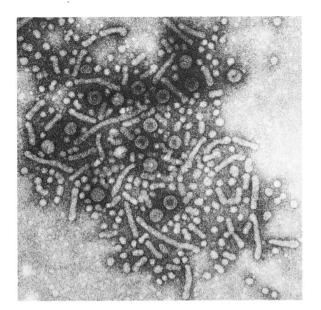 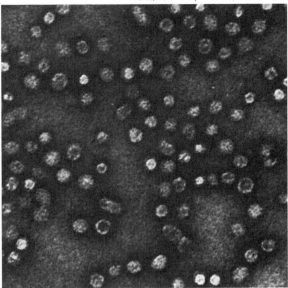

Photomicrographs reveal hepatitis B virus (left) and a new vaccine effective against it (right). The spheres in the vaccine are purified surface antigen particles that offer protection against hepatitis B. The vaccine was made from the blood plasma of persons who had contracted hepatitis B.

drug timolol cut deaths by more than one-third among patients after the first heart attack. The Norwegian study prompted the FDA not to require the usual lengthy domestic trials, and so the drug was approved in the U.S. much more rapidly than usual. Timolol was already in use for treating glaucoma.

Other drugs related to timolol, called beta blockers, also appeared promising in preventing second heart attacks. One called metoprolol was protective in a Swedish study. Another, propanolol, produced a 26% drop in mortality after the first heart attack in a National Heart, Lung, and Blood Institute study. The clinical trials of propanolol were discontinued early when the benefits of the drug became convincing. Propanolol is already widely used in the United States for relief of chest pain and irregular heart rhythm.

Beta blockers were challenged in 1981 by a group of drugs called calcium blockers, developed and extensively tested in Europe. The FDA approved a calcium antagonist, verapamil hydrochloride, for intravenous use for certain irregular heart rhythms. An FDA advisory committee recommended approval of the oral use of the drug for treatment of a variety of chest pains. On the basis of studies in the U.S. and in other nations verapamil was reported to be equal to or better than beta blockers in reducing chest-pain episodes and lengthening exercise time. The committee also urged approval of another calcium blocker, diltiazem, for treatment of coronary artery spasm and chest pain.

A new set of antibacterial drugs began to reach the market in 1981. Called third-generation cephalosporins, the drugs are less toxic to patients and more effective against more types of bacteria than were earlier drugs. The first of the new cephalosporins to be approved by the FDA was cefotaxime, which became available in May. The second, moxalactam, was approved in October and became available in December. Half a dozen related drugs also had applications pending or were in clinical trials, and more than ten others were in earlier stages of development. At many medical meetings during the year clinical reports emphasized the safety of the drugs and their effectiveness against microorganisms recalcitrant to other antibiotics. The drugs were expected to be most useful in hospitals with large burn, cancer, and surgical wards, where many patients have antibiotic-resistant infections that are difficult to combat. Clinical tests demonstrated efficacy against a wide variety of infections, including penicillin-resistant gonorrhea, meningitis, respiratory-tract bacterial infections, bone and joint infections, peritonitis, and complicated urinary-tract infections.

Because the third-generation cephalosporins are active against most organisms that cause hospital infections in the United States and because they have so few side effects, two special prospects were cited for the new drugs. One prospect is "blind" therapy—treating a very sick, hospitalized patient for an unidentified microorganism in an unknown site in the body without waiting for laboratory tests. The other prospect is "monotherapy"—treating deep-seated infections with a single broad-spectrum high-potency, low-toxicity cephalosporin instead of combining less powerful and more toxic drugs. Physicians were expected to take several years to sort out which of the new antibiotics

would be most effective for any given application.
— Julie Ann Miller

See also Feature Article: The Electricity of Life and Limb.

Skin diseases

Life-styles and high technology left their mark on dermatology in 1981 just as they had during the preceding decade. A new outbreak of a startling cutaneous syndrome primarily affecting homosexual men was noted during the year. By the year's end more than 150 cases of Kaposi's sarcoma and/or *Pneumocystis carinii* infections were reported in homosexual male populations, with clusters reported from New York City, San Francisco, Los Angeles, and Atlanta, Ga. Kaposi's sarcoma, described originally by Austrian dermatologist Moritz Kaposi in 1872, is a malignancy of the skin and internal organs. It is uncommon among Caucasians, usually occurring only in elderly men of Mediterranean extraction. More frequently it is seen among black African populations, suggesting a role for genetic, infectious, or geographic factors.

The alarming aspects of the new outbreak include its appearance in a totally new and unexpected population class; its association with various "opportunistic" organisms, such as *Pneumocystis carinii*, which are usually only pathogenic (disease-causing) in immunologically deficient individuals; and the aggressive behavior of the sarcoma—with several deaths already reported—in contrast to the unpredictable but usually slowly progressive spread of the disease in the more typical older patients. Why this syndrome has suddenly appeared is the subject of intense investigation.

Several technical medical achievements of the past decade have led to newly encountered skin lesions. Bone marrow transplants for various hematologic disorders have caused, in recipients, a graft-versus-host (GVH) reaction with skin involvement. Such patients, whose own weakened immune systems are, in effect, overwhelmed by the transplanted tissue, may suffer generalized skin eruptions or reactions. Despite treatment about half the patients who develop GVH die.

The public's unquenchable appetite for weight loss has left its mark on the skin recently via the introduction of intestinal bypass procedures for treatment of "morbid obesity." This surgical procedure, which gained popularity in the mid-1970s, produces skin lesions in up to 25% of those undergoing it. While a variety of findings were reported, one common feature was immunologically mediated damage to small blood vessels in the skin. In some of those affected the condition cleared up spontaneously, but others gained relief only after the bypass was dismantled.

Dermatologic side effects of hemodialysis for chronic kidney failure have been increasingly documented in the last decade. Dialysis patients commonly develop generalized pruritus (itching), and some have had blis-

Brown nodules (left) indicate the presence of Kaposi's sarcoma, a rare malignancy of the skin and internal organs that increased in frequency during the last year. At the right, a skin biopsy of Kaposi's sarcoma reveals nuclei that vary in size.

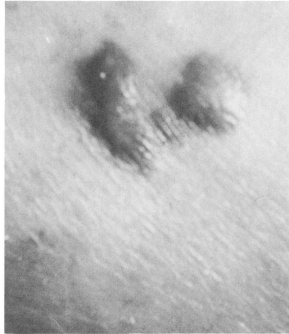
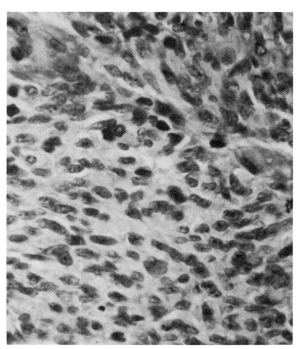

Photos, Centers for Disease Control, Atlanta

tering reactions or a disorder associated with increased skin fragility. Since 1977 several therapies, including use of short-wave ultraviolet light, have been developed to control the pruritus. Suggestions that hemodialysis might effectively treat psoriasis in otherwise healthy patients have not been confirmed by controlled studies done in the last two years.

Skin changes are also a prominent feature of the star medical headliner of the last two years, toxic shock syndrome (TSS). In this ailment patients display a profuse "sunburn type" of rash which often leads to the diagnosis. In some cases of TSS the skin may be the primary source of microbial colonization for this *Staphylococcus aureus*-induced entity.

New medicines. What was probably the most increasingly used skin medicine in 1981 is not generally even considered to be a drug by the public. Nonetheless, sunscreens now help prevent skin disease in millions of people worldwide. The rationale for sunscreens is to place a chemical that absorbs ultraviolet rays on the skin, thus shielding the skin itself from the acute and chronic effects of "solar irradiation." The highly refined sunscreens produced at present can both prevent sunburn (the acute effect) and also recently were shown to inhibit tumor development in research animals. The latter finding provides experimental support for what dermatologists have long observed: that decades of exposure to sunlight, especially in fair-skinned individuals, promotes actinic ("ray"-induced) changes in the skin, ranging from rough, red excrescences (actinic keratoses) to basal- and squamous-cell carcinomas and even, to some extent, to malignant melanomas.

After several years of testing a clinically active derivative of vitamin A was scheduled to reach the U.S. prescription marketplace in 1982. This synthetic retinoid, 13-*cis*-retinoic acid, has had a dramatic experimental impact on several distressing skin disorders. In 1979 investigators from the U.S. National Institutes of Health showed striking long-term benefits in patients with severe, scarring, antibiotic-resistant, cystic acne. In 1980 the drug was found to relieve some previously untreatable chronic conditions affecting keratinization (keratin is the skin's major structural protein). It is important to note that the success of this relative of vitamin A does not mean that vitamin A itself will successfully treat these same disorders, though some research with physician-supervised "toxic" doses of vitamin A has been continued.

Yet another derivative of vitamin A—tretinoin ("vitamin A acid"; brand-named Retin A)—is one of the two major advances in the topical (applied to the skin) treatment of acne of the last decade. Tretinoin can be especially useful in cases of mild, comedonal (blackheads and whiteheads) acne. The other major advance was a subject of furious competition in 1981, as drug makers scrambled for shares of the topical antibiotic market. During the last five years there has been a flurry of studies regarding the efficacy of clindamycin, erythromycin, and tetracycline applied as lotions to the skin. All are effective to some degree. It is also interesting to note that within a five-year span oral clindamycin first gained rapid, enthusiastic acceptance as a treatment for acne followed by a quick, virtual disappearance. An occasional side effect of the drug, a potentially severe bowel disorder (pseudo-membranous colitis), all but removed it as a clinical tool. Topical clindamycin remains relatively safe for acne therapy, and the systemic drug still has legitimate non-dermatological uses.

One of the premier therapeutic achievements in dermatology during the last decade involved a rather rare disease. Acrodermatitis enteropathica (AE) is an inherited disorder that appears in infancy and, without treatment, usually soon leads to death. The striking clinical findings include extensive skin erosions, hair loss, and profound bowel and behavioral disturbances. While the drug diiodoquin had for years been somewhat helpful in treating the disease, it came nowhere near the efficacy of another agent first tried by London physician E. J. Moynahan in 1973. This "magic bullet" for AE turned out to be elemental zinc.

Precisely why zinc so dramatically corrects the symptoms of AE is not known. Most patients with AE do have low serum zinc levels that are corrected by zinc supplements. It is also thought that inherited enzyme defects may influence availability of dietary zinc and that the consequent zinc deficiency in such persons contributes to defective immune responses.

At the same time that zinc began to be used to treat AE, skin lesions similar to AE were increasingly observed in patients receiving intravenous hyperalimentation, a chemical feeding process mainly used in patients who cannot absorb food from the gut. It was then found that many of these special "feeding" solutions were low in zinc. When zinc levels in the solutions were increased, the skin lesions disappeared.

Other recently developed medicines have also helped many with common skin disorders. In the last year ketoconazole was approved for systemic use in treating certain fungal infections. Two related drugs, clotrimazole and miconazole, also emerged in the past decade as effective topical agents in treating ringworm of the body, which in the past may have responded only to systemic medication.

In 1981 researchers reconfirmed a decade-earlier finding that helps some older patients suffering from herpes zoster (shingles). Giving systemic corticosteroids (cortisonelike agents) to selected patients with acute herpes zoster may reduce the incidence of post-zoster neuralgia, a nerve-related nagging or aching pain that can persist for months to years.

Smallpox victory; herpes failure. From a public health standpoint 1981 marked the fourth anniversary

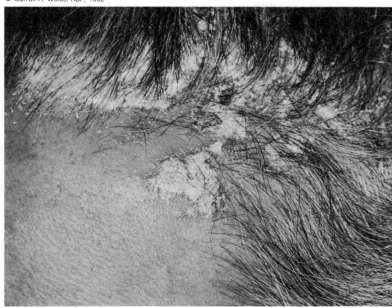

Psoriasis is among the many skin diseases for which the human leukocyte antigen (HLA) system has established genetic markers.

of mankind's foremost success in preventing a fatal infectious skin disease, smallpox. The last known case of naturally occurring smallpox was in October 1977. Subsequently, the World Health Organization removed smallpox from the list of regulated diseases effective Jan. 1, 1982. At the close of 1981 the only nation still requiring a smallpox immunization certificate for entry into that country was Chad despite a lack of scientific justification for the requirement. In fact, public health officials of many nations now urge patients not to allow themselves to be routinely vaccinated against smallpox, since occasional severe complications of vaccination with this live virus do occur and smallpox itself does not.

Another public health hazard remained noteworthy for its lack of a cure, though not for any lack of effort. The herpes simplex virus causes recurring infections ("fever blisters," "cold sores") primarily of mucous membranes about the mouth and genitalia. An estimated 30 million to 50 million people in the U.S. and countless more throughout the world suffer from it, and during the last decade several purported remedies have come and gone. Photo-inactivated dye-light therapy, levamisole, ether, and 2-deoxy-D-glucose all appeared promising, but none stood up to scrutiny. At this time herpes remains an epidemic in search of a cure. Fortunately, most patients eventually recover from the disease with or without treatment.

Diagnostic achievements. While traditional skin diagnosis largely depends on the eye of the beholder, three recent advances are on the microscopic and biochemical level. One recently maturing diagnostic tool involves immunofluorescence, the detection of immunologic activity in cutaneous tissues and the correlation of these findings with specific disease states. Both antibodies and complement components (mediators of immunity) may be deposited in diseased blood vessels, between epidermal cells, in other foci of the skin or hair follicles, and/or in blood serum. As now refined, these techniques aid in diagnosing blistering diseases, such as pemphigus vulgaris, bullous pemphigoid, and dermatitis herpetiformis; connective tissues entities such as lupus erythematosus, discoid lupus, and rheumatoid vasculitis; and numerous other disorders.

A second rapidly evolving diagnostic advance utilizes the human leukocyte antigen (HLA) system. Found on the surfaces of most human cells, these glycoproteins differ slightly from one person to another. These genetically transmitted differences allow an individual's immune system to distinguish foreign cells from his own. The HLA system serves as an important basis for matching compatible tissues (histocompatibility) in kidney and other organ transplants.

In 1972 the first association was made between a specific HLA type and a skin disease, dermatitis herpetiformis. Since then an avalanche of studies has established genetic markers for other skin diseases, including pemphigus vulgaris, psoriasis, Reiter's disease, and Behcet's disease. Although these "fingerprints" are not totally disease-specific, they are valuable diagnostic clues, and so the search continues for yet more associations.

Dermatologists have also been part of a larger effort to diagnose diseases in utero (before birth). While visualizing the fetus on ultrasound, teams in three countries secured fetal skin biopsies and in this way either confirmed or ruled out such severe genetically transmitted skin diseases as xeroderma pigmentosum

353

and several fatal varieties of epidermolysis bullosa.

Skin surgery. During the last year the U.S. Food and Drug Administration approved a purified bovine collagen extract for injection into human skin. This "implant" becomes incorporated into the connective tissue matrix of the patient's own skin. While the technique proposes to correct certain skin contour deformities, its success in the long-term cosmetic treatment of scars and other defects is not known.

In the last decade two other surgical procedures gained attention. In microscopically controlled fresh-tissue surgery the surgeon takes multiple small sections of tumor-filled or otherwise diseased tissue, immediately examines them microscopically, and then determines whether further tissue excision is needed to effect a cure. While relatively expensive and time-consuming, this technique has advantages in treating recurrent cancers and those in cosmetically sensitive areas. Argon laser therapy for obliterating certain skin lesions also recently gained some adherents. Though potentially scarring, it has become one alternative for removing tattoos and such vascular malformations of the skin as hemangiomas.

Future prospects. Basic research being done at present has promising applications in the near future. Plasmapheresis is a process in which blood plasma is removed from a patient, "filtered" to remove immunologic or other disease "factors," and then reinfused. It is being used in non-dermatologic disorders and is being tested for certain skin disorders. Monoclonal antibodies, a new generation of immunologic weapons, are being appraised as skin therapies and diagnostic aids. Rapidly expanding knowledge of mediators of inflammation, especially the prostaglandins and histamine, should lead to improved therapies. Accelerating research efforts to understand receptor sites within cells for the binding of corticosteroid molecules along with advances in neuro-hormone chemistry may also soon be the basis of important dermatologic applications.

—Steven Andrew Davis; Howard Maibach

Dentistry

Enrollment in U.S. dental schools continued to decline for the second consecutive year during 1981; tuition and fees for dental schools had climbed over 250% during the last decade, and schools were shifting the burden for revenue from federal to other sources. The American Dental Association (ADA) reported that freshmen enrollment nationally totaled 5,855 students in 1981, a 2.9% decline from the 6,030 in 1980. An even larger decrease was expected for the first-year class in 1982 because of an action by the U.S. Department of Health and Human Services abolishing requirements for institutions that are receiving capitation and construction grants. This new ruling permits dental and other health profession schools to reduce their first-year enrollment without fear of jeopardizing federal support, the ADA says.

According to an ADA survey, ever increasing tuitions are "pricing the lower middle class out of dental school. Studies of the applicant pool indicate that people from families with smaller incomes are dropping out at a more rapid rate than others." The study was analyzing the drop of dental school applicants, which by 1981 had declined 40% compared with 1975. The average first-year resident tuition and fees for public dental schools were $2,367 for the 1980–81 academic year, a 252% increase over ten years. Resident tuition and fees for private schools averaged $7,664 in 1980–81, a 266% increase over ten years earlier. To overcome the

Fractured incisors are shown before (left) and after (right) restoration with microfilled material, which has a much smoother surface than other substances used for filling teeth.

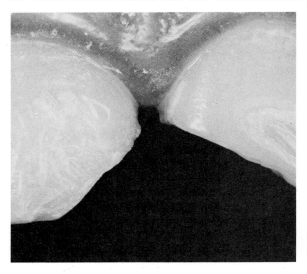
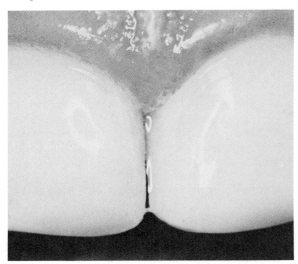

persistent decline in federal capitation funds, which dropped from 1973 to 1980 from an average of 12.1% to 4% of school budgets, dental schools were gradually shifting the burden for providing revenue away from the federal government to income from tuition, state appropriations, and dental school clinics.

Clenching and biofeedback. Coupled with relaxation therapy biofeedback has helped patients to overcome chronic jaw clenching and tooth grinding, a New York dentist reported. Speaking at the annual session of the ADA, Andrew Cannistraci said that bruxism, the habitual clenching and grinding of teeth, is a manifestation of tension. It has an enormously destructive effect on oral health, causing deterioration of restorations, periodontal or gum tissue damage, destruction of bridgework, excessive wear of teeth, discomfort for denture wearers, and jaw muscle spasms.

Until a few years ago dentists had difficulties relieving bruxism problems in patients. But the advent of biofeedback treatment has changed that picture. Therapy involves the use of a highly sophisticated and sensitive electromyographic (EMG) instrument that translates involuntary muscular tension into easily understood audio and visual signals. Electrodes in a headband are placed over the frontal forehead muscles in order to monitor levels of tension and relaxation. Earphones are then placed over the patient's ears to block out every sound except a beeper. When a predetermined level of EMG activity that signals tension in the jaw muscle area is monitored, the patient hears a high-pitched or rapid sound.

Natural-looking fillings. People can look forward to longer lasting and more natural-looking dental fillings for front teeth, a Harvard University dental scientist predicted. Leon Dogon said that the "restoration of cavities in the front of the mouth has always been of primary concern to the patient and the dentist. Both want to see the teeth returned to a very natural appearance, with the fillings undetectable." New "microfilled" materials show promise to offer advantages over conventional and composite (plastic) fillings.

The new materials consist of hard microsized crystals, similar in texture to very fine sand. This filler is then mixed with a resin for application to the tooth surface. "The microfilled materials, which have been available for about four years, offer extensive advantages for use on front teeth, where very smooth surfaces are necessary for the best aesthetic results. Studies show that the microfilled materials offer a much smoother surface texture than conventional materials, making them more like natural tooth enamel," Dogon explained.

Big sister sets example. A young patient's older sister or brother may be the dentist's best friend when it comes to reducing anxiety in the dental chair, suggested a Baylor College dental scientist. Whenever possible, a dentist should first have a youngster watch an older sibling sit in the chair and go through a "dry run" of the treatment. The child watching learns that a trip to the dentist is not scary and that quiet cooperation is the way to behave.

W. James Thrash of Dallas based his suggestion on theories of pain and human behavior. "Specifically, the pain one feels is largely related to the level of anxiety, which in turn is a response to fear. And since fear is a learned response, it also can be unlearned." According to such a theory one of the most effective ways to change a person's behavior is to have a role model demonstrate the desired behavior. In dentistry the closer the role model to the patient, the better. Thrash indicated that studies have shown that live models, especially related ones, are more effective teachers

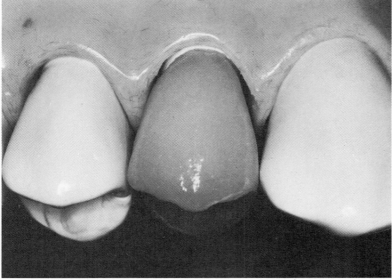

Ceramic crown is less expensive than gold and silver and is also preferable to metals because it does not obscure X-rays.

Courtesy, Ralph B. Sozio and Edwin Riley

than either films of children receiving dental care or explanations of dental care by a member of the dental office staff.

Early wisdom tooth removal. Even if they do not cause problems now, potentially bothersome impacted wisdom teeth should be removed early, suggests a University of Illinois dental scientist. Daniel M. Laskin explained that wisdom teeth, or third molars, are remnants of an age when human jaws were larger and could accommodate the molars without any problems. Today's wisdom teeth often do not break through the gum or, at most, are only partially visible. These totally or partially hidden teeth are called impacted.

If the impacted tooth will cause crowding or damage the second molars or the jawbone, the dentist will recommend that it be removed. On the other hand, if the adjacent teeth are not in good condition, or if other teeth are missing, the decision might be to try to save the wisdom tooth. Also, if the wisdom teeth grow in straight and can be maintained in healthy condition, they should be retained.

Chewing and dental problems. The way one chews as a child may be a clue to dental problems encountered as an adult, suggested two University of Florida dental scientists. A computer study of chewing habits of a test group of children and adults revealed that "normal chewing patterns may be helpful in assessing the effects of malocclusion (faulty bite) in both child and adult years," according to A. Page Jacobson and Charles Gibbs. By knowing a patient's normal chewing patterns, a dentist will be able to spot early signs of problems stemming from deviant chewing habits.

The study, which used a specially designed instrument to record graphically three-dimensional jaw movements during chewing, revealed marked differences in the jaw movement patterns between normal children and normal adults. The study also showed the changes that occur naturally in normal chewing patterns during the years of facial and body growth. With this advanced technology dentists will be able to detect developing malocclusion problems, and early detection will enable them to plan interceptive treatment at an early age.

Bite plate. A thin plastic device called a bite plate was being used increasingly by dentists to correct a variety of problems. It has proven to be useful for treating a number of problems, including advanced periodontal disease, bruxism, temporomandibular or jaw joint (TMJ) problems, and a collapsed bite.

The bite plate is a thin disk of acrylic resin that covers part of the hard palate. Behind the upper front teeth it is thickened and flattened so that it contacts the lower front teeth. This keeps the back teeth slightly apart when the mouth is closed. According to Marvin Simring of the University of Florida the bite plate therapy sometimes helps lost bone to be regenerated in patients with periodontal disease. In patients who clench their teeth the smooth surface of the bite plate helps correct problems in the way the upper and lower teeth meet.

Bite mark identification. Identification of human bite marks is providing the legal "last word" in an increasing number of criminal cases. Forensic dentistry, the science of matching bite marks to a cast of an individual's teeth, has provided legally accepted evidence in courts in California, Oklahoma, Illinois, Florida, Indiana, Oregon, and Kansas. According to Edwin Andrews, an Oklahoma City forensic dentist, teeth provide excellent evidence because each person's dental structure is unique. The teeth are the most durable part of the human body and can be identified long after a body has decomposed. Andrews cited a homicide case in Oklahoma City where bite marks were among supporting evidence that resulted in the conviction of a 22-year-old suspect.

Forensic dentistry also can often help in detecting battered child cases. Jaw fractures can be clues to a child beating, but they are sometimes difficult to spot, particularly if the child is seen long after the beating took place and the fracture has had time to heal. Dentists are required to report any suspected child-abuse cases to the proper authorities.

—Lou Joseph

Veterinary medicine

Concern over what has been termed the rights of animals was expressed with increasing frequency during 1981 by animal welfare groups opposed to the confinement rearing of livestock and poultry. The diversity of persons promoting this concept was evident from the roster of speakers at a two-day conference sponsored by the Chicago Anti-Cruelty Society. Factions included vegetarians who would ban the raising of animals for meat and academics philosophically opposed to limiting the freedom of animals. As spokesman for a moderate group, veterinarian Michael Fox, head of the Institute for the Study of Animal Problems within the Humane Society of the United States, urged a consumer boycott of pork to protest the conditions under which hogs are raised. Government research favoring the development of corporate hog farms was decried by small-farm advocates. Tom Grumbly, former associate administrator for the Food Safety and Quality Service of the U.S. Department of Agriculture, was concerned about human health hazards from chemical and antibiotic feed additives, the heavy use of which was related to large corporate livestock units.

Rebuttal to these views was presented elsewhere by representatives of the livestock industry, animal scientists, and veterinarians. According to John Herrick, veterinarian at Iowa State University, "Animals in confinement have the greatest of care, the most scientifically formulated ration in front of them at all

Laying hens (above) commonly are crowded in close quarters in wire cages, and veal calves (right) are often confined to small crates for 16 weeks. Animal welfare groups protested such practices.

times, their wastes instantly removed, carefully monitored ventilation and all the comforts needed for maximum performance. Animals are healthier than ever in their history of domestication and do not have to search for food, seek shelter and wallow in their waste. In general, animals are healthier than humans." This, Herrick contended, brought to consumers more and higher quality protein and also resulted in conservation of land and cessation of pollution of rivers and streams by animal waste. He conceded that abuses do exist but attributed them to inefficient producers who in the long run would put themselves out of business.

Another aspect of this controversy related to the growing conflict between animal welfarists and biomedical researchers. In this area Texas A & M veterinary scientist Michael Ballinger suggested that specialists in laboratory animal medicine were best equipped to bring the two factions together. He pointed to several bills pending before the U.S. Congress that would drastically limit the number of animals used in research, and said that they were being opposed by researchers who believed that testing drugs and chemicals on forms of life lower than those animals would not yield results applicable to humans. Because federal law requires extensive animal testing of any new product likely to have an effect on animals or humans, chemical and pharmaceutical companies are the largest users of laboratory animals.

As an outgrowth of attention being paid to the role of companion animals in human welfare, a symposium on Pet Loss and Human Emotion, held at the Columbia-Presbyterian Medical Center in New York City in March 1981, focused on the role that veterinarians can play when the human-animal bond is broken. Of the estimated 100 million contacts between veterinarians and pet animals annually, nearly 2 million are for the purpose of seeking or discussing euthanasia (humane termination of life) for a pet.

Reasons for euthanasia of animals include senility, relief of suffering from untreatable disease or intractable pain, and viciousness or unmanageability. In most instances there is a genuine bond between the animal and its owner, concerning the breaking of which Marc A. Rosenberg of the University of Pennsylvania School of Veterinary Medicine said, "The veterinarian in private practice has a preexisting relationship with the client which enables him to play a unique role in the management of euthanasia and grief." When the expression of grief appears to be abnormal, psychiatrists recommended that the veterinarian refer the client to a family physician, clergyman, or social worker.

Prepaid pet health plans continued to be offered, despite the fact that of about 30 launched since 1959 none has lasted longer than two or three years. One such plan offered in California since 1979 has just under 2,000 dogs and cats enrolled at annual fees of

$39 to $70, depending on age and size of the animal, with a maximum benefit of $500 per year and $5,000 lifetime. During the first 2½ years some 1,500 claims were paid, including 18 in one week ranging from $15 to $230 (average $88). Proponents of these plans pointed out that veterinary fees, although relatively low for the quality of services offered, are considered too high by some owners, who may therefore elect euthanasia for an ailing pet. Detractors have claimed that no plan can succeed until reliable actuarial data concerning illnesses and accidents incurred by pet animals are compiled and that the relatively low ratio of benefits to cost will not attract responsible owners who take good care of their pets.

For several years veterinarians in various parts of the U.S. have expressed concern over what they consider encroachment upon private practice by tax-exempt organizations, principally local humane societies. In 1981 a $250,000 clinic built with donated tax-deductible funds and operated by the Humane Society of Macomb County, Mich., was the object of a lawsuit brought by the Michigan Veterinary Medical Association and other interested parties, who claimed that the low fees charged by this clinic constituted unfair competition. Plaintiffs in the suit pointed to the substantial overhead expense represented by property and income taxes paid annually by private practitioners in addition to interest on their investment in facilities. The suit was settled in favor of the plaintiffs. The U.S. Internal Revenue Service later ruled that tax-exempt organizations must operate by the same rules imposed on private enterprise if they wish to provide veterinary services for a fee.

As a means for providing low-cost veterinary service limited to vaccinations and treatment of parasitism, a Pet Prevent-A-Care program operating from a van was begun in California in 1975. Two more van-trailer units were added in 1981 with some 600 clinics being scheduled at shopping centers, up from 200 during earlier years. According to founder Victor Giamattei, "Our market lies in the pet owner who has never established a relationship with a veterinarian and is unaware of what the profession has to offer." Public acceptance has been so enthusiastic, he said, that plans were underway to go nationwide through a franchise network.

In early 1981 a calf at the University of Utah's Artificial Organs Center was killed after surviving 267 days with a polyurethane heart, breaking the 221-day record for an animal with an artificial heart. Both hearts had been implanted by veterinarian Donald Olson, who had also removed an artificial heart implanted in a calf six weeks earlier and replaced it with the natural heart of its twin. This demonstrated the possibility of sustaining life in a human patient with a mechanical device until a natural heart transplant would become available.

The proceedings of a conference on research in animal agriculture to meet human needs in the 21st century pointed to a number of major developments in animal health that would substantially improve animal production. These included application of knowledge from past research, development of new technologies, and improvement of animal health-care delivery systems. One technique mentioned as having the potential for increasing animal resistance to disease was that of genetic engineering. A breakthrough in this area was announced in June 1981 by scientists at Genentech, Inc., who in cooperation with International Minerals & Chemical Corp. and the U.S. Department of Agriculture (USDA) succeeded in inducing bacteria to manufacture a vaccine effective against foot-and-mouth disease of cattle, sheep, and hogs. This was the first vaccine produced by gene splicing to be proven effective against a disease of animals or humans. According to U.S. Secretary of Agriculture John Block, it "can mean annual savings of billions of dollars and an increase in the world supply of meat." Commercial production of the vaccine, however, was not expected to begin until the mid-1980s.

Foot-and-mouth disease has occurred sporadically and at times in epidemic proportions throughout much of Europe for at least two centuries. In March 1981 the first outbreak in 13 years was reported in Great Britain, three weeks after the disease had appeared in Brittany on the French coast. This prompted the slaughter of several herds of cattle and hogs and the quarantine of some 70,000 animals within a 2,600-sq-km (1,000-sq-mi) area, which was successful in containing the outbreak. British animals and meat had been embargoed by the USDA until December.

With the enrollment of 1,172 women students at veterinary colleges of the U.S. and Canada for the 1981–82 school year, women accounted for 46% of the entering classes (more than 50% at some schools) and 40.4% of the total enrollment of 9,497. This represented an increase from 9.9% of 5,471 students in 1970–71 and 4.6% of 3,908 in 1961–62. By comparison, women accounted for 27.9% of total and 30.8% of first-year enrollment in medical schools during 1981–82.

—J. F. Smithcors

See also Feature Article: WHAT MAN HAS DONE TO DOGS.

Optical engineering

Optical engineering has traditionally dealt with the application of optical principles to devices such as photographic cameras, telescopes, binoculars, and motion-picture projectors. By 1982, however, the number of optical devices in common use had greatly expanded as had the role and required knowledge of the optical engineer. The past year marked a notable change in the field, with a new term, "photonic engineering," coming into common use to describe the expanded role of the optical engineer.

Optics is the science and application of devices using light for forming images, making measurements, or conveying information. Classical optics considered light as a propagating electromagnetic wave. This wave was treated as a particle, a photon, when the light interacted with matter, as when light was absorbed by a photographic film to record an image. In general, the photonic aspects of light were of less importance to optical engineers than were the geometrical and wave-propagation properties. However, the rise in importance of electro-optical systems, optical communications devices, and laser applications has required a greater awareness by the engineer of the broader aspects of the field. The term "photonics" or "photonic engineering" has been used for several years, but only in 1981 did it begin to find common acceptance. The use of this term illustrates the widened role of the engineer in the "new optics."

Several examples of this wider role appeared during the last year. These included the increased use of optical fiber communications, the introduction of laser-based devices in consumer products, and in many applications the coming replacement of photographic film by electro-optical detectors.

Videodiscs. The introduction of laser videodiscs into the home marked the first direct consumer market for laser-based devices. Videodiscs permit the recording of up to two hours of a television program on a single 12-in-diameter disc that could be played on a machine about the size of a normal record player; the picture is viewed on a conventional home television set. In 1981 there were two types of videodisc on the market, one in which the pickup of the image from the disc is accomplished electrically through a stylus and the other in which the picture signal is read from the disc using a laser and a photodetector. The optical approach had the advantage of allowing the record to be sealed within a transparent plastic cover, thus being immune to the effects of dust and damage that result from frequent handling.

The television signal in the optical videodisc is stored as a sequence of coded holes that are originally written onto a master disc using a high-power laser. Copies are made by contact printing the master onto the discs that are to be sold. The signal is read out by use of a low-power helium-neon laser that is focused by a lens to form a small spot on the disc. Variations in the amount of light reflected from the disc as the array of holes passes beneath the laser spot are sensed by a photodetector. Electronic circuitry decodes the light signal into a normal video signal that may be viewed on a normal TV set. The player includes many devices that cause the imaging lens and photodetector to move accurately from track to track of the disc while it is being played.

A single videodisc can hold more than 200,000 individual frames of pictorial information of quality and resolution sufficient for normal television viewing systems. The optical reading of these frames does not require contact with the disc during operation, thereby providing the capability of switching rapidly from one image to another. This led to what may in the long term be an even more significant market for the optical disc, that of a rapid-access, high-density, information storage device. Videodiscs are being used as input and storage devices for computers because they are cheaper

High-powered carbon dioxide laser cuts 0.63-centimeter- (0.25-inch-) thick titanium alloy at speeds up to 125 centimeters (50 inches) per minute.

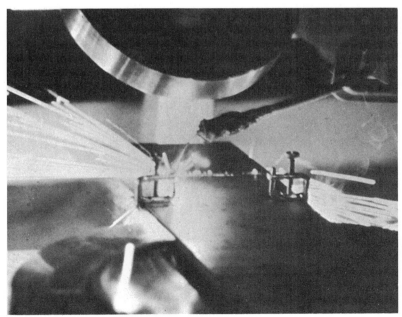

United Technologies Research Center

and more reliable than traditional magnetic storage devices. As yet, the writing or storage of data on these discs requires expensive, high-power laser equipment. Therefore, the major use of the discs at present is for volume storage of prerecorded data.

One demonstration of the potential use for optical disc technology was carried out in Cambridge, Mass., at the Massachusetts Institute of Technology. There a set of television images of Aspen, Colo., (chosen, presumably, because of its appropriate size) was written onto a single videodisc. These images covered every building in the town from several possible directions of view. An observer could then move through the city, viewing the entire path of his travel as if he were actually there because a computer selected the appropriate scenes from the videodisc and sent them to a television display for viewing.

The significance of this development is that it indicates the possibility of using videodiscs as an entirely new tool for research or teaching, since the input images could be generated from a computer as well as obtained from a television camera. The computer generation of images would allow a student or a scientist to view objects that have not yet existed or no longer exist.

The development of the technology described above represents a major achievement in optical engineering. The manufacture of compact, low-cost lasers that have sufficient lifetimes to permit such products to be built was an important aspect of the achievement. Less obvious difficulties that had to be overcome included the manufacturing of precise small lenses that serve to place the point image from the laser onto the disc track, and of the mechanical and electro-optical detectors that are used to guide the lens into position and focus. Finally the packaging of these components into a reliable unit provided an example of the extent to which the fields of optics and electronics have become closely related.

Cameras. The videodisc described above was the principal development that reached full prominence in 1981. Several other products that resulted from applications of optical engineering also emerged during the year. Among them was a portable holographic camera using thermoplastic-sensitive material rather than conventional silver halide film. The thermoplastic material permits instant viewing of the hologram "in place," and is erasable and reusable. This may permit wider use of holography in industry for testing and research.

The introduction of electronics continued in amateur and professional cameras with Polaroid Corp. introducing a "sun camera," which provides automatic balancing of available sunlight in shadows by a controlled built-in flash unit. A Japanese-made instant camera using a photographic system similar to that used in the Eastman Kodak instant camera was introduced on the Japanese market. Cameras that focus

automatically also became more prevalent in 1981, as the mid-priced automatic 35-mm model became the most rapidly growing part of the photographic equipment market. A move toward fully electronic cameras was made with the announcement by Sony Corp. of Japan of a miniature magnetic videodisc system for recording still pictures from a miniature camera by using a detector array in the focal plane rather than photographic film. The quality of such pictures is not as good as those produced on photographic film, but the disc containing the recorded pictures can be placed into a special player and presented on a home television set.

Lasers. Optical techniques for processing materials had by 1982 become significant in many industries. The principal application was that of welding or brazing metals and other materials that would otherwise be difficult to work. High-power lasers, principally carbon dioxide lasers, were used for the welding of most metals. They produced extremely high-tolerance welds. Laser welding was used on as massive an assembly as the copper sheathing for the hull of a ship.

A scanning laser ophthalmoscope was announced during the year. This device can be used by eye surgeons or optometrists to obtain specific data on the conditon of small portions of the eye and to view the retina on a television screen.

The use of high-power lasers for military purposes broadened with their employment in the field as target designators. The use of lasers as weapons was the subject of some progress and much controversy. The principal area of concern to optical engineers in utilizing lasers as weapons is that of the precise pointing and tracking of targets by the large-aperture telescopes necessary for placing sufficient laser energy density on a target to achieve its destruction. These requirements encouraged the development of new techniques for the active control of wavefronts, which would ultimately find more peaceful uses in the correction of atmospheric refraction errors on astronomical telescopes.

Optical materials. No major new optical materials were announced during the year. Some improvements in the homogeneity of fused silica and fused quartz mirror substrate materials were attained. For the visible wavelength region there was greater availability of infrared transmitting material in larger sizes and at lower costs.

Fabrication of complex non-spherical optical surfaces by single-point diamond machining became a commercial process, with several companies entering the field. As of 1982 the major impact of this new technology was in the areas of infrared reflecting optics and complex conical optics for high-energy resonator elements, but it was expected that a significant industry would materialize.

Telescopes. In the area of astronomy some progress was made toward the development of a new large-diameter-aperture telescope as the University of Cali-

Experimental infrared camera system can detect small variations in heat and create television pictures of warm objects, such as the subject's skin and lighted pipe (above left), in a dark room. The camera's image detector (above right) contains more than 8,000 sensing elements in an area the size of a dime.

fornia announced the beginning of a detailed design of a 10-m telescope using segmented mirrors. It appeared likely that future telescopes will have primary mirrors that are made up of many smaller segments, tied together to the required tolerances by servomechanisms which are controlled by optical alignment sensors. Engineers at Kitt Peak National Observatory in Arizona initiated the polishing of some trial mirror segments that may be the prototypes for most large telescopes in the future.

At the University of Arizona progress was made on the development of prototype telescope mirrors using a lightweight ordinary glass material. These mirrors will not be as stable with temperature as would those made from fused silica or quartz, but they are less expensive to build.

Fiber optics. The use of optical devices in communications continued to increase. In 1981 the Bell System announced plans for fiber optical links along the heavily populated corridor between Boston, Mass., and Washington, D.C., and also continued with construction of fiber undersea links.

Fibers for use in areas other than data transmission were also becoming more prevalent. The use of fibers as a method of illumination in otherwise inaccessible areas was common. Some new applications took advantage of the less desirable properties of fibers when used as light ducts. For example, fibers are often sensitive to temperature differences and mechanical stress-

es, and the transmission or polarization of the light through the fiber is modified to an extent proportional to the disturbing stress. For this reason fibers can then be used as pressure sensors, thermometers, and detectors for flourescent ultraviolet or other high-energy radiation.

One interesting new application of glass fibers is as a method of sensing the vibrations produced in the strings of an electric guitar, providing a means of detection and amplification that is not sensitive to local electric fields. Additional areas where optical devices using fibers have appeared include detectors that warn of structural failure, liquid level and flow sensors, seismic disturbance and strain sensors, and blood flow sensors.

Future prospects. During the next year there should be increased commercialization of electro-optical measurement techniques as well as significant new products incorporating the coupling of optical devices and microcomputers. Enhanced capabilities of laser videodisc systems can be expected, along with the introduction of compact audiodisc devices that employ optical recording techniques. An increase in the use of high-power lasers for both industrial and military uses is also likely. In addition, some observers believe that the replacement of photographic systems by compact electro-optical video recording systems may begin within the next two years.

—R.R. Shannon

Physics

In their efforts during the past year to understand, control, and in some cases even outdo the workings of the natural world, physicists grappled with the largest and smallest known objects in the universe as well as with some of the most difficult phenomena to observe or create. Quasars with radio lobes millions of light-years across taxed their comprehension; preparations for producing two exotic subatomic particles, their ingenuity; and the goal of an X-ray laser, their tenacity. The year also brought rewards as well as challenges, including practical results from two decades of fundamental work on the glassy metals and a more simplified theoretical picture, backed by experiment, of the structure and behavior of the atomic nucleus.

General developments

In recent months work toward a kind of Holy Grail of laser physics, the X-ray laser, surged forward with the report of laser emission in the far-ultraviolet region of the spectrum. Physicists also pondered the significance of the particle jets and extended regions of radio noise associated with quasars and offered some new reasons to remain optimistic about the future of controlled thermonuclear fusion.

Chasing xasers. The genetic code is lodged in DNA, a long-chain molecule that is very difficult to study directly. Scientists dream of being able to see the structure itself, reliably expanded a thousandfold. Mankind's understanding of genetic defects and of such diseases as cancer would improve enormously.

Such a possibility arose in 1981 from work of Geoff Pert and colleagues at the University of Hull in England, who took the first steps toward development of an X-ray laser, or xaser. Common lasers work in the optical region of the electromagnetic spectrum. They emit light that has all its component waves in phase, so that all the individual crests and all the troughs coincide. When these matched waves reflect from an object, they carry away from it more information than does an ordinary beam of light. By matching these reflected waves with a beam that has not been reflected and recording their interaction, a hologram is produced. This composite information can be used to make three-dimensional pictures of the object. (The most common form of holographic record is a plastic film that, when illuminated with a laser beam, projects a three-dimensional image.)

An X-ray laser would have this same capability. X-rays penetrate into the atomic structure of matter, deflecting from atoms that are about the same size as X-ray wavelengths. This holds out the possibility that an X-ray laser could make holograms of tiny molecules. Until now, much of scientists' knowledge of molecules has come by passing X-rays through crystallized forms of them and observing the shadowy interference pattern cast by the passing waves. This technique, X-ray crystallography, is like trying to identify actors in a play by their moving silhouettes—adequate for static portraits perhaps, but a poor aid in understanding the dynamics. Shadows moving in three dimensions can swell or shrink, and an observer watching them on a screen cannot know whether they are coming or going or actually enlarging. When there are many "actors"

Workers at the Lawrence Livermore National Laboratory prepare a 375-ton pair of interlocking, C-shaped superconducting magnets for its move into the Mirror Fusion Test Facility building. The magnet pair, the largest and most complicated superconducting device of its kind for fusion research in the world, will be used to "cork" one end of a tandem-mirror magnetic bottle designed for plasma containment. The superconducting coils consume only 100 watts to produce a magnetic field as high as 150,000 times that of the Earth. In February 1982 the magnet pair was energized successfully to its full design operating current.

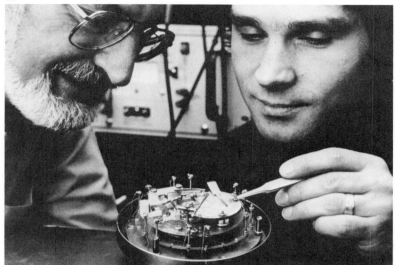

Physicists Heinrich Rohrer and Gerd Binnig of IBM's research laboratory in Zurich pose with an experimental vacuum chamber they used to detect the tunneling behavior of electrons across a thin barrier of vacuum. Electron tunneling, an effect of the wave nature of elementary particles, was described in quantum mechanical terms in the 1920s and first observed in thin solid barriers in 1957. Because the effect occurs in a vacuum over a distance of only a few angstroms, attempts at experimental detection have been plagued by severe vibration problems, which the Zurich researchers finally solved.

onstage—that is, groups or chains of molecules—the script becomes indecipherable. Thus an X-ray laser would be invaluable in understanding processes on small scales.

The extreme energy of X-rays leads to great difficulties in devising X-ray lasers. Normally, lasers operate by exciting atoms of a suitable material to a higher energy state. Then a primer wave of light travels through the material, triggering each atom to release a quantum of light as it decays from its excited state to one of lower energy. The primer drives a phase-coherent shower, and this cascade of photons is the pencil-thin light beam that emerges from the laser. At optical frequencies the primer wave is built up from multiple back-and-forth reflections from mirrors at opposite ends of the lasing material. No such easy solution works for X-rays, however, because no simple substance is known to reflect them.

Instead, Pert's group made the density of candidate atoms very high in order to make the initial photon wave sufficiently powerful to avoid the need for reflecting mirrors. Keeping a high density of atoms excited, all ready to lase, also demands a considerable influx of energy. This energy was provided by intense microwave radiation, delivered to a fiber of carbon. The fiber vaporized instantly, exciting the carbon atoms. As the hot cloud expanded, X-rays emitted by nearby atoms stimulated their neighbors. Amplification of the X-rays was observed as they passed down the confining tube. Although the actual emitted light was in the far ultraviolet, corresponding to the carbon atom's available excited states, extension of this method to higher frequencies, into the X-ray range, seems plausible.

To be useful the emitted pulses must be made reliably and often. This accomplishment lies a long way off. One factor is predictable, however: because of their very short wavelengths, X-rays act as great mag-

nifiers when used in a hologram. Illuminated by visible laser light, an X-ray hologram could be seen by the human eye through a microscope. There, the full three-dimensional image of molecular structures would appear, magnified by the ratio of the optical wavelength to the X-ray wavelength—at least a factor of a thousand. Though an "everyday" X-ray laser may lie years away, these recent results hold out the promise of a direct view of the intertwining of DNA, the embrace of life itself.

Wriggling jets. Cosmology is the science with the largest possible scale. The universe is about 20 billion light-years across, filled with galaxies swarming like bees. The largest object humans can see with the naked eye is a galaxy much like our own. The Milky Way and the Andromeda galaxy, M31, are near twins, dominating the smaller members of the Local Group of galaxies.

The largest known galaxies are the giant ellipticals, oblate spheroids containing a trillion stars, ten times more than our Galaxy. Often the fattest ellipticals sit serenely at the center of large clusters of galaxies. Probably they condensed out of the dense dust at the bottom of the cluster's gravitational well.

Clusters range from minor clumpings, like the Local Group, up to such enormous swarms as the Hercules Cluster with its 10,000 galaxies. Some astronomers believe they have detected signs of yet another scale above this, the supercluster. These conglomerations, if they exist, represent the largest dimension over which gravitational attraction can form structure.

Still, these are groups of objects. The fundamental building block of cosmology remains the single galaxy. It is unrepresentative, though, to think of these star swarms in terms of their optical images. In recent years astronomers have become aware that, seen through the new generation of radio telescopes, lone elliptical galaxies can appear very large indeed.

Peering at quasars, those enormously energetic objects found at the edge of the observable universe, astronomers have found filaments extending outward on both sides. At radio frequencies these look like jets of matter being ejected symmetrically from the bright quasar core. In 1980 studies of several such quasar jets showed that the astronomers had been narrowing their focus too much. Looking at much greater distances from the quasars, they found diffuse blobs of radio noise, aligned roughly with the central jets. These weak, diffuse regions may be "fossils" of some past event that ejected streams of particles in opposite directions from the quasar. The relatively bright, young jets then suggest that the direction of ejection has stayed about the same since that time.

But how much time? Here the separation of these blobs becomes all-important. One quasar seems to have satellite zones of radiation at opposite ends of an axis 75 million light-years long. These zones could be the "working surface," where beams of high-energy particles from the core strike the intergalactic gas, lighting up the places where they dissipate their energy. According to theory such beams probably cannot move faster than a tenth of the speed of light, since they will pick up slower moving gas as they propagate. Coupled with this velocity, the distance from the quasar to the blobs implies that the process has been going on for 100 million years.

This figure is close to the suspected lifetime of quasars themselves. Picture, then, a brilliant core of a huge elliptical galaxy, so bright and so far away that from Earth it looks like a point of light, a quasar. While this galaxy is still young, something starts spewing streams of electrons and protons out of its core. Slowly the beams push their way out against the pressure of the gas between the galaxies. The quasar labors its whole life to make the largest single structure known, the vast extended lobes of the beams, stretched along an ever-lengthening axis.

The answer to what could make this biggest of all

structures lies hidden deep in the quasar's core. Something explosive happens in quasars, consuming the mass equivalent of whole stars each year. Accumulating indirect evidence points to a basic black-hole "engine" that does indeed suck stars into a disk around the hole. As the stars spiral in, they break up. Somehow streams of high-energy particles are ejected along both axes of the disk, producing two beams that then break free of the quasar. It is impossible to see the disk, which probably is no larger than our solar system. Thus, to verify this model, one must look for some signature in the trails left by the outward-rushing beams.

Interestingly the radio jets are not straight. Some snake sideways or bend. In 1981 examination of the jets on both sides of the radio galaxy 3C 449 showed a pronounced wriggling. One explanation is that there is not one black hole at the quasar center but two in orbit about each other. Their orbits could cause the disk around one to tilt periodically. This action would then fan the beams around like a swiveling searchlight. This motion can project outward as a wriggling beam.

An alternate explanation is based on the assumption that the beams are very much like a stream of water confined to a hose. Just as a firehose carrying water tends to coil up in a helix, the beams may wriggle, too. The 3C 449 radio map can be reconciled with the theory of such firehose-like instabilities. The jets wander away from a straight path, displaying a wavelength consistent with a Mach number (ratio of the jet's speed to the speed of sound within it) of about ten. Thus these are literally supersonic jets.

Only further detailed study of the radio maps can distinguish between these two explanations, or perhaps suggest a new one. One fact is clear, however: these are the largest objects in the universe with a single cause. The largest of them is 25 times bigger than the entire Local Group. Ironically, the cause of it all may be a furiously energetic core smaller than the solar system, a black hole writing its signature on a cosmic scale.

Total intensity radio map of galaxy 3C 449 delineates the pronounced wriggling in the inner jets and outer radio lobes present on each side of the nucleus. Dashed line follows region of maximum intensity through the jets and lobes. Solid line indicates the direction that nuclear material was first ejected.

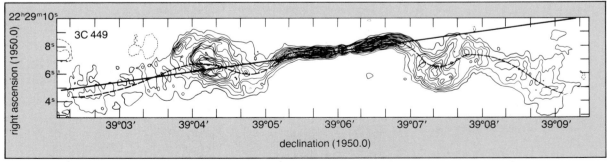

Reprinted courtesy of Phil Hardee and THE ASTROPHYSICAL JOURNAL LETTERS, vol. 250, p. L10, November 1, 1981, published, by the University of Chicago Press; © 1981 The American Astronomical Society

Eleven-ton, water-cooled electromagnet is readied at Westinghouse Electric Corp. for shipment to Princeton University. The coil is the first of 22 being made for Princeton's Tokamak Fusion Test Reactor.

Throwaway tokamaks. Steady progress toward controlled thermonuclear fusion was made in 1981. The toroidal plasma-confinement chambers called tokamaks achieved improved operating conditions at Princeton University and elsewhere. The most promising developments, however, occurred in smaller experiments designed to test new frontiers.

Tokamaks hold plasma in a doughnut-shaped magnetic bottle, heating it with electric currents until fusion occurs. Until recently plasma physicists believed that the bottle could be only slightly filled at best; the contained plasma could exert only about 3% of the pressure of the confining magnetic fields, or else the bottle would spring a leak. Exceeding the 3% limit apparently causes unstable "ballooning" in which the plasma squeezes out through ripples in the field lines.

But recent experiments at Columbia University, New York City, and the Max Planck Institute for Plasma Physics in Garching, West Germany, showed that above a plasma pressure of about 10% a new, favorable tendency develops in the tokamak. Complex changes in the plasma gradients result in a kind of feedback that can stabilize the ballooning. The experiments that revealed this behavior were small compared with the massive tokamaks themselves and showed plasma confinement for pulse times much longer than the growth times (a few microseconds) of the instabilities. This result suggests that tokamaks running at high plasma densities can be much more efficient, since the power yield rises with density.

Even better, high densities make possible fusion schemes that seemed only distant hopes. The conventional fusion reactor would combine nuclei of the heavy hydrogen isotopes, deuterium and tritium, yielding neutrons and energy. The neutrons move across magnetic fields, delivering their energy to a blanket of liquid lithium and damaging the reactor walls in the process. At higher densities and higher temperatures, however, deuterium will "burn" by itself, giving energy plus charged hydrogen instead of neutrons. The hydrogen is easily channeled away from the container boundaries by magnetic fields. This alternative would eliminate the lithium blanket and the many costly problems of wall contamination.

If high densities can be achieved, many theorists believe that the resulting reactor must have very high magnetic fields of about 150,000 gauss. Consequently the reactor must be smaller so that the volume devoted to such high fields is at a practical minimum. This requirement in turn rekindled interest in a remarkable idea first advanced in the late 1970s: the throwaway tokamak. A San Diego firm, Inesco, Inc., has proposed a compact doughnut design that produces about 1,000 Mw of power for about a month, burning deuterium and tritium. Then, as damage builds up in the reactor vessel, it is simply discarded. This route may be cheaper than providing expensive shielding, even though the vessels would cost several hundred thousand dollars apiece. Inesco argued that the energy gain from them would more than offset the cost.

—Gregory Benford

High-energy physics

In 1981 high-energy physics was dominated not so much by the results of an experiment as by preparations for one. This experiment, an attempt to produce neutral intermediate vector bosons (called Z⁰), will be an important new test of the well-established synthesis of weak and electromagnetic interactions, (see *1982 Yearbook of Science and the Future* Year in Review: PHYSICS: *High-energy physics*). The experiment involves novelties in design and execution, and one may predict that both the techniques used and their results will shape the high-energy physics of the next decade.

The unified theory of weak and electromagnetic interactions has successfully correlated several observed features of weak interactions and predicted new ones, in particular the so-called neutral-current interactions. The latter are weak processes in which the electric charge of the individual particles involved does not change; *e.g.*, in the elastic scattering of a neutrino by a proton. In the unified theory such processes are thought to take place by the exchange of a neutral particle of spin 1, the Z⁰, (*see* figure 1). Analogous processes, such as radioactive beta decay, occur by the exchange of a particle similar to the Z⁰ but electrically charged: the W particle. While the putative effects of Z⁰ and W exchange have been observed, the particles themselves have not. Evidently, an important test of the unified theory would be their actual production and confirmation that they indeed have the properties that theory ascribes to them.

On the basis of the unified theory it is possible to make fairly precise predictions of the rest energies of Z⁰ and W. The former is believed to be about 88 GeV (billion electron volts), while the latter is 78 GeV. These rest energies are about eight times higher then those of the heaviest particles yet discovered. It is this disparity that accounts for the fact that neither Z⁰ nor W has yet been observed.

In order to create a Z⁰ or a W in a collision between ordinary particles, enough kinetic energy must be available in the colliding particles to equal the rest energy of the created particle. This is difficult to achieve in a collision of a single energetic particle with a fixed target. A moving proton would need an energy of more than 5,000 GeV for a Z⁰ to be created in such a collision. Instead, physicists have turned increasingly to colliding-beam experiments to create new particles of high rest energy.

In such experiments two beams of particles with equal momentum but opposite direction are made to collide. It can be shown that all of the kinetic energy of the two particles is available for conversion into the rest energy of new particles. So in order to create a Z⁰ or a W, a minimum of 40–45 GeV of kinetic energy for each colliding particle is necessary.

The problem with colliding-beam experiments is that in an ordinary particle beam produced by a high-energy accelerator the density of particles is extremely small, much smaller than that in a very thin gas. Furthermore, if two such beams were crossed, each particle would only be near particles in the other beam for a very short time. The probability for any interesting collisions would be so low that the experiment would have little chance of success. In order to make colliding-beam experiments possible, it is necessary to get many more particles into a beam than is usually the case.

This type of high-density particle beam was first made possible some years ago through a device called a storage ring. A storage ring is essentially a ring similar to that of ordinary accelerators, in which magnetic forces are used to confine charged particles. The storage ring differs in that the particle orbits are stable over long periods of time, often many hours. Therefore, it is possible to "fill" the ring with the output of an accelerator over this long time period, thus accumulating many more particles than would be present in the accelerator. In some storage rings two types of particles, of opposite electric charge, are stored in this way, revolving in opposite directions. These oppositely directed beams can be made to meet, thus providing the conditions for a colliding-beam experiment.

Experiments of this type, using electrons and their antiparticles (positrons), have been performed for some years at several storage ring installations. But no electron accelerators exist that give enough energy to an electron and positron to produce a Z⁰ in a collision. Instead, physicists have turned to colliding beams of protons and antiprotons.

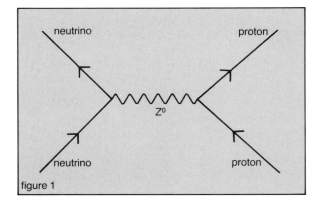

figure 1

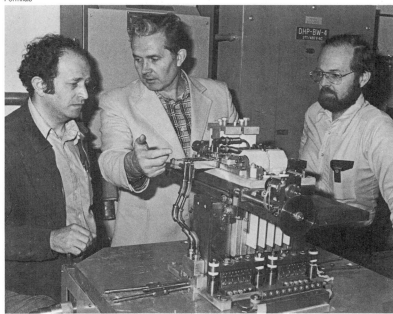

Physicists Carlos Hojvat (left) and Jim MacLachian (right) of Fermi National Accelerator Laboratory examine one of two newly arrived lithium lenses with Soviet colleague Gregory Silvestrov. The device, developed in the U.S.S.R., is intended to help focus an 80-billion-electron-volt proton beam onto a target for the production of antiprotons.

At the CERN laboratory in Geneva, Switz., a synchrotron that can accelerate protons to 400 GeV energy has been operated for some years. Antiprotons, however, do not occur in sufficient quantities in nature that they can be accelerated directly. Instead an indirect procedure has been devised. Antiprotons are produced when high-energy protons hit a target of ordinary matter. These antiprotons have energies of a few GeV. Furthermore, since they are produced in collisions, they come with a range of velocities, both forward and sideways. This range of velocities would make it impossible to store the antiprotons because such storage depends on a precise control of the orbital motion. It is therefore necessary to decrease the velocity range.

The variation in antiproton velocity can be thought to correspond to a "temperature" of the beam, with a higher temperature corresponding to greater variation. Two techniques for decreasing the velocity variation have been developed and have come to be known as "cooling" methods. The conceptually simpler method, known as electron cooling, involves an electrical interaction between antiprotons and electrons moving in the same region with about the same velocity. Because electrons are much less massive than antiprotons, they will have much less energy. In analogy with what happens when a hot object contacts a cold one, the antiprotons cool down by transferring most of their energy to the electrons and gradually approach a state in which there is very little variation in their velocities. Electron cooling was first proposed by the Soviet physicist Gersh Budker in 1967.

The CERN antiproton storage system actually uses a different method, called stochastic cooling, which ac-

complishes the same result. This method was invented by CERN physicist Simon Van Der Meer. Stochastic cooling involves the application of external forces to each particle in a beam such that any variation in velocity of the particle from the average behavior is reduced by the force. Sophisticated electronic techniques are required to exert precisely the right force on each particle, which is necessary for stochastic cooling to work. After the antiprotons are cooled and 100 billion are collected in a storage ring, they are transferred to an accelerator ring, in which their energy is increased to about 26 GeV. These antiprotons are then transferred through the action of magnetic forces to yet another accelerator, called the SPS, which accelerates them to 270 GeV. At the same time protons are being accelerated in the SPS to the same energy but in the opposite direction. The two groups of particles are allowed to collide within the SPS ring once they have reached their maximum energy, and any results of the collision are detected.

At CERN about 40 million antiprotons are produced each second with the right energies to be stored. Roughly one day's worth of production gives three trillion such antiprotons, if all could be stored. This number of antiprotons circulating rapidly in the ring, while still of very low density compared with ordinary matter, is sufficient to generate enough collisions to make interesting experiments possible.

In the modern theory of subatomic particles such entities as protons and antiprotons are believed to be composite objects, made up of simpler particles known as quarks and antiquarks. The proton is composed of three quarks bound together tightly, the antiproton of the corresponding three antiquarks. A high-energy collision between a proton and an antiproton can be thought of a collision between their constituent quarks and antiquarks.

Many processes can take place when a quark and antiquark collide, most of which have little to do with the production of Z^0 or W particles. Once in about a million such collisions, however, the quark and antiquark can annihilate, producing a Z^0 if their charges are equal and opposite, or a W if their charges have the same sign. It is such rare events that are of principal interest to the CERN experimenters.

Because the proton and antiproton contain quarks other than the ones that annihilate, a Z^0 or W will be produced together with several other particles, usually pions, that result from recombination of the remaining quarks and antiquarks. An important element of experiments to detect Z^0 and W is detecting them in a background of other particles. Both W and Z^0 are highly unstable and decay into lighter particles. Such decays are expected to occur in 10^{-23} seconds, so that the Z^0 and W must be detected through their decay products. Finding Z^0 is expected to be relatively easy. A few percent of the time it should decay into a pair of muons with no other accompanying particles. Muons are charged particles about 200 times heavier than their electron relatives. They are easy to distinguish from other charged particles because of the ease with which they travel through matter. Similarly, the Z^0 should sometimes decay into a pair of electrons.

Unfortunately when a proton and antiproton collide many other processes occur that can give rise to a muon pair or an electron pair, accompanied by a large number of pions. Therefore, it is necessary to find a way of picking out those muon or electron pairs originating in Z^0 decays. One way is to measure the total mass of the pair. This quantity can be determined from a measurement of the energy and momentum of each of the pair. If the pair originates in a Z^0 decay, the total mass of the pair will equal the Z^0 mass, whereas a pair originating from other processes would have no special reason to have this total mass. Therefore, if the mass of all muon pairs originating in proton-antiproton collisions is determined and the result plotted on a graph, something like figure 2 should be found. There will be a broad distribution corresponding to the uninteresting pairs, together with some excess of pairs at the mass value corresponding to Z^0 decays. Other techniques can be used to rule out alternative origins for such an excess.

The W will be more difficult to detect in proton-antiproton collisions because it decays into a muon and neutrino, the latter of which cannot be observed directly. Therefore, a total mass cannot be inferred, and the rare W production events cannot be distinguished in this way from other processes that produce single muons. Alternative methods for making this distinction

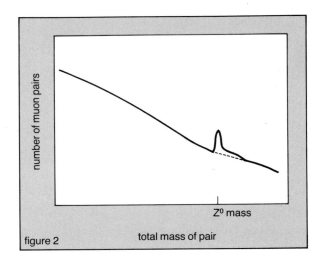

figure 2

have been proposed, but it remains to be seen whether they will succeed or whether new facilities with greater numbers of antiprotons will be needed to detect the W particle.

Once the Z^0 and W are detected, future experiments at proton-antiproton colliders or at projected high-energy electron-positron colliders should enable physicists to determine a variety of their properties and thereby gain new insights into the behavior of a class of fundamental particles that until now have been purely hypothetical.

—Gerald Feinberg

See also Feature Article: THE PHANTOM NEUTRINO.

Nuclear physics

The past year was a productive one for lines of nuclear research ranging from the most fundamental to the most applied. Substantial progress was made in unraveling some long-standing puzzles; at the same time a whole range of new questions opened up. For the first time scientists felt reasonably confident that they had a fundamental understanding of the nucleon-nucleon interaction.

Symmetries and simplicities in nuclei. One of the major triumphs in nuclear science in recent years has been the new understanding of nuclear structure, which includes not only the previously accepted models—vibration, rotation, collective, and shell—in their respective regions of validity but also the much broader transition regions in between, where previous models had been ineffective. This new understanding is based on the use of group theory as an organizing principle and the postulation of a central role for pairs of neutrons and protons (collectively called nucleons) coupled either to zero or to two units of angular momentum (see *1980 Yearbook of Science and the Future* Year in Review: PHYSICS: *Nuclear physics*). Substantial progress has been made in understanding specifically why these particular combinations are the important ones for nucleon-nucleon force. Although this use of group theory has led to the identification of important new simplicities in the behavior of the nuclear system and to previously unrecognized symmetries, all this work has been applicable only to the bound states of nuclei.

In an attempt to search for equivalent simplicities and symmetries in the unbound quantum states—in the scattering problems—Franco Iachello, Karl Erb, and Allan Bromley at Yale University examined the so-called molecular resonances that occur when, for example, two carbon-12 nuclei interact. During the year, in some beautiful experiments of Andrew Sandorfi at Brookhaven (N.Y.) National Laboratory, these molecular resonances were shown to correspond to actual states in magnesium-24 (^{24}Mg), wherein the 24 neutrons and protons at the appropriate energies reorganize themselves into two carbon nuclei moving in simple fashion with respect to one another. The Yale group found that it was possible to understand the characteristics of all 39 known resonances in the ^{24}Mg system within the framework of a single simple mathematical group, leading to a series of symmetries completely analogous to those found earlier in the examination of bound states. Edward Schloemer and his collaborators at Yale subsequently showed that the same mathematical treatment suffices to reproduce all the known characteristics of the molecular states in silicon-28, and indications are that this new and general simplicity is intrinsic in the interactions of all complex nuclei.

Nuclear molecules. Russell Betts of Argonne National Laboratory in Illinois and his collaborators pushed study of these molecular structures to ever heavier systems, higher spins, and higher energies. In studying the nickel-56 system they found, for example, states having 42 units of spin at energies some 70 MeV (million electron volts) above the nickel ground state and at ten times more energy than is required to allow the nickel to eject either a neutron or proton. From other measurements it is known that at these energies there are at least 100,000 states of the same spin per million electron volts of excitation energy; yet the new states discovered by Betts and collaborators have long lifetimes and appeared to have very weak coupling to the underlying complicated states. This shows that when the nickel nucleus is excited with as much as 70 MeV of energy, the 56 neutrons and protons rearrange themselves to look like two silicon-28 nuclei, again in simple motion with respect to one another. This behavior is truly remarkable for a 56-body quantum mechanical system and provides substantial new insight into such systems. It should be pointed out that 42 units of angular momentum is the highest spin yet definitely established in nuclear science and approach-

es the value, about 50 units, at which the nickel nucleus is expected to disintegrate spontaneously under centrifugal forces. It is under such conditions of extreme centrifugal stress that it becomes possible to test current knowledge of nuclear structure and dynamics in particularly sensitive fashion.

Exploring much heavier nuclear systems, Jack Greenberg of Yale, Dirk Schwalm of GSI in Darmstadt, West Germany, and Klaus Bethge of the University of Frankfurt in West Germany found evidence which suggests that even in the uranium-plus-uranium case molecular complexes form. In these collisions time scales are such that electronic shells form around the two colliding uranium nuclei as though they constituted a super nucleus with atomic number Z=184; such a super nucleus has what is called a supercritical electrostatic field in its vicinity, so much so that the inner "atomic" electrons are bound so tightly that they are pulled into the Dirac sea of negative energy electrons (see *1979 Yearbook of Science and the Future* Year in Review: PHYSICS: *Nuclear physics*). If a vacancy is produced in one of the inner atomic shells during the

View of spin spectrometer designed at Washington University, St. Louis, Missouri, shows several of the 72 scintillation detectors around its spherical scattering chamber. The device was built for Oak Ridge National Laboratory to examine nucleus-heavy ion collisions.

Oak Ridge National Laboratory

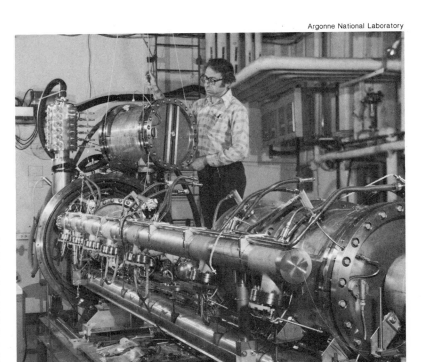

Scientist at Argonne National Laboratory near Chicago works on a section of the facility's new superconducting linear accelerator, which will boost the energy of heavy ions at about half the cost of operating a room-temperature equivalent. The accelerator should help investigators deepen their understanding of the forces that hold atomic nuclei together.

early stages of the collision and is subsequently carried into the Dirac sea, in principle it can be filled by one of the negative energy electrons, and an unaccompanied positron would be expected to emerge. This permits testing of the most precise physical theory known, quantum electrodynamics, in an entirely new way and in a situation in which it is the dominant effect rather than the very small correction that usually is the case.

Greenberg and his collaborators appear to have found the positrons expected on the basis of quantum electrodynamics. In addition they seem to have found a very surprising result: superimposed on the rather smooth spectrum of positrons originally expected are sharp lines representing groups of positrons all having the same energy. Although the situation remains open, the most attractive explanation at the moment, advanced by Walter Greiner and his collaborators at the Institute of Theoretical Physics in Frankfurt, is that instead of just colliding the two uranium nuclei form a molecular system that rotates and remains intact for a sufficiently long period to allow many positrons of the same energy to be emitted. If subsequent measurements confirm this hypothesis, it will mean that molecular phenomena are a characteristic feature of all nuclear interactions.

Deep inelastic scattering. One of the entirely new phenomena that becomes available for study in heavy ion collisions is deep inelastic scattering, first discovered by John Huizenga and his collaborators at the University of Rochester in New York. In this process the kinetic energy of the relative motion of massive colliding nuclei somehow is transformed into internal excitation of the products of the interaction; these products are then blown apart by their mutual electrostatic repulsion. Recent measurement by A. C. Mignerey and co-workers at the University of Maryland finally provided convincing evidence for the detailed mechanism whereby the energy transformation is carried out. It appears that when heavy nuclei collide a neck forms between them. Individual neutrons and protons are exchanged back and forth through the neck, heating up the product fragments and damping the kinetic energy of relative motion.

Further suggestion that this mechanism may indeed be the important one came from new calculations of Stephen Koonin of the California Institute of Technology and collaborators, who mathematically reproduced many of the observed features of the deep inelastic process—mass distribution, charge distributions, and the like—on the assumption of such individual nucleon transfer. To the extent that these studies are successful, they will represent the transfer from classical mechanics to quantum mechanics of the last two holdout concepts, friction and viscosity. Until now these have been the only major concepts of the classical domain that found no analogue in the quantum world.

Parity nonconservation in nuclei. To the limits of present measurements, the strong interaction that determines nuclear structure and nuclear interactions conserves parity; that is, anything that can happen in a right-handed way has a precisely equal probability of happening in a left-handed way. In contrast, the weak interaction that produces nuclear radioactivity is now well known to violate parity conservation, and processes governed by it can distinguish clearly between right-handed and left-handed activities. Because the strong interaction is about a trillion times stronger than the weak one, it has been very difficult to obtain any experimental measurement concerning the role of the weak interaction in nuclei.

One of the best ways to look for such effects is to scatter right- and left-handed polarized protons (protons with spins aligned either with or against their direction of motion from other protons and search for differences. This experiment, in fact, was done in the final days of the zero-gradient synchrotron accelerator at Argonne National Laboratory just before the machine was closed down in the fall of 1979, and, to the surprise of the physicists involved, an effect was observed that was ten times bigger than any predicted. Since all experimental data measured at low energies are described by present theories, the fact that these same theories fail by a factor of ten at 6 GeV (billion electron volts), where these most recent experiments were performed, suggests that for some totally unknown reason there is a strong dependence on energy of the weak interaction between neutron and protons. This conclusion, on the basis of the work of Nigel Lockyer and co-workers at Argonne, was supported by recent work of Homer Conzett and co-workers at Los Alamos (N.M.) National Laboratory at energies around 1 GeV, where again large parity-nonconserving effects were found.

These results are extremely important because they must be explained within the framework of the apparently successful unification of electromagnetism and the weak nuclear force carried out by Nobel laureates Steven Weinberg, Abdus Salam, and Sheldon Glashow.

Quantum chromodynamics. Quantum electrodynamics, the most precise physical theory yet available, has been shown to form a remarkably successful basis for the understanding of all electromagnetic phenomena. Work of Stanley Brodsky of the Stanford Linear Accelerator Center in California and others was making it increasingly clear that quantum chromodynamics can be expected to play the same role for the strong nuclear interaction, the so-called nucleon-nucleon force, whose elucidation has been a chief goal for experimentalists in nuclear and particle physics for the last several decades. Within the framework of quantum chromodynamics nuclei are no longer considered complexes of neutrons and protons exchanging mesons to give the observed binding but instead are more complicated collections of quarks exchanging gluons to provide the binding. For some time it had been assumed that the quark-gluon effects would be measurable only at extremely high energies. Calculations of Brodsky's group, however, showed that characteristic signatures of these quark-gluon phenomena will exist

at energies as low as a few billion electron volts, where measurements are even now possible, and may well persist to much lower energies, where they can be explored with the standard accelerators of nuclear physics. This is a particularly important development because it again ties together nuclear physics, particle physics, and cosmology at a fundamental level and at a level which, it is hoped, will permit direct experimentation.

—D. Allan Bromley

Solid-state physics

Discovering and controlling new solids with properties not found in nature is what solid-state physics is ultimately about. Some of these discoveries, like the transistor, have revolutionized the personal world of countless people. A crystal of silicon little bigger than a pinhead, made impure in a desired manner, replaced much more bulky and costly vacuum tubes and spawned a new age of space probes, computers, and a diversity of miniaturized electronic devices.

But the individual transistor was just the start. The next major step, the integrated circuit, or IC, sprung from knowledge of the way thousands of transistors and associated circuit elements could be squeezed on a crystal of silicon that was still only little larger than a pinhead. This development has drastically enlarged the electronics revolution such that its influence on the lives of whole populations, at least in the developed countries, is now unavoidable.

The IC is based on silicon in the form of a single crystal, the atoms of which are arranged in a completely orderly and predictable manner. Yet there are solids, called amorphous solids, in which the atoms have no such long-range order or predictability, and it would be profitable to make use of and control these solids as well. Just as there are advantages to crystalline order for some applications, there are cases in which the destruction of this order can give superior materials for specific uses.

Before one attempts to examine some of these cases, it is important to clear up some confusion that is common even among scientists. Such crystalline material as the pure single crystals of silicon used in IC's does not ordinarily occur in nature. Much more common are polycrystalline solids, which are made up of many single crystals (sometimes called grains) of finite size that are separated by grain boundaries. Although the orderliness or periodic arrangement of atoms within the crystal lattice is broken at these boundaries, polycrystalline solids are not amorphous. Even if the constituent crystals are only tens of atoms across, their presence can be detected by X-ray diffraction or other means. In amorphous materials order exists only in the arrangement of the first few atoms around any given atom due to the spatially constrained ways that atoms

371

can be packed around a central atom. Using modern methods of studying the arrangement of atoms in solids (principally X-ray, electron, and neutron scattering techniques), scientists can distinguish between amorphous and polycrystalline materials in a definitive manner.

During the past decade both theoretical and practical work went forward on amorphous semiconductors, with current interest focused principally on their potential for the conversion of solar energy to electricity (see 1982 *Yearbook of Science and the Future* Feature Article: A NEW WORLD OF GLASSY SEMICONDUCTORS). But exciting work also has emerged from a very different type of amorphous material, the glassy metals, and it is this class of solids that will be discussed below.

To many people the word glass first invokes the thought of a transparent object, perhaps a windowpane or a drinking tumbler. Scientifically the word "glass" has a very different meaning; it describes a material that does not crystallize when it cools from the liquid state but gradually becomes a solid without imposing any long-range order on its atomic structure.

Molten metal sprayed against a chilled rotating drum freezes rapidly into a ribbon of metallic glass. The machine produces 30 meters of ribbon per second.

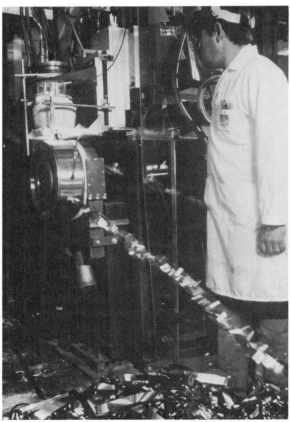

The more familiar glasses—sheet glass, optical lenses, and the like—are formed from metal oxides, semiconductor oxides, or both. This type of glassy material has been known for thousands of years because it is impossible to crystallize many of them, no matter how slowly they are cooled. On the other hand, early humans found that such other materials as water and metals transformed very abruptly from the liquid to the solid state, unlike the glasses. The abrupt change in these materials occurs when they suddenly crystallize from the liquid state.

In the 1950s a group of investigators led by Pol Duwez at the California Institute of Technology became intrigued with the idea of forming glassy metals by cooling from the melt. There was evidence going back to the 19th century that noncrystalline metals could be formed by odd processes; for example, by decomposition of unusual chemicals, by quenching certain metallic vapors directly into the metallic form, or by electrodeposition. No one, however, had ever formed a glassy metal directly from a liquid.

Duwez and his co-workers reasoned that this failure might be simply the result of not cooling the metal fast enough. It must take the atoms a finite, albeit a very small, time to arrange themselves in crystalline order. If they could just be "frozen" in place before this arrangement occurred, glassy metals could be formed. In 1960 the Caltech group reported their first success, using a method called splat cooling in which a drop of liquid metal is inserted between two chilled metallic plates. These plates were brought together so quickly and powerfully that the liquid drop is transformed into a thin sheet that cools extremely fast—about a million degrees per second. The solid so produced was found to lack all crystalline order. In their work Duwez and his co-workers had no success with pure metals but only with alloys. The first glassy metal made was an alloy of gold and silicon. With further research two key facts emerged: glassy metals had very exciting properties not found in crystalline material, and they could only be made from certain types of alloys.

Glass-forming metal alloys fall into three classes. The first comprises alloys combining noble or transition metals—*e.g.*, gold, palladium platinum, iron, nickel, or cobalt—with such nonmetals as boron, phosphorus, carbon, or silicon. The second comprises combinations of transition metals containing only a few *d*-shell electrons such as zirconium, niobium, or tantalum with those having *d* shells that are complete (*e.g.*, copper) or almost complete (*e.g.*, iron, cobalt, or nickel). It is the *d* shell of electrons that give the transition metals their very special properties; for example, ferromagnetism and mechanical strength. The shell is filled when it holds a total of ten electrons. The third class consists of alloys containing elements with two conduction electrons such as beryllium, magnesium, or calcium. These elements are alloyed with rather

Novel branding method for gem diamonds uses ion implantation through a foil stencil to create a surface region of altered electrical conductivity. The distinguishing mark, normally unseen (left), can be made visible temporarily (right) by giving the gem a static charge and dusting with a special powder.

similar metals such as zinc, aluminum, or titanium.

If the glassy metals had not demonstrated startling new properties, they would have remained simple curiosities. Because they were of practical interest, however, ingenious manufacturing methods were developed. In the early 1980s they were beginning to move into a manufacturing phase in which increase in production by a factor of 5,000 was predicted within eight years, from about 20,000 kg (44,000 lb) in 1981 to 100 million kg (220 million lb) in 1988.

One important property of the glassy metals has to do with mechanical strength. For example, their tearing energy is typically a thousand times larger than that of crystalline metals, signifying an enormous increase in strength. Glassy metals also can be bent and twisted to greater extremes without breaking.

In order to understand this tremendous difference in behavior between crystalline and glassy metals, it is important to realize that the crystalline order inherently leads to weakness. Crystalline materials contain defects associated with the crystalline order called dislocations. It is the movement of these defects along the ordered arrays of atoms that reduces the strength of crystalline materials. In glassy metals there is no such order and hence there are no such defects; their atoms

are arranged in a completely "tangled" manner. It is for this reason that these materials are so strong. Unfortunately the present, limited methods of fabricating glassy metals prevents them from being made in large sizes suitable for conventional structural elements.

Nevertheless, glassy metals have another exploitable property that, taken alone, is expected to stimulate exponential growth in production of these materials. This is a very special magnetic behavior that makes it advantageous to employ glassy metals in the transmission and use of electricity. For example, one expert calculated that 31 billion kilowatt-hours of electricity are lost annually in power-distribution electrical transformers in the U.S. alone. The special characteristics of glassy metals can remove the majority of this loss, saving more than a billion dollars a year. To this figure can be added other savings involved in the application of glassy metals to electric motors and related pieces of machinery.

Again, the solid-state physics associated with this special magnetic property has to do with the lack of order. Crystalline materials resist efforts to change the direction of their magnetization because of the constraints set by the orderly arrangement of atoms in the crystal; yet such switching of magnetic fields in solids

373

is necessary for operation of transformers, electric motors, and other devices. The resistance to magnetic switching results in consumption of electricity by the transformer. In the glassy metals there is no crystalline order to hinder the switching of direction of the magnetic field, and thus the electricity loss is reduced.

The special properties of the glassy metals have other important applications. One use is in light, high-frequency (4,000,000-Hz) motors for airborne use where weight reduction is so important. Another example relates to the application of microcomputers to automobiles. An important goal is the development of sensors that can detect and feed to the microcomputer critical information about the performance of the engine so that the microcomputer can make optimum changes in engine operation. One essential device is a piezoelectric or magnetic detector that tells the microcomputer of engine knock long before a human being could detect it. The glassy metals are sensitive piezomagnetic materials and thus may be excellent sensors for this application. Other applications envisioned or under development include magnetic shielding for audio recording heads, corrosion-resistant metals superior to stainless steel, brazing metals, and magnetic filters for water processing.

Once glassy metals began to be appreciated, the main hurdle to their use was the lack of practical manufacturing techniques. Work in this area was led by John Gilman in his former position as director of Allied Corporation's Materials Research Center, Morristown, N.J. Allied researchers Ho Sou Chen, Donald Polk, and Mendayam Narasimhan made systematic progress in understanding these materials and the ways they are formed. From this knowledge, processes were developed at Allied by which metallic ribbons could be continuously fabricated at a rate of 30 meters per second. The ribbon form is obtained by quickly moving the liquid alloy in thin streams over a chilled cylinder. In the early 1980s other manufacturing techniques, including ion implantation, were being explored. Coupled with continued fundamental research and a search for new applications, these efforts should make the glassy metals an important contributor to the technological future.

—William E. Spicer

Psychology

This review of the past year in psychology describes selected research in perception and cognition, looks at some developments in social psychology (and especially at those aspects that seem to be making it increasingly difficult to separate from experimental psychology), discusses some interesting recent facets of neuropsychology, animal psychology, and applied psychology, and concludes by summarizing selected developments in clinical psychology. If there is any single underlying theme to the work described, it is the renewed interest in affective variables—the "hot" cognitions and intentions that motivate so much of our subjective experience and behavior.

Perception and cognition. Subliminal perception has long been a much more popular—and respectable—problem for research and theory in the U.K. than in the United States. In this regard perhaps the most newsworthy event of the year was the publication by British psychologist Norman Dixon of a revision of his earlier book, *Subliminal Perception; The Nature of a Controversy* (1971). The new book, called simply *Preconscious Processing* (1981), should be much more influential, especially in the U.S., than the earlier work.

Experimental verifications and extensions of some of the basic work on this topic continued to appear. For example, a group of researchers from Dartmouth College and Haskins Laboratories, headed by Carol Fowler, published what appeared to be the first U.S. confirmation of Tony Marcel's Cambridge research on the influence of subliminal stimulation on lexical decision (the judgment as to whether a string of letters is or is not a word, with reaction time the critical measure). They concluded that "We are confident that the priming effects of words masked well below the recognition threshold are quite real" (*Journal of Experimental Psychology: General*, 1981, pp. 341–362).

These researchers have all used meaningful words as cues (primes) and targets. However, another positive demonstration published during the year used simpler cues. Glyn Humphreys, working at the University of Bristol in England, compared "direct" and "indirect" tests of associative priming from subliminally presented cues (*The British Journal of Psychology*, 1981, 23, pp. 323–330).

When a normal (supraliminal) presentation of either a digit or a letter cue is made first, the reaction time required to make an accurate alphanumeric judgment (digit or cue?) of a subsequently presented target character depends on whether the two stimuli are of the same type; that is, either both digits or both letters. If they are, "associative priming" occurs, and the alphanumeric judgment is reliably faster. Humphreys used subliminal, backward-pattern-masked presentation of the first cue. He reported that his subjects were unable to respond above chance level to the question "Was a digit or a letter shown?" after they had been exposed to the subliminal presentation of one or the other character but had not been shown a second (target) character. Nevertheless, the same subjects were able to categorize target characters reliably better when they were of the same category as the prime cue. This result can be interpreted to mean that information processing was effectively generated by the prime cue even when conscious identification of that character could not be made.

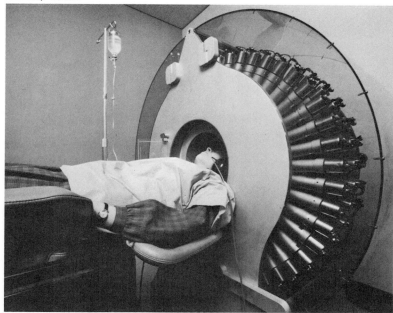

New possibilities in neuropsychology have been opened by the PET (positron-emission tomography) scan. The recently developed technique, which indicates such factors as blood flow, blood volume, and oxygen consumption, can be used to differentiate activities in various parts of the brain.

Subliminal stimulation promises to be a powerful research tool for a wide variety of problems in psychology, most obviously those related to cognitive functions. Now that the reluctance of U.S. experimentalists to utilize these techniques seems to be changing, more about preconscious processing and its potentially important research implications can be expected to appear in U.S. publications.

Social psychology. Social cognition has become the most important unifying concept within social psychology. While social psychologists were never as inclined as some others to disregard mentalistic constructs, many of them were behavioristically oriented. Now there are few topics in this field that are not directly, and often crucially, influenced by the social cognition concept. This does not mean that social psychologists have accepted cognitive concepts uncritically. One who has not done so is the University of Michigan's Robert Zajonc. In a recent, typically innovative report, Zajonc argued that affective judgments precede, rather than follow, cognition, as is assumed in the orthodox theoretical account.

An especially impressive demonstration of this proposition was reported by William Kunst-Wilson and Zajonc. They first obtained affective (like-dislike) ratings on a large number of randomly constructed octagons (black figures on white). They selected 20 of these that had neutral (indifferent) affective scores. Ten of these figures were then shown to new subjects, each a total of five times, using a tachistoscope. The exposure period of one millisecond (1/1,000 of a second) was too short to permit conscious identification of any of the figures, as demonstrated by the subjects' failure to

identify the shown, as compared with the unshown, figures above chance level. Nevertheless, these same subjects, when asked to rate the 20 figures on an affective scale, gave reliably higher ratings to those that had been subliminally shown than to those that had not. This demonstration of the effectiveness of prior experience as a determinant of affect, in the absence of any evidence of cognition (in the sense of knowledge), suggests a major limitation of the role of cognition.

Another indication of the wide-ranging style of modern social psychologists was the research conducted by John Cacioppo of the University of Iowa and Richard Petty of the University of Missouri, who took advantage of contemporary advances in psychophysiological techniques to relate implicit muscle reactions or electromyograms (EMG's) to the depth and affectivity of information processing. Their article in the May 1981 issue of *The American Psychologist* reviews the history of psychophysiology as well as their own research. They showed, for example, that changes in task-relevant EMG's (implicit lip movements), but not in task-irrelevant EMG's (nonpreferred forearm movements), parallel the superior recall—presumably reflecting "deeper" information processing—of self-referent responses ("Does this adjective apply to you?") as compared with orthographic responses ("Do these two words rhyme?").

Neuropsychology. Normally, the right and the left hemispheres of the brain are functionally coordinated as well as structurally connected, and any separation of functions is difficult to demonstrate. However, separation of basic functions can be shown by study of brain-damaged individuals, whether the damage results from

375

The Hearing Dog Program, developed by the American Humane Association, is designed to assist the hearing impaired to function in their everyday lives. Dogs are trained to alert their owners to such sounds as alarm clocks, doorbells, smoke alarms, and babies' cries.

disease or accident or is produced surgically, as in the brain-splitting operation that relieves severe epileptic conditions. (The brain-splitting experiments, first conducted on cats and monkeys and later on human patients by California Institute of Technology psychobiologist Roger Sperry, won him the 1981 Nobel Prize for Physiology or Medicine.)

In the main, the left hemisphere has been shown to be responsible for language and sequential skills, the right hemisphere for spatial relationships. The newest research suggests that this separation extends to affective responses. There appears to be an emerging consensus that positive affectivity is primarily a function of the left hemisphere, negative affectivity a function of the right hemisphere. Clinical evidence from patients with one hemisphere destroyed or severely damaged indicates that euphoria is likely to result when only the left hemisphere is intact and a kind of depression when only the right hemisphere is functioning. The typical balance between positive and negative affectivity thus seems to be another effect of normal hemispheric interaction.

It should be noted that thus far these relationships are only suggestive and are not yet accepted by all experts in the field of brain research. To illustrate the complexities involved, one can consider the patient whose damaged left hemisphere has destroyed his speech ability, as often occurs in war injuries. To what extent is the depression that accompanies this condition attributable to unchecked right-hemispheric operation, in accordance with the recent theoretical position outlined above, and to what extent is it a reaction to the loss of communication function? Clearly, much more in the way of refined clinical and, preferably, experimental research is needed before unambiguous brain-behavior relationships can be established.

Determination of unambiguous relationships in neuropsychology clearly depends upon sophisticated instrumentation. The widely available bodyscan CAT (computerized axial tomography) reveals only the brain's anatomy, but a new technique, the PET (positron-emission tomography) scan, differentiates activities of various parts of the brain. The PET scan traces radioactively tagged substances. It has been used, in demonstrations, to record the brain activities that occur in the right hemisphere when a cat raises its left paw. It can even differentiate which one of the cat's whiskers has been touched. In an even more fanciful application activation in the auditory cortex of a schizophrenic patient was tentatively interpreted as a "first demonstration" of a brain indication of hallucinatory voices.

Animal-human relationships. The relationship between people and animals was the focal point of a number of unusual events during the year. This relationship was the central topic of the first international conference on the "human/companion animal bond." The conference was convened at the University of Pennsylvania's four-year-old Center for the Interaction of Animals and Society and was directed by the head of the center, animal ecologist Alan Beck, author of *The Ecology of Stray Dogs* (1973). It attracted a rather wide variety of conferees, primarily veterinarians and psychologists but also humane society officers, social workers, ethologists, pet store owners, and philosophers.

The important role of pets in the psychological well-being of older people was apparently a major determinant of the conference. Pets appear to be a cost-effective means of countering the isolation and loneliness that trouble older people. Pets provide both direct emotional support and the feeling of being needed.

These opinions were buttressed by empirical results. Psychologist Aaron Katcher headed an investigation that attempted to determine social factors influencing the well-being of coronary patients. Surprisingly, the most important social predictor identified was pet ownership. Slightly over half of the 93 patients studied had pet animals. Only three of these patients had died after one year, compared with one-third of the others. Obviously this kind of study is preliminary, and much more detailed and better controlled investigations are needed. But the results, which were not anticipated, do confirm some earlier ones, such as a much-cited study by Roger Mugford in Yorkshire, England. Mugford gave a parakeet to one-half of a group of 48 old people (average age: 73) who lived alone; the other half received begonias to care for. Semiannual assessments of social adjustment were made by social workers, and at the end of three years it was reported that the bird owners were distinctly better adjusted.

The more active role of animals as human helpers was also receiving much attention. The American Humane Association started a program of training "hearing-ear" dogs as companions for deaf people; the dogs are trained to alert their owners to various meaningful sounds (*e.g.*, telephones, fire alarms). Tufts University began a project to train monkeys to aid severely disabled persons. One participant in this experimental project, a paralyzed young man, found a most useful companion in a capuchin monkey, Hellion. After a rather stormy period of adjustment, overseen by Mary Joan Willard, the Skinner-trained founder of the Tufts project, Hellion became a true companion. For example, she obtains for her human apartment mate special containers of food and drink from the refrigerator. In return she receives food pellets, released through a feeding mechanism manipulated by means of a laser attached to the mouth control of the wheelchair. Many problems remain to be solved, but the results thus far offer considerable promise of long-term rewards.

Applications. An important result of one of the continuing studies of recipients of special preschool training was announced at the annual meetings of the American Psychological Association. New York University psychologists Martin and Cynthia Deutsch were directing an ongoing study of some 1,200 poor black children from Harlem, who have been checked periodically since receiving special training in the 1960s. A subgroup of 158 young people were now in the 18–22-year age range. For the first time distinct gender differences were showing up. Males generally were doing better after special preschool training than their nontrained counterparts; higher percentages were enrolled in college (32 and 20%, respectively) or were gainfully employed (57 and 44%). Females, however, were faring no better for having had the preschool training; their percentages were approximately the same as the control percentages. The investigators suggested that differential social roles, traditional in the school system, might help to account for the emerging difference. They found some evidence that teachers were more likely to react negatively to the

self-assertiveness fostered by the training when it occurred in girls.

It is interesting that Project Head Start (which was modeled after the training program described above) was one social intervention program whose budget was not initially chopped by the Reagan administration. More than 300,000 children would be served if a proposed budget increase over the 1981 level was maintained.

The first annual Irvine Symposium on Environmental Psychology was convened at the Irvine campus of the University of California. If the participants' descriptions of ongoing and planned projects were any indication, it appeared that this field was ready to move more confidently into the arena of public policy. The empirical studies presented were concerned with such settings as markets, hospital emergency rooms, and residential care facilities for the elderly.

One of the most interesting studies reported was a comparison of supermarkets and farmers' markets by Robert Sommer, director of the University of California's Center for Consumer Research on the Davis campus. Perhaps the most surprising result was that the great majority (75 to 97%) of the specific items that shoppers were able to locate correctly in supermarkets were on peripheral rather than central aisles. A suggestion for future policy direction was made by an architect, who pointed out that architects are too busy with other problems to pay much attention to the findings of environmental psychologists; the proper recipients of such recommendations are the people who have the primary financial responsibility for the buildings to be constructed.

Clinical psychology. Several interesting developments in therapy were reported. The general tightening of purse strings by the Reagan administration stimulated renewed interest in short-term therapy (*see* Daniel Goleman's comprehensive review article in the August 1981 issue of *Psychology Today*). There was also continuing—if not accelerated—interest in family therapy, which involves "treating" all of the members of a family rather than only the one or more in whom the most disturbing symptoms occur. Even as efforts to find new drug treatments and uncover more biological bases of behavior disorders intensified, at the other end of the spectrum a new look was being taken at the small irritations in life that seem to combine to produce adjustment crises, as indicated by psychologist Richard Lazarus's "Hassle Scale."

The year was marked by the startlingly rapid development of "pop" psychology shows on radio and television, in which listeners or viewers are encouraged to call in and receive instant suggestions about their problems. These shows, some of them very successful financially, were viewed by many as a dangerous new fad, the therapeutic results of which were, to say the least, questionable. Developments on the political front included the initiation of a comprehensive test of the effectiveness of psychotherapy by the National Institute of Mental Health and the confirmation, by the refusal of the U.S. Supreme Court to hear an appeal, of an earlier legal decision against the Blue Shield policy of not reimbursing psychologists directly for services rendered to insurance holders.

—Melvin H. Marx

See also Feature Article: TWINS—NATURE'S TWICE-TOLD TALE.

Space Exploration

The first three manned orbital flights of the reusable space shuttle "Columbia" took place during recent months. Other highlights of 1981 included a 75-day stay in a space station by two Soviet cosmonauts and the Voyager 2 flyby of Saturn.

Manned flight

The space shuttle orbiter "Columbia" became the first spacecraft to return from orbit and land on the Earth like an airplane. In other developments the Soviet space station Salyut 6 was manned three times during the year as the U.S.S.R continued development toward a continuously manned modular space base.

Space shuttle. "Columbia" was rolled out to Kennedy Space Center's Launch Complex 39 at Cape Canaveral, Fla., late in 1980 for an extensive prelaunch check-

out that included a 20-second full-throttle burn of the three liquid oxygen/liquid hydrogen main engines. The first launch attempt was 20 minutes from lift-off on April 10, 1981, when the primary spacecraft general-purpose computers fed an incorrect timing signal to the backup flight system. Attempts to resolve the timing error failed, and the mission was postponed.

The STS-1 (Space Transportation System) crew of John Young and Robert Crippen entered "Columbia's" cockpit again on April 12 for a second countdown. This time software and procedural changes allowed the on-board computers to synchronize their timing correctly. "Columbia's" main engines and the two solid-propellant rocket boosters combined to provide 6.5 million lb of thrust at lift-off on April 12. The spent rocket motor cases separated 2 minutes 14 seconds after lift-off and were lowered by parachute into the Atlantic for recovery and reuse on a later flight. Main engine cutoff took place 8 minutes 36 seconds after lift-off, and the jettisoned liquid oxygen/liquid hydrogen tank coasted for half an orbit before breaking up on entering the atmosphere over a remote portion of the Indian Ocean.

Two burns of the orbital maneuvering system's (OMS) two 6,000-lb (2,725-kg)-thrust engines placed "Columbia" in an initial 133-n mi orbit. (One nautical mile equals 1.85 km.) Young and Crippen then set about activating the spacecraft's systems and also opened the huge payload bay doors in order to expose the space radiators for carrying away crew metabolic and spacecraft system heat loads; these amounted to approximately 70 BTU (British thermal units) per hour

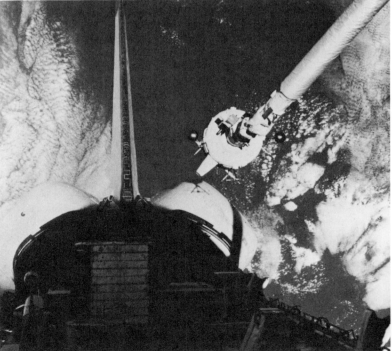

Remote manipulator system on the space shuttle "Columbia" was successfully tested during the shuttle's second and third flights. Eventually, the robot arm will be used to deploy and retrieve satellites.

NASA

instead of the predicted total of 90.

Except for minor problems "Columbia's" other systems performed normally during the two-day flight. The fuel cells were called on to produce about two kilowatts less electrical power than had been estimated before the flight.

When the payload bay doors were opened, the crew discovered that portions of 16 heat shield tiles were missing from the two OMS pods on either side of the vertical stabilizer. The pods were in an area of relatively low heating on reentry, and so the missing tiles posed little concern to the crew or to Mission Control.

Two additional OMS burns raised "Columbia's" orbit to 148 n mi early on the first day. While it carried no scientific or commercial payloads, "Columbia's" payload bay on the first orbital test flight contained instrumentation for thorough performance measurements of the orbiter's systems and flight-handling characteristics. Most of the two-day flight was flown with the payload bay facing the Earth and the tail facing toward the direction of orbit.

After a heads-down, tail-first, retrograde OMS deorbit burn, the crew maneuvered "Columbia" around to a heads-up, nose-first attitude. The deorbit burn took place over the Indian Ocean, and reentry into the atmosphere occurred just north of Guam in the western Pacific. Young and Crippen then successfully landed the orbiter at Edwards Air Force Base in California, touching down 54 hours and 20 minutes after lift-off.

Again in the Kennedy Space Center's orbiter processing facility "Columbia" was prepared for a second trip into space. A Canadian-built remote manipulator system, or robot arm, was installed on the left sill of the payload bay. An array of Earth-survey experiments, mounted on a European Space Agency Spacelab pallet, was lowered into "Columbia's" payload bay before the spacecraft joined its booster in the cavernous assembly building.

Preparations for the second flight were delayed in September when nitrogen tetroxide oxidizer being loaded in the forward reaction control system spilled down the right side of the spacecraft's fuselage during fueling operations at Launch Complex 39. Some 380 heat shield silica glass tiles were loosened by the oxidizer's solvent action on the bond holding the tiles to "Columbia's" aluminum skin. A buildup of contaminants that prevented proper seating of the oxidizer servicing fitting where it was connected to the orbiter service panel was the cause of the spill.

STS-2 crewmen Joe Engle and Richard Truly strapped themselves into "Columbia's" cockpit early on the morning of November 4. Late in the countdown two of the three hydrazine-fueled auxiliary power units (APUS) that drive hydraulic pumps aboard the spacecraft showed higher-than-normal gearbox lubricating oil pressures, and the launch attempt was scrubbed. The APU-driven hydraulic system gimbals the main engines during launch and powers actuators for elevons (surfaces that combine the functions of elevators and ailerons) and rudder during flight in the atmosphere.

Clogged filters and contaminants in the APU lubricating oil delayed the launch until November 12, when "Columbia" became the first spacecraft to make a second trip into space. Early in the flight a high alkalinity level was detected in the by-prouduct water of one of the three fuel-cell electrical power plants, and the decision was made to shut down the fuel cell after a drop in voltage. An alternate flight plan, established for such a contingency, was adopted by Mission Control and the STS-2 crew in order to gain the highest number of test objectives from a flight shortened from seven days to two. High-priority flight tests, such as checkout of the remote manipulator arm and activation of the Earth survey experiments, were grouped into the second day's activities, and some 90% of the flight's engineering objectives were met.

"Columbia" again descended into the atmosphere

NASA

Canisters of lithium hydroxide float past flight commander Jack Lousma in the weightless environment of space during the third flight of the space shuttle "Columbia" in March 1982. The photograph was taken by Lousma's fellow astronaut C. Gordon Fullerton.

>

Back on Earth after a week in the Soviet Salyut 6 space station in May 1981, cosmonauts Leonid Popov of the U.S.S.R. and Dumitru Prunariu of Romania autograph the Soyuz 40 descent module.

Authenticated News International

over the western Pacific and achieved a smooth landing on November 14 at Edwards Air Force Base. The third orbital test flight, of seven days duration, was flown March 22–30, 1982. With Gordon Fullerton and Jack Lousma as crew, STS-3 carried an array of space science experiments on a pallet in the payload bay. Also, further tests were run for the robot arm, including grappling and moving objects to and from their positions in the payload bay.

Soviet manned flight. Space station Salyut 6, in orbit since 1977, continued as the focal point of Soviet development toward continuous manned operations in space. Three pairs of cosmonauts lived aboard the station during 1981, one crew for 75 days.

Cosmonauts Vladimir Kovalenok and Viktor Savinykh were launched March 12 aboard Soyuz T-4 from Tyuratam and docked with Salyut 6 two days later. The supply vessel Progress 12, which had been docked to the space station after an unmanned flight, was undocked March 21 and vaporized in the atmosphere over the western Pacific. Soyuz 39, with crew Vladimir Dzhanibekov and Mongolian cosmonaut-researcher Jugderdemidyin Gurragcha, was launched the day after Progress 12's departure and docked with the space station on March 23.

During a week-long stay aboard Salyut Dzhanibekov and Gurragcha joined Kovalenok and Savinykh in undertaking life science and cosmic radiation experiments and studies. Soyuz 39 and its crew returned to the Earth March 30, landing near Dzehezkazgan, Kazakhstan.

Soviet cosmonaut Leonid Popov accompanied by Romanian engineer-cosmonaut Dumitru Prunariu lifted off on May 14 aboard Soyuz 40 to spend a week aboard Salyut 6. The two cosmonauts and their craft returned to the Earth May 22. After 75 days in space Kovalenok

and Savinykh landed in the U.S.S.R. on May 26.

Pursuing a modular space station concept, the Soviet Union launched Cosmos 1267 on April 24. The unmanned spacecraft underwent a separate flight test program in orbit while cosmonauts were aboard Salyut 6, but on June 19 it was docked with the space station by the Soviet control center. The space station under development envisions a central core with several docking ports at which modules built for specific tasks would be docked. Population of the modular space station would depend upon the type of mission underway.

—Terry White

Space probes

While the U.S. contribution to planetary science by means of space probes was perhaps at its greatest level ever in 1981, the year's achievements could be viewed as a finale. Budget restrictions by the administration of Pres. Ronald Reagan appeared to preclude future activity in this field of space exploration.

Probing the Sun. As 1981 began, Pioneer 6, orbiting the Sun since 1965, was still transmitting scientific data on the behavior of the solar wind and other associated phenomena. The probe had been designed with a lifetime of six months. During its 15 years of continuous operation Pioneer 6 made the first detailed measurements of the interplanetary medium, some spanning a half billion miles. Its data led to many discoveries about the Sun itself, the solar wind, solar cosmic rays, and the solar magnetic field. The probe teamed up with the West German-U.S. Helios satellite in 1975 to provide scientists with data concerning solar particles and fields close to the Sun in comparison with the particles and fields observed in near-Earth space. Information from Pioneer 6 continued to provide data to the U.S. National Oceanic and Atmospheric Administration for the prediction of solar storms.

The sister probes Pioneer 7–11 were also still active during the year, and they too were operating long beyond their expected lifetimes. On July 26 Pioneer 10 crossed what is often called the silver astronomical unit (AU), a point 25 AU from the Sun.

The major U.S. contribution to the International Solar Polar Mission (ISPM) venture with the European Space Agency (ESA) was canceled during the year by the government. The cancellation reduced the scope of the joint mission, which was to have one ESA probe and one U.S. probe in polar orbit around the Sun. The U.S. National Aeronautics and Space Administration (NASA) had signed a memorandum of understanding with ESA that spelled out what NASA would contribute to the international mission: one of the two probes, launched by the space shuttle; tracking and data reduction; and provision of the radioisotopic thermal electric generators for the ESA probe. Upon cancellation of the U.S. probe NASA Administrator James M. Beggs wrote to ESA that NASA "would use its best efforts to fulfill its remaining commitments in the original memorandum of understanding."

Despite the U.S. withdrawal ESA decided to continue development of its probe in the hope that NASA would honor the remainder of its promises to ISPM. "Europe's decision to go ahead with the solar polar mission following the NASA cancellation was made with our eyes open," said Vittorio Manno, scientific program coordinator for ESA. An offer to build the second probe in Europe and sell it to NASA, as a means of effecting savings, met with a NASA rebuff.

Venus revealed. The continued exploration of Venus by the U.S. also was effectively brought to an end by the Reagan administration late in the year when funds for the proposed Venus Orbiting Imaging Radar probe were dropped from the NASA budget. The Soviet Union, however, launched a pair of probes toward Venus as 1981 drew to a close. Venera 13 was launched on October 30, followed by Venera 14 on November 4. They arrived at the planet on March 1 and 5, 1982, respectively.

The two probes contained experiments provided by scientists in France and Austria. En route to Venus, the probes utilized French instruments to make measurements of gamma radiation in interplanetary space that permitted determination of the sources of such rays. The Austrian instruments detected and measured the interplanetary magnetic fields.

Venera 13 and Venera 14 each had a lander vehicle similar to the U.S. Viking, still transmitting from the surface of Mars. These craft had screw-jack sample gatherers, capable of scooping up soil and drilling into rocks in the adjacent area. Once aboard the spacecraft, the samples were analyzed by X-ray fluorescence, a technique with greater information capability than the

gamma-ray device used on the earlier Venera 9 and 10 probes. Also provided was an improved imaging system for pictures of the Venusian surface. Both landers touched down in areas selected by the Soviets from the maps made by the U.S. Pioneer Venus probe, one in the foothills of the mountainous Phoebe region near the planet's equator and the other 600 mi farther east.

Unlike the U.S. the Soviet Union was far from abandoning the investigation of Venus by probes. Yuriy Zaytsev, head of a department of the Institute of Space Research of the Soviet Academy of Sciences, wrote in the October 31 issue of *Sovetskaya Estoniya* of the types of future Soviet Venus probes that could be expected. These included Venus landers with radioisotopic power supplies for long life on the planetary surface, landers with television cameras, and: "Developments of the still more distant future may include planet rovers for traveling over the surface of Venus as well as craft capable of delivering Venus soil to Earth. . ."

More detailed information about Venus was revealed at the first International Conference on the Venus Environment, held in Palo Alto, Calif., from November 2–6. Most of the information derived from the 30 experiments of the six U.S. Pioneer Venus probes, one orbiter of which was still transmitting data as the year ended. Among the most significant findings were that there is evidence for two major, currently active volcanic areas on the planet, probably the principal vents for the internal heat of the planet. Apparently, Venus has a thicker crust than does Earth and has only one plate with little plate tectonics or movement. Data from the probes permitted calculation of complete, self-consistent models of the cloud system of the planet and its greenhouse effect. Additionally, there is evidence that Venus once had oceans such as those on Earth.

The volcanic regions are in Beta Regio and the Scorpion Tail of Aphrodite Terra. Beta Regio is a region larger than the Hawaii-Midway chain of islands and appears to be a huge, double-shield, volcanic structure. Aphrodite Terra is the planet's largest continentlike upland feature. Studies of gravity measurements were the basis for the assumption that Venus is a one-plate planet, with no continents floating on a liquid interior, as do those of Earth.

The clouds of Venus are upside down compared to those of the Earth. Unlike the atmosphere of Los Angeles and other U.S. cities the smog layer is on top of the clouds and is about 15 km (9.3 mi) thick. The Earthlike condensation clouds, composed of droplets of sulfuric acid, are present below 57 km (35.4 mi), extending down to 48 km (29.8 mi). The clouds vary in density and are patchy in distribution. They apparently produce only drizzles rather than hard rains.

Other findings include the fact that Venus absorbs most solar heat in its clouds, unlike the Earth which absorbs such energy in its surface. The Venusian cloud layer has a single convective circulation cell that carries heat from the equator to the poles. Earth, on the other hand, has three such cells for accomplishing the same task.

Venus at one time probably had liquid water oceans but lost them to space. Scientists believe that in the early days of the solar system, the Sun was some 30% less hot. At that time the atmosphere and environment of Venus could have been almost Earthlike. Evidence to support this hypothesis was found by the Pioneer probes' measurement of the ratio of deuterium to hydrogen; there is 100 times more deuterium relative to hydrogen on Venus than on the Earth. However, when the greenhouse effect began, water disappeared from the planet, and life, if any, with it.

Other data indicated that the Venusian atmosphere received far more chemical elements from the Sun than did Earth during the evolution of the solar system. The gases involved are argon-36 (^{36}Ar), krypton, and xenon, the so-called noble gases. Venus has 75 times as much argon-36, the primordial form of the gas, as does Earth in its atmosphere. It also has three times as much krypton as does the Earth. There is perhaps as much as 30 times more xenon, but there also could be far less than that amount.

Other studies found that most of the lightning on Venus occurs over the volcanic regions. Volcanoes on Earth also produce lightning. Soviet Venera probes revealed that the Venusian ashen airglow is 3 to 50 times brighter than a Class I aurora on Earth. However, other observations showed that there was much less lightning on Venus than had been expected.

In an interesting marriage of space science and the arts Fred Scarf of the TRW Corp. produced space music from his electric field detector aboard the Pioneer Venus Orbiter. It presented in sound such phenomena as a series of different structures in the Venusian ionosphere, precursors of Venus's bow-shock wave in the solar wind hours in advance of the crossing, time-compression of orbital events to show the size of various disturbances in the solar wind, and low frequencies encountered as the probe crossed the wake of Venus in the solar wind.

Looking toward Jupiter. The year was a frustrating one for NASA planetary scientists, especially those at the Jet Propulsion Laboratory (JPL) in Pasadena, Calif., where the Galileo Jupiter probe was being developed. The probe was originally scheduled for launch in 1985 by the space shuttle, using a Centaur upper stage to take it from Earth orbit into an interplanetary trajectory. Even as Galileo components were being completed and tested and $300 million had been spent on the program, it was canceled by the Reagan administration's Office of Management and Budget.

Scientists, in general, were appalled by the action. It meant the end of U.S. interplanetary exploration pro-

grams and the probable closing of JPL with the loss of 1,200 jobs. As a result James Van Allen, a pioneer in unmanned space exploration, began a campaign of letter-writing to presidential science advisor George Keyworth to solicit assistance in reversing the cancellation. He also made a personal appeal to the National Academy of Science's Space Science Board.

As 1981 ended, apparently the administration heeded the voices of Van Allen and others. The Galileo probe was reinstated but with some changes. The Centaur upper stage was eliminated, and so the probe would have to be restructured to utilize a solid-propellant inertial upper stage. Such a substitution would cause Galileo to require between 24 and 30 months longer to arrive at Jupiter, resulting in an increase in operational costs of some $40 to $50 million.

Ironically, science was benefiting from Galileo even before it was launched. Using technology derived from the development of the probe, JPL designed an unmanned, submersible, oceanographic research vehicle. It weighed 1,293 kg (2,850 lb) and could reach depths of 6,096 m (20,000 ft).

News from Saturn. During the year data from the probes Voyager 1 and 2 continued to both delight and mystify U.S. scientists studying the planet Saturn. Even though Voyager 1 had departed from the planet, the huge amount of data it left behind was providing material of great value. Among the legacy was the fact that Saturn's moon Titan has a diameter of 5,117 km (3,180 mi) with an atmosphere extending ten times farther above its surface than does that of Earth. Its temperature, at the surface, is about $-181.7°$ C ($-295°$ F).

Early in January NASA decided to target Voyager 2 for an encounter with Uranus after its Saturn mission was completed. The scheduled arrival date was set at Jan. 24, 1986, with the probe passing some 107,000 km (66,488.5 mi) above the planet's cloud tops. On August 24 Voyager 2 curved past Saturn's satellites Hyperion and Phoebe in order to make its closest approach to the planet on the following day. It passed approximately 101,400 km (63,000 mi) above the planet's cloud tops, only 3.1 seconds ahead of schedule. Its trajectory later took it past the satellites Iapetus, Titan, Dione, Mimas, Enceladus, Tethys, and Thea.

The Voyager 2 mission was termed a complete success by NASA even though there were anxious moments when the sensor scan platform of the probe malfunctioned as the craft passed behind Saturn, approximately four hours after the point of closest approach to the planet. (The problem reoccurred on September 8.) The platform was unable to move in its horizontal plane. A similar malfunction had taken place earlier on the Voyager 1.

Among the most intriguing yet mystifying discoveries of Voyager 2 was the detection of braided rings, apparently of the same type noted by Voyager 1 in the

F-ring of Saturn. Scientists had supposed that they must be related to accompanying "shepherding" satellites as those pictured by Voyager 1; however, no such satellites were detected in the Voyager 2 pictures, even though the pictures were of higher resolution. Voyager 2 concentrated its efforts on observing the 69,200-km (43,000-mi) ring plane on the planet's B-ring and its puzzling "spokes," the apparently braided F-ring and its satellites, the eccentric rings (C-ring and one in the Cassini division), and the Encke division. The new "kinked" rings were discovered within the Encke division. A movie was made of the B-ring and its spokes. It revealed a complex activity: spokes formed, others sheared out, and still others seemed to fade away. Other features of Saturn's rings included the fact that the A-ring appears to be reddish while the Cassini division and the C-ring are bluish.

Photographs of Saturn's various satellites also provided new information. Enceladus revealed a varied topography. First indications were that it resulted from tidal heating and frictional heat produced by the expansion and contraction of the satellite's crust. An image of Tethys showed an impact crater at least 400 km (250 mi) in diameter, almost one-third the diameter of the Moon. Pictures of Hyperion caused scientists to dub it a "thick hamburger patty" because of its unusual shape. The satellite apparently has its axis at an angle to the plane of its orbit. Iapetus is very dark. It has a density of 1.1, indicating a composition of 35% rock, 55% water, and 10% methane.

In commenting upon photographs of Iapetus, Carl Sagan of Cornell University, a member of the imaging science team, said: "One significant conclusion—still tentative, but there is more unanimity on this issue than there has ever been before—is that Iapetus is covered with a fairly thick stain of organic material. If you fold that in with the Titan story, you have an interesting perception of complex organic chemistry in the outer solar system."

Pictures of the Saturnian atmosphere made by Voyager 2 showed in fine detail its structure and complex dynamics. Numerous swirls and spots, more than those seen by Voyager 1, were viewed in the turbulent atmosphere. It was apparent that the planet's jet streams extended at least to lat 80° N. Other measurements showed strong temperature gradients with respect to latitude. They are significant because they represent masses of gas, the potential energy of which permits the calculation of wind velocities.

Finally, data from Voyager 2 showed that Saturn is surrounded by a torus (doughnut-shape) of plasma that has the highest temperatures known in the solar system. It consists largely of hydrogen and is centered on the orbits of the satellites Rhea and Dione; the temperature ranges between 600 million and 1 billion degrees F.

Halley's Comet. During 1981 the U.S. also bowed out of major participation in an international effort to study Halley's Comet by means of interplanetary space probes. The Reagan administration canceled NASA's Halley's Comet probe, leaving that body which draws near the Sun only once every 75 or 76 years to be studied in space by ESA, the Soviet Union, and Japan. Twice NASA unsuccessfully suggested a cooperative mission with ESA, with NASA having two instruments aboard ESA's Giotto probe in exchange for ESA's use of the NASA deep-space tracking network and other services. The only participation by NASA in Giotto is a minor one, the involvement of some 30 experiment coinvestigators. ESA worked out an agreement with the U.S.S.R. to exchange data that would assist it in making final adjustments to Giotto's trajectory for insuring the proper rendezvous with the comet.

The Soviet comet probes were to be two spacecraft, launched in late 1984 or early 1985, that would first fly by Venus, drop off landers, and then move on to a 1986 encounter with the comet. France was actively involved in the experiments aboard the Soviet craft. The two probes should provide a resolution of the comet's nucleus of from 152.4 m (500 ft) to 304.8 m (1,000 ft), while scientists hoped that Giotto would provide a resolution of 91.4 m (300 ft).

Panoramic view of the surface of Venus was transmitted to Earth by the descent module of the Soviet space probe Venera 14. The Venera 14 lander touched down on Venus March 5, 1982, and functioned for almost an hour before the planet's extremely high temperatures rendered it inoperative.

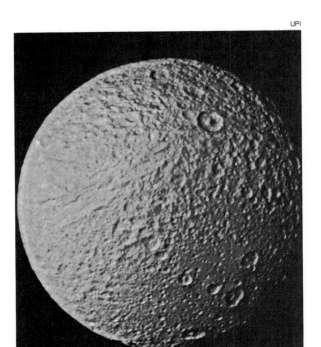

Saturn's moon Tethys was photographed by Voyager 2 from a distance of 282,000 kilometers (175,000 miles). Objects about 5 kilometers (3 miles) in size are revealed. Part of the satellite is heavily cratered.

A note on Mars. The financially hard-pressed NASA gratefully accepted $60,000 in 1981 (with an additional $40,000 expected later) from private contributors to fund data transmissions from the Viking 1 lander, still operational on the surface of Mars. Part of the money was to be used to continue data analysis from the probe. NASA officially renamed the Viking 1 lander the Thomas A. Mutch Memorial Station in honor of the scientist who headed the lander imaging science team and was killed in a mountain-climbing accident in October 1980.

—Mitchell R. Sharpe

Transportation

While concern about future petroleum supplies and costs continued to influence transport technology trends, the more immediate impact during 1981 was the constraint placed on many research and development programs by the continuing steep inflation in the United States and the inability of the U.S. economy to recover from a recession. Another important influence was the lessening of regulation. The stiff competition from deregulation in the airline industry plus the prolonged recession combined to force airlines to make major reductions in outlays of all types. The Lockheed Corp., seeing no relief in the immediate future, decided to stop making commercial aircraft and planned to discontinue production of its unprofitable L-1011 TriStar giant wide-bodied air transport after the last one is delivered in 1984.

The trucking industry also felt the sting of far greater competition because of deregulation and likewise had to cut back its outlays. On the other hand the railroad industry—long depressed financially—improved its status. The outlook in 1982 for all three transport industries was one of only moderate improvement.

Air transport. The first B-767, an advanced, new-generation, two-engine jet transport, completed its first flight tests, which were designed to prove its airworthiness. The tests were to take ten months, and as of early 1982 the Boeing Co. claimed that the overall development/production program was on schedule. The manufacturer's smaller new-generation transport, the B-757, underwent its first flight tests in February 1982.

Both aircraft feature extensive use of aluminum and composite materials to reduce weight and of high-technology wings to achieve 30–35% better fuel efficiency. The two-engine, wide-bodied B-767 seats approximately 200 passengers, while the two-engine, narrow-bodied 757 seats about 180. First deliveries were scheduled to begin in mid- or late 1982.

Despite the technological advances of the two new aircraft some U.S. airlines were demanding a smaller-capacity transport—about 150 seats—with fuel consumption and other cost savings sufficient to reduce total operating expenses by 25%. Major attention, therefore, was expected to be placed on research and development programs to produce such an aircraft for the large short-to-medium-range market.

Formal U.S. government approval of two-man flight crews for new, advanced aircraft such as the 767 was requiring extensive changes in flight-deck configurations. For example, the 767 was designed to use the Engine Indication and Crew Alerting System (EICAS), developed by a division of Rockwell International Corp. The EICAS will assume many of the tasks performed by a flight engineer on a three-man crew, such as continuous checks of the engines, the fuel supply, and the electronic and hydraulic systems. The Airbus Industrie's A300 transport was to feature a push-button device to replace the flight engineer. A lights-out situation indicates that the systems are functioning properly; a white light indicates an abnormal situation; and a red light indicates a failure. More advanced systems are expected to feature six cathode-ray tubes that visually display altitude, airspeed, aircraft attitude, navigation, weather, engine, and electrical system data.

The U.S. Federal Aviation Administration (FAA) approved a new electronic warning system designed to reduce sharply the chances of mid-air collisions. Called the Threat Alert and Collision Avoidance Sys-

Flight testing began during the year on the Boeing 767. The two-engine, wide-body plane was one of a new generation of jet transports designed to achieve greater fuel efficiency through the use of lighter weight materials and improved wing design.

tem (TCAS), it emits constant radarlike signals, or pulses, in all directions from the aircraft over a distance of up to 22 nautical miles. This, in effect, enables the aircraft to fly in the center of an electronic bubble, so that if any aircraft with a transponder penetrates it the TCAS-equipped aircraft will be alerted by both audio and visual signals. Commercial aircraft with more complex TCAS gear will be able to know instantly not only the intruder's exact position, distance, and altitude, but also whether to dive, climb, or maintain altitude to avoid a collision course.

The FAA admitted that the new warning system is not foolproof, since it cannot spot an intruding plane not equipped with at least a transponder. The agency noted, however, that all planes now operating in busy air lanes near major cities must be equipped with such equipment.

Despite the inherently better fuel consumption achieved by a turbine-driven propeller as compared with a jet or turbofan engine, the former's inability to propel air transports above speeds of 645 km/h (400 mph) proved its downfall in competition with the latter. At speeds higher than 645 km/h the propeller met excessive drag as the blade tip speed approached the speed of sound.

With the cost of fuel becoming the major expense confronting the airline industry, research on ways to overcome this propeller drawback has been underway for several years by both the U.S. National Aeronautics and Space Administration (NASA) and several major aerospace companies. As of 1982 the researchers were optimistic, predicting that by 1990 many airlines would be flying passengers in a new type of propeller-driven aircraft that would operate at savings of 15–20% in fuel consumption compared to turboprop planes designed in the 1950s.

One recent result of propeller research is the "prop-

fan," developed by the Hamilton Standard Division of United Technologies. It contains eight to ten blades that have a thin profile and are swept back, which not only permits greater efficiency but also reduces outside noise. Small-scale wind-tunnel tests indicate that propfans installed on high-speed transports would provide 20% better efficiency than a turbofan at speeds of about 885 km/h (550 mph); the efficiency would be even greater at 805 km/h (500 mph). While considerably more research on the propfan is required to solve problems such as the increased cabin noise it generates and its lack of compatibility with advanced high-speed swept-wing airframes, proponents visualize its use in the 1990s for 80–160-passenger, shorthaul aircraft that spend most of their time in climbing and descending.

During the year the Technical Center of the FAA announced plans to crash a deactivated Boeing 720 aircraft by remote control in California's Mojave Desert in 1984. Its tanks would be full of a special fuel that is not expected to create the huge fireball that often occurs when a jetliner crashes. The $10 million project, jointly sponsored by the FAA and NASA, was seeking to develop anti-misting fuel additives as inhibitors to fire. The Technical Center claimed that the best candidate for such an additive is FM-9, a British-developed anti-misting kerosene powder.

An FAA Sikorsky CH-53 helicopter became the first aircraft to navigate using satellite information taken from a special receiver and processed for the pilot's display. Using the U.S. Department of Defense's Navstar satellite system as its primary navigational guidance, the helicopter flew a 160-km (100-mi) course from the FAA Technical Center in Atlantic City, N.J., to Cape May, N.J., and back. The purpose of the experiment was to determine the feasibility of using these military satellites for civil aviation purposes. In evalu-

Boeing Vertol 234, the world's largest commercial helicopter, was one of six to be operated by British Airways, chiefly between Aberdeen, Scotland, and North Sea oil platforms.

ating the accuracy of the satellite guidance the Center called the flight "nothing short of spectacular."

While the frequently predicted comeback of the airship for commercial air and freight transport still did not materialize in 1981, another project could, if successful, take it a major step closer to realization. Through a $4.7 million research grant from the U.S. Department of Agriculture's Forest Service the Piasecki Aircraft Corp. of Philadelphia began building a "Heli-stat," four surplus Sikorsky H-34J helicopters linked to the bottom of a 105-m (343-ft) blimp envelope discarded by the U.S. Navy. Plans call for turning the Heli-stat over to the U.S. Forest Service in May 1982, for the start of three years of demonstration tests to determine if the craft can be used successfully in logging operations.

The four helicopters are to be linked with the blimp by means of aluminum tubes and by a centralized control system that will permit them to operate in unison. The craft is to be designed to be able to lift up to 25 tons of logs for transfer from out-of-the way forest areas to places where they can be cut into lumber at less cost than by the use of straight helicopters or trucks on service roads.

Highway transport. U.S. auto and truck manufacturers received a major blow when the U.S. Supreme Court refused to consider their requested reversal of a lower court's upholding of the U.S. Environmental Protection Agency's particulate standard for diesel cars and light-duty trucks. This EPA standard will require such motor vehicles, beginning with model year 1985, to make sharp reductions in the particulates emitted in the exhausts of their diesel engines.

The EPA developed its standard for public health reasons, mostly because the particulates contain some chemicals that are thought to be carcinogenic (cancer-causing). The agency also pointed out that diesel particulates are especially dangerous because they are overwhelmingly in the small-size range—less than 1/10,000 of an inch across—and are thus inhaled and lodged in the deepest part of the lungs.

Three major motor vehicle builders—General Motors Corp., Mercedes Benz, and Volkswagen of America—joined in the appeal. GM warned that the new standard could force the shutdown of production of fuel-efficient diesel cars and light trucks in the model year 1985 unless it is modified. The company claimed that the only way to comply with the standard would be to use a trap oxidizer. This device collects the solids in the exhaust through the use of some type of heavy-duty filter and then burns them off by means of thermal oxidation, a process that requires temperatures of at least 450° C (840° F). The process is very complex and requires electronic sensors and actuators to perform the oxidizer's function properly. General Motors claimed that the oxidizer is not sufficiently advanced technologically to be used by that date. Accordingly, strong efforts to modify the standard by means of legislation were expected.

A similar particulate standard was scheduled to be put into effect in 1986 for heavy-duty trucks, which emit 60–100 times the amount of particulates emitted by automobiles. This would also require a trap oxidizer for compliance. Automakers expected to gain support for their efforts from a study by the U.S. National Academy of Sciences, which found that while the EPA particulate standard for diesel cars for 1982 models is practical and prudent for protecting human health and the environment the much tougher 1985 standard could prove too costly for the industry.

Another company was added to the list of firms promising a breakthrough in the near future that will allow batteries to become economically feasible for use in electric automobiles in limited-range, low-speed urban travel. All such batteries to date have serious problems, such as high initial purchase costs, heavy weight, too limited range before recharging, and poor acceleration capabilities. However, C&D Batteries, a subsidiary of the Allied Corp., announced "the most revolutionary discovery in battery technology since the lead-acid battery came into use a century ago." C&D claimed that it was close to final development of a new, lightweight battery that could be in widespread use in electric cars in five to ten years.

According to C&D the battery would use either polyphenylene, a conductive polymer discovered by Allied researchers, or polyacetylene, a polymer developed by University of Pennsylvania researchers. Both are said to have unusual characteristics. Polyphenylene produces high voltages and does not deteriorate in air, while polyacetylene, which must be sealed from the air, can be produced in plasticlike sheets. The latter, thus, would make it possible for auto batteries to be made in unusual shapes, such as flat, for mounting in the side panels of the car.

C&D claimed that the energy storage capacity of both batteries is three times that of a lead-acid battery and that both can withdraw energy ten times as fast. Another advantage is the lack of fumes from the electrolyte.

The Fruehauf Corp. unveiled an experimental trac-tor-trailer combination, called the FEV2000, which was developed largely to demonstrate the remaining potentials of energy efficiency in truck technology. The unit is 18 m (60 ft) long, consisting of a 15-m (50-ft) trailer and 3-m (10-ft) tractor. It features side skirts along the entire length, an integral air flow foil at the front, and a unique boattail at the rear, all of which reduce drag. Also included are an air dam at the bumper to reduce underbody air drag, skirts at the drive wheels, and a seal at the tractor-to-trailer interface. Overall, these many features reduce drag by 57% compared to the configuration of a standard tractor-trailer vehicle.

Reduction of mechanical drag is accomplished by the use of radial-ply tires, a more efficient train package on the tractor, and use of lightweight materials. The main objective is to cut the use of costly fuel, and the experimental vehicle would do this by 40%. While its estimated 39% boost in cargo capacity would also be possible, the unit as built conflicts with current regulations in most U.S. states. One limits truck widths to 245 cm (96 in), and the new vehicle is 260 cm (102 in) wide. Another is its 18-m length, as opposed to the 17-m (55-ft) limit in most states. These and other regulatory conflicts are reasons why the experimental vehicle is not for sale, although its technological advances undoubtedly will be applied—even if in only a limited way—to existing truck-trailer combinations.

United Parcel Service (UPS) announced its first package-delivery van equipped with a new engine capable of saving up to 40% of the fuel now used by existing vans. UPS planned to build ten more such vans for fleet operations throughout the country if EPA approves the engine as meeting its emission standards. The engine has been modified so that it does not re-

UPI

Officers at police headquarters in Tokyo monitor the city's computerized traffic-control center. The computers analyze data, transmitted by over 5,000 sensors, on the number and speed of passing vehicles and use the information to regulate approximately 4,800 traffic signals.

France's TGV ("train of great speed") covered the 425 kilometers (265 miles) from Paris to Lyon in 2½ hours on its first commercial run, September 27, 1981.

quire either pre-mixing of fuel and air or the use of fuel with a high octane rating. Compared to a conventional gasoline engine, this new model has demonstrated improved idling performance and fuel savings of up to 38% in start-stop delivery driving and up to 20% in highway driving.

Pipeline. The government of Panama gave approval during the year for construction of a 90–100-cm (36–40-in) petroleum pipeline across the nation to link the Pacific and Atlantic oceans. The $170 million project became possible after Standard Oil Co. (Ohio) announced that it would not build its proposed pipeline to move Alaskan crude oil from Long Beach, Calif., to refineries in the Middle West.

The Panama line, to be designed and built by Morrison-Knudsen Co., Inc., was to consist of 83 km (52 mi) of 100-cm-diameter and 43 km (27 mi) of 90-cm-diameter pipe. It was to originate near Puerto Armuelles and terminate at a new marine terminal at Chiriquí Grande on the Caribbean Sea. The route would cross just about everything bad for a pipeline builder—mud, swamps, mountains, and rock. There would be 26 major water crossings, many over rivers with swift currents; at the largest ones the pipe must be coated with concrete to provide negative buoyancy. The mountain range crossing would require sufficient booster power to push the oil to a maximum elevation of 1,060 m (3,500 ft).

Designed for an initial throughput of 600,000 bbl per day, and ultimately 800,000 bbl, the pipeline is expected to cut as much as 20% from the $5 per bbl cost of transporting Alaskan crude oil across the Panama Canal. Construction was scheduled to be completed in late 1982.

Railroad transport. The French National Railroads unveiled what it proclaimed to be the fastest passenger train in the world. Called the TGV—an acronym for Train de Grande Vitesse, or "train of great speed"—its maximum cruising speed was 255 km/h (160 mph) although it was designed to be capable of reaching 380 km/h (235 mph).

The railroad had spent $1.6 billion since 1970 on the development of the train, which consists of eight cars joined together as a single unit without a break. The sleek aerodynamic shape, the low center of gravity because of an 45-cm (18-in) reduction in height as compared with conventional trains, the use of engines at both ends that generate 6,300 kw, and operations on continuous welded rails all combined to permit such great speeds. The train was so powerful that it could climb gradients up to 3.5% without loss of cruising speed. Because the speeds were so great the engineer had to use a special console in the engine cab to read track signal information on digital readouts.

The initial operational route was between Paris and Lyon, a distance of 425 km (265 mi). The trip took about 2½ hours, part of the route being traversed at slower speeds because of ordinary track. This was about 1¼ hours faster than the previous passenger-train schedule. By 1983, after the tracks are upgraded to permit TGV service, the route was to be extended to Marseille.

The U.S. Navy's missile-carrying hydrofoil ship "Pegasus" heads across Puget Sound prior to sea trials off California. A commercial passenger-carrying version was to be introduced in 1982.

The most innovative of many technological innovations to stimulate the interchange of rail and truck freight service moved into the operational stage of development. This was the RoadRailer, a highway trailer equipped with both rear-end rail and rubber-tired wheels that are interchangeable for both rail and highway travel. When on rails, the front end of the first unit links to the rail locomotive similarly to a highway trailer linking to a tractor. Each following unit links to the rear of the forward RoadRailer, thus making up a train without the need for any piggyback cars. This reduces weight sharply for rail travel—though increasing it somewhat for highway travel—in order to achieve large fuel savings.

Officials of the Burlington Northern Railroad Co. reported an impressive performance by the RoadRailer train in an operational test run between Chicago and Seattle, Wash., a distance of nearly 2,820 km (1,750 mi). The unusual freight train was made up entirely of 48 RoadRailers. A Burlington Northern spokesman said that the train sustained 95-km/h (60-mph) speeds on level track, crossed two mountains, and completed the long trip at an average speed of 68 km/h (42 mph). As for fuel conservation, he said that the train averaged 35 vehicle-kilometers (22 vehicle-miles) per gallon compared to 18 vehicle-kilometers (11 vehicle-miles) per gallon for conventional piggyback trains.

The Illinois Central Gulf Railroad (ICG) began the first daily commercial RoadRailer service on its 595-km (370-mi) route between Memphis, Tenn., and Louisville, Ky. ICG planned to operate the 80-unit train, under lease from the builder, Bi-Modal Corp. of Greenwich, Conn., in 16-hour overnight service for one year.

The firm was optimistic that the train would be successful, and, if so, it planned to add more such trains along other routes.

Trailer Train Co. officially introduced its new "4-Runner" intermodal rail freight car, which was designed for industrywide use and was expected to be formally approved by the Association of American Railroads. In 1981 it already was in revenue service on the Burlington Northern Railroad, and the Union Pacific Railroad ordered 100 cars for service by the end of 1981.

The new car has a number of unique features. In a departure from the design of virtually all U.S. rail equipment each of its wheel assemblies contains just one axle and set of wheels rather than two, resulting in a significant weight reduction. Its ride is cushioned by the same shock absorbers used by France's new high-speed passenger train. Its overall length of 57 m (191 ft) permits close fastening, with drawbars, of four independent skeletonized units that can carry four 14-m (45-ft) highway trailers. The trailers are loaded and unloaded by overhead or side cranes, and they are close enough to one another to reduce air turbulence and to eliminate the possibility that rear doors might be opened by thieves.

Water transport. The first U.S. deepwater port for unloading crude oil directly from supertankers began operations in 1981 off the Louisiana coast. The Louisiana Offshore Oil Port consists of three mooring buoys, where the tankers transfer their oil via a flexible floating hose to a huge 142-cm (56-in) underwater pipeline (the largest ever laid in the U.S.) for transfer to the pumping station about 2,440 m (8,000 ft) from the

389

buoys. From there the oil is pumped through a 120-cm (48 in) underwater line a distance of 31 km (19 mi) to a shore storage facility for later transfer to the Capline pipeline system.

Lockheed Aviation Services, a subsidiary of Lockheed Corp., began developing a central computer service for transoceanic ship routing. With a major goal of conserving fuel, the proposed SeaPlan would provide routings based on such data as weather, oceanography, ship performance, navigational aids, and customer needs. The company expected to test the innovation on a Greek shipping line in 1982. If the test proved successful, SeaPlan would be made commercially available in early 1983.

A commercial passenger-transport version of the Jetfoil, a high-speed hydrofoil made by Boeing Co., was scheduled to begin service in 1982. The vessel, named Bima Samudera 1, was to be delivered in its commercial passenger version but would have a quick-change capability to allow seat removal and rapid replacement with communication and navigation equipment for open-sea patrol functions. Its cost was approximately $13.7 million. The hydrofoil would be able to maintain level flight above the water by means of a computer control system that uses wave-height input to adjust the attack angle of the vessel's submerged foils.

The world's largest containership, "Frankfurt Express," entered service during the year for Hapag-Lloyd AG. The 51,540-deadweight ton ship was scheduled to serve the Europe–Far East route. Propelled by twin diesels, the twin-hulled vessel can stow containers in up to nine layers below deck and up to three layers above deck.

—Frank A. Smith

U.S. science policy

One of the last official deeds of U.S. Pres. Jimmy Carter was to reaffirm his consistent support of real growth in federally funded research and development by providing for an increase of 18.5% overall in his proposed budget for fiscal year 1982. The National Science Foundation (NSF) was slated to receive a jump of 23.5%. But budgetary proposals of outgoing administrations rarely survive intact, and the determination of incoming Pres. Ronald Reagan to reduce federal expenditures overall offered advance notice that change was in the wind.

Federal budget cuts. The magnitude of the change, however, was more in the nature of a force-10 gale. Even before the new administration had appointed any senior science officials to the major departments of the government, David Stockman, the new director of the Office of Management and Budget (OMB), began to hack away not only at research and development (R and D) funding in Carter's fiscal 1982 budget but also

at that allocated to the remaining months of the fiscal 1981 budget.

The exception to this process was R and D associated with national defense. The Reagan administration saw a public mandate to build national security while cutting heavily into non-defense expenditures as a means of reducing inflationary pressures. Although President Carter had specifically singled out basic research as an obligatory responsibility of the federal government, his successor rarely mentioned the subject during his campaign. The closest approach that policy scouts of a worried scientific community could find in the Reagan camp was a brief passage from a February 1981 OMB document, *A Program for Economic Recovery*. It was not reassuring:

The merit of research and development is without question. However, in times of fiscal austerity even some promising investments in science and technology must be restrained and new undertakings postponed.

By March 1981, however, it was no longer necessary for the science leadership to look for storm signals. The gale was blowing full blast. Within six weeks after taking office the new administration announced its revision of the budgets for fiscal 1981 and 1982. In dollar terms the proposed outlay of $21.0 billion for national defense R and D in Carter's 1982 budget was to be raised to $21.7 billion, while non-defense R and D was to be cut from $20.7 billion to $18.1 billion, more than 12.5%.

As instructions went out from OMB to the various executive agencies, the fine structure of the Reagan science policy became even more apparent. Proposed outlays for research programs for solar and other non-nuclear alternatives were drastically cut; by the end of 1981 the Department of Energy was being skeletonized amid discussions of its eventual absorption by other agencies.

The Carter initiatives to support joint government-industry programs of industrial innovation were rejected almost in their entirety; the economic philosophy of the Reagan administration relied on tax reductions rather than demonstration projects to provide the necessary incentives to private enterprise. But to the academic scientific community the most alarming developments were those associated with OMB instructions to the NSF.

The latter agency is the only federal entity primarily concerned with the support of science education and basic research. Thus there was concern over the fact that the fiscal 1981 budget it inherited from President Carter was cut by $82 million and its fiscal 1982 budget by more than $123 million. Of even greater concern to the scientific leadership, however, was that the NSF was not given the authority to allocate those drastic cuts according to its own wishes. Instead, it was ordered by OMB specifically "to selectively reduce or eliminate some ... programs while maintaining on-go-

Budget director David Stockman's efforts to reduce non-defense government spending included cuts in federal funding of research and development.

ing support for its critical responsibilities in the advancement of science."

OMB regarded as "critical" those programs supporting basic research in the natural sciences and engineering. A 20.5% increase given by the Carter administration to the NSF engineering directorate was untouched by OMB. But the social and behavioral sciences were severely cut, especially the social and economic sciences—from $40.1 million to $10.1 million. The science education program was, in the jargon of the new era, virtually "zeroed out." Of the $111.9 million that had been allocated for its activities by the Carter 1982 budget, only enough was left to support second- and third-year fellowship commitments. Especially painful to many scientists was a decision to eliminate an already budgeted $75 million program to upgrade scientific instruments, this after the apparently successful culmination of a hard-fought campaign to persuade several administrations that the growing obsolescence of U.S. laboratory equipment was to a large extent the most serious threat facing the national scientific endeavor.

The final blow to the NSF program—smallest in terms of actual dollars but of overriding importance to a large segment of the scientific community—was a set of decisions to reduce support for U.S. participation in the International Council of Scientific Unions and eliminate it entirely with respect to the International Institute for Applied Systems Analysis. The former provides the principal mechanisms for international collaboration among scientists in such ventures as the International Geophysical Year and the Global Atmospheric Research Program. The latter is an association of scientists from the advanced countries of the world which attempts to wrestle with problems of a transnational nature that may be subject to technical analysis,

such as global energy needs and environmental pollution that crosses national boundaries.

Another blow to international scientific cooperation came during the year when the U.S. National Aeronautics and Space Administration (NASA) reported that it could not fund its projected role in the International Solar-Polar Mission, an agreement between the U.S. and a consortium of 11 European countries for a joint mission to make a three-dimensional map of the Sun and its space environment through a pair of instrumented space vehicles to be launched in 1985. The sudden and unilateral announcement by the U.S. that it could not afford the joint mission raised serious questions among scientists of other countries concerning the reliability of future U.S. agreements.

One of the peculiarities of the U.S. scientific community is that although its members share common interests and objectives with respect to federal support, instances of organized political effort on its own behalf are quite rare. When they do take place, they are more likely to originate from perceived threats to their independence than from concerns about funding.

The impact of the administration budget cuts in March, however, suggested that even for the scientific elite, there were limits. Although the OMB staff concerned with the science budget insisted that the directed reductions in the NSF budget were based entirely on objective analyses of the productivity of specific areas of NSF support, the more outspoken members of the scientific leadership, notably Philip Handler, then president of the National Academy of Sciences, insisted that the cuts were the manifestations of ideological bias—against sociological and economic research on one hand and international cooperation on the other.

To the extent that there was bias in the Reagan administration against behavioral research, it was

391

broadly distributed; the research budgets of all the major agencies dealing with problems of mental health were heavily cut. The Alcohol, Drug Abuse, and Mental Health Administration was ordered to eliminate virtually all social research in its program.

The response from the affected scientists was not slow in coming. In the words of the Social Science Research Council:

Regardless of how the proposed cuts in the NSF (and other federal social science research) budgets were interpreted, they set in motion a train of events that is perhaps unprecedented in the history of the social sciences.... At first, social scientists, with help from their colleagues in the physical sciences, spoke out against the proposed cuts, in letters, telegrams, testimony, and in person, to those who might influence the final budget levels. By April, social scientists [as well as research psychologists, anthropologists, and an unprecedented alliance from other scientific disciplines] were beginning to work through existing organizations and were even creating new ones to influence Congress in its deliberations and decisions on social science research budgets.

One of the more fiery statements to the Congress was made by Zvi Griliches, chairman of the Department of Economics at Harvard University, in his testimony before the House Subcommittee on Science, Research, and Technology:

... no reasoned case has been made that social-science research is either valueless or of lower scientific quality than other NSF-supported research. I can, therefore, attribute the motivation for such selective cuts only to vindictiveness, ignorance, and arrogance.... Those suggesting these cuts do not seem to want to know what good economic policy can or should be ... The country is embarking on one of the largest macro-economic policy experiments in our history, with very little research support for it, and they do not even want to know how to measure its effect, how it is doing, and what its consequences might be!

Efforts to gain support from friends in the Congress were only partially successful; many members of the Congress were moved to give the Reagan plan a fair trial, and the Congressional budget-making process was in some disarray. Perhaps the most significant effect of the extraordinary effort of the scientific community on behalf of their beleaguered colleagues was that in September, when the Reagan administration—faced with the prospect of a calamitous deficit—called for a further 12% cut in all non-defense funding, there was some attempt to cushion the social and behavioral sciences from the second blow. By the end of 1981 Congressional action had increased the fiscal 1982 funding for social and economic sciences by the National Science Foundation to $17.6 million from the original severely cut figure of $10.1 million.

But the prospect of an across-the-board cut of 12% on all non-defense research and development brought great alarm to the rest of the scientific community. Because the proposed cuts were to apply to the budget of the fiscal year to begin on October 1, the directors of federally funded research laboratories began to send out dismissal notices to members of their permanent staffs. They also began to make telephone calls to the scientific leadership. So urgent were the calls and so pervasive was the alarm within the academic scientific community, that the National Academy of Sciences within a period of weeks took the unprecedented step of inviting the leaders of the U.S. scientific community to a meeting at the Academy in Washington on October 26 and 27, and then asked the top science officers in the federal government to meet with them. The objectives of the conference were to find out what was happening to the historic nurturing relationship between the federal government and academic science and to try to reach some agreement on how to minimize the damage that most feared.

Attending the meeting from the OMB was its principal officer responsible for R and D outlays, Frederick Khedouri. He had grim news for those seeking reassurance on continuing federal support:

... I think the one thing that it is important to understand is that this Administration has a really radically different attitude towards the budget than previous administrations have demonstrated ... [W]e are hopeful of establishing a target for federal direction of resources in the economy as a whole ... and once we've established this target we will not lie passively and watch events overtake the target ... We do not want to see a continued increase in pressure for the federal government to support more and more of the scientific endeavor, because I think that would lead ultimately to an unfortunate loss of independence and politicization.

His unbending approach was echoed, in part, by the subsequent remarks of George A. Keyworth II, head of the White House Office of Science and Technology Policy. Keyworth reminded the audience that U.S. science remained in a healthy position and that "the reaction in some areas is lacking realism." He suggested that the prospective reductions in federal funding would not be as harmful as many of those in the audience feared, since they would more likely be drawn from the development and demonstration sections of the overall R and D budget, as opposed to academic research.

A statement issued by the conferees also highlighted the need to protect "longer—term research, in contrast to development and demonstration." If further reductions are required, they said, the proposed 12% across-the-board cuts should be avoided in favor of a more analytical approach, employing inputs from the affected communities. Some of the funds earmarked for defense should go to basic research in recognition of its contributions to military technology; the production of scientists and engineers should be maintained at an adequate level; and the instrumentation and facility base "on which future scientific and technological advance depends" should be revitalized.

Because the contributions by industry to the overall national budget for R and D have been increasing rapidly in recent years relative to federal allocations, suggestions were made at the Academy meeting and elsewhere that in a thriving economy industry may be able to compensate for the slowdown in federal support of fundamental research. Not so, said Edward E. David, Jr., president of Exxon Research and Engineering, Inc. He estimated that it would require a tripling of industrial contributions to academic research over the next decade to compensate for the proposed cuts in federal support in the fiscal 1982 budget.

Biotechnology. There was one area, however, where industry was more than eager to support academic research. And in the process of doing so it was generating a range of difficult questions for those concerned with the independence of academic research. The field was biotechnology, and the interest was in the extraordinarily attractive products of recombinant DNA (deoxyribonucleic acid) research, almost all of it coming from university laboratories. The potential for sudden wealth, for both small and large industries and also for individual scientist-entrepreneurs, was quite dramatic.

Opportunities for joint enterprises of mutual benefit gave rise to a number of approaches from industry to major research universities, but not all of them were welcomed by the affected faculties; one such case occurred at Harvard University in 1980. A similar furor arose in the biology department at the Massachusetts Institute of Technology in 1981, but with a different outcome. MIT was approached by a wealthy entrepreneur, Edwin C. Whitehead, with a proposal to establish the Whitehead Institute for Biomedical Research under the direction of David Baltimore, a Nobel laureate on the MIT faculty who was internationally famed for his work in molecular biology. The proposal called for Whitehead to spend $20 million on construction and facilities, $5 million a year on operating expenses, and to leave an endowment of $100 million at his death. In addition, he offered a gift of $7.5 million to MIT's biology department as a "gesture of friendship."

One of the proposal's unique—and, to the faculty, troublesome—features was that the laboratory would share in the most precious privilege accorded to any faculty—granting tenure to selected individuals of merit. The proposal called upon MIT to grant full academic teaching appointments to 20 scientists who would be appointed by the officers of the institute.

Several members of the department protested loudly and publicly, but with the assurance that no individual would be named to the faculty who did not meet MIT criteria the biology faculty eventually voted to accept the proposal. During the year a number of similar enterprizes were launched at other major research campuses across the country. It appeared likely that the unfavorable prospect for federal funding played no small role in these developments, but there was also a certain inevitability in the process given the extraordinary financial promise of much of the contemporary research enterprise. Nevertheless, there was unease in the minds of many who saw an inevitable decline in the traditional interaction of bench scientists who were working in the same university laboratory but for different industrial sponsors.

Teacher shortage. The increasing overlap between the interests of university research laboratories and the output of high-technology industries gave rise to other fresh concerns in 1981. One had to do with the number of qualified scientists and engineers who were prepared to work in the high-technology companies. A leading physicist calculated that if the production of physicists continued on its present downward slope, the country would within a few years be turning them out at the rate it had been before the first Soviet spacecraft shocked the nation in 1957. Others pointed out that the sudden eagerness for engineers and mathematicians in the computer industry had driven up starting salaries for new Ph.Ds to an astonishing average of $33,516. Universities consequently could no longer

Culver Pictures

In 1925 the nation's attention was focused on Dayton, Tennessee, where a high-school teacher, John T. Scopes (seated at table, fifth from right), was tried for breaking a state law by teaching Darwin's theory of evolution. William Jennings Bryan, the most famous political orator of his day, led the prosecution, and the great lawyer Clarence Darrow (center, leaning against table) headed the defense. The trial ended in Scopes's conviction, but he was later acquitted by the state supreme court on a technicality. The teaching of evolutionary theory again became a political issue in the early 1980s.

compete in the marketplace, raising the question of where the next generation of technically trained people would come from if there were no competent teachers. The pinch was already hurting the military. In October the chief of the U.S. Air Force Systems Command reported 1,100 engineering vacancies in the Air Force, 500 in his own corps.

Nor were concerns limited to higher education. A report issued by the National Research Council lamented that only one-third of the nation's high schools offered more than one year of science and mathematics and that only 100,000 high-school students study calculus compared to 5,000,000 in the Soviet Union. Japan, the report added, graduates five times as many engineers as the U.S.

Creationism controversy. The coincidence of these findings with the announcement by the Reagan administration that it was eliminating science and engineering education from the NSF budget was worrisome—but even more worrisome to some was the sudden threat of a resurgent animosity to the teaching of biological evolution in public schools.

The Darwinian theory concerning the evolution of species, while accepted by the vast majority of the scientific community, is offensive to many individuals who accept a literal reading of the Old Testament. A counter-Darwinian movement, calling itself "scientific creationism," has come to challenge the accumulated body of research in evolution, geology, and astrophysics by raising unresolved questions in Darwinian theory and by offering what it considers evidence of a simultaneous creation of all known species of plants and animals.

Traditionally, the arguments of creationists have been met with cold scorn from the leaders of the scientific community, and their appeals for equal attention in the teaching of biology were effectively rebutted by the argument that creationism was a religious belief and had no place in the teaching of science. But in 1981 a new issue arose. The creationists, with some support from individuals with scientific training, began to argue that the unresolved questions in Darwinian theory and the purported evidence of simultaneous creation established a basis for teaching the subject as an alternative scientific theory.

Within a period of months bills were offered in several states that would require biology teachers to teach both theories or neither. A handful of individual teachers of biology and colleagues who had been crying in the wilderness with regard to the impending assault on academic freedom by the new creationists began to pick up allies. The signing by the governor of Arkansas on March 19 of a bill that ordered public schools to "give balanced treatment to creation-science and to evolution-science" sent shock waves through the scientific community. For the first time biology teachers found support, not only from their own professional society, but also from the National Academy of Sciences, the American Association for the Advancement of Science, and, most important for the science teachers of Arkansas, the American Civil Liberties Union.

The ACLU brought its big guns to Arkansas and trained them on the hapless young state attorney general obliged to defend the constitutionality of the law. The December trial was over in ten days, and Judge William R. Overton declared the law to be invalid in terms strong enough to satisfy even the most ardent evolutionist.

Creationists, however, did not accept defeat. They argued that the case had not been properly handled and that the legislation had been flawed. They also promised to be back, and it appeared at the end of the year that the battle would be joined once again, this time in Louisiana, where a similar bill had been enacted on July 21.

—Howard J. Lewis

Scientists of the Year

Honors and awards

The following article discusses recent awards and prizes in science and technology. In the first section the Nobel Prizes for 1981 are described in detail, while the second is a selective list of other honors.

Nobel Prize for Chemistry

The 1981 Nobel Prize for Chemistry was divided equally between Kenichi Fukui of Kyoto University, Japan, and Roald Hoffmann of Cornell University, Ithaca, N.Y., in recognition of their independent contributions to the development of a remarkably reliable generalization concerning the influence of the electronic structures of molecules on the course of reactions that they undergo. Some commentators assessed their theory as the most important advance in chemistry during the second half of the 20th century.

An achievement of this magnitude naturally did not occur suddenly, nor did it have a single origin. The evolution of its theoretical basis can be traced to a revolution that took place in the science of physics more than 50 years ago. Between 1929 and 1954 Nobel Prizes for Physics were awarded to Louis de Broglie, Werner Heisenberg, Paul A. M. Dirac, Erwin Schrödinger, Max Born, and Wolfgang Pauli. The prizes rewarded the achievements of these European physicists during the late 1920s, when they participated in the discovery of some unsuspected properties of electrons and in the development of an accurate mathematical description of their behavior in atoms and molecules.

One of the new properties of electrons was their wave nature, predicted by de Broglie and demonstrated by others, who showed that beams of electrons produce interference patterns just like those formed by light waves and water waves. Still other scientists found, by studying the effects of magnetic fields on the wavelengths of light emitted by atoms, that each electron acts as if it spins on its own axis. Given these clues to the nature of the systems with which they were dealing, Schrödinger and Heisenberg formulated an analysis of the dynamics of electrons that soon came to be called the "new" quantum mechanics, the successor to the "old" quantum mechanics conceived by an earlier generation of Nobel prizewinners: Max Planck, Albert Einstein, Niels Bohr, James Franck, and Gustav Hertz. The new quantum mechanics proved so versatile and general that Dirac viewed it as the basis for a complete understanding "of a large part of physics and the whole of chemistry."

Dirac has lived to see his insight vindicated by the granting of Nobel Prizes for Chemistry to Linus Pauling in 1954, Robert Mulliken in 1966, Gerhard Herzberg in 1971, and Fukui and Hoffmann in 1981; all of these scientists demonstrated that the results of quantum mechanical calculations can be used to understand many details of the structure and behavior of bulk matter.

Most of the substances of interest to chemists are composed of particles called molecules, which are assemblages of atoms held together by the mutual attraction of pairs of neighboring atoms for pairs of electrons that occupy the region between those atoms. The linkages between atoms, keeping them at particular distances and angles, are called covalent bonds, and chemical reactions are events in which old molecules disappear and new ones appear as old bonds break and new ones form. Although dozens or hundreds of covalent bonds may be present in a molecule, only a few of them are susceptible to change under ordinary circumstances, and much of the success of the experimental chemist depends on the ability to recognize these and to choose conditions that favor the breaking or formation of a covalent bond between selected atoms. In recent decades the cultivation of this art has grown into a specialized branch of chemistry focused on the mechanisms of reactions; that is, the sequences of motions of atomic nuclei and electrons that accompany the conversion of one set of molecules into another.

A large body of mechanistic results has been generalized into principles that account for many categories of reactions and that guide chemists in the selection of procedures appropriate to the synthesis of new materials. The reactions that have become best understood are those in which a sequence of bond-breaking and bond-forming steps result in the creation and destruction of a succession of transitory, unstable intermediate species. In a class of reactions that remained little

Kenichi Fukui

Wide World

Roald Hoffmann

understood until Fukui, Hoffmann, and the late Robert B. Woodward published the results of their investigations, several covalent bonds undergo changes all at once without the formation of any detectable intermediates.

The achievements of Fukui and Hoffmann are based on the quantum mechanical descriptions of molecular structure that are provided by the solution of a differential equation first formulated by Schrödinger. This equation, when written in the form appropriate to a chosen molecule, takes into account the interactions among all the electrons and atomic nuclei present in that molecule as well as the wave properties of those entities. The solution of the equation defines an open-ended set of discrete, stable energy states—called orbitals—that the electrons can occupy. Each orbital is identified with the value of its energy and with a particular region of space where the electrons are located. Under ordinary conditions two electrons occupy each orbital of the set that has the lowest total energy. There will always be one or two electrons in an orbital of higher energy than any other; these are the least tightly bound of all the electrons in the molecule. Every molecule also has an unlimited number of vacant orbi-

tals; if one or two more electrons are added, the stablest arrangement is that in which the new arrivals enter the vacant orbital that has the lowest energy.

Exact solutions of the Schrödinger equation yield results in excellent agreement with experimental observations, but for decades such solutions remained curiosities to most chemists because they were applicable only to molecules too simple to be of practical interest and were obtainable only by difficult and unfamiliar mathematical techniques. Over the years, however, chemists have become better acquainted with the concepts and relevance of quantum mechanics, while much of the mathematical rigor of the subject has been relieved by the development of qualitative descriptions of the types of orbitals most common in organic compounds. These lack the precision of those obtainable by extended calculations, but they are adequate for introducing the ideas advanced by the current Nobel laureates.

In 1954 Fukui published his first exposition of the concept that the crucial process in many chemical reactions consists of an interaction between the highest occupied molecular orbital of one compound and the lowest unoccupied orbital of another. In effect, the first molecule shares its most loosely bound electrons with the second, which accepts them at the site at which they can become most tightly bound. The interaction can be visualized as the formation of a new, occupied orbital that has properties intermediate between those of the two former ones. Fukui designated these labile orbitals "frontier orbitals" and provided examples of their significance in reactions used to produce important classes of organic compounds, including polymeric materials produced by the combination of different kinds of components.

Hoffmann undertook the research that led to his share of the Nobel Prize when in 1962 he joined forces with Woodward. (Woodward, who was to win the Nobel Prize for Chemistry in 1965 for his unparalleled successes in synthesizing complicated compounds that occur in nature, was probably the most influential organic chemist of the twentieth century.) Their immediate goal was to find a mechanistic explanation of the unexpected outcome of a reaction that Woodward and his colleagues had hoped to use in synthesizing vitamin B_{12}. Along the way they showed that several previously reported reactions take place in a way that can be correlated with an identifiable symmetry in the mathematical descriptions of the molecular orbitals that undergo the most change, and that this symmetry is absent in other known cases in which reaction does not occur. Their conclusions, expressed in a set of statements now called the Woodward-Hoffmann rules, account for the failure of certain cyclic compounds to form from apparently appropriate starting materials, though others are readily produced. The rules also explain why, when the rings in certain cyclic compounds are broken, the product consists of only one of several compounds that might have been expected by a chemist unaware of the rules. Furthermore, they provide the reason for the exact reversal of the symmetry requirements of reactions that are promoted by heat as opposed to those that are facilitated by light.

Though the scope of Fukui's frontier orbital interpretation is greater, Hoffmann and Woodward's theory had the advantages of being presented in one of the most widely circulated chemical journals in the world, in a qualitative and semipictorial form easily grasped by most organic chemists, and under Woodward's name. The Woodward-Hoffmann rules, promulgated in journal articles and in their book *The Conservation of Orbital Symmetry* (1970), were instantly accepted and have withstood numerous tests when applied to situations not previously examined. Many observers share Hoffmann's opinion that, had Woodward lived, he would have joined John Bardeen and Frederick Sanger as a winner of two Nobel Prizes in the same field.

Fukui was born in Nara Prefecture, Japan, in 1918. He took little interest in chemistry before enrolling at Kyoto University, where he earned a Ph.D. in engineering in 1948. During his years at the university he became intrigued by the theoretical challenges of chemistry and has made that science his lifework. He joined the faculty of engineering at Kyoto before attaining his doctorate and has been professor of hydrocarbon physical chemistry since 1951. His publications on the significance of frontier orbitals were written in a mathematical style, and they attracted little attention until they were shown to be connected to the later work of Hoffmann and Woodward.

Fukui's career is reminiscent of that of the 19th-century U.S. physicist J. Willard Gibbs. Though both were trained as engineers, their best-remembered achievements belong in the context of scientific theory. Both published their ideas in forms not immediately comprehended by those who later benefited most from them, in journals that were not widely circulated. The merits of the work of both men went largely unrecognized in their native countries until established foreign scholars perceived their significance and ensured their integration with the mainstream of science.

Hoffmann was born in Zloczew, Poland, in 1937 and emigrated to the United States in 1949. He graduated from Columbia University and pursued postgraduate studies at Harvard, where he was awarded the Ph.D. in 1962 upon completing a dissertation under the direction of William N. Lipscomb (the Nobel laureate in chemistry in 1976). He remained at Harvard for the next three years, collaborating with Woodward in framing the principles of the orbital symmetry theory. In 1965 he joined the faculty of Cornell University, where he was named John A. Newman Professor of Physical Science in 1974.

Nobel Prize for Physics

Three scientists who have revolutionized spectroscopy, the analytical study of the interaction of electromagnetic radiation with matter, shared the 1981 Nobel Prize for Physics. Half of the prize was awarded to Kai M. Siegbahn of the University of Uppsala, Sweden; the other half was shared by Nicolaas Bloembergen of Harvard University and Arthur L. Schawlow of Stanford University.

Siegbahn was cited for formulating the theoretical principles that underlie the technique called ESCA (electron spectroscopy for chemical analysis) and for refining the instruments necessary for carrying it out. ESCA depends upon a fundamental phenomenon, the photoelectric effect, which was discovered in the 1880s by the German physicist Heinrich Hertz. The effect consists of the emission of electrons by a material that is struck by a beam of electromagnetic radiation; it is displayed by all kinds of materials—solid, liquid, or gaseous—and is brought about by radiation of many wavelengths—visible, ultraviolet, X-rays, and gamma rays. Its existence is one of the key pieces of evidence that supports the modern view of the dual nature of matter and radiation, either of which can exhibit the properties of waves or of particles depending on the circumstances and the procedures used to observe and measure them.

Einstein's Nobel Prize, in 1921, was awarded specifically in recognition of his analysis of the photoelectric effect, which he had published in 1905. (Einstein believed that his work on the theory of special relativity was more significant, however, and devoted his Nobel lecture to that topic.) He showed that the energy of the radiation that causes a material to emit an electron must be exactly equal to the sum of two other quantities of energy: the first is the amount required to dislodge the electron from its bound state in the material, and the second is the kinetic energy possessed by the electron as it moves away.

The energy of the radiation—usually X-rays—used to liberate electrons can be controlled precisely. Siegbahn's achievement was to develop ways of measuring the kinetic energies of the ejected electrons accurately

Kai M. Siegbahn

Wide World

enough to permit the determination of their original binding energies. He was able to show that particular binding energies can be uniquely identified with the chemical element to which the electron had been bound and even with the ionic or molecular environment of an atom of that element. The compound sodium thiosulfate, for example, contains atoms of the element sulfur in two different states of combination; irradiation of a tiny sample of this substance with X-rays ejects electrons that had been bound with energies characteristic not only of sulfur but of the two states of that element in the compound.

In the late 1960s Siegbahn and his collaborators wrote two books in which they presented the theory and practice of ESCA. During the 1970s their technique was adopted in laboratories throughout the world for analyzing many kinds of materials, including the particles present in polluted air and the surfaces of solid catalysts used in petroleum refining.

Siegbahn—the son of Karl Manne Siegbahn, who received the Nobel Prize for Physics in 1924 for his discoveries relating to X-ray spectroscopy—was born in Lund, Sweden, in 1918. He was awarded a Ph.D. in physics by the University of Stockholm in 1944. In 1951 he was appointed professor at the Royal Institute of Technology in Stockholm, and in 1954 he moved to the Physics Institute of the University of Uppsala.

The Siegbahns, father and son, were the sixth parent-child pair to win Nobel Prizes. The others have been Pierre and Marie Curie, who won the physics prize in 1903 (Marie Curie also won the chemistry prize in 1911), and their daughter, Irène Joliot-Curie, who shared the chemistry prize in 1935; Sir J. J. Thomson and his son, Sir G. P. Thomson, who won the physics prizes in 1906 and 1937, respectively; Sir William Bragg and his son, Sir Lawrence Bragg, who shared the physics prize in 1915; Niels Bohr and his son, Aage Bohr, who won the physics prizes in 1922 and 1975, respectively; and Hans von Euler-Chelpin, who shared the chemistry prize in 1929, and his son Ulf von Euler, who shared the prize for medicine in 1970.

The unraveling of the physical principles that are

Nicolaas
Bloembergen

Harvard University

the basis of the laser and the maser had already brought Nobel Prizes to Charles Townes of the U.S. and Nikolay Basov and Aleksandr Prokhorov of the Soviet Union in 1964 and to Alfred Kastler of France in 1966. The idea of stimulated emission of radiation had been advanced by Einstein in 1917 and confirmed by several observers during the 1920s and 1930s, but the incentive for exploiting it in devices that amplify electromagnetic waves arose only after the spectacular growth of microwave technology that accompanied the development of radar during World War II.

Lasers are particularly useful in spectroscopy because they produce very intense beams of light, very nearly all of the same wavelength; they also can generate extremely brief pulses of radiation. All of these features have been incorporated into spectroscopic technology since the first laser was demonstrated in 1960. Bloembergen and Schawlow, who both are noted for their originality as well as their skills as teachers and experimentalists, earned their share of the Nobel Prize by investigating phenomena that depend for their very existence upon lasers.

Among Schawlow's accomplishments was an ingenious demonstration of a way to circumvent an inherent difficulty in classical measurements of the wavelengths of radiation emitted or absorbed by atoms and molecules. The problem arises from the motion of these particles—especially those in gases—in all directions at the same time that they are interacting with the radiation. This motion affects the wavelength of the radiation emitted or absorbed in the same way that the motion of an automobile affects the pitch at which its horn is detected by the ears of a stationary listener. The result of these so-called Doppler shifts of frequency is that an absorption or emission spectrum (a graph of intensity against frequency or wavelength) does not consist of a series of sharp peaks, each corresponding to a transition between two well-defined energy states; instead, the peaks are broadened and smeared into rounded and overlapping hills and valleys from which it is difficult and sometimes impossible to pick out the desired information.

Schawlow's method of locating precisely the wavelengths of light absorbed by the hydrogen atom required a laser that could be tuned like a radio transmitter to emit a sharp signal at any freqency within a wide interval. He directed the laser beam through a sample of hydrogen, where part of its energy was absorbed by those atoms moving at the particular velocity leading to a Doppler shift that made their absorption frequency exactly match that of the beam. After striking a mirror, the returning beam also was partly absorbed but by atoms for which the Doppler shift was opposite to that of the atoms that had absorbed part of the forward beam. A graph of the intensity of the reflected beam against the frequency, which was gradually varied, had the shape of each Doppler-broadened absorption peak of

Arthur L. Schawlow

hydrogen except at the frequency at which the Doppler shift was zero, as if the hydrogen atoms were stationary. (Few, if any, of the atoms were actually stationary, but those moving at right angles to the laser beam do not undergo the Doppler shift.) At that frequency the returning beam would have to have been partly absorbed by the same group of atoms that had already absorbed energy from the forward beam, but because they had done so, they could not do it again. Therefore, the intensity of the reflected beam rose abruptly at the frequency of light absorbed by stationary hydrogen atoms.

The result of this experiment was a set of highly precise values of the frequencies of radiation that the hydrogen atom absorbs; these, in turn, led to more accurate knowledge of the quantized energy states of the atom and to an improved value of one of the fundamental physical constants, the Rydberg constant.

Bloembergen became involved with the fundamentals of masers and lasers while he was engaged in his doctoral research at Harvard University in the late 1940s under the direction of Edward M. Purcell, who was to share the Nobel Prize in 1952 for investigations of the effect of magnetic fields on the absorption of microwaves by atomic nuclei. Within two years after Townes's group had demonstrated the first maser in 1954, Bloembergen had applied his knowledge of microwave absorption in working out the specifications for an improved version of the maser that has become the most widely used microwave amplifier. In 1957 he and his co-workers built the improved device in a form suitable for amplifying the weak radiation that hydrogen atoms emit at a wavelength of 21 cm.

The laser, which extended the scope of the maser to radiation of optical wavelengths, was introduced in 1960. In the following year Bloembergen directed his efforts to the study of the properties of matter illuminated by laser beams. James Clerk Maxwell in the 19th century had presented a satisfactory explanation of the

nature and behavior of electromagnetic radiation that does not appreciably alter the properties of the media through which it propagates. The electric and magnetic fields within a laser beam, however, are so intense that they induce observable changes in the properties of matter (such as the index of refraction) that govern the behavior of light beams. Maxwell's laws are inadequate for these situations, just as Newton's laws do not suffice for subatomic particles, but Bloembergen and his associates recast Maxwell's formulations to take the new effects into account, thereby establishing the theoretical basis for a new scientific specialty called nonlinear optics. Numerous practical applications of nonlinear optical phenomena have already been developed; these include an extension of the scope of laser spectroscopy by providing means of producing laser beams of previously unavailable wavelengths and a promising method of inducing unusual chemical reactions by focusing energy in such a way as to break a selected covalent bond within a molecule containing many such bonds.

Bloembergen was born in Dordrecht, The Netherlands, in 1920 and received bachelor's and master's degrees from the University of Utrecht before that school was closed by the Germans during World War II. In 1946 he accepted a research appointment at Harvard, where he undertook the studies for his doctorate. His Ph.D. was granted by the University of Leiden in 1948. Returning to Harvard, he became an associate professor in 1951 and since then has held several endowed professorships; in 1980 he was named the Gerhard Gade University Professor (a title once held by Purcell). He became a U.S. citizen in 1958.

Schawlow was born in Mount Vernon, N.Y., in 1921; shortly thereafter his family moved to Canada, and he attended the University of Toronto, receiving his Ph.D. in 1949. In that year he became a research associate at Columbia University, where he joined Charles Townes in the maser-laser project that led to Townes's share of the Nobel Prize for Physics in 1964. Townes and Schawlow wrote *Microwave Spectroscopy*, a monograph published in 1955. In 1951 Schawlow had married Townes's sister Aurelia and joined the Bell Telephone Laboratories. After returning to Columbia as a visiting professor in 1960, he moved to Stanford. In 1978 he was appointed J. G. Jackson and C. J. Wood Professor of Physics.

Nobel Prize for Physiology or Medicine

Sharing the 1981 Nobel Prize for Physiology or Medicine were three investigators of the workings of that most complex of all the biological structures that have evolved in the billions of years since life originated on the Earth, the human brain. Half of the prize was awarded to Roger W. Sperry of the California Institute of Technology, Pasadena, for his studies of "the func-

Roger W. Sperry

tional specialization of the cerebral hemispheres;" that is, the differences in the ways that the two halves of the brain deal with the information made available to them by the senses. The other half of the prize was shared by David H. Hubel and Torsten N. Wiesel, both of the Harvard University Medical School, Boston, for their collaborative discoveries concerning "information processing in the visual system;" that is, the mechanisms by which the brain builds up a meaningful image of the outside world from the sensations produced by light falling on the millions of sensitive cells present in the retinas of the eyes.

Neurologists have recognized for a long time that the two halves of the human brain are not completely redundant as are the kidneys or the lungs. A person is not fundamentally affected by the loss of one lung or one kidney because these paired organs are simple duplicates; either can perform the task normally shared by the pair. The cerebral hemispheres, on the other hand, although they are superficially alike, have been shown to differ in their responses to perceptions of the surroundings and in the kinds of mental tasks that they undertake. Evidence for these differences began accumulating in the 19th century, much of it from observations of the psychological effects of injuries that affected different parts of the cerebral cortex. For example, obstruction of the left anterior cerebral artery commonly results in paralysis and loss of sensation on the right side of the body as well as impairment of speech.

Sperry, regarded by many experts in his field as the world's leading authority on the brain, developed many of the surgical and experimental techniques that are necessary in testing theories concerning distinguishable mental activities and in locating the regions where they take place. The studies leading to his Nobel Prize evolved from experiments he conducted in the late 1940s at the University of Chicago on fish in an investigation of the transfer of learning from one side of the brain to the other. This work was extended to mammals—cats, monkeys, and chimpanzees—during the 1950s in Sperry's laboratories at Chicago and later at Pasadena, by disconnecting the halves of the brain by cutting through two groups of nerve fibers. One of these was the transverse bundle called the corpus callosum or the great cerebral commissure; the other was the optic chiasm, the crossover at which the optic nerves branch so as to carry information from each eye to both sides of the brain.

The first problem that Sperry wanted to solve was to find the exact function of the corpus callosum. Earlier investigators had severed this bundle of fibers but had found that the animals appeared to be practically unaffected; their learning ability, coordination, behavior, and responsiveness were those of normal animals. Sperry, however, invented new procedures that made it possible to teach one-half of the brain to perform some task and then test the other half for its ability to perform the same task. The results of this project clearly showed that the corpus callosum serves the important function of transferring information between the two hemispheres, enabling the intact animal to choose its actions by integrating the complementary but different mental processes that take place in the two halves of the brain.

The results obtained with these so-called split-brain cats and apes were carried over to human beings in the early 1960s. Two neurosurgeons, Joseph Bogen and Philip Vogel, encouraged by the rapid recovery of the animals after surgery and their apparently good health, applied the nerve-cutting procedure, called commissurotomy, to a few patients suffering from epilepsy that had been uncontrollable by all other treatments. After recovering from the operation, the patients experienced relief from their epileptic seizures and improvement of their general health; they also permitted Sperry and his co-workers to evaluate their psychological condition.

These evaluations fully confirmed the conclusions that had been reached from the studies of simpler animals. A long series of tests showed that the left hemisphere is superior to the right in assembling logical sequences that are expressed in speech or writing, while the right hemisphere is superior at recognizing faces, copying drawings, or distinguishing objects by feeling them.

Sperry, who was born in Hartford, Conn., in 1913,

earned a bachelor's degree in English literature and a master's degree in psychology from Oberlin (Ohio) College and a doctorate in zoology from the University of Chicago in 1940. He then became an associate of Karl Lashley, first at Harvard University and then at the Yerkes Laboratories of Primate Biology in Orange Park, Fla. In 1946 he joined the faculty of the University of Chicago and in 1954 moved to the California Institute of Technology as Hixon Professor of Psychobiology. In 1979 Sperry was awarded the Albert Lasker Basic Medical Research Award; he thus joined several other recent Nobel science laureates who had received Lasker prizes before being selected by the Nobel committees.

Hubel and Wiesel, who met when they were both associated with the Johns Hopkins University Medical School in Baltimore, Md., have been partners in research on the visual system of mammals since 1959, when they and the late Stephen W. Kuffler joined the faculty of the Harvard Medical School, becoming the nucleus of its department of neurobiology. One of their outstanding achievements was the analysis of the flow of nerve impulses from the eyes to the primary visual cortex, which is located in the occipital lobes of the cerebrum. They used tiny electrodes to detect the electrical discharges that occur in individual cells of the brains of monkeys as the retina responds to patterns of light.

The retina of each eye contains about 150 million light-sensitive cells called rods and cones. The responses of these cells to stimulation by light are relayed and combined through a complicated array of neurons arranged in successively deeper layers of the retina. The impulses pass through this data-processing network and ultimately reach the ganglion cells, of which there are approximately one million. The long projections, or axons, of these ganglion cells are the fibers making up the bundle called the optic nerve, which transmits the visual information, already considerably modified during its journey, to two relay stations, the lateral geniculate nuclei. Each of these, in turn, passes its share of the impulses along to the primary visual cortex of the right or left side of the cerebrum. Hubel and Wiesel demonstrated that every small patch of the retina corresponds to a small region of the visual cortex; the visual cortex, in other words, constitutes a map of the retina.

Their work revealed many of the structural and functional details of the primary visual cortex of the monkey. They found, for example, that the cells present in this region can be distinguished according to the degree of complexity of their action. The simplest cells are those that respond to impulses relayed by the geniculate nuclei from only one eye. These simple cells, in turn, stimulate cells of the next higher order of complexity: at this stage partial integration of the information from both eyes takes place. Even at this level of the hierarchy of cells the responses are produced by very small bits of the original stimulus. The organization of these bits into a mental image of the entire perceived object is a still more sophisticated operation that may take place in unexplored layers of the visual cortex or even in a different part of the brain.

The research of Hubel and Wiesel proved that many of the details of visual cortical function are determined by genetic mechanisms that operate during prenatal development, but that visual experience during the first few months after the birth of the animal can modify them to some extent. Their results support the view that prompt surgery is imperative in correcting certain eye defects that can be detected in newborn children.

Wiesel was born in 1924 in Uppsala, Sweden, and earned a medical degree from the Karolinska Institutet in Stockholm. After remaining there for a year as an instructor in physiology and as a member of the committee that selects winners of the Nobel Prizes in Physiology or Medicine, he accepted a research appointment at the Johns Hopkins University Medical School in 1955. He moved to Harvard in 1959 and was named the Robert Winthrop Professor of Neurobiology in 1974. He remained a Swedish subject.

Hubel was born in Windsor, Ont., in 1926 and attended McGill University in Montreal, receiving a bachelor's degree in 1947 and a doctorate of medicine in 1951. He held positions at the Montreal Neurological Institute, the Johns Hopkins University Medical School, and the Walter Reed Army Institute of Research in Washington, D.C., before joining the faculty of the Harvard Medical School in 1959. In 1965 he became professor of neurophysiology and, in 1968, was appointed George Packer Berry Professor of Neurobiology, a chair named for the former dean who brought Hubel and Wiesel to the Harvard Medical School. Hubel became a U.S. citizen in 1953.

—John V. Killheffer

(Left) David H. Hubel; (right) Torsten N. Wiesel

Harvard Medical School

AWARD	WINNER	AFFILIATION
ANTHROPOLOGY		
MacArthur Prize Fellow Award	Shelly Errington	University of California, Santa Cruz
MacArthur Prize Fellow Award	Lawrence Rosen	Princeton University, N.J.; Columbia University, New York, N.Y.
ARCHAEOLOGY		
MacArthur Prize Fellow Award	Ian Graham	Cambridge, Mass.
Roald Fryxell Medal	Karl W. Butzer	University of Chicago, Ill.
ARCHITECTURE		
Gold Medal of the American Institute of Architects	Romaldo Giurgola	Mitchell/Giurgola Architects; Columbia University, New York, N.Y.
International Pritzker Architecture Prize	Kevin Roche	Hamden, Conn.
ASTRONOMY		
Amateur Achievement Award of the Astronomical Society of the Pacific	George E. Alcock	Cambridgeshire, England
Catherine Wolfe Bruce Medal	Riccardo Giacconi	Harvard University and the Center for Astrophysics, Cambridge, Mass.
Eddington Medal	P. J. E. Peebles	Princeton University, N.J.
Gold Medal of the Royal Astronomical Society	Maarten Schmidt	California Institute of Technology, Pasadena
Henry Russell Lectureship	Riccardo Giacconi	Harvard University; Harvard/Smithsonian Center for Astrophysics, Cambridge, Mass.
James Craig Watson Medal	Stanton J. Peale	University of California, Santa Barbara
MacArthur Prize Fellow Award	Joseph H. Taylor	Princeton University, N.J.
Newton Lacy Pierce Prize	Bruce Margon	University of Washington, Seattle
Robert J. Trumpler Prize	Richard Kron	University of Chicago, Ill.
Steacie Prize	Georges Michaud	University of Montreal, Quebec, Canada
CHEMISTRY		
Alan T. Waterman Award	W. Clark Still	Columbia University, New York, N.Y.
American Chemical Society Award in Inorganic Chemistry	Roald Hoffmann	Cornell University, Ithaca, N.Y.
American Society of Biological Chemists-Merck Award	Martin D. Kamen	University of California, San Diego
Arthur C. Cope Award	Frank H. Westheimer	Harvard University, Cambridge, Mass.
Bingham Medal	James L. White	University of Tennessee, Knoxville

AWARD	WINNER	AFFILIATION
Buck-Whitney Award	Jack H. Freed	Cornell University, Ithaca, N.Y.
Carl Wagner Memorial Award	Allen J. Bard	University of Texas, Austin
Chemical Pioneer Award	Robert L. Banks	Phillips Petroleum Co.
Chemical Pioneer Award	Ralph Landau	Halcon International
Creative Polymer Chemistry Award	Louis J. Fetters	Institute of Polymer Science, University of Akron, Ohio
Ellis R. Lippincott Medal	George C. Pimentel	Lawrence Berkeley Laboratory, Calif.
Garvan Medal	Sara Jane Rhoads	University of Wyoming, Laramie
Gold Medal of the American Institute of Chemists	Milton Harris (Retired)	Gillette Co.
Herty Award	Jacob H. Goldstein	Emory University, Atlanta, Ga.
International Award in Heterocyclic Chemistry	Henk V. van der Plas	State Agricultural University, Wageningen, The Netherlands
James Flack Norris Award in Physical Organic Chemistry	Andrew Streitwieser, Jr.	University of California, Berkeley
Leo Hendrik Baekeland Award	Barry M. Trost	University of Wisconsin, Madison
Marlow Medal	G. S. Beddard	Royal Institution, London, England
Marlow Medal	Graham Fleming	James Franck Institute, University of Chicago, Ill.
National Academy of Sciences Award in Chemical Sciences	Gilbert Stork	Columbia University, New York, N.Y.
Outstanding Contribution to Chemistry Award	Duane A. Tewksbury	Marshfield Medical Foundation, Wis.
Pauling Award Medal	Henry Taube	Stanford University, Calif.
Percy L. Julian Outstanding Research Award	James W. Mitchell	Bell Laboratories
Perkin Medal	Herbert C. Brown (Emeritus)	Purdue University, West Lafayette, Ind.
Peter Debye Award in Physical Chemistry	Peter Rentzepis	Bell Laboratories
Robert A. Welch Award in Chemistry	Paul D. Bartlett	Texas Christian University, Fort Worth
Rosenstiel Award for Excellence in Basic Medical Science Research	Elias J. Corey	Harvard University, Cambridge, Mass.
Rosenstiel Award for Excellence in Basic Medical Science Research	Bengt I. Samuelsson	Karolinska Institutet, Stockholm, Sweden
Rosenstiel Award for Excellence in Basic Medical Science Research	Frank H. Westheimer	Harvard University, Cambridge, Mass.
Royal Medal	Geoffrey K. Wilkinson	University of London, England
Royal Society of Chemistry Award for Main Group Element Chemistry	Alan Cowley	University of Texas, Austin
Wolf Prize in Chemistry	Joseph Chatt	University of Sussex, England

AWARD	WINNER	AFFILIATION
EARTH SCIENCES		
Arnold Guyot Memorial Award	Mary R. Dawson	Carnegie Museum of Natural History, Pittsburgh, Pa.
Arnold Guyot Memorial Award	Robert M. West	Milwaukee Public Museum, Wis.
Arthur L. Day Medal	Donald L. Turcotte	Cornell University, Ithaca, N.Y.
Arthur L. Day Prize	Gerald J. Wasserburg	California Institute of Technology, Pasadena
Award for Outstanding Achievement in Bioclimatology	Harold C. Fritts	Laboratory of Tree-Ring Research, University of Arizona, Tucson
Award for Outstanding Contribution to the Advance of Applied Meteorology	J. Stewart Marshall (Emeritus)	McGill University, Montreal, Quebec, Canada
Carl-Gustaf Rossby Research Medal	Cecil E. Leith, Jr.	National Center for Atmospheric Research, Boulder, Colo.
Charles Chree Medal and Prize	Keith A. Browning	Royal Signals and Radar Establishment, Malvern, England
Charles Doolittle Walcott Medal	Martin F. Glaessner (Emeritus)	University of Adelaide, South Australia
Clarence Leroy Meisinger Award	Robert A. Houze, Jr.	University of Washington, Seattle
Cleveland Abbe Award for Distinguished Service to Atmospheric Sciences	Henry G. Houghton (Emeritus)	Massachusetts Institute of Technology, Cambridge
Cleveland Abbe Award for Distinguished Service to Atmospheric Sciences	Joachim P. Kuettner	National Center for Atmospheric Research, Boulder, Colo.; World Meteorological Organization, Geneva, Switzerland
Elliott Cresson Medal	M. King Hubbert	U.S. Geological Survey
G. K. Warren Prize	John T. Hack	George Washington University, Washington, D.C.
Henryk Arctowski Medal	Thomas M. Donahue	University of Michigan, Ann Arbor
International Meteorological Organization Prize	Bert Bolin	International Meteorological Institute, Stockholm, Sweden
James B. Macelwane Award	Ronald G. Prinn	Massachusetts Institute of Technology, Cambridge
James B. Macelwane Award	David Southwood	Imperial College of Science and Technology, London, England
James B. Macelwane Award	Donald J. Weidner	State University of New York, Stony Brook
John Adam Fleming Award	Thomas M. Donahue	University of Michigan, Ann Arbor
MacArthur Prize Fellow Award	Stephen Jay Gould	Harvard University, Cambridge, Mass.
MacArthur Prize Fellow Award	John Imbrie	Brown University, Providence, R.I.; University of Rhode Island, Kingston

AWARD	WINNER	AFFILIATION
MacArthur Prize Fellow Award	Paul G. Richards	Lament-Doherty Geological Observatory, Palisades, N.Y.; Columbia University, New York, N.Y.
Mary Clark Thompson Medal	William A. Berggren	Woods Hole Oceanographic Institution, Mass.
Maurice Ewing Medal	Manik Talwani	Lamont-Doherty Geological Observatory, Palisades, N.Y.; Columbia University, New York, N.Y.
National Academy of Sciences Award for Initiatives in Research	Kerry E. Sieh	California Institute of Technology, Pasadena
Penrose Medal	John Rodgers	Yale University, New Haven, Conn.
Second Half Century Award	James R. Holton	University of Washington, Seattle
Second Half Century Award	Hans R. Pruppacher	University of California, Los Angeles
Vetlesen Prize	M. King Hubbert	U.S. Geological Survey
Walter H. Bucher Medal	Jack E. Oliver	Cornell University, Ithaca, N.Y.
William Bowie Medal	Herbert Friedman (Retired)	Naval Research Laboratory, Washington, D.C.

ELECTRONICS AND INFORMATION SCIENCES

Duddell Medal and Prize	Bruce A. Joyce	Philips Research Laboratories, Redhill, England
Herman Skolnik Award	Robert Fugmann	Farbwerke Hoechst, Frankfurt, West Germany
Marconi International Fellowship Award	Arthur C. Clarke	University of Moratuwa, Sri Lanka
Senior Award of the Institute of Electrical and Electronics Engineers	Bishu S. Atal	Bell Laboratories
Senior Award of the Institute of Electrical and Electronics Engineers	Manfred R. Schroeder	Drittes Physikalisches Institut, University of Göttingen, West Germany
Stuart Ballantine Medal	Amos E. Joel, Jr.	Bell Laboratories

ENERGY

American Chemical Society Award in Petroleum Chemistry	Irving Wender	University of Pittsburgh, Pa.
Coates Award	H. V. Drushel	Exxon Research and Development Laboratories
Enrico Fermi Award	Rudolf E. Peierls (Emeritus)	University of Oxford, England; University of Washington, Seattle
Enrico Fermi Award	Alvin M. Weinberg	Institute for Energy Analysis, Oak Ridge (Tenn.) Associated Universities
Ernest Orlando Lawrence Memorial Award	Martin Blume	Brookhaven National Laboratory, Upton, N.Y.

AWARD	WINNER	AFFILIATION
Ernest Orlando Lawrence Memorial Award	Yuan T. Lee	University of California, Berkeley
Ernest Orlando Lawrence Memorial Award	Fred R. Mynatt	Oak Ridge National Laboratory, Tenn.
Ernest Orlando Lawrence Memorial Award	Paul B. Selby	Oak Ridge National Laboratory, Tenn.
Ernest Orlando Lawrence Memorial Award	Lowell L. Wood	Lawrence Livermore National Laboratory, Calif.
Howard N. Potts Medal	A. Uno Lamm	Hillsborough, Calif.
Peter Mark Memorial Award	Lawrence L. Kazmerski	Solar Energy Research Institute, Golden, Colo.
William R. Cherry Award for Outstanding Contributions to Photovoltaic Science and Technology	Joseph J. Loferski	Brown University, Providence, R.I.

ENVIRONMENT

Distinguished Service Award of the American Institute of Biological Sciences	Peter H. Raven	Missouri Botanical Garden, St. Louis
Environmental Award of the American Institute of Chemical Engineers	A. Roy Price	Merichem Co.
F. J. Zimmermann Award in Environmental Science	John M. Wood	Gray Freshwater Biological Institute of the University of Minnesota, Navarre
J. Paul Getty Wildlife Conservation Prize	Maria Tereza Jorge Padua	Director of National Parks, Brazil
J. Paul Getty Wildlife Conservation Prize	Paulo Nogueira Neto	Secretary of the Environment, Brazil
MacArthur Prize Fellow Award	John P. Holdren	University of California, Berkeley
M. S. Tsweet Chromatography Medal	Arnaldo Liberti	University of Rome, Italy
M. S. Tsweet Chromatography Medal	Robert E. Sievers	Cooperative Institute for Research in Environmental Sciences, University of Colorado, Boulder

FOOD AND AGRICULTURE

Chemical Pioneer Award	Quentin F. Soper	Eli Lilly and Co.
Cyrus Hall McCormick Gold Medal	Theodore E. Stivers, Jr.	Decatur, Ga.
John Deere Medal	Claude H. Pair (Retired)	U.S. Department of Agriculture
John Scott Medal	Quentin F. Soper	Eli Lilly and Co.
Rank Prize	Hamish Munro	U.S. Department of Agriculture
Royal Medal	Ralph Riley	Agricultural Research Council, London, England

AWARD	WINNER	AFFILIATION
LIFE SCIENCES		
Albert Lasker Basic Medical Research Award	Barbara McClintock	Cold Spring Harbor Laboratory, N.Y.
Edgar Tillyer Award	Leo M. Hurvick	University of Pennsylvania, Philadelphia
Edgar Tillyer Award	Dorothea M. Jameson	University of Pennsylvania, Philadelphia
Eli Lilly Award in Biological Chemistry	Harold M. Weintraub	Fred Hutchinson Cancer Research Center, Seattle, Wash.
Frederic Ives Medal	Lorrin A. Riggs (Emeritus)	Brown University, Providence, R.I.
Gilbert Morgan Smith Medal	Luigi Provasoli	Yale University, New Haven, Conn.
Herbert A. Sober Award	Efraim Racher	Cornell University, Ithaca, N.Y.
H. P. Heineken Prize	C. Weissmann	University of Zürich, Switzerland
H. P. Robertson Memorial Lectureship	Stanley Cohen	Vanderbilt University School of Medicine, Nashville, Tenn.
James Murray Luck Prize	Victor A. McKusick	Johns Hopkins University School of Medicine, Baltimore, Md.
James Van Lanen Distinguished Service Award	Henry R. Bungay	Rensselaer Polytechnic Institute, Troy, N.Y.
MacArthur Prize Fellow Award	Michael T. Ghiselin	University of Utah, Salt Lake City
MacArthur Prize Fellow Award	Richard C. Mulligan	Harvard University Medical School, Boston, Mass.
MacArthur Prize Fellow Award	Robert S. Root-Bernstein	Salk Institute, San Diego, Calif.
MacArthur Prize Fellow Laureate Award	Barbara McClintock	Cold Spring Harbor Laboratory, N.Y.
Madison Marshall Award	George Wald	Harvard University, Cambridge, Mass.
National Medal of Science	Philip Handler	Former president of the National Academy of Sciences, Washington, D.C.
Pfizer Award in Enzyme Chemistry	Richard R. Burgess	University of Wisconsin Medical School and the McArdle Laboratory for Cancer Research, Madison, Wis.
Richard Lounsberg Award	Philip Leder	Harvard University, Cambridge, Mass.
Ross G. Harrison Prize in Developmental Biology	Donald D. Brown	Carnegie Institution of Washington, D.C.
Scientific Medal	M. P. Hassell	Imperial College of Science and Technology, University of London, England
Scientific Medal	J. R. Krebs	Edward Grey Institute of Field Ornithology, University of Oxford, England
Selman A. Waksman Award	I. C. Gunsalus	University of Illinois, Urbana

AWARD	WINNER	AFFILIATION
U.S. Steel Foundation Award in Molecular Biology	Joan A. Steitz	Yale University, New Haven, Conn.
Weiss Medal	E. J. Land	Christie Hospital and Holt Radium Institute, Withington, England
Weiss Medal	A. J. Swallow	Christie Hospital and Holt Radium Institute, Withington, England
Willard Gibbs Medal	Bert Vallee	Harvard University Medical School, Boston, Mass.
Wolf Prize in Medicine	Stanley N. Cohen	Stanford University, Calif.
MATERIALS SCIENCES		
A. L. Patterson Award	Wayne A. Hendrickson	Naval Research Laboratory, Washington, D.C.
Dickson Prize for Science	John W. Cahn	Center for Materials Science, National Bureau of Standards, Gaithersburg, Md.
International Award in Plastics Science and Engineering	Roger S. Porter	Materials Research Laboratory of the National Science Foundation, Washington, D.C.; University of Massachusetts, Amherst
Karl J. Bayer Medal	Allen S. Russell	ALCOA
MATHEMATICS		
Frank Nelson Cole Prize in Number Theory	Robert P. Langlands	Institute for Advanced Study, Princeton, N.J.
Frank Nelson Cole Prize in Number Theory	Barry Mazur	Harvard University, Cambridge, Mass.
John J. Carty Award	Shing-Tung Yau	Institute for Advanced Study, Princeton, N.J.
Leroy P. Steele Prize	Nelson Dunford (Emeritus)	Yale University, New Haven, Conn.
Leroy P. Steele Prize	Eberhard Hopf (Emeritus)	Indiana University, Bloomington
Leroy P. Steele Prize	Jacob T. Schwartz	New York University, New York, N.Y.
Leroy P. Steele Prize	Oscar Zariski (Emeritus)	Harvard University, Cambridge, Mass.
MacArthur Prize Fellow Award	Gregory V. Chudnovsky	New York, N.Y.
Salem Prize	Peter Jones	University of Chicago, Ill.
MEDICAL SCIENCES		
Albert Lasker Clinical Medical Research Award	Louis Sokoloff	National Institutes of Health, Bethesda, Md.
Alfred P. Sloan Prize	César Milstein	Medical Research Council Laboratory of Molecular Biology, Cambridge, England
Alfred P. Sloan Prize	Wallace P. Rowe	National Institutes of Health, Bethesda, Md.

AWARD	WINNER	AFFILIATION
Bristol-Myers Award for Distinguished Achievement in Cancer Research	Van Rensselaer Potter	McArdle Laboratory for Cancer Research, University of Wisconsin, Madison
Charles F. Kettering Award	E. Donnall Thomas	Fred Hutchinson Cancer Research Center, Seattle, Wash.
Charles S. Mott Award	Takashi Sugimura	National Cancer Center Research Institute, Tokyo, Japan
Gairdner Foundation International Award	Michael S. Brown	University of Texas Health Center at Dallas
Gairdner Foundation International Award	Wai Yiu Cheung	University of Tennessee Center for Health Sciences, Memphis
Gairdner Foundation International Award	Joseph L. Goldstein	University of Texas Health Center at Dallas
Gairdner Foundation International Award	Georges Köhler	Institute for Immunology, Basel, Switzerland
Gairdner Foundation International Award	César Milstein	Medical Research Council Laboratory of Molecular Biology, Cambridge, England
Gairdner Foundation International Award	Elizabeth Neufeld	National Institutes of Health, Bethesda, Md.
Gairdner Foundation International Award	Saul Roseman	Johns Hopkins University, Baltimore, Md.
Gairdner Foundation International Award	Bengt I. Samuelsson	Karolinska Institutet, Stockholm, Sweden
Gairdner Foundation International Award	Jerry H. C. Wang	University of Manitoba, Winnipeg, Canada
Harold Lamport Award for Young Investigators in Physiology and Biophysics	David B. P. Goodman	University of Pennsylvania School of Medicine, Philadelphia
Harvey Prize in Human Health	Hans W. Kosterlitz	University of Aberdeen, Scotland
International Gold Medal for Excellence in Research in the Disease of Alcoholism	Harold Kalant	Addiction Research Foundation of Ontario; University of Toronto, Ontario, Canada
Inventor of the Year	Donald Ausmus	Independence, Mo.
Isaac Schour Memorial Science Award	Edward J. Kollar	University of Connecticut, Storrs
Jacob F. Schoellkopf Medal	Gabor Markus	Roswell Park Memorial Institute, Buffalo, N.Y.
Louis and Bert Freedman Foundation Award for Research in Biochemistry	Eric J. Simon	New York University School of Medicine, New York, N.Y.
MacArthur Prize Fellow Award	H. John Cairns	Harvard School of Public Health, Boston, Mass.
MacArthur Prize Fellow Award	Raphael C. Lee	Massachusetts Institute of Technology, Cambridge; Massachusetts General Hospital, Boston

AWARD	WINNER	AFFILIATION
Paul Ehrlich-Ludwig Darmstaedter Prize	Stanley Falkow	Stanford University Medical Center, Calif.
Paul Ehrlich-Ludwig Darmstaedter Prize	Susumu Mitsuhashi	Gumma University, Maebashi, Japan
Ramón Magsaysay Award	Pramud Karan Sethi	Mahavir Viklang Sahayata Samiti, Sawai Mansingh Medical College, Jaipur, India
Sidney S. Kaliski Award of Merit	C. W. Daeschner, Jr.	University of Texas, Galveston
Wightman Award	Louis Siminovitch	University of Toronto; Hospital for Sick Children, Toronto, Ontario, Canada
William S. Middleton Award	Norman Talal	University of California School of Medicine; Veterans Administration Medical Center, San Francisco

OPTICAL ENGINEERING

AWARD	WINNER	AFFILIATION
Adolph Lomb Medal	Won-Tien Tsang	Bell Laboratories
Charles Hard Townes Award	C. Kumar N. Patel	Bell Laboratories
David Richardson Medal	Charles A. Burrus, Jr.	Bell Laboratories
Frederick Ives Medal	Lorrin A. Riggs (Emeritus)	Brown University, Providence, R.I.
Rank Prize	Charles Eliott	Royal Signals and Radar Establishment, Malvern, England
Rank Prize	Calvin F. Quate	Stanford University, Calif.
R. W. Wood Prize	Linn F. Mollenauer	Bell Laboratories
Simrad Prize in Electro-Optics	Halvor Heier	Central Institute for Industrial Research, Oslo, Norway
Simrad Prize in Electro-Optics	Jakob Stamnes	Central Institute for Industrial Research, Oslo, Norway

PHYSICS

AWARD	WINNER	AFFILIATION
Albert A. Michelson Medal	Hermann P. J. Haken	University of Stuttgart, West Germany
Apker Award	Mark B. Ritter	Montana State University, Bozeman
Frank H. Spedding Award	Georg A. Busch (Emeritus)	Laboratory of Solid State Physics, Eidgenössische Technische Hochschule, Zurich, Switzerland
Franklin Medal	Stephen W. Hawking	University of Cambridge, England
Glazebrook Medal and Prize	Godfrey H. Stafford	Rutherford Appleton Laboratory, Chilton; St. Cross College, University of Oxford, England
Gold Medal of the Acoustical Society of America	Harry F. Olson (Retired)	RCA Corp.
Grand Prix de Physique Jean Ricard	Paul Rebut	Joint European Torus (JET)
Guthrie Medal and Prize	J. C. Ward	Macquarie University, North Ryde, New South Wales, Australia
Harry Diamond Award	Martin Greenspan	Silver Spring, Md.

AWARD	WINNER	AFFILIATION
Holweck Prize	David J. Thouless	University of Washington, Seattle; Yale University, New Haven, Conn.
James Clerk Maxwell Prize	John H. Nuckolls	Lawrence Livermore National Laboratory, Calif.
John Price Wetherill Medal	Frank F. Fang	Thomas J. Watson Research Center, Yorktown Heights, N.Y.
John Price Wetherill Medal	Alan B. Fowler	Thomas J. Watson Research Center, Yorktown Heights, N.Y.
John Price Wetherill Medal	Webster E. Howard	Thomas J. Watson Research Center, Yorktown Heights, N.Y.
John Price Wetherill Medal	Frank Stern	Thomas J. Watson Research Center, Yorktown Heights, N.Y.
John Price Wetherill Medal	Phillip J. Stiles	Brown University, Providence, R.I.
John T. Tate International Medal	Pierre Aigrain	Groupe Thomson, France
J. Robert Oppenheimer Memorial Prize	Maurice Goldhaber	Brookhaven National Laboratory, Upton, N.Y.
J. Robert Oppenheimer Memorial Prize	Robert Marshak	Virginia Polytechnic Institute and State University, Blacksburg
Karl Taylor Compton Prize	Melba N. Phillips (Emeritus)	University of Chicago, Ill.
MacArthur Prize Fellow Award	Douglas D. Osheroff	Bell Laboratories
MacArthur Prize Fellow Award	Steven Wolfram	California Institute of Technology, Pasadena
MacArthur Prize Fellow Award	George Zweig	Los Alamos National Laboratory, N.M.
Max Born Prize	Cyril Domb	King's College, University of London, England
Max Planck Medal	Kurt Symanzik	Deutsches Elektronen-Synchrotron, Hamburg, West Germany
Medard W. Welch Award	Harrison B. Farnsworth (Emeritus)	Brown University, Providence, R.I.
Navy Superior Civilian Service Award	Bruce J. Faraday (Retired)	Naval Research Laboratory, Washington, D.C.
Norsk Data Physics Award	Kjell Johnsen	Brookhaven National Laboratory, Upton, N.Y.
Otto Klung Prize	Gerhard Mack	Theoretical Physics Institute II, University of Hamburg, West Germany
Particle Physics Prize	Kjell Johnsen	Brookhaven National Laboratory, Upton, N.Y.
Prize for Industrial Applications of Physics	Alec N. Broers	IBM
Simon Memorial Prize	A. J. Leggett	University of Sussex, Brighton, England
Thomas Young Prize	Nicholas J. Phillips	Loughborough University of Technology, England
Walter Schottky Prize in Solid State Physics	Klaus von Klitzing	Technischen Universität, Munich, West Germany
William F. Meggers Award	George W. Series	University of Reading, England

AWARD	WINNER	AFFILIATION
Wolf Prize in Physics	Freeman Dyson	Institute for Advanced Study, Princeton, N.J.
Wolf Prize in Physics	Gerard t'Hooft	State University of Utrecht, The Netherlands
Wolf Prize in Physics	Victor Weisskopf	Massachusetts Institute of Technology, Cambridge
Wright Prize	Luis W. Alvarez (Emeritus)	University of California, Berkeley
Wyld Propulsion Award	John F. Kincaid	Applied Physics Laboratory, Johns Hopkins University, Baltimore, Md.

PSYCHOLOGY

American Association for the Advancement of Science Socio-Psychological Prize	Gary W. Strong	Systems Service Institute, University of Louisville, Ky.
Distinguished Contribution to Psychology in the Public Interest	Herbert C. Kelman	Harvard Center for International Affairs, Cambridge, Mass.
Distinguished Professional Contribution Award	Jack I. Bardon	University of North Carolina, Greensboro
Distinguished Professional Contribution Award	Carl Eisdorfer	Montefiore Hospital and Medical Center, New York, N.Y.; Albert Einstein College of Medicine of Yeshiva University, New York, N.Y.
Distinguished Professional Contribution Award	Jane W. Kessler	Case Western Reserve Mental Development Center, Cleveland, Ohio
Distinguished Scientific Award for the Applications of Psychology	Anne Anastasi	Fordham University, New York, N.Y.
Distinguished Scientific Contribution Award	David M. Green	Harvard University, Cambridge, Mass.
Distinguished Scientific Contribution Award	Irving L. Janis	Yale University, New Haven, Conn.
Distinguished Scientific Contribution Award	James L. McGaugh	University of California, Irvine
MacArthur Prize Fellow Award	Robert Coles	Concord, Mass.
MacArthur Prize Fellow Award	Howard E. Gardner	Boston University, Mass.

SPACE EXPLORATION

Collier Trophy	The individuals and organizations responsible for developing and demonstrating the feasibility of the "Columbia" space shuttle	
Langley Medal	Charles S. Draper (Emeritus)	Charles Stark Draper Laboratory, Inc., Cambridge, Mass.; Massachusetts Institute of Technology, Cambridge
Langley Medal	Robert T. Jones	Ames Research Center, Moffett Field, Calif.
Presidential Citizen's Medal	Alan M. Lovelace	NASA

AWARD	WINNER	AFFILIATION
TRANSPORTATION		
George H. Henderson Medal	Louis T. Klauder	Louis T. Klauder and Associates
Goddard Award	John F. Yardley	McDonnell Douglas Astronautics Co.
Wright Brothers Memorial Trophy	Dwane L. Wallace (Retired)	Cessna Aircraft Co.
SCIENCE JOURNALISM		
American Association for the Advancement of Science-Westinghouse Science Journalism Award	Barbara Burke	*Journal,* Ithaca, N.Y.
American Association for the Advancement of Science-Westinghouse Science Journalism Award	Henry S. F. Cooper	*New Yorker*
American Association for the Advancement of Science-Westinghouse Science Journalism Award	Stuart Harris	Public Broadcasting Service
American Association for the Advancement of Science-Westinghouse Science Journalism Award	Eliza Hobson	WEVO radio, Concord, N.H.
American Association for the Advancement of Science-Westinghouse Science Journalism Award	Fay Joyce	*Times,* St. Petersburg, Fla.
American Association for the Advancement of Science-Westinghouse Science Journalism Award	John Mansfield	Public Broadcasting Service
American Association for the Advancement of Science-Westinghouse Science Journalism Award	Charles Stafford	*Times,* St. Petersburg, Fla.
American Institute of Physics-U.S. Steel Foundation Science Writing Award in Physics and Astronomy	Eric J. Chaisson	Harvard University; Harvard/Smithsonian Center for Astrophysics, Cambridge, Mass.
Dorothea Klumpke-Roberts Award	Dietrick Thomsen	*Science News*
James T. Grady Award for Interpreting Chemistry for the Public	Albert Rosenfeld	*Science 81;* University of Texas Medical School, Galveston

AWARD	WINNER	AFFILIATION
MISCELLANEOUS		
American Association for the Advancement of Science-Newcomb Cleveland Prize	Robert Axelrod	Institute of Public Policy Studies, University of Michigan, Ann Arbor
American Association for the Advancement of Science-Newcomb Cleveland Prize	William D. Hamilton	Museum of Zoology, University of Michigan, Ann Arbor
Bradford Washburn Award	Roger Tory Peterson	Old Lyme, Conn.
Delmer S. Fahrney Medal	Arthur M. Bueche	General Electric Co.
National Academy of Sciences Public Welfare Medal	Paul G. Rogers	Former congressman from Florida
Sanford Fleming Medal	David Suzuki	Canadian Broadcasting Corp.
Scientific Freedom and Responsibility Award	Morris Baslow	New City, N.Y.
Scientific Freedom and Responsibility Award	Paul Berg	Stanford University, Calif.
Scientific Freedom and Responsibility Award	Maxine Singer	National Institutes of Health, Bethesda, Md.
Scientific Freedom and Responsibility Award	Norton Zinder	Rockefeller University, New York, N.Y.
Vannevar Bush Award	William O. Baker (Retired)	Bell Laboratories
Westinghouse Science Talent Search	1. Reena B. Gordon	Midwood High School, New York, N.Y.
	2. Ronald M. Kantor	Riverdale Country School, New York, N.Y.
	3. Ogan Gurel	Stuyvesant High School, New York, N.Y.
	4. Helen E. Getto	Lane Technical High School, Chicago, Ill.
	5. Theron W. Stanford	San Marino High School, Calif.
	6. Mitchell Tsai	Theodore Roosevelt High School, Kent, Ohio
	7. Niels P. Mayer	Corona del Mar High School, Calif.
	8. Noam D. Elkies	Stuyvesant High School, New York, N.Y.
	9. Saechin Kim	Bronx High School of Science, New York, N.Y.
	10. Lynne P. Snyder	Smithtown High School West, N.Y.

Obituaries

Barnett, Stephen Frank (Aug. 10, 1915—Aug. 18, 1981), British veterinarian, made important contributions to the understanding of tick-borne diseases in livestock and hence to the control of such diseases and the improvement of tropical agriculture. He was particularly noted for his work on East Coast fever, a protozoan disease of cattle, and he acted as adviser to many countries in Africa, South America, and the Middle East. Barnett studied at the Royal Veterinary College in London and in 1939 joined the Kenya Department of Veterinary Services. After obtaining his doctorate at the University of London in 1947 he continued his research in Chicago and East Africa before becoming university lecturer in animal pathology at the University of Cambridge in 1964.

Breit, Gregory (July 14, 1899—Sept. 13, 1981), Russian-born physicist, was a highly esteemed theoretical physicist, who in 1942 joined the Manhattan Project in Chicago and began making designs for an atomic bomb. Although Breit resigned from the project to embark on ballistics research at the Aberdeen Proving Ground, Md., his expertise was needed again some seven years later when scientists feared that an explosion of a hydrogen bomb might set off a worldwide chain reaction. Breit's calculations discounted this theory, and he backed up his conclusion with tests using a new cyclotron at Oak Ridge (Tenn.) National Laboratories. He was also credited with helping to develop the resonance theory of nuclear reactions and with contributing to the first "atom smashers." For the latter he was awarded a National Medal of Science in 1967. During his long career Breit taught at the University of Minnesota (1923–24), was a physicist in the department of terrestrial magnetism at Carnegie Institution (1924–29), and served as professor at New York University (1929–34), the University of Wisconsin (1934–47), Yale University (1937–68), and the State University of New York at Buffalo (1968–73).

Breuer, Marcel (Lajos) (May 21, 1902—July 1, 1981), Hungarian-born architect and designer, was instrumental in creating modern furniture and building designs that were indicative of a technological age. Breuer was a leading exponent of the International Style, which was characterized by the use of open space and utilized reinforced concrete construction. From 1920 to 1928 he studied and then taught at the famous Bauhaus school of design. Under the tutelage of its master, Walter Gropius, Breuer designed prefabricated housing and modular furniture. In 1925, inspired by the shape of bicycle handlebars, he fashioned his classic Wassily chair, which featured leather straps slung across a tubular steel frame. In 1928 Breuer set up his own architectural firm in Berlin and created the Cesca chair, a tubular steel dining chair with a cane back and seat. During this time he completed two out-standing projects: the Harnischmacher House (1932) in Wiesbaden, Germany, and the Dolderthal Apartments (1934–36) in Zürich, Switz. Breuer then worked for a brief period in London with the architect F. R. S. Yorke. He designed laminated plywood furniture that became widely imitated. In 1937 Breuer accepted a teaching position at Harvard University's School of Architecture and joined his old associate Walter Gropius. Together with Gropius he designed a series of wood-frame houses that combined elements of the International Style and American materials, resulting in a light, boxlike structure similar to many of his earlier European projects. Examples of this style were Breuer's house at Lincoln, Mass. (1939) and the Chamberlain cottage, Wayland, Mass. (1940). After Breuer's move to New York in 1946, his work became more heavy and sculptural. Some of his major commissions included the Sarah Lawrence College Theatre, Bronxville, N.Y. (1952); UNESCO Headquarters, Paris (1953–58; with Pier Luigi Nervi and Bernard Zehrfuss); St. John's Abbey, Collegeville, Minn. (1953–61); De Bijenkorf department store, Rotterdam, Neth. (1955–57); the IBM research center, La Gaude, Var, France (1960–62); the Whitney Museum of American Art, New York City (completed 1966); and the headquarters for the Department of Housing and Urban Development (HUD), Washington, D.C. (1963–68). Among his numerous awards and tributes Breuer received the coveted gold medal of the American Institute of Architects in 1968, and in 1976 he received the gold medal of the French Académie d'Architecture. He retired in the same year.

Coon, Carleton S(tevens) (June 23, 1904—June 3, 1981), U.S. anthropologist and archaeologist, often conducted anthropological studies in conjunction with archaeological investigations and was the author of the highly controversial work *Origin of Races* (1962). In 1949 Coon unearthed approximately 31,000 agricultural artifacts, some dated at about 6050 BC, while exploring Belt Cave in northern Iran. Two years later he returned to Iran and excavated Hotu Cave, which contained thick rock deposits that revealed an unbroken cultural sequence encompassing the Iron Age, Bronze Age, and New Stone Age. Beneath a layer of rock that had fallen from the ceiling of the cave, Coon found layers of sand and gravel from the last glacial period. Nearly twelve meters (39 ft) down he discovered the fossilized bones of human beings. These findings culminated in the publication of *The Story of Man* (1954), which traced the history of man 50,000 years from the Ice Age to modern times. Coon set forth the controversial theory that five distinct major races of man existed before the emergence of *Homo sapiens* as the dominant species. This theory was disputed and then largely ignored by scientists. Coon, who received both undergraduate and graduate degrees from Harvard University, spoke ten languages, including some

415

used by the tribes he studied. He taught anthropology at his alma mater before becoming professor of anthropology at the University of Pennsylvania and curator of ethnology at the University Museum in Philadelphia in 1948. Coon was a prolific writer, and some of his other notable works included: *Tribes of the Rif* (1931), *The Races of Europe* (1939), *A Reader in General Anthropology* (1948), and *The Seven Caves* (1957). His autobiography, *Adventures and Discoveries,* was to be published posthumously.

Corner, George Washington (Dec. 12, 1889—Sept. 28, 1981), U.S. anatomist and embryologist, specialized in analyzing the function of hormones in the female reproductive system and, with Willard M. Allen, identified the hormone progesterone, an ingredient used in oral contraceptives. Their findings led to the development of birth control pills, many of which contain a mixture of a synthetic progestational agent and a small amount of estrogen. Corner received (1913) his M.D. from Johns Hopkins University and taught there and at the University of California until 1923. He then served (1923–40) as professor of anatomy at the University of Rochester School of Medicine, director (1940–55) of the department of embryology at the Carnegie Institution in Washington, historian (1955–60) of the Rockefeller Institute, and executive officer (1960–77) of the American Philosophical Society in Philadelphia.

Darlington, Cyril Dean (Dec. 19, 1903—March 26, 1981), British biologist, was Sherardian professor of botany at the University of Oxford (1953–71) and the author of remarkable and sometimes controversial works on human population and genetics. The first of these, *Recent Advances in Cytology* (1932), virtually established nuclear cytology as a scientific discipline. It appeared while Darlington was a member of the staff at the John Innes Horticultural Institution, which he had joined in 1923. He also served as director there from 1939 to 1953. His second major book, *The Evolution of Genetic Systems* (1939), adopted a still broader perspective in its study of population and evolution and had a far-reaching effect on the development of biological ideas. In 1969 Darlington published *The Evolution of Man and Society,* a wide-ranging synthesis of human genetics and cultural history in which the author drew controversial political conclusions from his study of the role of genetic variations. A fellow of the Royal Society from 1941 and recipient of its Royal Medal in 1946, he was president of the Genetical Society (1943–46) and a foreign member of the Italian Accademia Nazionale dei Lincei and the Royal Danish Academy of Sciences and Letters.

Delbrück, Max (Sept. 4, 1906—March 9, 1981), German-born molecular biologist, with Alfred D. Hershey and Salvador E. Luria won the 1969 Nobel Prize for Physiology or Medicine for research and discoveries on bacteriophages (viruses that infect bacteria). After

Max Delbrück

Delbrück earned his Ph.D. in physics at the University of Göttingen in 1930, he worked with Otto Hahn and Lise Meitner just prior to their discovery and investigation of uranium fission. While serving as a research assistant at the Kaiser Wilhelm Institute for Chemistry in Berlin (1932–37), Delbrück became interested in molecular genetics and the manner in which complex molecular systems can replicate themselves identically. He began his pioneering work on bacteriophages while on the faculties of the California Institute of Technology (1937–39) and Vanderbilt University (1940–47). Through a key experiment in 1939, he discovered a one-step process for growing bacteriophages in bacterial cells by which new virus particles would be formed and the cell would die. Delbrück and Hershey also discovered that the genetic material of different kinds of viruses can combine to create new types of viruses. In 1947 Delbrück returned to the California Institute of Technology, where he was professor of biology until his retirement in 1977.

Denny-Brown, Derek Ernest (June 1, 1901—April 20, 1981), New Zealand-born neurologist, was professor of neurology at Harvard University from 1941 to 1972 (J. J. Putnam professor, 1946–67) and an authority on the neuropathology of the nervous system. Denny-Brown was educated at the Otago University, New Zealand, and at Magdalen College, Oxford, before holding posts at the National Hospital and Guy's Hospital in London. He later worked at St. Bartholomew's Hospital and, again, at the National Hospital. His published works included *The Basal Ganglia* (1962) and *Cerebral Control of Movement* (1966). Denny-Brown was made an Officer of the Order of the British Empire in 1942.

Douglas, Donald Wills (April 6, 1892—Feb. 1, 1981), U.S. aircraft designer, was the pioneering founder (1920) of the Douglas Aircraft Co. and the manufacturer of the twin-engine DC-3 (military C-47) transport, which ushered in the era of mass airline travel and played a major role in the Allied air victory during World War II. Besides developing such military aircraft as the A-20 attack bomber, the A-3D jet attack bomber, the SBD (Dauntless) dive bomber, and the D-

558 and X-3 research planes, Douglas designed the Cloudster, the first airplane to lift more than its own weight in payload, and the World Cruiser biplane, which completed the first around-the-world flight in 1924. After the war his company manufactured the DC-8, DC-9, and DC-10 jet transports and the A-4 (Skyhawk) attack bomber. In the late 1950s the company began producing rockets and guided missiles, including the Nike Ajax, Nike Zeus, Honest John, Sparrow, and Genie. His company also designed and developed (1955) the Thor intermediate-range ballistic missile, which later evolved into the highly reliable Delta space launch vehicle used by NASA. In 1957 Douglas retired, and ten years later the Douglas Aircraft Co. merged with the McDonnell Aircraft Corp.

Fisk, James Brown (Aug. 30, 1910—Aug. 10, 1981), U.S. physicist, helped develop microwave magnetrons for high-frequency radar during World War II as an electronic research engineer at Bell Telephone Laboratories, which he joined in 1939. Fisk served as president of Bell Laboratories from 1959 to 1973, and under his leadership research teams developed the transistor, industrial lasers, and satellite communications systems. Fisk also established a reputation as a tough negotiator and on more than one occasion left Bell to serve the U.S. government. Under Pres. Dwight D. Eisenhower, he headed a U.S. government scientific delegation that negotiated nuclear disarmament with Nikita S. Khrushchev. He also served under Presidents John F. Kennedy and Lyndon B. Johnson. In 1947 Fisk was named first director of the division of research of the Atomic Energy Commission but resigned in 1948 to become Gordon McKay professor at Harvard University. In 1973, a year before his retirement, Fisk became chairman of the board of Bell Laboratories.

Fletcher, Harvey (Sept. 11, 1884—July 23, 1981), U.S. physicist, headed the scientific research team that developed and demonstrated (Jan. 24, 1934) stereophonic sound, a system of sound recording and reproduction that utilizes two or more independent sound channels of information. This discovery revolutionized

Harvey Fletcher

the motion-picture and recording industries, which subsequently produced movies, phonograph records, and magnetic tapes featuring stereophonic sound. After earning a Ph.D. from the University of Chicago, Fletcher served for five years as head of the physics department at Brigham Young University in Provo, Utah. He then joined (1916) the staff of Bell Telephone Laboratories. In 1933 he was named head of Bell's physical research lab, overseeing pioneer work in the fields of speech, music, and hearing. In 1949 he moved to Columbia University in New York City and three years later returned to Brigham Young as director of research. There he also served as chairman of the engineering department, dean of the College of Physical and Engineering Sciences, and professor of physics. Even after his formal retirement Fletcher continued to write scholarly papers analyzing the sounds of musical instruments and to experiment at his echo-free laboratory at Brigham Young. His work on the fundamentals of psychoacoustics is detailed in *Speech and Hearing* (1929).

Glueckauf, Eugen (April 9, 1906—Sept. 15, 1981), German-born scientist, was head of the radiochemistry branch at the Atomic Energy Research Establishment (AERE), Harwell, and made a notable contribution to the management of nuclear wastes. Glueckauf studied at the Technische Hochschule in Berlin but left Germany in 1933 to escape Nazi persecution. He joined the staff of Imperial College, University of London, then went to Durham Colleges (later University) to conduct research on atmospheric gases. In 1947 he was appointed to the chemistry division at Harwell and continued his earlier work on the separation of gases. He became one of the first to investigate disposal of nuclear wastes in glass. Glueckauf also contributed to the development of seawater desalination and to the study of diffusion of fission products. He published numerous scientific papers on these and other topics. One of his major achievements was his early proposal for a self-contained site for the recycling and disposal of nuclear wastes. Glueckauf was elected a fellow of the Royal Society in 1969. After retirement in 1971 he served as a consultant to the Atomic Energy Research Establishment until 1980.

Handler, Philip (Aug. 13, 1901—Dec. 29, 1981), U.S. biochemist, was president (1969–81) of the National Academy of Sciences and an internationally acclaimed biochemist who made significant studies on pellagra, a disfiguring disease that disturbs mental and nervous function and causes a red sore tongue and gastrointestinal disturbances. After earning a Ph.D. in biochemistry at the University of Illinois, Handler in 1939 joined Duke University to help conduct research on pellagra. Handler found that the disease, which afflicted people in the Southeast living on corn-based diets, was caused by poor-quality corn products that prevented the human body from manufacturing its own nicotinic acid.

He was instrumental in the passage of a North Carolina law making it mandatory to fortify cornmeal products with nicotinic acid, iron, and riboflavin. During World War II Handler and a group of scientists developed the pressure bandage used to treat severely burned soldiers; the bandage eliminated inflammation and toxicity and saved hundreds of lives. In other research at Duke University Handler studied the relationship between diet and high blood pressure in kidney disease. He concluded that a low-protein diet would relieve hypertension but would also reduce the production of a key hormone, ACTH, by the pituitary gland. During his career Handler was credited with discovering at least 15 enzymes. In 1950 he was named chairman of the biochemistry department at Duke, where he remained until his 1969 appointment as president of the National Academy of Sciences.

Harrison, Wallace Kirkman (Sept. 28, 1895—Dec. 2, 1981), U.S. architect, played a leading role in designing such magnificent New York City structures as the United Nations headquarters, Rockefeller Center, Lincoln Center for the Performing Arts, and the Metropolitan Opera House, as well as the Empire State Plaza in Albany and the Trylon and Perisphere theme center for the 1939 New York World's Fair. After World War I, Harrison studied at the École des Beaux-Arts, Paris, returning to New York to work for Bertram Goodhue. Harrison was then invited by Wiley Corbett to become his partner in the firm of Corbett, Harrison & MacMurray, which was asked to join other architects in the design of the Rockefeller Center complex. Later, Harrison was appointed head of an international team of consultants working on the UN headquarters. In 1945 he formed a partnership with Max Abramovitz and established Harrison & Abramovitz, which became one of the largest architectural firms in the U.S. Their design specialty was office buildings, including the Alcoa Building in Pittsburgh, Pa. (1953) and the Socony Mobil Building in New York City (1956). Harrison's design for the First Presbyterian Church in Stamford, Conn., with its fish-shaped interior and luminous

Wallace Kirkman
Harrison

stained glass windows, was also highly regarded. In 1979 Harrison established his own firm in Rockefeller Center.

Hassel, Odd (May 17, 1897—May 11, 1981), Norwegian chemist, shared the 1969 Nobel Prize for Chemistry with Sir Derek Barton of Britain for their work in determining the actual three-dimensional shape of certain organic compounds. After studies at Oslo, Munich, and Berlin universities, Hassel returned to Oslo as lecturer in 1925. His early work in crystallography resulted in an important book, *Kristallchemie*, which appeared in English and Russian translations. In 1934 Hassel was appointed professor at the University of Oslo, where he headed the physical chemistry department until his retirement in 1964. After research in crystallography Hassel turned to the study of the structure of gas molecules by means of electron diffraction; this led to the establishment of conformational analysis, the study of the three-dimensional geometric structure of molecules. The Nobel Prize-winning work proved to be vital in the creation of synthetic molecules used in developing new drugs.

Kardiner, Abram (Aug. 17, 1891—July 20, 1981), U.S. psychoanalyst, together with Monroe Meyer and Bert Lewin founded (1930) the New York Psychoanalytic Institute, the first psychiatric training school in the U.S. In the 1950s he joined the Columbia University faculty and was director of Columbia's Psychoanalytic Institute. Kardiner, who graduated from Cornell University Medical College, New York City, had just completed his psychiatric residency at Manhattan State Hospital on Ward's Island when Sigmund Freud accepted him as a student-patient for six months in Vienna. When Kardiner returned to the U.S., he discarded Freud's teachings about latent homosexuality but was more accepting of his Oedipal theory, which he considered the crux of Freud's teachings. Kardiner was a leading proponent of a school of psychiatry that combined psychoanalysis and cultural anthropology and that emphasized the interplay of culture with the psyche. He also wrote several clinical books, including *The Individual and His Society* (1939; with Ralph Linton), *The Psychological Frontiers of Society* (1945; with others), *They Studied Man* (1961; with Edward Preble), and *My Analysis with Freud* (1977).

Krebs, Sir Hans Adolf (Aug. 25, 1900—Nov. 22, 1981), German-born biochemist, shared the 1953 Nobel Prize for Physiology or Medicine with Fritz A. Lipmann of the U.S. and was professor of biochemistry at the universities of Sheffield (1945–54) and Oxford (1954–67). Krebs began his work in metabolic biochemistry in Berlin and Freiburg before Hitler's rise to power prompted him to leave Germany for England. In 1935 he was appointed lecturer in pharmacology in Sheffield, where he continued his pioneering study of the synthesis of urea and the oxidation of carbon compounds in living creatures to produce carbon dioxide.

Sir Hans Adolf Krebs

During World War II he undertook nutritional research. He also directed the Medical Research Council's unit for research in cell metabolism. After retirement in 1967 Krebs continued research at the Radcliffe Infirmary, Oxford. He was made a fellow of the Royal Society in 1947 and knighted in 1958.

Lacan, Jacques (April 13, 1901—Sept. 9, 1981), French psychologist, acquired extraordinary celebrity status in France after the publication of *Écrits* (1966) and gained an international reputation as an original, controversial, and, for some, inspiring interpreter of the work of Sigmund Freud. He claimed to have purged Freudian psychoanalysis of the distortions introduced by post-Freudians and emphasized the primacy of language as the mirror of the unconscious mind. His work was associated with the fashionable theories of structuralism, and its influence extended well beyond the field of psychoanalysis to make him one of the dominant figures in French cultural life during the 1970s. Lacan founded the École Freudienne in Paris but dissolved it in 1980. He intended to replace it with a new school, still more closely aligned to Lacanian orthodoxy. He also wrote poetry and published several volumes of *Séminaires*.

Lancefield, Rebecca Craighill (Jan. 5, 1895—March 3, 1981), U.S. bacteriologist, while conducting research at Rockefeller Institute (now Rockefeller University) created a system of classification of more than 60 different types of Group A streptococcal bacteria. Lancefield's studies were vital in proving that one type of streptococcal bacterium could cause a number of diseases, including scarlet fever, erysipelas, or a sore throat; physicians previously had believed that each type of clinical infection was caused by a specific type of streptococcal bacterium. Lancefield's research also led to a more efficacious treatment of streptococcal infections related to such conditions as scarlet fever, rheumatic fever, and glomerulonephritis, an acute inflammation of the kidneys. Lancefield graduated from Wellesley (Mass.) College and in 1918 became a technical assistant at Rockefeller Institute. She later obtained a Ph.D. in immunology and bacteriology at Co-

lumbia University. Lancefield spent her entire career (1918–80) at Rockefeller University.

Link, Edwin Albert (July 26, 1904—Sept. 7, 1981), U.S. inventor, was the innovative developer (1929) of the Link flight simulator, a mechanical device used to train millions of military and commercial airline pilots to make instrument landings. At first Link's invention was distributed to amusement parks, but in 1934, after dozens of U.S. Army pilots had been killed making landings, Link's "blue box" was bought to train new pilots. In 1935 he founded Link Aviation Inc. and served as its president until the company became a subsidiary of General Precision Equipment Co. in 1954. He then became president of General Precision until it merged with the Singer Co. in 1968. Link, who was also responsible for introducing trainers for jet fighters, bombers, and transpolar celestial navigation, unveiled (1958) a high-density air navigation system that helped pilots avoid air collisions. During his later years Link turned increasingly to oceanographic exploration because he was convinced that the ocean held the key to food and energy for future generations. In order to facilitate undersea archaeological pursuits Link co-developed (1960) the "Sea Diver," a bullet-shaped underwater scooter that towed a diver behind it. In the same year he co-invented the "Shark," a mobile, unmanned television camera used to explore the ocean depths and relay photos to a ship via cable. His other contributions included: the "lock-out submarine deep diver," the first submersible with an exit hatch for divers; the "submersible, portable, inflatable dwelling," an air-conditioned underwater home for undersea workers; and the "Sea Link," a rotorless helicopter able to transport four persons down to a depth of 457 m (1,500 ft). In 1980 Link was named recipient of the Charles A. Lindbergh Award, given for achievement in science and technology combined with preservation of the natural environment.

Malina, Frank Joseph (Oct. 2, 1912—Nov. 9, 1981), U.S. aeronautical engineer, was a pioneering rocketeer who with Theodore von Kármán founded in the late 1930s what became known in 1944 as the Jet Propulsion Laboratory (JPL). Malina, who earned a Ph.D. from the California Institute of Technology in 1940, served as the first director of the JPL from 1944 to 1946. In 1942 he formed Aerojet-General, which became a major aerospace firm. He and Kármán developed solid-fuel rockets that gave propeller-driven aircraft faster takeoffs, and they also helped design (1945) the WAC Corporal, one of the country's first high-altitude sounding rockets. Their original research helped the U.S. put the first man on the Moon. In 1946 Malina moved to France to join UNESCO's scientific division, which he later headed.

Martin, Sir James (1893—Jan. 5, 1981), British engineer, invented the Martin-Baker aircraft ejector seat, a safety device for military aircraft that has protected over 4,700 airmen in their escape from fighter planes. The seat was first tested in 1946, and Martin steadily improved the design to keep pace with the development of supersonic aircraft and to protect pilots ejecting at high altitudes. He trained as an engineer in Belfast before founding the Martin Aircraft Co. in 1929, which five years later became the Martin-Baker Aircraft Co. Martin was also responsible for improving the armament of World War II fighter aircraft and for inventing a device to cut barrage balloon cables. He was knighted in 1965, was named Officer of the Order of the British Empire and Commander of the Order of the British Empire and received the Royal Aero Club Gold Medal.

Moses, Robert (Dec. 18, 1888—July 29, 1981), U.S. builder, who more than anyone else transformed the New York landscape with a gigantic network of 35 highways, 12 bridges, 810,000 ha (2 million ac) of parks, 658 playgrounds, numerous housing projects, and two hydroelectric dams, all of which influenced planning in other U.S. cities. Moses studied political science at Yale, Oxford, and Columbia universities before entering New York politics in 1914. From 1924 to 1968 Moses, who never held elective office, maneuvered his power so that he maintained 12 separate city posts simultaneously. He was unwavering in his vision, so much so that he would threaten to resign if his plans were not implemented. He spent huge sums of money because he knew politicians would never leave a half-finished project as a monument to their own incompetence. Some of his most gigantic undertakings included Lincoln Center, the 1964 World's Fair, Shea Stadium, the Triborough Bridge, and Jones Beach State Park. He was also instrumental in bringing the UN building to the East River waterfront. In 1928 Franklin D. Roosevelt was elected governor of New York, and Moses's rise in power abruptly ended. The two spent endless hours in bitter controversy, and Roosevelt forced Moses out of his position as secretary of state of New York. However, Moses did hold onto his parks jobs owing to public support. When Fiorello H. La Guardia became mayor of New York City in 1933, Moses was appointed head of the City Parks Department and head of the Triborough Bridge and Tunnel Authority. In 1934, in his first and only bid for elective office, Moses ran for governor and lost by a record 800,000 votes. During the 1940s and 1950s he built huge public housing towers, which became less and less attractive to the public. In 1959, his popularity waning, Moses relinquished his city posts and became president of the World's Fair. He lost most of his state jobs in 1962 when Nelson Rockefeller unexpectedly accepted his routine resignation. In 1968 Moses was stripped of his last post. His accomplishments were placed under critical scrutiny when the book *The Power Broker*, by Robert Caro, was published in 1974. The 1,246-page work won Caro a Pulitzer Prize. He acknowledged Moses as "the greatest builder in America," while Moses's critics continued to point up the immensity and impersonality of his projects.

Northrop, John Knudsen (Nov. 10, 1895—Feb. 18, 1981), was one of the most ambitious aircraft designers in the history of aviation and an early proponent of all-metal airplane construction and the flying-wing airplane design. Northrop co-founded Lockheed Aircraft Corp. in 1927 and designed the Lockheed Vega monoplane, which set many speed and endurance records. In 1928 Northrop founded the Avion Corp. (bought by United Aircraft and Transport in 1930), where he developed the Alpha (1930), one of the first modern, low-wing monoplanes. He left United in 1931 to form the Northrop Corp. in El Segundo, Calif. There he constructed the Northrop Gamma, the A-17 and A-17A attack planes, the Navy BT-1 dive bomber, and various other military craft for foreign countries. In 1937 the company became the El Segundo division of Douglas Aircraft Co. Northrop's pioneering spirit led him to found Northrop Aircraft Inc. in 1939 and to design such planes as the XB-35 flying-wing bomber; the YB-49, a jet-powered version of the XB-35; the N-1M, the world's first successful all-wing plane; the P-61 Black Widow night fighter; the F-89 Scorpion jet fighter; and the B-35 and B-49 bombers for the U.S. Air Force. Northrop retired as director in 1952, and his company was renamed Northrop Corp. in 1959. During World War II he employed wounded hospitalized veterans for small assembly jobs related to his night fighter. After the war Northrop established a prosthetic department, where he developed an improved prosthetic arm and hand.

Oakley, Kenneth Page (April 7, 1911—Nov. 2, 1981), British anthropologist, used scientific methods of analysis to expose the 1953 Piltdown hoax. The Piltdown skull, allegedly discovered in Sussex in 1912, had been accepted as the remains of *Eoanthropus*, a primitive man who provided the "missing link" between man and ape. Oakley's application of fluorine analysis for dating, using a technique he had developed, proved that the remains were fraudulent. He studied at University College in London and earned a Ph.D. in 1938. He worked with the Geological Survey and the British Museum (Natural History) and investigated sites in Britain and abroad. Oakley also contributed articles and chapters to major publications in the field of paleontology and published his own *Frameworks for Dating Fossil Man* (1964). Besides winning the Prestwich and Henry Stokes Memorial medals, he was a fellow of the British Academy and of University College and served as president of the Anthropological Section of the British Association in 1961.

Piccard, the Rev. Jeanette Ridlon (Jan. 5, 1895—May 17, 1981), U.S. scientist and Episcopal priest, made a historic ascent into the stratosphere when in 1934 she piloted a spherical balloon of 17,000 cu m

(600,000 cu ft) in volume to a height of 17,557 m (57,564 ft) above Lake Erie with her husband, Jean Piccard, as her aide. During her ascent Piccard made studies of the cosmic rays in the stratosphere and became the first balloonist in the U.S. to fly successfully through a layer of clouds. Piccard, who held a B.A. in philosophy and psychology, an M.A. in organic chemistry, and a Ph.D. in education, had a wide range of interests. From 1964 to 1970 she was consultant to the director of NASA's Johnson Space Center, and in her mid-70s she began theological studies. In 1971 she was ordained a deacon of the Episcopal Church and in 1974 was the eldest of 11 women to be ordained priests.

Rosen, Samuel (1897—Nov. 5, 1981), U.S. ear surgeon, discovered that otosclerosis, a deafening condition in which the bony wall dividing the middle and inner ear thickens, could be alleviated by mobilizing the tiny stapes (or stirrup) bone, one of the chain of minute bones in the middle ear that transmit sound vibrations from the eardrum membrane. During a 1952 diagnostic operation Rosen made a probe of the stapes bone to ensure that it was rigid before proceeding with fenestration surgery; he found that his patient's hearing was completely restored when he pried loose the fixed stapes. This delicate surgery, on the tiniest bone in the human body, revolutionized ear surgery when its effectiveness was finally recognized in 1955. Rosen, who conducted these operations while on the staff of Mount Sinai Hospital in New York City, met resistance from colleagues, who, he felt, resented his political stands, and possibly the loss of high fees surgeons had been earning for fenestration surgery. Rosen introduced and demonstrated his technique in at least 40 countries, never accepted a fee for operations outside New York, and donated his instruments so instrument makers could study their unique design. In addition to his affiliation with Mount Sinai, Rosen was professor emeritus of otolaryngology at the College of Physicians and Surgeons of Columbia University.

Sondheimer, Franz (May 17, 1926—Feb. 11, 1981), German-born scientist, with R. B. Woodward was the first to achieve total synthesis of a nonaromatic steroid, a procedure used in the preparation of cholesterol and cortisone. Sondheimer conducted this work at Harvard University in the early 1950s and continued his research after his appointment to the Syntex Pharmaceutical Co. research laboratories in Mexico. In 1956 he became head of the organic chemistry department at the Weizmann Institute of Science in Israel. There his work on compounds of benzene proved what had until then only been predicted by theory and consequently had far-reaching implications for the whole field of organic chemistry. In 1964 he returned to England and worked as research professor at the University of Cambridge (1964–67) and later at University College, London. He made further notable contribu-

tions to the synthesis of organic compounds and attracted collaborators from many countries to his laboratories. He was elected a fellow of the Royal Society in 1967.

Speer, Albert (March 19, 1905—Sept. 1, 1981), German architect, was Hitler's chief architect and the minister for armaments and ammunition in the German government from 1942 to 1945. Tried at Nürnberg, he was the only leading Nazi to plead guilty to war crimes, and he served 20 years in Spandau prison, Berlin. Speer studied architecture and taught at the Technical University in Berlin before joining the Nazi Party and being chosen to design the stadium in Nürnberg, the Berlin Chancellery, and other massive monuments of Nazi architecture. He became a personal friend of Hitler, who mesmerized his young protégé and in 1942 appointed him to succeed Fritz Todt as armaments minister, responsible for the slave labor that supported the German wartime economy. Speer proved successful and even raised production from 1942 to 1944, despite increased Allied bombing. He also showed re-

Keystone

Albert Speer

markable foresight by encouraging the production of synthetic substitutes for oil. But Speer was also one of the first to foresee Germany's eventual defeat and in 1945 was one of a group that attempted to kill Hitler. Later Speer expressed his guilt and remorse for German war crimes and admitted responsibility for what had been done by the Nazi government. After his release from Spandau in 1966 he wrote *Inside the Third Reich* (1970), in which he admitted and attempted to come to terms with his management of the German industrial machine, which, he said, had presented him with a great challenge and given him "incredible satisfaction."

Stanner, William Edward Hanley (Nov. 24, 1905—Oct. 8, 1981), Australian anthropologist, helped found the Australian Institute of Aboriginal Studies in Canberra and the Gallery of Aboriginal Australia. Stanner was professor of anthropology and sociology at the Australian National University from 1964 to 1970. After studying at the London School of Economics, he conducted research work in Kenya and after World War II became founding director of the East African Institute of Social Research, Makerere, Uganda. As a newspaper reporter during the 1930s he became aware of the plight of the Aborigines and began to campaign on their behalf. Stanner was a member of the Commonwealth Council for Aboriginal Affairs from 1967 to 1977 and in 1979 became a founding member of the Aboriginal Treaty Committee. His broadcast lectures, "After the Dreaming," reached a wide audience, and he published *White Man Got No Dreaming* (1979), a collection of articles. Stanner was appointed Companion of the Order of St. Michael and St. George in 1972.

Trippe, Juan Terry (June 27, 1899—April 3, 1981), U.S. aviation pioneer, significantly influenced the formation and expansion of the international airline industry as the founder of Pan American World Airways. After serving as a naval aviator during World War I, Trippe became president of Long Island Airways, which he founded in 1922 with some friends from Yale University. From 1924 to 1926 he headed Colonial Air Transport, which secured the first Post Office contract to deliver U.S. airmail on a route between New York City and Boston. In 1927 Trippe felt that the domestic competition was increasing, so, having acquired an airmail route between Miami and Havana, he entered the international field with a single Fokker three-engine monoplane. Successful in establishing himself as a far-sighted leader in the aviation business, Trippe was at the forefront of nearly every major development in commercial aviation during the next 40 years. Under his direction Pan Am became the first airline to fly across the Pacific and Atlantic oceans; to order commercial jets (1955), which effectively halved flying time and made air travel a popular form of transportation; and to buy the wide-bodied Boeing 747 jets (1966) for long-distance travel. Trippe also pioneered the use of amphibian "clipper" planes for low-fare service on the North Atlantic (1952) and the concept of selling overseas flight tickets to be paid on an installment basis (1954). After retiring as president and chief executive director of Pan Am in 1968, he served as honorary chairman of the board.

Urey, Harold Clayton (April 29, 1893—Jan 5, 1981), U.S. chemist, was awarded the 1934 Nobel Prize for Chemistry for his discovery in 1931 of deuterium, a heavy isotope of hydrogen. After earning his Ph.D. from the University of California at Berkeley in 1923, Urey studied the theory of atomic structure with Niels Bohr in Copenhagen. In 1929 he joined the faculty of Columbia University, where he discovered deuterium while working with George M. Murphy and Ferdinand G. Brickwedde. Urey had correctly predicted that the distillation of liquid hydrogen would contain the heavy isotope. The discovery led eventually to the development of the hydrogen bomb, which uses deuterium and the heavier hydrogen isotope tritium as its fuel. During World War II Urey worked for the top-secret Manhattan Project, where his research on the separation of uranium isotopes by gaseous diffusion was a major contribution to the development of the atomic bomb. In spite of his pioneering efforts in atomic research Urey later campaigned for an international ban against nuclear weapons. After the war he moved to the University of Chicago and in 1947 published a paper on the thermodynamic properties of isotopic substances that provided much of the theoretical basis for isotope geochemistry. At Chicago Urey also began his studies of astrophysics and the origins of the solar system. In a celebrated experiment in 1953 he and a graduate student, Stanley Miller, demonstrated that the Earth's primordial ingredients of methane, ammonia, hydrogen, and water could have been forced by lightning discharges to combine into amino acids, the building blocks of protein. His book *The Planets: Their Origin and Development* (1952) was the first systematic and detailed chronology of the origin of the Earth, the Moon, meteorites, and the solar system. Urey left Chicago in 1958 to join the faculty of the University of California at San Diego (La Jolla), where he continued his investigations of geochemistry, the history of the solar system, and the origins of life. During the 1970s he helped analyze the Moon rocks retrieved by the Apollo astronauts and served as a consultant on the Viking misions to Mars.

Yukawa, Hideki (Jan. 23, 1907—Sept. 8, 1981), Japanese physicist, was awarded the 1949 Nobel Prize for Physics for his theories on subatomic particles. In 1935 Yukawa proposed that mesons (small energized particles) were responsible for binding protons and neutrons in atomic nuclei. During his tenure (1949–53) as visiting professor at Columbia University in New York City, Yukawa's theory on the existence of mesons was confirmed in laboratory tests, and he became Japan's first Nobel laureate. After Yukawa graduated from Kyoto Imperial University, he lectured there briefly (1932–33) before serving on the faculty at Osaka Imperial University (1933–39). In 1939 he returned to Kyoto, where he continued his theoretical work. Yukawa was invited to the Institute for Advanced Study in Princeton, N.J., in 1948 and in the following year became visiting professor at Columbia University. He returned to his alma mater in 1953 and served as director of Kyoto University's Research Institute for Fundamental Physics until his retirement in 1970.

Contributors to the Science Year in Review

C. Melvin Aikens *Archaeology.* Chairman, Department of Anthropology, University of Oregon, Eugene.

D. James Baker, Jr. *Earth sciences: Oceanography.* Acting Dean, College of Ocean and Fishery Sciences, University of Washington, Seattle.

Fred Basolo *Chemistry: Inorganic chemistry.* Professor of Chemistry, Northwestern University, Evanston, Ill.

Louis J. Battan *Earth sciences: Atmospheric sciences.* Director, Institute of Atmospheric Physics, University of Arizona, Tucson.

Rudy M. Baum *Chemistry: Physical chemistry.* San Francisco Bureau Chief, *Chemical & Engineering News* magazine.

Gregory Benford *Physics: General developments.* Professor of Physics, University of California, Irvine.

Keith Beven *Earth sciences: Hydrology.* Assistant Professor, Department of Environmental Sciences, University of Virginia.

Harold Borko *Electronics and information sciences: Information systems and services.* Professor, Graduate School of Library and Information Science, University of California, Los Angeles.

D. Allan Bromley *Physics: Nuclear physics.* Henry Ford II Professor and Director, Wright Nuclear Structure Laboratory, Yale University, New Haven, Conn.

John Davis *Architecture and civil engineering* (in part). Engineering Consultant and Technical Writer, Virginia.

Steven Andrew Davis *Medical sciences: Skin diseases* (in part). Assistant Clinical Professor of Dermatology, University of California, San Francisco.

Warren D. Dolphin *Life sciences: Zoology.* Professor of Zoology, Iowa State University, Ames.

F. C. Durant III *Electronics and information sciences: Satellite systems.* Aerospace Historian and Consultant.

Robert G. Eagon *Life sciences: Microbiology.* Professor of Microbiology, University of Georgia, Athens.

Gerald Feinberg *Physics: High-energy physics.* Chairman, Physics Department, Columbia University, New York City.

Lawrence E. Fisher *Anthropology.* Director of Graduate Studies, Department of Anthropology, University of Illinois, Chicago.

David R. Gaskell *Materials sciences: Metallurgy.* Professor of Metallurgy, University of Pennsylvania, Philadelphia.

Richard L. Gordon *Energy.* Professor of Mineral Economics, Pennsylvania State University, University Park.

C. David Gutsche *Chemistry: Organic chemistry.* Professor of Chemistry, Washington University, St. Louis, Mo.

Robert Haselkorn *Life sciences: Molecular biology.* F. L. Pritzker Professor and Chairman of the Department of Biophysics and Theoretical Biology, University of Chicago.

Harvey J. Hindin *Electronics and information sciences: Communications systems.* Communications Editor, *Electronics* magazine, New York City.

John Patrick Jordan *Food and agriculture: Agriculture.* Director, Colorado State University Experiment Station, Fort Collins.

Index

This is a three-year cumulative index. Index entries to feature and review articles in this and previous editions of the *Yearbook of Science and the Future* are set in boldface type, *e.g.,* **Astronomy.** Entries to other subjects are set in lightface type, *e.g.,* Radiation. Additional information on any of these subjects is identified with a subheading and indented under the entry heading. The numbers following headings and subheadings indicate the year (boldface) of the edition and the page number (lightface) on which the information appears.

> **Astronomy 83**–256;. **82**–254; **81**–254
> archaeological findings **82**–250
> extraterrestrial catastrophe as cause of
> species extinction **82**–124
> honors **83**–402; **82**–404; **81**–401
> optical telescopes **81**–198
> physics research **83**–363

All entry headings, whether consisting of a single word or more, are treated for the purpose of alphabetization as single complete headings and are alphabetized letter by letter up to the punctuation. The abbreviation "il." indicates an illustration.

Acknowledgments

56   Illustration by Leon Bishop; photos, (top) Russ Kinne—Photo Researchers; (bottom) M. P. L. Fogden—Bruce Coleman Inc.

63   Illustration by Leon Bishop

108   (Top, left and bottom, right) Charles L. Martin, DVM, MS, Dip. American College of Veterinary Ophthalmologists, Professor, Department of Small Animal Medicine, University of Georgia; (top, right and bottom, left) Gary M. Bryan, DVM, Washington State University, Pullman

109   Charles L. Martin, DVM, MS, Dip. American College of Veterinary Ophthalmologists, Professor, Department of Small Animal Medicine, University of Georgia

119   The Bettmann Archive

133   (Top, right) Adapted from "Lake Lisan: The Pleistocene Precursor of the Dead Sea," Z. B. Begin, A. Ehrlich, and Y. Nathan, GEOLOGICAL SURVEY OF ISRAEL, Jerusalem, Bulletin no. 63, pp. 6–7, November 1974; (bottom) adapted from "Climatic Fluctuations During the Holocene as Reflected by the Dead Sea Levels," David Neev and John K. Hall, in Deon C. Greed (ed.), Desertic Terminal Lakes, Proc. of the International Conference on Desertic Terminal Lakes, held at Weber State College, Utah, May 2–5, 1977, pp. 53–60

139   (Bottom) From "Glycerol and β-carotene Metabolism in the Halotolerant Alga Dunaliella: A Model System for Biosolar Energy Conversion," by Ami Ben-Amotz and Mordhay Avron, TRENDS IN BIOCHEMICAL SCIENCES, vol. 6, no. 11, pp. 297–299, November 1981

162, 167, 169   Illustrations by Bill Peterson

213–215, 218–226   Illustrations by John Draves and Ron Villani

216–217   (Top) Adapted from "The Search for New Families of Elementary Particles," by David B. Cline, Alfred K. Mann, and Carlo Rubbia, © January 1976 by Scientific American, Inc. All Rights Reserved

218   (Bottom, left) From "Solar Neutrinos: A Scientific Puzzle," John N. Bahcall and Raymond Davis, Jr., SCIENCE, vol. 191, no. 4224, pp. 264–267, January 23, 1976

Now there's a way to identify all your fine books, and carry papers, personal belongings and books around with you with flair and style. As part of our continuing service to you, Encyclopaedia Britannica is proud to be able to offer you the fine quality items shown on the next page.

Booklovers will love the heavy-duty personalized **Ex Libris** embosser. Now you can personalize all your fine books with the mark of distinction, just the way all the fine libraries of the world do.

The fashionably designed tote bag, decorated with the Britannica thistle, has been specially made for our patrons. Constructed from heavy-duty canvas, it gives you an easy, convenient way to carry books, papers, personal belongings, even shoes or any other daily necessities.

To order either of these items, please type or print your name, address and zip code on a plain sheet of paper along with the description and quantity of the items you are ordering (note special instructions for ordering the embosser). Please send a check or money order only (your money will be refunded in full if you are not delighted) for the full amount of purchase, including postage and handling, to:

Britannica Home Library Service
Attn: Yearbook Department
Post Office Box 6137
Chicago, Illinois 60680

(Please make remittance payable to: Britannica Home Library Service)

IN THE
BRITANNICA TRADITION
OF QUALITY...

EX LIBRIS
PERSONAL EMBOSSER

A mark of distinction for your fine books. A book embosser just like the ones used in libraries. The 1½″ seal imprints "Library of _____" (with the name of your choice) and up to three centered initials. Please type or print clearly BOTH full name (up to 26 letters including spaces between names) and up to three initials. Please allow six weeks for delivery.

Just **$20.00**

plus $2.00 shipping and handling

ENCYCLOPAEDIA BRITANNICA
TOTE BAG

This stylishly designed tote bag is useful for carrying your books, records, papers —even a spare pair of shoes. Warm earth-brown, sturdy cotton canvas, to withstand hard school use or as a shopping carry-all. Britannica thistle emblem in light golden color adds attractive style accent. Two extra pockets for small items and sundries. Please allow two to three weeks for delivery.

Only **$12.95**

plus $2.95 shipping and handling

This offer available only in the United States.
Illinois residents please add sales tax.